D1571982

A SILVER CAMP
CALLED

CREEDE

A CENTURY OF MINING

BY RICHARD C. HUSTON

Under the Auspices
of the
Creede Historical Society
Creede, Colorado

WESTERN REFLECTIONS PUBLISHING COMPANY®
Montrose, CO

ISBN 1-932738-10-X

Library of Congress Control Number: 2004113382

Cover and text design: Laurie Goralka Design

First Edition
Printed in the United States of America

Western Reflections Publishing Company®
219 Main Street
Montrose, CO 81401
www.westernreflectionspub.com

FRONTISPIECE

Commodore Workings — Creede Mines — 1978

Courtesy of Pan Eimon

A pen and ink drawing of the Commodore Numbers 3 and 4 Levels from the Commodore Number 5 Level.

Pan Eimon is an international artist who has lived, made art, and shown it around the world. Pan Eimon's paintings and drawings are in homes, offices, and corporate collections in many countries. Her art has been shown in an exhibit sponsored by the U.S. Embassy in Managua, Nicaragua; in the United Nations show in Mendoza, Argentina; was the first American artist presented at the National Gallery in Mongolia; and been shown in many galleries in the United States.

Eimon's husband, Paul Eimon, played an important role in Creede Camp's second boom.

DEDICATION

THIS BOOK IS DEDICATED to the miners and mill hands who worked in the mines and mills of Creede Camp during its century of mining. John R. Jackson, a Creede native, prospector, miner, mine manager and developer, self-made geologist and mineralogist, writer, and poet, is the inspiration behind this book.

John's desire to save Creede Camp's history, along with his knowledge of the subject, made him the most important contributor to the story of Creede Camp. Documents such as books, newspapers, mining periodicals, and geologists' reports, as well as interviews, provided the historic framework for the book, but John's knowledge of the people involved in the camp's history and his stories about them gives the book a most important and interesting human touch.

John R. Jackson

John is descended from a family that has called Creede home throughout its century of mining.

John's grandfather, William T. Jackson, Sr., was born at Siler Hill, North Carolina, in 1861. He migrated to Colorado in the 1880s, first to Gregory Gulch near Central City, then to Leadville, and finally to Creede during the first boom in the 1890s. The Jackson family, William, Sr., his wife Selma, and two daughters, lived in a small cabin in Bachelor where he worked at the Last Chance and Amethyst Mines. The family moved to a cabin in Stringtown, located in the narrow canyon of Willow Creek between the present town of Creede and North Creede. Then he worked in the Commodore Mine. He died in his early fifties from the effects of silicosis, a common disease among miners of that era.

John's father, William T. "Billy" Jackson, Jr., was born and spent his childhood in Bachelor before the family moved. He continued the family's mining tradition after serving with the U.S. Marines during World War I. He married Alice Davis, a rancher's daughter, in 1921. William, Jr., like his father, contracted silicosis and had to give up mining. He was elected Mineral County Treasurer in 1928 and served in that post until his illness forced him to resign in 1957. He also served as undersheriff, clerk of district and county courts, and Creede's city clerk.

John Jackson, one of the four children of William, Jr., and Alice, was born in Creede in 1927 and grew up during the camp's hard times. Before military service in Europe during World War II, John's first mining job in 1944 was drilling "uppers," holes drilled upward by hand to widen the Commodore No. 5 Tunnel during its re-opening by the Emperius Mining Company. The work was directed by John's father. He returned to Creede after his military service and became an apprentice in the Amethyst Mine. John and Gavin Skinner then leased mining property in the upper Amethyst Mine in 1948 under the name J & S Mining Company after the Emperius Mining Company had abandoned the upper workings.

William, Jr., secured a lease on the Phoenix Mine in 1949 from the Moffat Estate Company, and John, his son, explored the northern extension of the Solomon-Holy Moses Vein System on the Phoenix property. His efforts resulted in the discovery of rich lead ore. The Outlet Mining Company was organized to mine the ore, and John was made mine manager in 1951. John leased the Holy Moses group of claims in 1954 under the name of Jackson Mining Company and again developed a rich but, unfortunately, small ore body. In 1958 he purchased the Midwest Mine. An exploration company was formed in 1968 with the help of the Phipps family of Denver and the Colorado Fuel and Iron Corporation of Pueblo. A tunnel was driven 2,500 feet; however, the Crane Corporation bought CF&I in 1971 and cancelled the project before the ore zone was reached.

John left Creede in 1976 to work for the Freeport Exploration Company in Nevada, prospecting for precious metals where the tools were diamond drilling, advanced geology, and geophysics. He retired from mining in 1989 to a small ranch near Cathedral in Hinsdale County, Colorado, and then moved to Cedaredge, Colorado, where he now resides.

John's interests go far beyond mining and related fields. He wrote a series of stories about Creede and its citizens for a local newspaper, the *Mineral County Miner and South Fork Tines,* and is the author of a series of booklets filled with humorous stories about the life and times in Creede Camp. John also is a poet. Several of his poems are included in this book.

FOREWORD

THE FIRST RECORDED PRODUCTION of silver from the Creede Mining District in the "Silvery San Juans" of southwestern Colorado was in 1884 and the last in 1988, a period of a century plus five years. There was no production in the depression years of 1931 and 1932 and likely none in several of the years between 1884 and the first official published production in1891. The district produced an estimated five million tons of ore that contained more than $700 million of gold, silver, copper, lead, zinc, and fluorspar, based on average commodity prices listed in the U.S.G.S. *Minerals Yearbook* for 2000. An estimated 182 miles of mine workings — shafts, tunnels, drifts, raises, and winzes — were excavated in the Creede Mining District.

The little town of Creede, Colorado, is located on the headwaters of the Rio Grande River at an elevation of 9,350 feet. The town is readily accessible by Colorado State Highway 149 that intersects U.S. Highway 160 at South Fork, between Alamosa and Durango, and continues through Creede up the Rio Grande River over the Continental Divide to Slumgullion Pass and Lake City, Colorado. The highway, named the "Silver Thread Scenic and Historic Byway," passes through some of the most beautiful scenery in Colorado — the San Juan Mountains. Professor Arthur Lakes of the Colorado School of Mines described Creede and the San Juans in a 1903 article titled "Creede Mining Camp" in Volume 23 of *Mines and Minerals:*

> *"It not infrequently happens that the abodes of the precious metals are among some of the grandest, ruggedest, and most picturesque scenery. They are often, too, hidden away in some of the seemingly most inaccessible spots on the face of the globe; inaccessible to all other eyes except the prospector to whom no height is inaccessible, and the mining man, who, provided the ore is rich enough or in large enough quantities, guesses he will find a way to it and bring it out somehow. This is particularly true of the little mining camp of Creede, just on the border of the rugged San Juan Range and on the edge of the great San Luis Park.*

*"After traversing an area of park-like country diversi-
fied by steep plateaus of volcanic rock, we see on the right
of us a dark narrow gash in one of the steepest and most
precipitous parts of the mountains. It is suggestive of one
of those narrow, dark, inaccessible canyons that sometimes lead like a natural gateway into the heart of the
range. This is the portal to the mining camp of Creede,
which was discovered in 1892 by the prospector Creede,
and during the reign of silver boomed, but has since qui-
eted down to a steady producing camp of silver and lead.*

*"Twice has the little town, crowded into the narrow,
precipitous canyon, been burnt out by fire, and twice has
it been rebuilt, and for safety the principal portion is now
located outside the canyon in the open river flat. As we
enter the grand portal between vertical cliffs upward of
2,000 feet high, of columnar rhyolite and massive
andesite, we form some conception of the difficulties early
encountered and the mighty work in bringing water, in
boring tunnels into vertical cliffs and spanning the canyon
and bringing down ore from the otherwise inaccessible
cliffs by wire and bucket tramways. We see, too, the relics
of past big mills and the handsome new buildings of present mills, showing that though not what it once was, men
have not lost faith in the wealth of the camp and the camp
is far from becoming a has been."*

I grew up in the San Luis Valley and was well aware of the natural beauty of the rugged San Juan Mountains. While growing up, I
spent considerable time camping and fishing in the summer and ski-
ing in the winter in the mountains around Creede.

My first job out of high school in 1949 was as a trail rider with
the U.S. Forest Service maintaining trails in the remote areas of the
upper Rio Grande River drainage, a job that still has pleasant memories for me. At the end of that summer I began my college education at the Colorado School of Mines in Golden, Colorado. While
attending Mines, my free summer time was spent working for the
Emperius Mining Company at Creede, learning the business of mining from the ground up. I began as a mucker shoveling rock, pulling
ore out of a chute, hand tramming ore in a one-ton car, and sorting
ore at the ore bin. Then I was advanced to miner's helper, and finally
to drift and stope miner. I learned basic mining skills and in the

process developed a great admiration for those who earn their living working in underground mines.

I will never forget my first day in the Commodore Mine at Creede. I reported for work on night shift (4:00 P.M. until midnight) with a hard hat, carbide lamp, lunch in a paper sack, and no water. A small cave-in, or a "sluff" in miners' terminology, occurred between the day shift coming out of the mine and the swing shift crew going in. We left the train that was taking us to work, climbed over the muck pile, and continued on our way on foot. I was assigned to load ore into a one-ton car from a chute, hand tram it to an ore pass, dump it, and then repeat the cycle until the end of the shift — all alone with no one within shouting distance. My work station was on a level a hundred or more feet above the main level. On the way up the ladder, I burned a hole in my lunch sack with my unfamiliar carbide lamp and the lunch went down the ladder way. I got awfully thirsty, and after realizing I had no water, decided to drink out of a trickle of water coming into the drift. The water was loaded with sulfates and the result was diarrhea. What a day! No water, no lunch, and diarrhea in a place totally void of light except for the feeble beam supplied by my carbide light. I worked alone and completed the shift even though I was exhausted, hungry, thirsty, and ill. I'm still surprised that I went back to work the next day!

After graduation from Mines and time in the military service, I returned to the San Luis Valley and worked for Paul Davis, a mining engineer who had spent time in Creede both as an engineer and a miner. One of my jobs with Paul was surveying in the Creede mines where I first met John Jackson. I left the San Luis Valley for a job at the Climax Molybdenum Mine near Leadville, Colorado, where I spent eleven years. Afterwards, I worked at AMAX's Henderson Mine in Colorado and the Twin Buttes Mine in Arizona. Projects late in my career took me to Europe, South America, Russia, China, and Mongolia.

When I retired, I decided to write a book about the history of Creede Camp and its miners who taught me much about mining and people. My Creede experiences have been the source of pleasant memories for me all these intervening years.

Several books have been written about Creede in the 1890s when the town was one of the last, and perhaps the wildest, of the mining boom towns in the West. This book is not about those times but about the prospectors, the discoverers of the rich veins, those who invested their time and money to develop the mines, and, most importantly, those who worked in the mines during Creede's century of mining.

I want to acknowledge those who helped me in my effort to document Creede Camp's history. First, I want to thank the Creede Historical Society for supporting me. I especially thank John Jackson for his encouragement and contribution to Creede Camp's story. Paul Davis, Ed Johnson, and Robert Boppe also provided encouragement and stories about the miners and historic events at Creede. Les Turnipseed, Gene Dooley, and others who worked in the mines have also provided much help. Mary Johnson and Marge Hosselkus, long-time Creede residents, gave accounts about life and individuals in Creede that are included in the book. Mildred (Hosselkus) Hoffman, former wife of Fred Baker of Bulldog Mountain fame, provided information about him. Charles Melbye, ex-president of Minerals Engineering Company, and William Wilson, who was president of Creede Mines, added greatly to the historic details of Creede during the second boom. Wilson provided me a copy of Judson Slater Hubbard's unpublished book about A.E. Humphreys, an early Creede investor. This filled in several blanks about Creede history. Stanley Dempsey, president of Royal Gold, provided invaluable information on Creede Camp during the 1940s from his collection of Colorado Mining Association yearbooks.

Phil Bethke and Paul Barton, geologists with the U.S. Geological Survey, and David Huston, my son and a geologist for the Australian Geological Survey, reviewed and critiqued the description of Creede Camp's geology. Paul Eimon, deeply involved in Creede's second boom, provided geologic and historical information about Creede, particularly a report by V.V. Clark that was invaluable in deciphering the camp's history. Pan Eimon, Paul's wife, graciously allowed her pen and ink drawings to be included in the book. Joel Tankersley, an ex-Creede second generation miner, kindly drew pencil sketches of miners specifically for the book.

Hugh Matheson, president of CoCa Mines, Inc., provided information about Creede Camp's final days as a mining district, as did Martin Nelson, a geologist who worked at Creede from 1983 to 1990 for Pioneer Nuclear, Inc., Minerals Engineering Company, and CoCa Mines. Robert Nye of Nycon Resources, Inc., described how he found a fabulous pitcher and tray made of Creede silver at an antique store. He also provided a picture of these items. Tyrus Poxson provided a brief history of the Emperius Mining Company that greatly added to information I had gathered from mining periodicals of the time. John Schofield described his work of surveying the Baker mining claims covering the Bulldog Mountain Mine for patent. Mrs. Robert Wardell, Clerk of the Mineral County Court, provided information on mining litigation at Creede and the Costilla Combined Courts, San Luis, Colorado. She also located old court records of perhaps the first court case concerning water pollution from a mining operation in Colorado. Thomas Howell, an old friend from high school days, gave information about his father, Dr. Thomas Howell, who was an officer in a company that almost discovered the very rich Bulldog Mountain Vein System fifty years before it was developed and mined.

The staffs of the University of Arizona Libraries, the Arthur Lakes Library and Geology Museum at the Colorado School of Mines, the Denver Public Library's Western History Collection, the Colorado Historical Society's Stephen H. Hart Library, the Linda Hall Library of Kansas City, Missouri, and the Nanini Branch of the Tucson Public Library all contributed to research for the book. Special thanks go to Sandra Howard and Jan Jacobs of the Creede Historical Library, Rebecca Lintz of the Stephen H. Hart Library, and John Talbot, an ex-Creede miner who helped me by researching old records at the Arthur Lakes Library.

Pictures used throughout the text came from many sources, including the U.S. Geological Survey and Bureau of Mines, the Creede and Colorado Historical Societies, the Denver Public Library's Western History Collection, the Library of Congress, the Colorado Mining Association, and the Monte Vista (Colorado) Historical Society. John Jackson provided pictures of Creede miners and mines that he had taken over the years or were in his personal collection. Dave Bunk, Sandy Kroll, Ken Wyley, Will Foreman, and David Huston graciously allowed the use of their pictures. Will took pictures of the miners driving openings for the Creede Mining Museum. Les Turnipseed and Dave Bunk allowed me to include copies of their Creede mining company stock certificates in the book.

Last, but certainly not least, I wish to thank Duane Smith of Fort Lewis College in Durango and Maureen Pierre of La Jolla, California, for the encouragement they have given me during the preparation of the manuscript.

Richard C. Huston
Tucson, Arizona

TABLE OF CONTENTS

PROLOGUE

THE CREEDE MINING DISTRICT is located in the center of the San Juan Mountains in Colorado. The San Juans are called the "Alps" of America for good reason. They are picturesque and beautiful with high rugged peaks separated by deep valleys carved by water, wind, and glaciers. The broad, crescent-shaped valley of the Rio Grande River in the vicinity of Creede is an unusual feature in the San Juans where narrow, steep canyons are the norm. The Rio Grande spills out of the narrow, constricted Box Canyon southwest of Creede into a wide and gently sloped valley that abruptly turns north from its previous southeast course as if repulsed by an obstruction to its normal direction of flow. The wide, gently sloped valley follows a sweeping curved north, then east past Creede, where it slowly turns south around Snowshoe Mountain to Wagon Wheel Gap where it again enters a narrow canyon and resumes a southeast course. Elevations vary from the 14,000-foot San Luis Peak on the Continental Divide to a low of 8,000 feet where the Rio Grande emerges from the San Juans. Verdant forests of spruce, pine, fir, and aspen, flower-dotted open meadows, rushing mountain streams, and sparkling lakes complete the landscape. Deposits of valuable metals, including gold, silver, copper, lead, and zinc have been found throughout the San Juans and have produced a large portion of Colorado's mineral wealth. The landscape and mineral deposits both result from the geological processes that created these mountains.

IN THE BEGINNING

San Juan geology and ore deposits have been the center of scientific study and geologic research beginning in 1895 by the U.S. Geological Survey and continuing to the present. Others, such as mining company geologists, contributed to our knowledge of the San Juans, primarily in the late twentieth century. The U.S. Geological Survey's systematic study of the San Juans began with Whitman Cross, in 1905.[1] The first comprehensive report on the Creede district geology and ore deposits by Emmons and Larsen was published by the U.S. Geological Survey in 1923.[2] A very thorough study of geology and ore deposition in the Creede district by Steven and Ratté in 1965 was fundamental in defining geology of the Creede district and vicinity.[3] The Survey chose Creede in the late 1950s as a site for detailed research into the "anatomy and physiology" of a typical ore deposit.[4] This research continued into the 1990s.

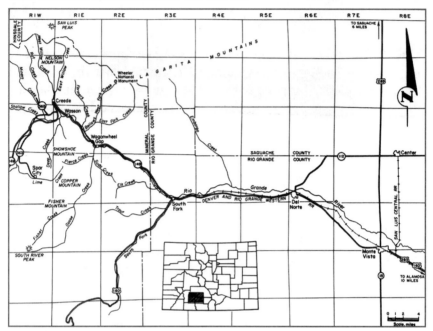

Location Map, Creede, Colorado

Creede was selected by the U.S. Continental Scientific Drilling Program as the site of deep drill holes to test the "roots" of the Creede ore deposits. The results of all this research were published in 2000 in the Geological Society of America's *Special Paper 346, Ancient Lake Creede* and is the reference, by and large, for this geologic history of the Creede area.

The San Juan Mountains are the largest erosional remnant of a much larger volcanic shield that covered what is now the southern Rocky Mountains up to a depth of 4,000 feet. The San Juans now cover an area of about 9,600 square miles and contain about 9,000 cubic miles of lava and other volcanic rocks. The volcanic rocks that mostly make up the San Juan Mountains are geologically young, the final product of geological processes that have been active for more than a billion years.

The oldest rocks in south-central Colorado are about 1.8 billion years old. These rocks were originally deposited as sediments at the bottom of an ancient sea. Subsequently the rocks were buried and

Black Canyon of the Gunnison — 1984
Photo by David Huston

heated, which caused them to change, or "metamorphose," into
"metamorphic" rocks termed "gneisses" and "schists" by geologists. A gneiss is a relatively coarse-grained rock that contains bands
with differing mineral content, whereas a schist is a finer-grained
rock with minerals such as micas aligned to give the rock a foliation
pattern. At great depths, the heat causing the metamorphism can
melt the rocks to produce molten rock called "magma." If not
erupted to the surface, the magma cools and solidifies into coarse-
grained "igneous" rock such as granite. This period of metamorphism and magmatism extended from 1.7 to 1.5 billion years ago
and accompanied mountain building or "orogenesis." Although
these metamorphic and igneous rocks are covered by volcanic rocks
in the Creede area and cannot be seen, they are well exposed in the
Black Canyon of the Gunnison River some 45 miles north and along
the highway in the narrow canyon south of Ouray.

Like all mountain ranges in geologic time, these mountains eroded to form an erosional surface, or "unconformity," as it's called by geologists. By the beginning of the Cambrian geologic period, about 540 million years ago, the region that was to be the San Juan Mountains was again under water. It remained under water for another 500 million years, during which time gravel, sand, and mud were deposited and formed rocks such as conglomerates, sandstone, shale, and limestone.

Ouray, Colorado — 1996

Photo by the Author

Again, these rocks are not exposed around Creede, but they create the spectacular mountain scenery around Ouray, further to the west. It is a quirk of nature that fossils, such as corals, clams, and other shellfish, can be found in these sedimentary rocks more than 10,000 feet above sea level.

The geological processes that formed the rugged San Juan Mountains and rich silver deposits of the Creede area began in earnest about 35 million years ago with the development of scattered volcanos. Volcanic activity occurs when a large body of molten magma is forced into the earth's crust. If magma is ejected through weak zones in the crust to the surface, the result is a rapidly cooled, fine-grained rock ranging from silica-poor, dark gray basalt through andesite and dacite to light gray or pink, silica-rich rhyolite.

The magma in the magma chamber is very hot (1,300 to 1,800 degrees Fahrenheit) and contains dissolved gases, mostly water vapor, under high pressure. As the magma rises toward the surface, the confining pressure is reduced and the dissolved gases separate from the magma much like they do when the cork on a champagne bottle is removed. As a general rule, basaltic magma is very fluid and remains so when the gases separate and therefore erupts as relatively fluid molten lava, as is the case in Hawaii's volcanic fields. On the other hand, rhyolitic magma is quite viscous, so the gases do not bubble away but may blow the magma apart into particles. Both modes of volcanic eruption occurred in the San Juans. The magma that created the first volcanos in the San Juan Volcano Field were basaltic to andesitic magmas, which produced non-explosive lava flows, like those in Hawaii. These lava flows coalesced to form about two-thirds of the total volume of the volcanic shield that covered the southern Rocky Mountains.

Over a period of one to two million years, about 28 million years ago, the character of magma in the San Juans changed from dominantly andesitic to rhyolitic. The character of volcanism also changed, becoming more explosive, more like the Mount St. Helens eruptions in Washington state. Geologists call the products of such explosive volcanism "pyroclastic" rocks. The term pyroclastic is derived from Latin for "fire broken." Catastrophic explosive pyroclastic eruptions forced large quantities of volcanic ash into the atmosphere. These hot ash clouds spread over the region, settled, and formed layers of volcanic tuff, 3,000 feet thick in places. This volcanic tuff consists of particles of rock that range from dust to small pebbles, with occasional fragments several feet in diameter. If the deposited layers are thick and hot enough the particles may be "welded" together by heat and pressure to form competent rock of varying degrees that resists erosion or, if not welded, may remain soft and easily eroded. Examples of both extremes are found near Creede. The high cliffs along Willow Creek north of Creede are typical of a strongly welded tuff. The Wheeler Geologic Area, the "Ghost City of the San Juans" twenty miles east of Creede, is an outstanding example of erosion of a non-welded tuff forming a most unusual series of spires and other fanciful shapes with incredible coloration, as if from another world.

The eruption of large volumes of magma to form extensive tuffs in the San Juans resulted in the formation of "calderas." Calderas are roughly circular segments of the earth's crust bounded by ring-shaped fractures, or faults, in the earth's crust that form when magma is ejected from a magma chamber, leaving a void. The roof of the chamber loses its support and collapses, leaving a roughly circular depression called a caldera at the surface. The tuffs and calderas of the central San Juan cluster are widely studied as exceptional sites of explosive volcanic processes. The floors of these calderas are uplifted by the pressure of the magma reintroduced into the chamber that created the caldera in the first place.

High Cliffs North of Creede — 2001

Photo by the Author

Wheeler Geologic Area — 1998

Photo by the Author

No fewer than seventeen large volume pyroclastic ash-flows erupted from the San Juan calderas. About a third of these calderas have economically significant mineralization. The Creede area was buried by immense ash-flows of more than 2,000 cubic miles that erupted from nine overlapping calderas, known as the Central San Juan Caldera Cluster, over a period of 1.5 million years. Calderas in the central cluster have diameters ranging from 7.5 to 46.5 miles for the La Garita caldera, one of the largest in the world. For compari-son, the Mount St. Helens eruption ejected 0.14 cubic miles of magma and left a crater 1.25 miles in diameter. Small potatoes compared to the volcanic activity in the San Juans!

Eruptions the size of the La Garita caldera are very rare and would be counted as one of the greatest catastrophes in nature, comparable to the impact of an asteroid. None have taken place during the world's recorded history.

Stages of Development of Resurgent Calderas

(Modified from Smith and Bailey)[5]

I. Regional doming of early intermediate composi-tion lavas and breccias.

II. Pyroclastic eruptions.

III. Caldera collapse.

IV. Post-collapse volcanism and sedimentation.

V. Resurgence and contin-uous sedimentation.

VI. Major ring-fracture volcanism.

Large volume pyroclastic ash-flows form incandescent,

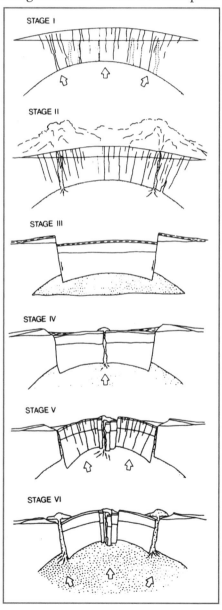

ground-hugging clouds that are fluidized and supported by hot gases, which are released and heated from the magma during eruption. These clouds race along at speeds of up to 325 feet per second or 220 miles per hour. Compare this with ash-flows during the later stages of the Mount St. Helens eruption on May 18, 1980, which had speeds of 100 feet per second. Ash-flows can move over hills and travel up to 100 miles.[6]

The ages of each of the San Juan calderas are indicated in parentheses in millions of years on the adjacent map.[7] The ragged outlines of the calderas indicate huge landslides that carried portions of the caldera walls into their craters. Note that later calderas overlapped those formed earlier in geologic time.

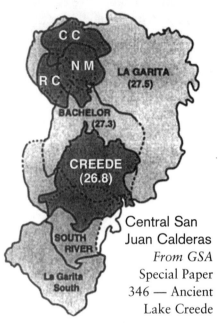

Central San Juan Calderas
From GSA Special Paper 346 — Ancient Lake Creede

Tuff formed from the La Garita caldera ash-flow has been identified sixty miles beyond the edge of its source caldera, across the present San Luis Valley and beyond. The La Garita ash-flow is among the largest in the world.

The Creede caldera, the youngest in the central San Juan cluster, developed about 26.8 million years ago. Mineralization in the Creede Mining District was deposited on the Creede caldera's northern margin approximately a million years after its collapse in faults that displaced the Creede Formation.

The Creede caldera is located immediately south of, and overlays, the Bachelor caldera. Other mineral deposits around the periphery of the Creede caldera include the Spar City district along its southern margin and the Wagon Wheel Gap fluorspar deposit along the eastern margin. Hot springs are located at Wagon Wheel Gap and Antelope Springs southeast and southwest of Creede respectively. Eruption and subsidence of the near-circular caldera occurred at the same time and a very large mass of welded tuff and landslide material from the sides of the caldera accumulated in the subsiding area, 7.8 miles in diameter. Magma re-entered the original chamber and caused the resurgence of a domed core (Snowshoe

Mountain) in the center of the caldera with slopes as steep as forty-five degrees. As the central dome rose, a moat formed around the dome and filled with water — ancient Lake Creede.

In the beginning, the lake was in a closed basin. Water flowing into the lake evaporated, so no water flowed out. Much like California's Mono Lake, ancient Lake Creede became very salty. Sedimentary materials were deposited in the lake in the northerly portion of the moat and formed shales and sandstones. Travertine, or calcium carbonate, was also deposited and represents mineral spring activity during sedimentation. The resulting sedimentary

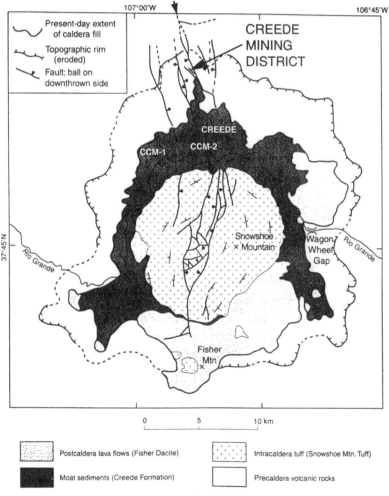

Arrows indicate line of Section on Figure 3

Geologic Map of the Creede Caldera

From GSA Special Paper 346 — Ancient Lake Creede

rocks were named the Creede Formation.[8] Dating has indicated that the Creede Formation was deposited in a period of no more than 234,000 years. Later lava flows completely filled the southeastern portion of the moat. The ancestral Rio Grande breached the eastern wall of the Creede caldera 23 to 21 million years ago and, for the first, time water flowed out of the lake.

About 26 million years ago, volcanism in the San Juans diminished and shifted to the eruption of basaltic and rhyolitic lavas concurrent with the beginning of regional extension faulting associated with the opening of the Rio Grande Rift. The Rio Grande Rift, a feature of movement in the earth's crust that forms basins and ranges, cut New Mexico in half and split Colorado up the middle to the vicinity of Leadville. It has been likened to a plowed furrow in a field with raised shoulders and filled with soil. In the San Luis Valley area, the Sangre de Cristo and San Juan Mountains represent the raised shoulders of the rift and the valley the furrow filled with soil — up to 30,000 feet of it! During the opening of the Rio Grande Rift, the Colorado Plateau region, including the San Juans, appear to have been rotated 15 degrees clockwise. Basaltic lavas erupted intermittently until about five million years ago.

The core of the earlier Bachelor caldera that collapsed immediately north of the Creede caldera was uplifted as a resurgent dome. As the dome rose, the brittle, welded tuff that had filled the caldera fractured, or as geologists say, "faulted," along the top of the dome instead of stretching. This faulted block, or Creede graben, dropped down relative to the rising sides of the dome. This process is shown in "Stages V and VI — Stages of Development of Resurgent Calderas," shown on page 7. The German word "graben," meaning "ditch," comes from the geologic term "horst and graben," used to describe the geology of "basin and range" topography prevalent in Nevada where narrow mountain ranges parallel adjoining flat-bottomed basins. The mountains, or "horsts," are uplifted blocks of the earth's crust separated by faults from the adjoining basins or downthrown "grabens." The Creede graben is bounded by four fault zones; the Alpha-Corsair and Bulldog Mountain on the west, and the Amethyst and Solomon-Holy Moses on the east. These are shown on the "Map of the Creede Mining District, Colorado."

Ore deposition occurred in the Creede Mining District about 25 million years ago following the collapse of the Creede caldera and the formation of ancient Lake Creede. At that time a body of molten rock formed, penetrating the earth's crust beneath the northern part

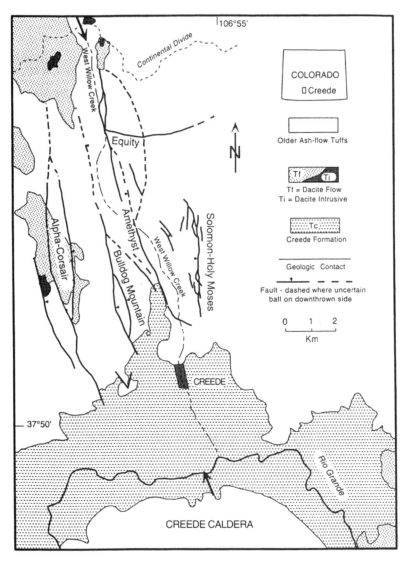

Map of the Creede Mining District, Colorado
*(Arrows indicate section showing Model of Hydrothermal
Ore Deposition)*
From GSA Special Paper 346 — Ancient Lake Creede

of the Creede Mining District. Heat from the cooling and crystal-
lization of this body created a circulating hot water or "hydrothermal" system that drew in saline waters from ancient Lake Creede.
The lake derived its moisture from rain and snowmelt primarily
from the highlands to the north and waters given off from the cooling body of solidifying rock. These waters mixed and boiled in open

fractures along faults of the Creede graben as they approached the then-existing surface. As the mixture's temperature and pressure dropped, the amount of minerals that could be carried in solution was dramatically reduced. As a result, silver and base metal minerals were deposited from solution to form a vein-type deposit. The deposit is termed an "epithermal" deposit by geologists, as it was formed about 1,500 feet below the existing surface.

The waters then discharged from the Amethyst fault zone into the top of the Creede Formation through an ancient stream channel filled with sedimentary rock where economic minerals were also deposited. The Wagon Wheel Gap fluorspar deposit was formed about 21 million years ago as part of another epithermal mineral system.

A high plateau, punctuated by volcanic cones and the remnants of caldera rims, resulted from volcanic activity. Erosion of the plateau surface formed a bench and table land topography. A period of regional uplift between five and two million years ago that raised the Creede area as much as 3,000 feet resulted in rapid erosion, and is commonly called the canyon cycle of erosion in the southern Rocky Mountains. Down-cutting by the Rio Grande River during this period removed the top half of the Creede Formation in the caldera moat and exhumed the Creede caldera, thus forming the wide, gently sloped river valley we see today. This period of erosion exposed the tops of the Creede ore deposits to oxidation by the elements.

The apex of the veins near the surface were commonly leached and low grade. The richest parts of the vein were below the leached portions of the veins as silver, and other minerals leached from above were re-deposited near the water table. These enriched ores were exposed at the surface in only the Last Chance and Amethyst Mines. In fact, if the deep canyons of East and West Willow Creeks had not been cut following the regional uplift of the Southern Rocky Mountains between two and five million years ago, which exposed the enriched ores, it is possible that the ore deposits at Creede would not have been discovered.

The Bulldog Mountain deposit was not found by the thousands of prospectors and miners who walked over Bachelor Mountain in the 1890s because its small exposed barite veinlets attracted no determined exploration, and discovery awaited the fundamental geologic studies by U.S.G.S. scientists in the late 1950s.[9]

Epithermal mineral deposits are characterized by low-temperature minerals, open-space filling in veins, and near-surface deposition. The

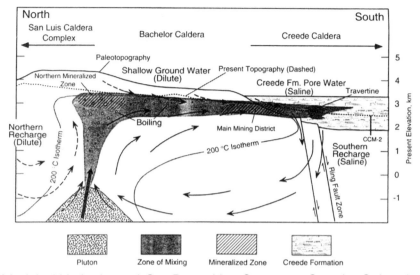

Model of Hydrothermal Ore Deposition System at Creede, Colorado
From GSA Special Paper 346 —Ancient Lake Creede

economic minerals in the Creede deposits include gold, silver, argentite (silver sulfide), galena (lead sulfide), sphalerite (zinc sulfide), and chalcopyrite (iron-copper sulfide). They are associated with gangue, or non-economic minerals, including quartz, chalcedony, rhodochrosite, barite, chlorite, pyrite, hematite, siderite, and adularia. Anglesite (lead sulfate) and cerussite (lead carbonate) occurred, along with rich pockets of native silver, in oxidized portions of the veins mined in the early days of the district. The Bulldog Mountain Mine is well known for crystallized minerals including native silver and barite, as well as cuprite, mimetite, pyrargyrite, pyrostilpnite, and roasasite.[10] The Commodore Mine on the Amethyst Vein System has been a source of classic specimens of silver minerals, sulfides, and gangue minerals since the 1890s. Cuprite, turquoise, and the rare mineral ktenasite are also known from this mine.[11] The Amethyst Vein received its name from the purple amethyst quartz crystals found in it. A beautifully banded rock consisting of massive amethyst and white quartz found in the Amethyst Vein was named "sowbelly" by the early miners because it reminded them of salt pork.

The canyon cycle of erosion, along with glaciation in the past million years, has formed the San Juan Mountains as we know them today. The Pleistocene Epoch, an interval of two million years, ended about 11,000 years ago and was a time of repeated climatic changes. This included the last ice age when continental ice sheets covered much of North America and glaciers were present in moun-tainous areas, even in the tropics. Evidence of glaciation exists in the Creede area. The Rio Grande and its tributaries were intensely glaciated during Pleistocene time as indicated by "hanging valleys" formed on the tributaries of the Rio Grande. These hanging valleys were formed as the glacier gouged away the sides of the river valley as it moved downstream. Glacial debris along area streams and a termi-nal moraine a few miles upstream from Creede give further evidence of the glacier. The world's climate began a warming trend about 20,000 years ago, and the ice sheet and glaciers retreated. They were gone 7,000 years ago except for small remnants.

Fossils are found in the Creede Formation and are similar to those from the slightly older Florissant lake beds near Colorado Springs. Fossil studies identified twenty-two plant genera.[12] Carbonized plant, feather, and insect remains can be found in fine-grained, brown shale partings. Fossils have been found at sites near the intersection of the Creede airport road and Colorado Highway 149 and near the Five- and Seven-Mile Bridges on Highway 149.

ANCIENT MINERS

The Pleistocene ice age had a dramatic effect on the world. Much of the world's water was tied up in ice, thus lowering the ocean levels and creating a land bridge between Asia and North America in the vicinity of the Aleutian Islands. Early man migrated to North America from Asia across this land bridge, called "Beringia." There are indications that this migration of Paleo-Indians started as early as 50,000 years ago and continued until migrants had made their way to the southern tip of South America.

About 25,000 years ago, these Paleo-Indians learned a new technology — making functional tools such as knives, scrapers, and projectile points out of stone, especially flint, chert, and obsidian. In order to provide the raw materials for making tools, the flint, chert, and obsidian had to be found and mined by ancient miners.

A record of over 10,000 years of human occupation is preserved in the upper Rio Grande River drainage. As the glaciers retreated and the climate warmed, large animals moved into the higher elevations during the warmer months. Paleo-Indian hunter-gatherers followed these animals as they migrated. Two locations, the Linger and Zapata kill sites, where these hunters butchered an extinct bison species were found in the 1930s near the Great Sand Dunes National Monument in the San Luis Valley. More kill sites have been found since. Large mammals, such as the mammoth, mastodon, large bison, and saber-toothed cats, became extinct near the end of the Pleistocene time. Some researchers feel that this was the result of over-hunting by the Paleo-Indians.

The Black Mountain Folsom site, located eleven miles west of Creede, was a seasonal camp used by Folsom hunters 10,600 years ago. Folsom hunters were Paleo-Indians who lived in North America at the time of the last glacial age. They were given the name "Folsom" after their fluted arrowheads were found near Folsom, New Mexico. The site was discovered in 1977 by Marilyn Montorano and Vincent Spero, a Forest Service archeologist, while investigating an area being considered for a timber sale.[13]

The Smithsonian Institution, in cooperation with the U.S. Forest Service and the San Luis Valley Archeological Network, studied the site beginning in 1991. Folsom projectile points, scrapers, and other tools were found. Chert for the tools came from several sources, but the majority came from a source on the headwaters of the Piedra River thirty-two miles distant. The Black Mountain Folsom site and Piedra River source of the chert were connected by trails and it is likely that the Folsom people wintered at lower elevations in the San Juan basin. They passed the source of the chert and mined it on their way to their summer camp where they manufactured points and other tools. Thus, the first miners in the Creede area arrived 10,600 years ago! Other Folsom sites likely exist in the Creede area since Folsom artifacts have been found at different places around Creede.[14]

The Indian tribes throughout the pre-history period hunted in the upper Rio Grande area during the summers but never became permanent dwellers there. For thousands of years they migrated into San Luis Valley over Poncha Pass to the north, Mosca and Medano Passes to the east, and the Wolf Creek Pass area to the southwest as attested to by the many artifacts they left behind in their travels. The Utes inhabited the San Juans when the white man arrived in the region. Projectile points have been found in Phoenix Park on East Willow Creek north of Creede, suggesting that Phoenix Park was a summer camp site for the Utes. The Wagon Wheel Gap hot springs was an important locale to the Indians, who believed that the springs had curative powers. There is no evidence that the Indians used minerals found in the Creede ore deposits.

EARLY HISTORY

The Spanish colonization of New Mexico did not extend into the upper Rio Grande River drainage even though the Spanish apparently explored the area. A small number of Hispanic families settled in the San Luis Valley, not too far from the established New Mexican settlements, as early as 1833. The first permanent settlement established in Colorado was at San Luis in the southern San Luis Valley in 1851.[15] The town of Loma was settled in 1859 on the north bank of the Rio Grande across the river from what was to be the American town of Del Norte. These Hispanic settlers irrigated their fields with water from the Rio Grande and grazed their animals in the wide, grassy meadows on the valley floor. They did not go into the mountains looking for other treasures.

In 1860, a small party of American prospectors, known as the Baker party, followed the Rio Grande upstream from the Mexican settlements in the San Luis Valley into the San Juans looking for gold. By one account, they crossed the Continental Divide at the headwaters of the Rio Grande into the Animas River drainage where they prospected at Baker's Park. Wagon Wheel Gap, downriver from Creede, was supposedly named for a wheel that was found along the old trail through the gap, presumably from a Baker party wagon. The author still likes the story he heard as a child about how Wagon Wheel Gap got its name. The Indians stretched a rope strung with scalps across the gap and weighted it in the center with a settler's wagon wheel! Not very likely, but intriguing to a youngster.

The Baker party did not find the gold they hoped for and, after a hard winter in the mountains, left for the east the next spring. By 1870, mining activity in the western San Juans had greatly increased after several years of inactivity. In fact, there was enough traffic along the Rio Grande for Del Norte to become the supply center for the San Juan mines in 1871.

The treaty of 1868 between the U.S. Government and the Ute Indian tribe gave the Utes the exclusive right to that portion of Colorado west of the 107th meridian and south of an east-west line fifteen miles north of the 40th parallel. This included most of the San Juans and no miners, farmers, or ranchers were allowed on Ute land. The 107th meridian passes north and south a few miles west of Creede. The first miners into the San Juans were, therefore, trespassers. A council was held at the Los Pinos Indian Agency in August, 1872, to resolve land disputes created by the miners, but the Utes refused to leave the mining areas. The federal government sent Felix Brunot, chairman of the federal government's Peace Commission, west to get the Utes to sign a treaty ceding about four million acres of mineral lands. This they did, but they would not give up agricultural lands. The Brunot Treaty of 1873 rescued the San Juan miners from their status as trespassers by paying the Utes twelve cents an acre for the disputed lands. What a bargain, or on the other hand, a monumental theft! The Utes were expelled from the mining areas of the San Juans in 1873. A Del Norte paper printed this poem:[16]

> *Then shout the glad tidings,*
> *Triumphantly sing;*
> *The San Juan is opened,*
> *We've busted the ring.*

Ultimately the Utes were expelled from all of Colorado in 1879 after the Meeker massacre, except for the Southern Ute Indian Reservation located on the southern edge of the state west of the 107th meridian.

EARLY TRANSPORTATION

Development of the San Juan mines depended on the construction of access roads for the transportation of people, heavy mining machinery, and supplies. The first wagon road into the area was built along the Rio Grande from Del Norte to Antelope Springs, southwest of the present Creede. Antelope Park was the site of San Juan City, Hinsdale County's first county seat. A group of Del Norte businessmen formed a company, the Del Norte and San Juan Toll Road, to build the road in 1873.[17] The road was ultimately extended over the Continental Divide at Stony Pass at an elevation of 12,600 feet above sea level and dropped down Cunningham Gulch into Howardsville. It followed the route earlier prospectors had taken

Stony Pass
Road on the
East Side
of the
Continental
Divide —
1998
Photo by the
Author

into the western San Juans. By far the most difficult section of the road was over Stony Pass. It was built by Major E.M. Hamilton in 1872 to haul heavy machinery to the Little Giant Mill.[18]

By 1881, a second road had been constructed to Lake City over Spring Creek and Slumgullion Passes. It branched off from the Stony Pass Road at Antelope Park and was financed by a company formed in Del Norte in June 1875, called the Antelope Park and Lake City Toll Road. The road was constructed in the summer and fall of 1875. A toll of $2.50 for each wagon with one pair of horses was charged, with an additional fifty cents for each additional pair of horses. Pack animals were charged twenty cents each and a saddle horse twenty-five cents. The loose cattle, mules, and horses were rated at twenty cents each and sheep and goats five cents per animal. Barlow & Sanderson initiated regular stagecoach service to Lake City from Del Norte in 1876. The company's Concord stages had a capacity of thirteen passengers and were pulled by teams of six horses.[19]

The Denver and Rio Grande Railway extended its narrow-gauge railroad system over La Veta Pass to Alamosa in 1878. Del Norte continued for a time to be the supply center for the mines and the settlers in the upper Rio Grande since it was connected by an easily traveled wagon road to Alamosa and the rail terminus. Rails were laid southwest to Chama, New Mexico, in 1880, then to Durango, Colorado, in 1881, and on to Silverton in 1882 to provide direct rail service to the San Juan mines west of the Continental Divide. This, of course, was the death knell for the wagon road over Stony Pass, a difficult and dangerous route at best, particularly during the winter months. The Lake City road continues to this day as Colorado State Highway 149.

SETTLING THE UPPER RIO GRANDE

Tom Boggs, brother-in-law of Kit Carson, located at Wagon Wheel Gap in 1840.[20] He was most likely the first permanent settler along the upper Rio Grande. Very few settlers located in the area until transportation for supplies in and products out was available.

Construction of the railroad to Alamosa and roads into the western San Juans provided access into the upper Rio Grande River valley for settlers. Pastoral land along the Rio Grande in and adjacent to the broad crescent-shaped valley formed in the moat of the Creede caldera millions of years ago was opened for homesteads in accordance with the Homestead Act of 1872. This law gave individuals the opportunity to claim and patent up to 160 acres of land in the public domain if certain age and citizenship requirements were met. In addition, the homesteader had to build a residence on the land and live there at least six months out of the year for each of five years. These early settlers built permanent structures to protect against the terribly cold, snowy weather during the winters on the upper Rio Grande and became the first permanent residents of the area.

The Homestead Act was passed by Congress as an incentive for people to settle the West. More than 200 homesteads were filed on in the upper Rio Grande between 1880 and 1929 from Pearl Lakes to the Old Riverside Ranch downstream from Wagon Wheel Gap.[21] Many individuals important to the history of Creede Camp homesteaded land along the Rio Grande.

The oldest homestead was patented in 1880 by Major Martin Van Buren Wason. He expanded his homestead by purchasing additional land. At one time he owned or controlled over 2,000 acres between Wagon Wheel Gap and Creede where he raised fine horses and cattle.[22]

Wason was born in Vermont in 1823. He went to South America at the age of eighteen where he was successfully involved in mining in Brazil and Panama. He came to Colorado in 1871 from Wyoming before finally settling in the upper Rio Grande. M.V.B. Wason died at his ranch in 1903 in his early eighties.[23] He had a very active role in the history of early Creede, as will be described in a later chapter.

Mystery surrounds Harriet Louise Wason, wife of M.V.B. Wason. A story that made the rounds at the time was that she was traded to Wason by a band of Indians for some horses. Actually, she was born in England and educated in Pennsylvania. She married Henry H. Wilcox, an Englishman, after the Civil War. They had several children and in 1875 the Wilcox family settled in Del Norte. Shortly thereafter Wilcox left, and Harriet filed for divorce. She and Wason were married in November 1877. She lived on the Wason Ranch until her death on August 16, 1904.[24]

EARLY TOURISM

The upper Rio Grande has always been a mecca for hunters and fishermen from the time of the Folsom people to the present time. A tourist hotel was opened at Wagon Wheel Gap in 1876. Many of the early ranches provided room and board to hunters and fishermen. Fishermen from the San Luis Valley took the morning train to Creede, stopped off along the Rio Grande and fished all day, and then caught the evening train from Creede back home. The beautiful scenery of the surrounding mountains and valleys attracted tourists to the area, making tourism an important factor.

Wagon Wheel Hot Springs Hotel and Bath — 1905
Courtesy of the Denver Public Library Western History Collection

Fishing at Wagon Wheel Gap — Photo by W.H. Jackson, 1880
Courtesy of the Denver Public Library Western History Collection

The Denver and Rio Grande Railroad extended its tracks from Alamosa to South Fork in 1881 and from South Fork to Wagon Wheel Gap in 1883. Trees along the railroad right-of-way were hand hewn and cut into railroad ties. Square hewn stumps were still visible in 1955, showing that the tie-cutters first shaped ties from the tree trunks with an axe, and then cut the tree down. The line was built primarily to carry visitors to the hot springs west of Wagon Wheel Gap that supposedly had medicinal and therapeutic properties. General William Jackson Palmer, founder of the Denver and Rio Grande Railroad, visited the hot springs as early as 1880 and decided to promote them as a tourist attraction. At his direction, the line was extended to Wagon Wheel Gap. General Palmer owned an interest in the hot springs property that had been developed with overnight lodging facilities and a large stone bathhouse. The General would invite his friends to visit the Wagon Wheel Gap Hot Springs Resort, bringing them by private train to the resort and then lavishing them with relaxing dips in the hot springs, fantastic trout fishing, and gourmet dining. In fact, Palmer had Beaver Lakes on Goose Creek, a short distance away from the resort, stocked with trout, up to 250,000 of them, for his guests. Service to Wagon Wheel Gap was discontinued in 1889 because of heavy snows in the winter and the expense of putting the track back in shape in the spring.

Wagon Wheel Gap circa 1873

Sketch by Thomas Moran

CHAPTER 1

DISCOVERY

AS ONE MIGHT EXPECT, PROSPECTORS and miners traveling the road past Creede on their way to the mining areas of the San Juans were curious about possible mineral treasures to be found in the hills surrounding the Rio Grande. The first economic mineralization was found by prospectors on what is now known as the Alpha-Corsair fault zone near Sunnyside, a small camp about two miles southwest of Creede. Sunnyside was nearer to the wagon road along the Rio Grande and more accessible for prospecting by those early pioneers traveling to the western San Juans. Mineral locations were made here as early as the 1870s but were allowed to lapse. Perhaps the discovery on Deep Creek was one of them. A Mr. Gay, who was the Santa Fe Railroad's general freight agent at Topeka, Kansas, stated that he first found Creede in an article in *The Denver Republican*, April 8, 1892:

> *"According to Mr. Gay, the camp was first located by himself and four others, J.C. McKensie [John C. MacKenzie], John Bernitt, James Wilson, and a man named Jackson. This was in 1876, before the days of the Leadville boom and long before N. C. Creede was ever near the place.*
>
> *"It was in the winter of 1876 that Mr. Gay and his companions first struck ore near the banks of Deep Creek about one mile west of Willow Creek. The party prospected around the region for two or three years and developed a quantity of low grade ore. This was not very profitable and Mr. Gay returned to the railroad business in 1878, while McKensie and Bernitt continued operations for some time longer."*

The Deep Creek Mining and Milling Company was formed[1] but there is no record of any mine development at the Deep Creek area. It is most likely Gay was talking about the prospecting that John C. MacKenzie did at Sunnyside where he located the Alpha claim just above the confluence of Miners and Rat Creeks in 1883. He sold the claim to two brothers, Richard S. and J.N.H. Irwin, in 1885. The Irwins also located the Diamond I and Hidden Treasure lodes near the Alpha claim and actively prospected and developed their claims until 1890.[2] Their ore was concentrated in an "arrastre." Arrastre is the Spanish name for a crude device in which ore is crushed by a heavy stone pulled around a dish-shaped vessel by a rope attached to a long pole rotating about a central pivot and powered at the other end by a horse or mule. The crushed ore was then concentrated by gravity, that is, by water washing the lighter worthless rock away while the heavier valuable minerals settled and were saved. The concentrates were transported to Del Norte by ox team.[3] This early operation was unprofitable because of the inefficient methods used and the high cost of transportation, even though it was reported that assays of ore near the surface ran 1,000 ounces of silver to the ton.[4]

MacKenzie, along with H.M. Bennett and James A. Wilson, located the Bachelor claim on the south end of the Amethyst fault zone about July 1884. Some low-grade ore was taken out of shallow workings and taken to Sunnyside by pack animals where it was unsuccessfully treated in the arrastre.[5]

There is no record of any new discoveries from 1886 until August 1889, when N.C. Creede, E.R. Naylor, and G.L. Smith located the Holy Moses claim on what is now called Campbell Mountain. The name "Holy Moses" was taken from the exclamation made when the value of the find became apparent.[6]

The next summer N. C. Creede located the Ethel claim and C. F. Nelson located the Solomon, Ridge, and other claims. Creede and Nelson jointly located the Phoenix claim on October 2, 1889. These claims are two to three miles up East Willow Creek from the present-day town of Creede and are on the Solomon-Holy Moses fault zone. The mining district that was formed after these discoveries was called the King Solomon district, east of and nearly continuous with the Sunnyside district. The two districts were joined together to form the Creede district.

Creede and his partners worked the claim and took out some very good-looking silver ore. Major Lafayette E. Campbell, Creede's old army buddy from Fort Kearney, Nebraska, was then quartermaster of the Fort Logan military post. Creede turned to him when capital was needed to develop the Holy Moses claim. Campbell, in turn, interested David H. Moffat and Sylvester T. Smith, both from

Denver, in the Holy Moses. Moffat was the president and Smith the general manager of the Denver and Rio Grande Railroad. In October 1890, the Holy Moses was sold to Campbell, Moffat, and Smith for a sum of $70,000.[7]

The Holy Moses Mining Company was organized in October 1890 with Moffat as president, Smith vice-president, and Campbell treasurer and general manager. Creede was employed at $40 per month to prospect for the company and was to receive a third interest in any new discoveries he made.[8]

The announcement of the sale of the Holy Moses was the first notification to the outside world that an important discovery had been made and the news created a boom. Hundreds of prospectors descended on the area before snow fell in the fall of 1890. Most of the first prospecting effort was on Campbell Mountain. Ex-senator Thomas M. Bowen purchased the Ridge, Hiram, Mexico, and other properties on East Willow Creek owned by Charles F. Nelson for $21,000. His purchase inspired confidence in the district.[9]

The Holy Moses Mine — circa 1890
Courtesy of the Creede Historical Society

By the spring of 1891, the prospecting frenzy expanded into other areas, particularly on Bachelor Mountain, where the Bachelor claim had been located in 1884 on the Amethyst fault zone. Some of the richest finds in the district were made on the Amethyst fault zone that spring after the snow melted. John C. MacKenzie and W.V.

McGilliard located the Commodore claim in April 1891.[10] The New York claim was located on June 1, 1891, by Charles Born, who was grubstaked by S.D. Coffin and George K. Smith of Platoro, Colorado.[11] A few days later Born became dissatisfied with the claim and told Smith he could have it. Smith accepted and relocated the New York claim in his name. Theodore Renniger and Julius Haase, grubstaked by Ralph Granger and Eric Von Buddenbock, two butchers from Del Norte, Colorado, located the Last Chance claim in June 1891.[12] Creede visited the site of their discovery and, impressed with the indications of rich silver ore, prevailed on Renniger and Haase to define their claim. Creede then located the Amethyst claim adjacent to the Last Chance in the names of D.H. Moffat, L.E. Campbell, and himself.[13] Charles F. Nelson found and located the Del Monte claim in January 1891.[14]

The story behind the location of the Last Chance claim is rather interesting. An article in *The Denver Republican* of July 13, 1897, reported that:

> *"Ralph Granger and Eric Von Buddenbock were partners in a butcher shop in Del Norte before Creede became known as a mining camp. One morning early in 1890 two men entered the shop to buy some salt side. They were going into the hills above Wagon Wheel Gap, they said, on a prospecting trip. They dallied, talking mining and luck and suddenly, or as suddenly as Ralph Granger could say it, for he was neither quick in thought, speech or action, he exclaimed: 'I'll give you all the grub you can use for a month if you'll let me and Buddenbock in on what you find'. The prospectors, Theodore Renniger and Julius Haase, looked at the scant allowance of food which their means allowed them to buy, and with the more certain prospects of good food than a silver mine, they simultaneously agreed to live well at the expense of the butcher firm for one month in their weary lives. The provisions all told amounted to $13 and with them Renniger and Haase set out."*

Renniger hailed from Platoro and carried the mail to Summitville, the first gold camp in the San Juans. Haase was a resident of Del Norte at the time. One fine morning in June, the two men made their way to the Creede area and camped about a quarter mile from a pleasant grassy spot on Bachelor Mountain, where their three burros wandered off for some serious grazing. Renniger (Haase according to some) noticed that the burros were missing. He caught up with the errant animals, berating them in three languages, kicking and pelting them with rocks to move them along. As burros will do, they did not budge. Renniger (or Haase) sat down to wait the burros out. He began to casually chip at an outcrop of rock and struck a vein showing rich silver ore. Renniger (Haase) offered up thanks to the three burros and named the discovery the Last Chance. The very rich Last Chance Mine was discovered because of three obstinate burros!

Julius Haase sold his interest in the Last Chance to his three partners for $10,000 and left the prospecting business. In November 1891, Renniger and Von Buddenbock sold their third interests to a group of capitalists, Mr. Ward of New York, I.Z. Dickson of Denver, Jacob Sanders of Leadville, and Henry R. Wolcott and Senator Edward O. Wolcott, both of Denver, for $65,000 each. Ralph Granger kept his one-third interest, even though his partners offered him $100,000 for it.[15]

The Amethyst claim was named for the purple amethystine quartz, rich in silver, found at the discovery site. The name was also given to the Amethyst fault zone that contained most of the Creede ore bodies. The Amethyst turned out to be one of the most prolific mines in the district. Although the discovery of the Holy Moses was largely responsible for the intense exploration around Creede, it was the discovery of rich ore in the Last Chance that resulted in the rapid development of the district. However, Creede Camp was born the day Nicholas C. Creede drove the claim stake of the Holy Moses Mine!

JOHN MACKENZIE

John MacKenzie was born in Halifax, Nova Scotia, on January 22, 1838. He learned the trades of silversmithing and watchmaking and became knowledgeable in metallurgical methods of the time. In 1861 he went to the gold fields at Mooseland, Nova Scotia, where he began his lifelong occupation as a prospector and miner. He successfully explored for gold on the Essequibo and Caroni Rivers in British Guiana for that country's government. His health suffered because of the hot, damp climate and he moved to Colorado after a couple of years. After spending time in the vicinity of Georgetown, he left for Silverton in the San Juans. For some reason, he did not continue on to Silverton, but set up camp on Rat Creek, settling at Sunnyside.[16]

In addition to his prospecting, he owned and operated a sawmill in Sawmill Gulch, had a hunting lodge at lower Sunnyside, and filed on and patented a homestead on Miners Creek.[17] McKenzie Mountain was named after him. He died on October 14, 1894, at Del Norte and was buried in the Del Norte cemetery. He left no will, was not married, and a brother in Halifax was his only known relative.[18]

RICHARD IRWIN

Richard Irwin was born in Montreal, Canada, on September 29, 1841. At the age of seventeen, he crossed the plains to Camp Floyd, Utah, where he was employed for a short time as an express rider. In 1859 he was an Indian trader in the Wyoming territory, was an overland express rider in early 1860, and, in the summer following, began his career as a miner when he joined the Pike's Peak gold rush. He was a successful miner in Gilpin County for six years before prospecting throughout the West and western Canada. He had interests in British Columbia, as well as at Irwin, Cripple Creek, and Creede, Colorado.[19]

Irwin first visited Creede in 1885 when he and his brother, J.N.H. Irwin of San Francisco, purchased the Alpha claim. The Irwin brothers mined their claims until 1890. Richard Irwin was in Cripple Creek, Colorado, in 1891. N.E. Guyot remembered him:

> "Dick Irwin, the celebrated prospector, whose memory is perpetuated in the still existing town of Irwin, in Gunnison County, Colorado, made my assay shop his headquarters during the fall of 1891. Every alternate day, after ranging the hills and sampling the shallow workings on prospects, especially on Battle Mountain, Irwin would run his own samples in our furnace.
>
> "Irwin's results were not satisfactory to him, and after buying a small interest in the Hidden Treasure lode from Lafe Fyffe, which claim was purchased subsequently by the Portland Mine, Irwin departed for the Kootenay [British Columbia] country. At that time I think he was about fifty-five years old — a courteous, silent man. But his skepticism could not be veiled. He paid a few hundred dollars for his interest in the Hidden Treasure, and no doubt made a handsome profit, but he was another of the old-timers who saw little that was impressive on Battle Mountain."[20]

The Portland Mine was one of the important mines in the Cripple Creek District. Richard Irwin helped organize the towns of

Rosita and Irwin in Colorado and the adjacent mining districts. He returned to Sunnyside in 1893 for a short period of time when he re-opened the Alpha Mine. *The Creede Candle* reported on January 19, 1894, that Richard Irwin and family would move to Cripple Creek where Irwin would mine for gold and let the silver stay in the Alpha until the price of silver rose. Irwin wrote a letter to the editor of *The Creede Candle* that was published on January 13, 1893:

> *Honor to Whom Honor is Due*
> *To the Editor of the Candle:*
> *Will you kindly correct a mistake made in your sum-mary of the Creede Mining District published in your last issue, and in which I am credited with the discovery of the old Sunnyside mines.*
> *When Charles F. Nelson and I first came here from Tombstone, Arizona in March 1885, we found the origi-nal discoverer of this camp, John C. MacKenzie, with his partners, James Wilson (who died last spring of pneumo-nia at Wason's Ranch) and John Birnett (now of White Hills Camp, Arizona), all at work on the Bachelor Mine, and Henry C. Bennett, still of Sunnyside, joint owner in the Alpha Mine with Mr. MacKenzie. My brother, J.N.H. Irwin of San Francisco, and I soon after bought the Alpha from them in August 1885.*
> *Mr. MacKenzie, an old and successful Georgetown and Geneva, Colorado miner deserves the credit of keep-ing this camp alive for 10 years, and until Mr. Creede came over the range and discovered the Holy Moses, since which time you have given us a history of the great Creede camp. Yours, etc.*
>
> *R.S. Irwin*

NICHOLAS C. CREEDE

Nicholas C. Creede's early life is somewhat of a mystery.[21] His brother, or half-brother according to some, Jerome Harvey, stated that Creede was born on a farm near Fort Wayne, Indiana, in 1841. His given name was William H. Harvey. His father died when he was four and at twelve he had to support himself. He drifted to Iowa, where he worked on a farm. Others say he was born early in 1848 and lived with his family in Iowa until he was eight. One story about his early life declared that he loved a girl whom his brother, Jerome, also loved. The girl jilted William for Jerome and William renounced his family, home, and name, and adopted the alias — Nicholas C. Creede. According to Jerome Harvey, Creede changed his name from Harvey in 1886 or 1887 while living in Julesberg, Colorado, because of some trouble with the Indians. Major Lafayette E. Campbell, a business associate of Creede's for many years who knew Creede as far back as 1865 under the name of Creede, stated in an interview in *The Denver Republican* of July 13, 1897, that: "The Iowa Harveys are only half brothers of Creede. His father died when he was only eight years old and soon afterwards his mother married a widower named Harvey by whom she had children."

At the age of eighteen he moved to Omaha, Nebraska, the jumping off place for pioneers moving further west. There he spent time cutting timber along the Platte River and then floating the logs down to Omaha and selling them. About 1862 or 1863, Indian troubles broke out in the territory west of Omaha. The Pawnee and Sioux were engaged in tribal warfare at the time and both tribes considered white settlers as their enemies. At the height of this disturbance, the Pawnee showed a desire to be friendly with the white people but the Cheyenne joined with the Sioux in warfare against the settlers. In order to meet this threat, Captain Frank North organized his famous Pawnee Scouts, Pawnee Indian braves led by white officers, who rode across the plains guarding wagon trains and defending settlers against the hostile Indians. Nicholas Creede enlisted in the Pawnee Scouts. His ability was speedily recognized by Captain North, who made Creede a first lieutenant within a very brief period after his enlistment. He fought the Indians for seven years in Nebraska and Dakota and, because of his bravery, was known as the great "war chief." He became fluent in the Pawnee language.

For three or four years, Captain North's Pawnee scouts acted as armed guards for the men constructing the Union Pacific Railroad across the Great Plains. Lieutenant Creede frequently held command of the entire body of scouts during this period in the absence of Captain North.

Major Campbell in his newspaper interview also stated that: "I knew him (Creede) as far back as 1865 when I was in the Army, and he was a lieutenant in the Pawnee Scouts. He was not a man of remarkable intellect or much education, but his honesty was incorruptible; he was gallant, brave, persistent, and a man of indomitable will."

While with the Pawnee Scouts, Creede traveled to the Dakotas and saw the mining activities in the Black Hills where he was bitten by the gold and silver bug. Toward the close of the 1860s, the Indian hostility lessened. Creede mustered out of the Pawnee Scouts and settled in Julesburg, Colorado, where he traded with the Indians for a short period of time.

In 1870, with the desire for wealth uppermost in his mind, Creede moved to Pueblo, Colorado. The following spring he moved to Del Norte, Colorado, where he went on unsuccessful prospecting trips into the neighboring hills. He then traveled to Elizabethtown, New Mexico, in the winter of 1871, staked a placer claim, and made nine dollars in three days.

He returned to Pueblo for a few years, leaving in the spring of 1873 for Custer County, Colorado, where he again led the lonely life of a prospector. He prospected without success in the area where the famous Bassick Mine was located at a later date. From there he prospected in the San Juan country and Chaffee County. Then he went to Leadville, Colorado, nearly dying from pneumonia at California Gulch. He traveled back to Chaffee County in 1878, where he located the Monarch Mine and founded the mining camp of the same name about twenty miles west of Poncha Springs. Creede sold his claims at Monarch for $3,000. This was his first successful prospecting venture.

Not one to give up easily in his search for wealth, Creede returned to the San Luis Valley, where he located the Bonanza and Twin Mines south of the mining camp of Bonanza in the Cochetopa Hills. He developed the Twin Mines and subsequently sold it for $10,000, after which he made a prospecting circuit that took in Utah, Nevada, Arizona, and California. The trip occupied some years but was not financially profitable.

In 1888, N.C. Creede formed a prospecting and mining partnership with George L. Smith and Charles H. Abbott of Salida for four years. Smith and Abbott furnished the money and Creede commenced prospecting at Bondholder on Spring Creek, a tributary of Cebolla Creek, north of Creede across the Continental Divide.

The first claim of record in the Spring Creek Mining District at Bondholder was staked by Creede on August 23, 1887. He named it the Ruby Silver and described it as being on the headwaters of Spring Creek about three miles westerly from a bald mountain on the Continental Divide. He filed on two more claims in 1887 and 1888. Creede then came to the Creede area from the north, believing that he was following the extension of a vein he had prospected at Spring Creek on the west side of the Continental Divide.[22]

The U.S. Geological Survey's study of the Creede ore deposits many years later proved that Creede's belief was correct. Strands of the Amethyst fault do cross the Continental Divide at Spring Creek and indicate a link between the Creede ore deposits and mineralization at Bondholder.

Just before the dissolution of Creede's agreement with Smith and Abbott, he found rich silver-bearing float while prospecting on what is now called Campbell Mountain north of the present town of Creede. Eagerly he followed the float to its source and his quest for wealth ended in the discovery and location of the Holy Moses claim in August 1889.[23]

CHARLES F. NELSON

Charles F. Nelson will always be known and remembered as one of the locators and founders of the now famous camp of Creede, though he named the camp after his friend and fellow prospector, Nicholas C. Creede. Nelson was born in Copenhagen, Denmark, in 1845. Canfield described Mr. Nelson's prospecting and mining activities as follows:

> *"In 1885, Mr. Nelson, who with Dick Irwin had been prospecting in Rosita and Ruby camps, happened to be at a new camp which had just been started below Tombstone, Arizona. Here they learned that discoveries of gold had been made near what is now Creede. Nelson at once started for the new field and Irwin accompanied him. They reached the spot in March 1885. Here they learned that gold had been found, but in small quantities. Mr. Nelson resolved to prospect around Sunnyside. Here he made some locations which he afterwards sold out to Irwin. In 1887 Mr. Nelson in company with John C. Mackenzie went on a hunting trip across the range from Sunnyside and came to Cascade Creek, a branch of Cebolla Creek. Late in the fall they learned that N.C. Creede had been prospecting in that locality. The next spring as soon as they could get across the range they went over ready to find a new field for prospecting. They found Mr. Creede had just come back to the locality to continue prospecting. Nelson and Creede stayed there all of the summer of 1888. The two compared notes frequently, and Nelson told what he knew of the country*

*across the range. It was decided to trace the belt over, and
after staying there that winter, the two crossed the range
in the spring of 1889. After prospecting a while that
spring, Nelson went down into the valley and spent the
summer in the vicinity of Sunnyside. Creede hunted over
what is now Campbell Mountain, and in the summer
located the Holy Moses. In September, Nelson heard of
the discovery Creede had made and came over from
Sunnyside and has been in the camp ever since. In
November, Nelson and Creede each built himself a cabin
at a point on Nelson gulch. They spent the winter there.
Creede and two men working on the Moses, and Nelson
and one assistant sinking on the Phoenix. In May of 1890,
Nelson located the Solomon, and in August, found the
Ridge. In January 1891, Mr. Nelson went up Bachelor
Hill, on which were the old Bachelor and Manhattan loca-
tions, and following the float, found and located the Del
Monte claim."* [24]

In the winter of 1890-1891, Nelson built a cabin in Creede
Camp. The first church services in the new camp were held in his
cabin by the Reverend Sanderson of Denver in the summer of 1891.
Nelson, upon hearing that there was a preacher in camp who could
not find any place to preach, insisted that he use his cabin whenever
he wished.[25]

Nelson gave an interview to the *Denver News* while on a trip to
Denver that was reported in *The Creede Candle* (dates not known):

"Mr. Charles F. Nelson of Creede is in town and is a
guest at the Brunswick. Learning that Mr. Nelson was one
of the original two men who discovered the rich deposits at
Creede, being in company at the time with N.C. Creede,
after whom the camp has been named, a representative of
the News called upon him last night to get some trustwor-
thy information about the latest aspirants for wealth and
mining honors among the many rich towns and camps of
Colorado. Mr. Nelson gave an interesting description of
how the body of ore at Creede was discovered.

"My friend Creede and myself were out. He was
prospecting for Mr. George L. Smith and E.R. Nacley,
both of Salida, the latter being president of the First
National Bank of that town. I was prospecting on my*

own account. Early in July 1890, we came into the Willow Creek country. The year previous we had been working on the other side of the range and following the mineral belt which was discovered on that side we came over in July before alluded to — 1889. Creede discovered the Holy Moses, which was the first mine discovered in Creede camp. The name of the mine was adopted in an interesting way. When George L. Smith looked at some of the float he had picked up — he turned it over in his hands and ejaculated 'Holy Moses! that looks good.' And Holy Moses was henceforth the name of the property.

"This was the first mineral discovered in Creede. Then an extension of the Holy Moses was made, called the Cliff, and about this time, October 2, 1889, I discovered the Phoenix. 'How, you ask?' Well, Creede and I concluded to take a hunting trip, and in trying to make a trail for our horses so as to get down to the creek bottom, as there was a very difficult descent, I discovered the lode and the location of the Phoenix was the result. This was the sum total of discoveries for 1889. But during the winter Creede and myself stuck to the properties and worked on them — he and his help on the Holy Moses, while my assistants and myself hammered away at the Phoenix. There we were high up on the mountains, in the midst of the most magnificent scenery in Colorado — for the Creede country is marvelous in its scenic beauty — it is like an exaggerated continuation of the Grand Canon [sic]; the naked cliffs rising up perpendicularly for 1,000 to 1,500 feet — and rock effects that would send a Bierstadt or a Moran into an ecstacy of artistic delight. I cannot say however, that we enjoyed the scenery very much that winter. The snow was four feet deep; we were seven miles from a post office and snow shoes were our only means of locomotion. Besides it was colder than charity, and on one or two occasions hungry mountain lions followed us with anything but friendly tread. You may rest assured that we did not await any emphatic expression of their sentiments, however.

"In 1890, when the snow melted, we saw that the inaccessibility of the mines demanded a better outlet to Willow Creek, so we spent the summer in making trails and prospecting instead of working our mines.

"*About the middle of September a party consisting of Captain L.E. Campbell, Jim Brown and Eben Smith, well-known engineers representing Dave Moffat, came up and examined the Holy Moses Mine, their examination resulting in the sale of the property a few weeks later, including the Cliff extension and the Ethel, the latter having been discovered in July 1890. The consideration was $65,000.*

"*During the summer while trailing and prospecting, as I told you about before, other discoveries had been made. I located the Solomon and the Ridge Mines. By the way, the district is called 'King Solomon Mines', or rather 'mining district' after Rider Haggard's marvelous story, and promises to equal those legendary caves of treasure in a very modern and substantial manner.*

"*Other discoveries quickly followed. The lucky finds of Creede and myself became bruited abroad, and Thomas M. Bowen was one of the first operators to come in and inspect our treasure. He seemed so well-satisfied that he purchased from me the Solomon group of mines, including the Solomon, Ridge, the Hiram, the Mexico, and some outside property. The consideration was $21,000. Prospectors began coming in droves as soon as the wealth of the country had been advertised by the investments I spoke of before. The fabulous resources of the entire Willow Creek country in the vicinity of Creede began to be realized. [N.C.] Creede discovered in May 1890, or about that time, the vast deposit of ore now know as the Mammoth, as well as its extension, the Eclat. He sold the Mammoth to Moffat and Campbell — Capt. Campbell — for $5,000.*

"*It would take columns to recite the other prospects discovered between then and now. I only wanted to show you what a very short time it took to place Creede Camp among the leaders in the mineral districts. But the most important strikes were made last summer, and Creede, from an original population of two, is now a bustling burg of about 1,200 souls, every mother's son of whom has a splendid opportunity to achieve a competence. The recent history of the district is too well-known to Denverites to need repetition. The vast deposits of the Amethyst and Last Chance Mines — among the latest* *discoveries, being found in August seem to authorize the name given the district, 'King Solomon Mines'. The ore runs about $170 to the ton, and is growing richer all the time. About five car loads a week are shipped to the Denver Sampling Works; it is very easy to mine the ore; it needs no sorting and there are five foot veins in both the Amethyst and Last Chance, which are all in pay ore. I have been prospecting and operating mines for nineteen years, in Colorado, Nevada, Utah, New Mexico, Arizona, and California, and I have never seen a better indication for a prosperous mining district, when its immature age is taken into consideration, than that which presents itself in the King Solomon district.*

"*As the reporter was about to leave his interesting companion, he was called back.*

"'*By the way, don't forget that the Denver & Rio Grande runs right into the heart of Creede and we all thank Dave Moffat for putting us in quick communication with the outside world.'*

"*Mr. Nelson will return to the King Solomon district in a few days and continue the prosecution of development work on several of his prospects.*"

CHARLES BORN

Charles Born immigrated from Germany in the early 1860s and for fourteen years worked for Steinway & Company, the New York piano manufacturer, as a cabinet maker. He moved to Del Norte in 1879 and then to Silverton in 1880 where he engaged in cabinet making. He returned to Del Norte where he lived until the discoveries at Creede attracted his attention. In addition to being one of the locators of the famous New York Mine, he held some patented claims in the district. He left Creede and went to Arizona where he located some valuable copper claims in the Constellation and Lynx Creek districts. Charles Born died in June 1908, at the age of sixty-six in Prescott, Arizona.[26]

S.D. COFFIN

S.D. Coffin is one of the pioneers of the Creede Camp, having gone there in December 1890. He built the first house in Jimtown, began work on Mammoth Mountain, and located the Rio Grande, Silver King, Mary Anderson, and other claims, including the New York claim on the Amethyst Vein. Mr. Coffin had the rare luck to be on the ground floor when the Amethyst and Last Chance lodes were discovered. The Last Chance people, in order to get a full claim, amended their survey to include Mr. Coffin's New York claim, and started litigation to clear title of their claim. A compromise was reached to resolve the difficulties between the New York and Last Chance owners, which resulted in the formation of the Consolidated New York Company.[27]

JULIUS HAASE

Julius Haase sold his share in the Last Chance Mine to his partners for $10,000. One story has it that he had to stay and help work the mine until it yielded his $10,000. Haase was born in Germany in 1858. Clarinda K. Sewell related Haase's story in a newspaper article in the *Monte Vista Journal*:

> *"The Haase Hay Ranch, known as the Hess Ranch, was purchased by the real discoverer of the Last Chance Mine and is the first Creede mining money thus far discovered to be invested in land upon which the purchaser planned to make his home. The ranch remained in the family for many years and is still in operation today within the holding of McNeill in the Rock Creek area and has always been in native grass."*

After receiving payment for his share in the Last Chance, Haase returned to Germany to visit his foster mother who had cared for him during childhood. Both parents, Julius Albert Hasse, Sr., and Katerene Guilstine Hasse, died of cholera just a week apart in August 1859, when he was nine months old. The seven years following his stay with his foster mother were spent in an orphanage where he was sent to work for "rich farmers," as he called them. At fourteen, he ran away from the orphanage and joined a merchant ship as a cabin boy. For the next fourteen years he worked on ships. In 1885, he jumped ship in Brooklyn, New York, then worked as a longshoreman and on a river boat for the next two years. An uncle in Del Norte, Otto Lewis, wrote to Julius that "this is a beautiful country and you could find gold almost anywhere." Haase arrived in Del Norte in 1885. He was disappointed that Del Norte was such a small place.

Upon returning from his visit to Germany, he purchased a hay ranch on Rock Creek south of Monte Vista for $7,000. He asked his neighbor, Tony Telinde, if he knew any nice girls who wanted to get married. Telinde said yes, that he had a daughter who would make a good wife. Telinde's daughter and Haase were married October 6, 1892 and set up housekeeping on the ranch. Haase died September 15, 1925, and his wife in 1955. Both are buried in the Rock Creek cemetery southwest of Monte Vista.[28]

ERIC VON BUDDENBOCK
Eric Von Buddenbock toiled during his life at what work he could find, and his wife added to the family's income by taking in washing. As a result, her health suffered. After he had received $65,000 for his share of the Last Chance Mine, he made his wife stop working and hired servants to take care of the household duties. Shortly thereafter he bought a pretentious two-story home in Del Norte. He then purchased the Philip Rengel Brewery in Del Norte. Von Buddenbock's wife died not long after their good fortune. After his wife's death, Von Buddenbock and his three sons moved to Trinidad, Colorado, where they continued in the brewery business. Von Buddenbock was one of the butchers who grubstaked Haase and Renniger when they located the Last Chance claim.[29]

RALPH GRANGER
Ralph Granger continued living in Del Norte after retaining his one-third interest in the Last Chance Mine. He was the other Del Norte butcher who grubstaked Haase and Renniger. Just prior to his good fortune, he married the daughter of a Baptist minister in rural Iowa. They settled in a modest frame house in Del Norte and their neighbors agreed that Mrs. Granger was a model housewife. When income from the mine became available, the Grangers moved into a much larger house in Del Norte that was furnished with the finest that money could buy. Granger was generous with his new-found wealth. None of his or his wife's family were ever in need afterward. However, Mrs. Granger was not happy. She told her neighbors that she had been happier when she had to do Ralph's washing. The Grangers moved to California shortly thereafter.[30]

The following pictures of five discoverers are from *Mines and Mining Men of Colorado*.[31]

Nicholas C. Creede

John MacKenzie

Richard Irwin
and Family

Charles F. Nelson   S.D. Coffin

CHAPTER 2

HERE COMES THE RAILROAD

FOR ANY MINING VENTURE TO BE SUCCESSFUL, an economical method must be found to transport the ore or concentrates to the smelter for treatment and, subsequently, to transport the resulting metal to market. In the early days of mining in the West, the railroads fulfilled this need. Governor John Evans of Colorado had made the statement that "Colorado without rails is comparatively worthless."[1] At first, until the railroad arrived at newly found mining districts, furnaces were constructed near a producing mine to smelt the ores from that specific mine. As more mines were developed, the owner of the furnace purchased ores from them for smelting and, if the arrangement was profitable, other plants were erected in the district to carry out the business of smelting and producing the final metal products.

As an example of the greater economy of smelting the ores near the mine instead of shipping crude ore a long distance, consider the case of a rich silver-lead ore, typical of those then produced in Colorado. A ton of the typical rich ore contained about 100 troy ounces of silver to the ton and four to six per cent lead. The 100 ounces of silver, when smelted out of the crude ore, weighs less than nine pounds and takes up the space of a cube measuring less than 2.75 inches on a side. Lead, at six per cent, weighs 120 pounds per ton of ore. The cost of shipping the 129 pounds of metal is much less expensive than shipping 2,000 pounds of crude ore by a factor of about sixteen to one weight-wise and much more when volume is considered.[2]

The first successful silver-lead smelter in Colorado, Leadville's Harrison Reduction Works, was constructed in 1877 by Edwin Harrison, president of the St. Louis Smelting and Refining Company.[3] Eilers and Billing erected a smelter at Leadville in 1879 that later became the Arkansas Valley Smelter, which processed much Creede ore. At the end of 1880, eleven or twelve smelters were

in operation in the Leadville district.[4] The Leadville smelting industry eliminated the great cost and difficulties in shipping crude ore to
the St. Louis and other eastern smelters, which led to the success of
early mining at Leadville. The Leadville success led to the establishment of a silver-lead smelting industry to serve other mining districts
in Colorado, including Creede Camp.

The enriched oxidized silver ore found at Creede was not suitable for mechanical concentration methods used at the time and,
therefore, was shipped direct to the smelters without any prior
treatment. In fact, close-by smelting was a necessity for the development of mining at Creede. The oxidized ore at Creede was a
siliceous fluxing ore that commanded a favorable rate from the
smelters. Much of the ore treated by the smelters was carbonaceous
in nature, having been produced from ore bodies in limestone strata
at Leadville, Aspen, and other mining camps. The slag produced by
smelting these ores was viscous and the smelters needed silica flux
to mix with the carbonaceous ores to produce a more fluid slag that
allowed a better separation of the metal values, making it easier to
handle during the smelting process. Therefore, the smelters were
more than happy to pay a premium for siliceous Creede ore with a
high silver value rather than process a viscous slag or add silica flux
that had no metal values.

Smelters were established in Colorado at Denver, Pueblo,
Durango, and Trinidad, where rail transportation for all kinds of
ores, fluxes, and fuel was available and cheaper than in isolated districts.[5] Creede had a railroad nearby that could deliver crude ore to
the smelters at Leadville, Denver, Pueblo, and Durango at a reasonable cost so there was no need for a smelter near the mines.

General William Jackson Palmer, the first president of the
Denver and Rio Grande, had extended the narrow gauge rails to
Wagon Wheel Gap in 1883, only ten miles from Creede, to serve the
tourist business. David H. Moffat and Sylvester T. Smith, who purchased Creede's Holy Moses Mine along with Major L.E. Campbell,
were men with broad railroad experience. They were fully aware of
the necessity of a railroad to Creede in order to serve the mines, both
in transporting people, materials, and machinery into the district
and ore out to the smelters. Earlier mine development, such as at the
Alpha at Sunnyside, had failed primarily because of the high cost of
transportation for their ore.

David H. Moffat succeeded William C. Jackson as president of
the Denver and Rio Grande Railway in early 1887. Moffat had been

in Colorado from the early days. He started a stationery and book
store in Denver in 1860, but a few years later became a cashier at
Denver's First National Bank. He and Jerome B. Chaffee, who
became one of Colorado's first U.S. senators, invested in the mining
business. Colorado Governor John Evans interested Moffat in rail-
roading in the open spaces of the West. He became treasurer of the
Denver Pacific and later was associated with the Denver and South
Park and the Denver and New Orleans Railroads. Moffat took over
the presidency of the Denver and Rio Grande Railroad in the spring
of 1887, after having considerable financial and investment experience and a "hands on" part in the development of Colorado's rail
system. Sylvester T. Smith was general manager of the railroad during Moffat's tenure. Together they improved the railroad's competi-
tive position by improving road beds, straightening curves, and
lowering grades, all of which cost money. Moffat recommended that
the Denver and Rio Grande build an extension from Wagon Wheel
Gap to serve the Creede mines and, because of his investments in
them, he could promise the railroad considerable traffic and revenues. His request was turned down. He angrily resigned as president of the Denver and Rio Grande in August 1891, after the foreign
stockholders, mostly those from England and the Netherlands,
demanded that dividends be paid instead of the profits being spent
for improvements. Moffat told the press that he felt the directors in
New York wanted to follow a policy he thought was injurious to the
railroad. Smith was relieved of his duties as general manager when
he advised, in no uncertain terms, that the proposed extension from
Wagon Wheel Gap should be built.[6]

Moffat spent $75,000 of his personal funds to extend the tracks
to Creede with an understanding that it would be turned over to the
Denver and Rio Grande upon his recovery of the construction costs.
Construction began in the summer of 1891 and was completed the
following December by the Rio Grande and Gunnison Company.
The track had a water grade from Wagon Wheel Gap to Jimtown
(the present-day town of Creede) through flat terrain that lent itself
to fast, cheap construction. The railroad was extended up East
Willow Creek above Creede to a point where it connected with the
terminal of the Holy Moses aerial tramway. The tracks along East
Willow Creek were laid at four and one-half per cent, making it difficult to hold cars in place.[7] The section was ultimately abandoned.
A Western Union telegraph line was erected along the tracks. The
first mail train reached Creede on December 10, 1891, over the new

line that was called the Rio Grande Gunnison Branch of the Denver
and Rio Grande Railroad.[8] The mines began shipping ore to the
smelters immediately, producing ten to twelve cars of ore, or from
100 to 120 tons, daily.[9]

A through train was run daily to Creede from Denver, Colorado
Springs, and Pueblo to which was attached a regular line of Pullman
sleeping cars. Connections could also be made to Grand Junction,
Aspen, Leadville, and Ouray via Salida. In 1892, the railroad fare
from Denver was $15.35; from Pueblo, $11.45; from Cañon City,
$11.45; from Leadville, $12.85; from Aspen, $17.70; from Grand
Junction, $20.60; from Ouray, $18.35; from Silverton, $18.65.[10]

A tremendous number of people came to the new, already-crowded
silver camp on the railroad — by one estimate, 200 passengers got off
the train from Alamosa each day. The trains were jammed when they
arrived — men sat on each other and hung onto the vestibule platforms.
The daily train from Alamosa consisted of twelve to fifteen coaches,
sometimes more. The first depot was a tent. The depot platform, which
had been hurriedly built, was piled with wooden barrels and boxes,
burlap bags, beer kegs, pot-belly stoves, furniture of all kinds, bed mat-
tresses, packing cases — and even small steam boilers. Because of the
extreme hotel shortage, the railroad rented out as many as ten Pullman
cars on a siding as hotel accommodations.

Freight Depot at Creede

Courtesy of the Denver Public Library
Western History Collection

The sketch was made by a reporter who visited Creede early in 1892, writing about the new camp in a booklet, *Creede Camp*, published by *The Rocky Mountain News*. He found the Rio Grande's freight station piled high with merchandise waiting to be claimed by consignees. Many of the reporter's comments about Creede are included in Chapter 6.

An early traveler, Richard Harding Davis, wrote about his impressions when he arrived in Creede in 1892 by rail: "The train stopped at the opening of this gully, and its passengers jumped out into two feet of mud and snow. The ticket and telegraph office on one side of the track was situated in a freight car with windows and doors cut out of it, and with the familiar blue and white sign of the Western Union nailed to one end; that station was typical of the whole town in its rawness and in the temporary and impromptu air of its inhabitants."[11]

The cost of constructing the railroad was equaled by revenues in the first four months of operation. Moffat turned the line over to the Denver and Rio Grande Railroad as he had agreed![12]

The First Train to Creede — Photo by E.F. Hilton, 1892
Courtesy of the Colorado Historical Society

CHAPTER 3
POLITICS AND THE PRICE OF SILVER

THE PRICE OF SILVER at the time of Creede's discovery was set not by supply and demand but by legislative fiat. The currency system of the United States from the beginning of the republic had always been based on "bimetalism," or the use of both gold and silver, in the country's coinage. The ratio between the two metals was set at sixteen to one, that is, sixteen times as much silver in silver dollars as there was gold in gold dollars. California's Gold Rush of 1849 upset the ratio when large quantities of mined gold dropped the value of gold. Consequently the value of silver, being in shorter supply, increased to a high of $1.326 per troy ounce in 1868 and silver dollars, containing about an ounce of silver, were melted down and sold for the higher value. As a result, the U.S. Congress passed an act in 1873 that ended the coinage of silver dollars and placed the country on a gold standard.

The silver strikes in the West reversed the roles of the metals again. Silver was plentiful and gold less so. The mine owners and most Westerners demanded that the government purchase silver at the old ratio of sixteen to one and called for an end to the demonetization of silver. The Act of 1873 was dubbed "the crime of 1873" in the West. The Bland-Allison Act of 1878, passed by Congress over President Hayes' veto, instructed the U.S. Treasury to purchase not less than two and not more than four million dollars of silver per month. The Treasury bought $24 million that was coined into silver dollars. This resulted in each silver dollar being worth less than ninety cents in gold.

The West favored free coinage of silver at the ratio of sixteen to one with no limits on quantity, but in 1885, the newly elected president, Grover Cleveland, was against it. By 1890, congressmen from the western silver states had enough power in Congress to force the passage of the Sherman Silver Purchase Act of 1890. The price of silver immediately climbed to $1.50 per troy ounce from $0.84, almost doubling the value of silver overnight. This price increase assured the start of the Creede "boom." The high price, however, did not hold. It had fallen to $0.85 an ounce in March 1892. An *Engineering and Mining Journal* editorial of the following April 2nd had this to say:

> "*The Market Price of Silver — During the past week the price of silver reached the lowest point ever recorded. On Monday the London quotation was 39 pence per troy ounce, which was equivalent to 85.6 cents here, but the metal was offered by New York dealers at 85 cents per ounce, at which price the gold value of the silver in a silver dollar was worth 65.7 cents. Since then the price has risen slightly, being quoted today at 87 1/2 cents. It is absurd to say that silver is suffering any 'injustice' or 'demonetization,' or that any 'crime' has been committed against it, to account for the decline in value to these figures. The value of silver, as of everything else, is governed by the law of supply and demand.*
>
> "*The production of silver has been going on for the past ten years at a constantly increasing rate, and while the consumption has increased, both for coinage and industrial purposes, and by the hoarding of the United States Government (under the act of July 14, 1890), it has been far outstripped by production.*
>
> "*The future course of the silver market may be predicted with as much certainty as that of any other metal, where the United States Government continues to buy 54,000,000 ounces per annum or not. The price will decline until the output is restricted, by the weaker mines closing down and production more nearly approximates consumption.*
>
> "*We shall not be surprised to see the price of silver decline to 80 cents per ounce before the end of this year, and, should this country adopt free coinage, it would in time go far below this, for that would remove the largest purchaser for the metal who would pay gold for it.*"

According to some, the Sherman Silver Purchase Act of 1890 was at least partially responsible for the "Panic of 1893," as it

helped create a lack of confidence in the government's fiscal poli-
cies in the country as a whole. Even though the causes of the panic
were more psychological than real, people were out of work and
banks closed. President Cleveland called Congress into a special
session on August 7, 1893, to repeal the Sherman Act. The House
of Representatives voted to repeal immediately, but the Senate
delayed until October of 1893. The price of silver dropped from
$0.83 per troy ounce to $0.62 in four days after repeal. In addition to the repeal, the government of India stopped the coinage of
silver. Repeal of the Sherman Act and India's abandoning silver
essentially ended silver mining in the West and signaled difficult
times at Creede Camp.

Mineral Industry, a mining industry periodical published by The
Scientific Publishing Company, had the following commentary in
their 1893 summary of the industry:

> *"For the silver mining industry, the year 1893 was one
> which in history will rank with 1873. The demonetization
> of silver, begun in the latter year, was finally completed in
> 1893 by the repeal of the Sherman Act in the United
> States, which withdrew the last of the great nations of the
> world from the futile attempt to uphold the price of the
> metal. ... The industrial uses of the metal cannot com-
> mand a price that will secure a large production.*
>
> *"The production of silver in the United States in 1893
> was not so much smaller than the previous year as might
> have been expected from the general closing down of the
> mines, but this was due to the fact that all the smelting
> works had large stocks of ore which they smelted after the
> output of the mines had ceased. It was not, therefore,
> until August or September that there began to be a per-
> ceptible reduction in the out turn of silver, but in the
> autumn many of the works, including all those in
> Leadville, blew out their furnaces for lack of ore."*

The effects of the repeal of the Sherman Act was felt in Creede
by mid-1893 as reported in *The Denver Republican*, June 30, 1893:

> *"All the producing camps have practically stopped
> shipping, the owners preferring to let the silver lie in the
> ground rather than sell it at the present low price. The
> Amethyst was the first to reduce force and did so early in
> the week. The New York and Chance and Bachelor will*

ship no more after tomorrow until the price goes up. Development is going ahead in all the big mines without intermission, and all are working small forces to keep out the water, protect the properties, and open new ground."

The *Creede Candle*, July 7, 1893, had this to say:

"Last Chance Cuts Working Forces — The Last Chance which has been running full handed up to that time, cut its force in half yesterday, letting out 75 men and continuing that number at work. They were the last to close for the reason that their contract with the Leadville smelter kept them up. The New York and Chance is completely shut down but the Amethyst continues to give employment to about 40 in developing and protecting the property."

The *Engineering and Mining Journal* made the following comments several months after the drop in the price of silver:

September 16, 1893:

"The mining industry of the State of Colorado is slowly recovering from the collapse caused by the sudden fall in the price of silver. At Creede some of the most important mines, such as the Amethyst, Last Chance, and New York, have recently resumed operations. There are symptoms of revival at Leadville, and Aspen will not remain quiet long. At the Denver smelters the stocks of ore have been considerably reduced and more ore is now being purchased than has been the case since the end of June.

"The southwestern portion of the State — the 'Silvery San Juans' — is still in a woeful condition, owing to the closing down of the mines. How severe has been the blow to business of this particular section is best indicated by the falling off in the earnings of the Rio Grande Railway, which for August were $469,300, as compared with $931,000 for the corresponding month last year. At Leadville only abut 550 men are at work, or about one-quarter of the force employed two months ago."

November 18, 1893:

"When in the last days of June the silver market collapsed, Colorado seemed on the verge of utter ruin. The

business of silver mining received the shock first, but its effects extended to the other diversified industries of the State. It is pleasing, therefore, to chronicle a recovery which promises to be all the more permanent for its slowness. Silver mining has been recommenced at Leadville, Creede, and other districts, but only in a half-hearted way. Vigorous development of the mines and extensive shipments of ore are in most cases postponed until the effect of the repeal of the Silver Purchase Law can be measured."

The repeal of the Sherman Act did not shut down silver mining at Creede, but seriously impacted it. The U.S. Geological Survey credited Mineral County with the production of 4,897,684 ounces of silver valued at $3,820,194 in 1893. In 1894 the figures were 1,866,827 ounces valued at $1,176,164. The 1894 silver production was only 38 per cent of that of 1893 and the 1894 value of the silver produced was only 31 per cent of the 1893 value.[1]

The battle for "free silver" was not over. The national election of 1896 was bitterly fought between the Democrats and Republicans, and one of the most contentious issues was the silver versus gold question. The Republican Party's convention produced a plank favoring gold in their platform. Colorado's Senator Henry Teller and thirty-three other western senators walked out of the Republican convention in protest. The politicos of the time expected that the Democrats would follow the Republican lead and include a gold plank in their platform. This, however, did not happen. William Jennings Bryan, an ex-Populist from Nebraska, made his famous speech at the convention with the sentence: "You shall not press down upon the brow of labor this crown of thorns, you shall not crucify mankind on a cross of gold." He won the Democratic nomination for president with "free silver" as his primary issue. Unfortunately for Bryan, the silver issue did not resonate with the voting public. Many Democrats defected to the Republican side and, as a result, William McKinley won the election. The country went on the "gold standard" in 1900.

The price of silver was set by the law of supply and demand from the demonetization of silver in 1893 until 1918, when the Pittman Silver Act was passed by the U.S. Senate. Politics and the price of silver will be revisited later in the history of Creede Camp.

Senator Edward O. Wolcott of Colorado, a self-described "Silver Republican," visited France and England to promote "international bimetalism." He attempted to persuade the Europeans to accept bimetalism and offered them tariff favors if they did so. The European countries on the gold standard were unwilling to abandon gold, and Wolcott's mission failed. Senator Wolcott was part of the syndicate that purchased the Last Chance Mine at Creede. An interesting side note to Senator Wolcott's involvement in mining at Creede is the pitcher and tray, made from Last Chance silver, on permanent display at the Colorado School of Mines Geology Museum in Golden, Colorado. Its description says:

> *"Edward O. Wolcott was U.S. Senator from Colorado between 1889 and 1900. Born in Massachusetts, he moved to Colorado in 1871, and practiced law in Georgetown until 1879, when politics took him to Denver. There, earnings from his law practice supplemented by his returns from mining and smelting interests made him a millionaire. He and his brother, Henry, lived in victoria splendor at 'Wolhurst,' their Denver mansion.*
>
> *"In 1888 Wolcott was elected to the Senate. A magnificent orator and elegant dresser, he was very popular on the East Coast; but his continued support of the anti-silver Republican party in the 1890s eventually cost him his Colorado backing. (Many Coloradans, including Wolcott, had gotten rich on silver. The Republicans were against unrestricted silver coinage.) Wolcott was voted out of office in 1900.*
>
> *"Creede was the site of Colorado's last big silver strike and was one of the wildest boomtowns of all. The boom began in 1889, when N.C. Creede claimed the Holy Moses Mine, and continued until the Sherman Silver Purchase Act was repealed in 1893. The price of silver fell abruptly from $1.29 to $0.50 per ounce, forcing closure of all but the richest mines.*
>
> *"The Last Chance Mine was found in August 1891, by two broke prospectors from Salida who sold it for a few thousand dollars in November 1891. The new owners included Henry Wolcott, of Denver, and Jacob Sanders of Leadville. The Last Chance Mine became the second largest producer of rich ore in Creede, returning huge profits to the owners. In the first year of operation, it produced over $1,600,000. Sanders apparently shared*

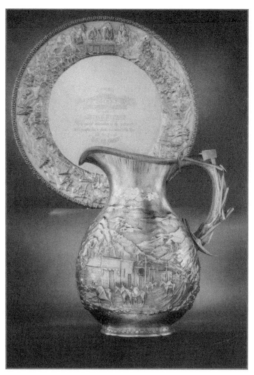

Wolcott Pitcher and Tray
Courtesy of Robert Nye

his good fortune with Edward Wolcott, prompting Wolcott's gift of the pitcher and tray.

"The tray is made from a single piece of silver alloy weighing 85.7 troy ounces. It has a rim of hand-chased repoussé work depicting Colorado mining and mountain scenes. The engraving says: 'Made of silver from the Last Chance Mine, Creed Camp Colorado, and presented to Jacob F. Sanders[2] with grateful appreciation of the generosity which prompted him to divide his interest in the mine with his friend Edw'd O. Wolcott.'

"The pitcher weighs 75.2 troy ounces. It is a hand-raised jug made in two halves that were soldered together, a lost art in pieces so large, a technique in which a flat circle of silver is hammered in concentric circles over a series of anvils with frequent annealings. The decoration is hand-chased repoussé work showing scenes of Creede.

"The alloy used in these pieces was a special melt made at Kirk Factory of Baltimore, Maryland with

bullion from the Last Chance Mine. The alloy is '11 ounce,' a silver quality used by S. Kirk & Son until 1896. It is 11 parts fine silver to 1 part copper, or 0.917 fine. (Sterling silver is 0.925 fine.)

"The pitcher and tray courtesy of Robert E. and Wilma E. Nye."

The location of the Wolcott Pitcher and Tray, or even their very existence, was not known until about 1983 when Robert Nye, a Denver mining man, happened to be visiting a friend in Indianapolis, Indiana. A local antique dealer called Robert's friend asking if he had ever heard of "Greed," Colorado. The dealer said that he had received a large silver tray and pitcher with an inscription about Greed, Colorado, and that he could not find Greed on a Colorado map. Robert was intrigued by the conversation and decided to accompany his friend to the antique dealer's shop. After inspecting the pieces and determining that they were, in fact, important historical items and should be saved, Robert purchased the pitcher and tray from the antique dealer. Robert then located an individual who had been vice-president of the Kirk Silver Factory in Baltimore and asked him to restore and appraise the value of the items. The appraised value was $160,000! Robert and his wife, Wilma, donated them to the Colorado School of Mines Geology Museum in 1988.[3]

CHAPTER 4
THE PROSPECTORS

AFTER WORD GOT OUT that rich discoveries had been made at Creede Camp, thousands of prospectors descended on the area. Four factors were responsible: first, the discovery of rich ore; second, established smelters and the coming of the railroad; third, the high price of silver; and fourth, American mining laws that encouraged the individual prospector, the "common man," to discover valuable minerals and to profit from his efforts. Most, if not all, of the major mineral deposits in the West discovered at the turn of the century were found by the prospector. Unfortunately, the number of prospectors profiting from their efforts was very small indeed. The chances of finding an economic mineral deposit by prospecting methods of the time were a bit better than playing the lottery, and far from being a sure thing.

Mines and Mining Men of Colorado described prospecting at Creede Camp:[1]

> *"The sale of the 'Moses' to Moffat, Campbell, and Smith was to the mining world like a flash of lurid lightning out of a clear sky. It became known at once, as such things always do, and the miners resolved that when $70,000 is paid for a hole not much deeper than a cellar, in a district before unheard of, there was something going on. Where there is one good property, there are likely to be more. Though is was late in the year, a rush commenced at once. Dozens of men tramped up the long road from Del Norte. They came from all parts of the state, and bore upon their brawny backs their tools, bed, and kitchen.*
>
> *"Across the mountains from the San Juan country and other parts of the southwest came men singly, in pairs, and by squads. When night came they rolled themselves in their blankets and slept in the cradle of the silent hills. A hundred Jasons each night counted the gems on Orion's*

glorious girdle. The storekeepers of the San Luis Valley were quick to seize upon the opportunity, and rustled goods up as fast as they could. Though the great mass of prospectors of the state knew nothing of the happenings in that out-of-the-way corner, it was but a short time until the camp contained several hundred people, and was entitled to assume the air of a frontier metropolis.

"In the winter of 1890-91 there was not such a head of steam on — no such irresistible tide of vim and enthusiasm. They weren't sure what they had yet. The discoveries on Campbell Mountain were all that was in sight, so they plastered that hill over with claims two or three deep and sat down to hibernate until the snow went away. In the long winter months, they talked of the railroad and its coming. They well knew that without it their properties would be of little value, no matter how large the ore bodies might be. Relying on Moffat's influence, however, not a man but believed the musical clang of the rail and the spike would be heard in the gulch when the season opened. With the first days of spring another flood of newcomers came in and began to wait for the indispensable railroad. Month after month went by and there was no sign of a move by the Rio Grande. Then Creede received its setback. As it has set the pace in all other directions, so it did in having experience. When scarcely born it met its reverse and conquered. While new men continued to come in, many of the old ones drifted away, unable to indulge in the luxury of idleness. Most of them have doubtless hit the trail back again before this time. All were not too poor or too faint-hearted to stand at their guns. While the feeling in the camp during the period of endured stagnation was not, by any means, as cheerful as it might have been, the prospecting was continued without cessation. Men began to wonder if there was not something else in that region besides Campbell Mountain. They found there was and here again this camp showed its kite-shaped capacity for beating the record. Aspen and Leadville were a long time learning that they had large inheritances than those in the neighborhood of the best discoveries, but Creede's young energy had a swifter hand. This is the way it came about, showing what bull-headed good fortune some people enjoy."

When the prospectors made their way to Creede, some by Pullman car, they found a land that was inhospitable to their profession. The high altitude, long and bitterly cold winters, steep mountainous terrain, and the lack of infrastructure to supply their physical needs made their lives difficult. They lived in tents, slept on the ground, ate simple food made with ingredients — salt, soda, beans, flour — that could be stored without refrigeration, supplemented by trout from the streams and venison. The prospectors were alone most of the time except for the company of their burros and horses.

Technology available to the prospectors in their exploration for minerals was indeed very limited. Few of them had much knowledge of geology and mineralogy. The ones who did, such as N.C. Creede, were the most successful prospectors. Others such as Julius Haase and Theodore Renniger were just plain lucky. The most common method of finding a mineral deposit at the time was to find float, a piece of rock broken from a vein that contained quartz or other diagnostic minerals, along a stream or water course where it had been washed down by floods over the years. The prospector then traced the pieces of float upstream until he found no more. He searched the hillsides hoping to find an outcrop of the vein from whence the float came, a slow, tedious, backbreaking process. Assay offices in the towns analyzed specimens of float and mineralized rock for gold, silver, and other valuable metals for the prospector as the values were not easily determined by visual inspection.

Once the prospector filed on his claim, the hard, physically demanding work of proving its mineral value began. The only tools available to them were picks, shovels, wheelbarrows, hand steel, and hammers to drill holes in the rock for dynamite, and hand windlasses, or perhaps a horse whim to lift the broken rock and earth from the prospect pit or shaft.

There was a difference of opinion in the camp as to the nature of the ore deposits in 1892 when little was understood about the geology of the district. Many of the prospectors, probably from the Leadville district, strongly believed the theory of blanket or "flat" veins similar to those found at Leadville; others depended entirely on the fissure vein theory. One early geologist stated: "It is hardly logical, however, to expect a blanket vein in the eruptive mass. Its nature is against any such conclusion."[2] Other geologists identified a strata of the Creede Formation that formed in "Ancient Lake Creede" as the Lower Carboniferous, known as the "Leadville blue

Prospectors at Creede, Colorado — 1890
Courtesy of the Colorado Historical Society

limestone."[3] This, no doubt, gave some credence to the blanket vein theory. In reality, nearly all the Creede deposits were of the fissure vein type. Claims were staked on the west slope of Monon Hill in 1894 or earlier on the outcrop of a silver deposit along the contact of volcanic tuff and the Creede Formation.[4] Monon Hill was the only exception to fissure veins until 1919 when Fred Monkemeyer found silver in a "flat" vein near the top of Bachelor Mountain.[5] Monkemeyer's discovery was also along the contact between the volcanic rocks and the Creede Formation in the ancient stream channel filled with sedimentary rocks as described in Chapter One.

The anniversary issue of *The Creede Candle* of January 6, 1893, recaps the camp's first full year and had this to say about expenditures for development:

> *"It is no exaggeration to say that $750,000 have been expended in the camp in search of ore. The thousands of prospectors who have worked with pick and shovel single-handed have sunk or driven tunnels, cuts, shafts, and drifts sufficient that if one were joined to the other the whole would make, at a close figure, a tunnel ten miles long. Had all this work been put onto one piece it would have tunneled under every mountain that forms any considerable part of the camp's mineral field and fairly laid the secrets all bare to the miner. But it is not dead work, nor lost work. Some of it per se was of no avail, but it all helped to define the belt and direct the intelligent worker.*

*It has served its purpose and many of the claims on which
ten feet of it was done can be had by any one who wishes
to try his luck. This sort of work is a necessity in mining
as the blanks are to a lottery. A prospector will locate fifty
claims before he finds the one to which he pins his faith
and stands by, swears by, hopes on, and will fight for if
necessary."*

Prospecting in the silver districts of the West, including Creede,
was greatly reduced, if not eliminated, after the dramatic drop in the
price of the metal in 1893. Prospectors left Creede Camp by the
thousands, many of them going to Cripple Creek, the gold camp
that was "booming" at the time. The better mines in the district continued to produce ore and the population of Creede dropped to that
necessary to staff the mines and provide services for the miners.
Creede's 1895 population was 1,400,[6] a dramatic drop from the
"boom" population of 10,000, by some estimates.[7]

Some of the prospectors or individuals providing grubstakes
held on to their claims or sold them to mining investors for good
sums of money. Several became wealthy, including at least two millionaires — Creede and Granger, men of modest means before their
good fortune. The Creede Mining Exchange was active in 1892 and
1893 to facilitate the sales and purchases of mining claims and
properties. Edmund Kirby in an article in the March 19, 1892, issue
of *The Engineering and Mining Journal* had this comment:

*"The surface of both mountains is covered with loca-
tions, most of them based upon a 10-ft. hole in the wash or
in the barren rock, without either vein or ore, and all these
are consequently absolutely void under the law, but
notwithstanding this fact a number of such claims are being
purchased for large sums in cash. Many valid locations,
however, have been made by uncovering one of the numerous veins and many sales are being made of these claims."*

The Creede Candle, Volume I, 1892, reported the following sales.[8]
Most likely there were many others that were not reported:

January 7, 1892:
*"The St. Charles joins end lines with the Bachelor on
the south and has a good showing for the vein. Last week
an option was given on it by C.C. Cotton to Jones &
Seeley, the tie contractors, for $5,000."*

January 14, 1892:

"Mr. A.L. Lawton on Monday completed the purchase of a 5/8 interest in the Cleopatra for Mr. Byers and others of Colorado Springs and the papers have been signed. The price paid was at a the rate of $40,000 for the property or $25,000 for the interest. Those who sold were D.S. Cotton and Geo. A. Brewer, who held 1/4 each., A.H. Major, Finley Frazee and Peter Ross, holding 1/8 together."

January 21, 1892:

"Sale of all the Whale and half of the Beaver and the Creede, all on Bachelor Hill reported. Also the sale of the Lena, Tenderfoot, Slide, Colorow and Annie. A quarter interest in the Salem on west Bachelor changed hands."

January 28, 1892:

"The McGinty lode, thought to be an extension of the Ethel, was taken up today by L.S. Cornell. The price was reported is $8,000. Denver parties purchased a half interest in the Stringer lode this week."

February 18, 1892:

"Monday last two new discoveries there were sold to good mining men of Pueblo for $20,000 cash. They are the Foundation and the Feenan."

March 10, 1892:

"Alex Taylor sold Baltimore group for $15,000."

March 17, 1892:

"The Commodore was located by W.P. McGilliard and J.C. MacKenzie and by them sold in December to I.L. Johnson for $10,000. The present owners are A.E. Reynolds and E.L. Shear of Aspen."

August 26, 1892:

"Completion of sale of the Del Monte, with C.F. Nelson, the original locator, as general manager and W.F. Hogan as superintendent."

September 9, 1892:

"The Happy Thought sold to Major T.H. Norton, R.C. Ralphsnyder, and G.C. Dewey for $15,000."

January 6, 1893:

"Report has it that a sale of a three-fourths interest in the Nancy Hanks was made during the week to C.J. Hughes of Denver for $60,000. By the same token the property is to be worked for a mine under the management of Frank G. White."

Barnes compiled a list of mining claims filed in the Creede district from the pages of *The Creede Candle* published in 1892. He found that 271 individual claims had been filed that year.[9] The *Report of the Colorado State Bureau of Mines for 1897* stated: "The county records (Mineral County) show 1,896 lode claims, 325 lode claims patented, and 10 placer claims of record." A map titled, "Official Surveys of Creede Camp," by Shrive B. Collins, U.S. Deputy Mineral Surveyor, 1903, and as copied by Don C. LaFont, County Surveyor, 1933, shows that 359 claims had been issued patents by 1903. Only a handful of claims proved to have a true economic value.

THE MINING ACT OF 1872

The Mining Act of 1872, much maligned these days, was passed by Congress and signed by President Ulysses Grant on May 10, 1872, to promote the development of the mineral resources of the United States.[10] It replaced the first General Mining Act of July 26, 1862, which was enacted to replace the local rules of individual mining camps in California and Nevada. The Act of 1872 is based on the principle that the right of ownership of mineral property depends upon two distinct elements — discovery and development. Discovery is made the source of title and development, or working of a mine, the continuance of that title. The law has been amended many times since 1872. The law, in its simplest form without complicated side issues, in effect at the time of the Creede discovery is described below.

Federal lands valuable for their mineral content were reserved from sale unless otherwise expressly directed by law. The law stated that "all valuable mineral deposits in lands belonging to the United States, both surveyed and unsurveyed, shall be free and open to exploration and purchase, and the lands in which they are found to occupation and purchase by citizens of the United States and those who have declared their intention to become such, under regulations prescribed by law, and according to the local customs or rules of miners in the several mining districts, so far as the same are applicable and not inconsistent with the laws of the United States."[11]

The law was written to benefit the "common man," as was the Homestead Act, and defined the "claim" system of mining law. It allowed individuals to discover, claim, develop, and ultimately own mineral deposits on federal lands as opposed to the "concession" system used in many other countries, where the state selects the concessionaire for exploring mineral lands and for operating any mines they find. The concessionaire then pays rents, taxes, or royalties to the state.

The claim system originated in the early days of mining in the United States. In places such as California during the Gold Rush, it developed as a method of determining on the spot the ground that an individual was allowed to work and the conditions in which he could hold on to it. This became necessary to preserve order. All the discoverer of a claim had to do was file notice of it with the county in which the claim was located and pay a nominal filing fee. This was a real problem for the Creede prospectors, as the district was claimed by three counties!

The Act of 1872 defined two types of mining claims — lode and placer claims. Placer claims were of little importance in the Creede district, so all definitions herein are about lode claims.

The Act defined lode claims as those upon veins or lodes of quartz or other rock in place bearing valuable mineral deposits. It also defined them as having a maximum length of 1,500 feet, a maximum width of 600 feet, and no more than 300 feet on each side of the vein at the surface or the apex of the vein. In addition, the Act called for parallel end lines and monuments set at the claim corners and at the point of discovery. The point of discovery had to be within the boundaries of the claim.

Sufficient discovery work is required to disclose the existence of a vein and, where possible, its general course and indication that the vein contains valuable minerals. According to the local rules of miners in the Sunnyside and King Solomon districts, the maximum claim width was 300 feet until sometime after 1900, and the point of discovery had to be defined by a discovery shaft or pit ten feet square and ten feet deep.

In order to hold the claim, the claimant had to perform assessment work each year and file an affidavit with the county authorities. Failure to perform the required assessment work subjected the claim to relocation or abandonment. Title to the claim could be obtained through the patent process. First, the owner had a survey made of the claim by a mineral land surveyor working under the authority of the

U.S. Government's General Land Office. The surveyor made a plat of the claim, any conflicting claims, and other adjacent claims. This survey plat was then filed with the General Land Office and other proper authorities and posted on the claim. The owner then filed a patent application with the General Land Office. If no title problems were discovered, a patent was issued to the owner that conveyed: 1) the exclusive right of possession and enjoyment of all the surface included within the limits of the location, as described in the patent, subject only to pre-existing easements; and 2) all veins, lodes, and ledges throughout their entire depth, the tops or apexes of which lie within the boundaries, the right to pursue the vein in depth outside of such boundaries being limited.[12]

The Act of 1872 was called the "Apex Law," famous to some and infamous to others. Simply stated, the apex rule in the law states that the claimant has an extralateral right to any vein that has its apex, or outcrop, on the surface, within the boundaries of his location. An extralateral right gives the claimant the right to mine the vein downward beyond vertical projections of the sidelines of his claim but within vertical planes defined by the parallel end lines of the claim. The apex rule holds even if the vein is followed beneath another's claim that does not hold the apex. This rule was based on an "ideal" situation, not on real geologic conditions. This created ownership problems and prolific litigation in most mining districts, including Creede. In fact, a cottage industry of lawyers and mining engineers was created to represent mining companies in litigation over extralateral rights. Litigation in the Creede district created serious problems in developing the mining properties, as will be addressed in Chapter Seven. One Creede case, *Del Monte Mining Company vs. Last Chance Mining Company*, went all the way to the Supreme Court of the United States in 1898 for settlement.[13] The ruling in this case set an important precedent that helped define the Apex Law. *The Mining Reporter*, August 16, 1906, had this comment:

> *"Mining Laws and Litigation — The development of mining has proved the inefficiency of the mining law as it now stands on the statute books of the United States. Those who first undertook to frame our mining laws set for themselves a difficult task, but it is not presumptuous to say that those who now undertake to revise them will find they have attacked a many-sided problem. Laws may be made for the government of people, but when it comes*

to ore deposits, veins, geological conditions, etc., we find
that nature abhors a straight line, and will not be coerced
or confined by hard and fast boundaries or sharp theoret-
ical conditions."

The Mining Act of 1872 had the positive effect of allowing the
"common man" prospector to discover mineral deposits in the West
and for some of them to profit as individuals; however, the law had
some unintended negative effects on mining. The *Mining Engineers'*
Handbook, in describing the "claim" system of mining law as promulgated by the Mining Act of 1872, stated:

"Where consolidation of claims is prohibited, the
result is waste and many failures; where claims are per-
mitted to be held without systematic development, no
good results to the country at large, nor to the claim
holder; and it is criticized as being a system which,
although it may appear at first sight to encourage individ-
ual enterprise, in reality leads to great waste of capital and
unorganized energy." [14]

It will become apparent that such was the case at Creede Camp
as its mining history unfolds.

CHAPTER 5

THE EARLY
INVESTORS

MANY ECONOMIC ENTERPRISES must have three basic
ingredients to be successful — land, labor, and capital. In the mining business, land is equated to a mineral deposit that can be economically exploited. Labor is provided by individuals working in
the mine for wages and other compensation. Capital is provided by
investors to pay for mine development and required facilities such as
hoisting and power plants, mine machinery, warehouses, means of
transporting ore to the railroad, housing for the miners, and so on.

As a rule, the investors who financed the first mining ventures in
the Creede district were wealthy individuals who made their fortunes elsewhere and were willing to risk venture money in the
prospectors' newly discovered mines. Creede mine investors came
from all parts of the United States, as far away as New York. Several
of the original discoverers became investors, including Nicholas C.
Creede, Ralph Granger, and Charles F. Nelson. Unfortunately, most
of the prospectors did not have the financial resources necessary to
develop their mines and sold them to mining investors or, as Creede,
Granger, and others did, became partners with the investors instead
of selling their claims outright.

The first mining company in the Creede district was the Holy
Moses Mining Company, organized in October, 1890. David H.
Moffat was its president, Sylvester T. Smith was vice-president, and
L.E. Campbell was treasurer and general manager.[1] The Bachelor
Mining Company was incorporated in 1891, with David H. Moffat,
Sylvester T. Smith, Frederick F. Struby, Julius E. French, and John T.
Herrick as Directors.[2] *The Creede Candle*, Volume I, 1892, listed
sixty-six mining companies incorporated in 1892 to do business in
the Creede district. A majority of the companies were capitalized for
one million dollars and issued a million shares of stock valued at one
dollar per share. Only the following companies were successful in
developing producing mines:

Cleopatra Mining Company: Directors — E. Eaton, R.L. Lawton, A.A. McGovern, Colorado Springs; N.C. Merrill, Ness City, Kansas; J.S. Byers, Poncha Springs; A.A. Hurd and A. Lawton. Incorporated February 5, 1892.

King Solomon Mining & Milling Company: Incorporators — N.C. Creede, William Gelder, and L.L. Bailey; Directors — N.C. Creede, President; S.K. Hooper, General Passenger Agent of D&RG, E.E. Humphrey, Surveyor General for Colorado; Geo. W. Robinson, President and Treasurer of the National Bank of Pueblo. Incorporated March 17, 1892.

Del Monte Mining Company: Directors — H.P. Lillibridge, J.G. Shields, L.G. Lurst, Chas. Adams, W.J. Wilcox, L.R. Enrich, H.K. Devereaux, J.S. Stevens, and Godfrey Kissal. Incorporated March 17, 1892.

Park Regent Consolidated Mining Company: Directors — O.P. Poole, A.W. Rucker, H.J. Sisty, W.J. Wolfe, D.C. Halcom, Charles S. Noble, and A.D. Davis. Incorporated March 17, 1892.

Nelson Tunnel & Mining Company: Incorporators — C.F. Nelson, A.W. Brownell, J.P. Wallace, B.F. Kelley, W.J. Swift, E.N. Mayner, and C.A. Miller. Incorporated April 1, 1892.

Last Chance Mining & Milling Company: Directors — Ralph Granger, Willard P. Ward, Jacob F. Sanders, S.Z. Dickson, and Henry R. Wolcott. Incorporated April 1, 1892.

Kreutzer Sonata Consolidated Mining Company: Incorporators — Louis Weiss, Edward J. Howard, Harry J. Sistry, D.O. Hausee, and James Rice. Incorporated April 15, 1892.

Eunice Mining Company: Incorporators — H.R. Henderson, W.H. Leves, Frank Mead, Frederick Robinson, Jr., and M.R. Crowell. Incorporated April 15, 1892.

Amethyst Mining Company, Inc.: Directors and Officers first year — D.H. Moffat, President; N.C. Creede, Vice President; Walter S. Cheesman, Secretary and Treasurer; L.E. Campbell, General Manager. Incorporated May 20, 1892.

Stanhope Mining Company: Directors — Charles W. Enos, L.F. Kimball, John C. Clinton, John R. Thurston,

Carleton Ellis, W.S. Connor, and Thomas C. Brainard. Incorporated May 20, 1892.

400 Acre Diamond Drill Consolidated Mining Company: Directors — Fine P. Ernest, George R. Swallow, George F. Coleman, Howard C. Chapin, A.F. Hazeltine, H.C. Downey, and Theodore H. Thomas. Incorporated June 15, 1892.

New York Chance Mining Company (Consolidation of the New York, Last Chance, and Annie Rooney): Directors — Henry R. Wolcott, Albert E. Reynolds, Owen E. Levre, Isaac L. Johnson, Charles L. McIntosh, S.Z. Dickson, and Jacob Saunders. Incorporated June 24, 1892.

Bristol Head Mining Company: Directors — David P. Keiller, Donald Cameron, F.R. Miller, Charles E. Marvin, Ernest G. Miller, William T. Roundtree, and Harry Seversen. Incorporated August 19, 1892.

White Star Mining Company: Directors — R.W. English, E.W. Waybright, D.W. Houston, Thomas Kelley, and F.W. Betts. Incorporated July 1, 1892.

Creedmoor Mining Company: Incorporators — Senator Thomas Bowen, Lou Mercer, and George D. Nickel. Incorporated October 7, 1892.

Golden Eagle Consolidated Mining Company: Directors — Roderic F. Kavanaugh, John H. Van Ness, L.N. McLane, Alex B. McKinley, and C.G. Worden. Incorporated December 2, 1892.

The Cleopatra Mining Company, Baltimore-Creede Mining Company, 400 Acre Diamond Drill Consolidated Mining Company, Happy Thought, and Golden Eagle Consolidated Mining Company were combined into one corporation, the United Mines Company, in 1894.[3]

The Commodore Mining Company was incorporated in the State of Colorado on May 14, 1895; Albert E. Reynolds, president, and C.F. McKenney, secretary.[4]

A majority of the early mining companies were organized to develop mines on the Amethyst Vein System — the Bachelor Mining Company on the south, then in sequence toward the north, the Commodore Mining Company, Nelson Tunnel & Mining Company, New York Chance Mining Company, Del Monte Mining Company, Last Chance Mining & Milling Company, Amethyst Mining

Company, United Mining Company, and Park Regent Consolidated Mining Company.

The Holy Moses Mining Company, Eunice Mining Company, Creedmoor Mining Company, and King Solomon Mining & Milling Company developed mines on the Solomon-Holy Moses Vein. The Kreutzer Sonata Consolidated Mining Company had property on the Alpha-Corsair Vein at Sunnyside where ore was mined by the Irwin brothers in 1885.

Three of the early mining companies were organized to resolve questions of ownership complicated by the Mining Act of 1872, the Apex Law, which was described in Chapter Four. The New York Chance Mining Company was a consolidation of three claims to eliminate ownership litigation based on the Apex Law. The Bristol Head Mining Company was organized by the owners of the Commodore and Amethyst Mining Companies to mine ground claimed by both companies under the Apex Law. The United Mines Company consolidation was prompted largely to settle a number of apex questions. These conflicts are described in detail in Chapter Seven.

Hundreds, perhaps thousands, of investors financed the development of the Creede mines. Some made fortunes but most did not. Some of the investors had a lasting impact on the history of Creede and their biographies are included in the following pages. Influential individuals from Denver were among the investors, including Walter S. Cheesman, David H. Moffat, and U.S. Senator Edward O. Wolcott, Colorado's "Silver Republican" senator who commissioned the pitcher and tray made of Last Chance silver. Two of the men involved in the original discovery of Creede's riches, Nicholas C. Creede and Ralph Granger, became self-made millionaires as investors in the mines they discovered or grubstaked. Another discoverer, Charles F. Nelson, along with J. P. Wallace of Creede and Robert B. and John T. Wallace of Monte Vista, Colorado, had the foresight to drive the Nelson Tunnel, the salvation of the mines on the Amethyst vein system. Biographies of Creede, Granger, Nelson, and Moffat up to the time of discovery and the completion of the railroad were started in previous chapters and will be concluded in this chapter.

NICHOLAS C. CREEDE

Nicholas C. Creede, after his discovery of the Holy Moses claim in August, 1889, and its sale to Moffat, Campbell, and Smith, was employed by the newly organized Holy Moses Mining Company.

Creede visited the site of discovery of the Last Chance claim in August, 1891, and traced the outcrop for some distance. Impressed with the surface indications, Creede prevailed on Renniger and Haase to define the Last Chance claim and then located the Amethyst claim next to the Last Chance claim in the names of Moffat, Campbell, and himself.[5] The location of the Amethyst claim was the true beginning of Creede's fortune.

Nicholas C. Creede died from a morphine overdose in the summer house at his residence in Los Angeles, California, the evening of July 12, 1897, according to an article in *The Denver Republican* of July 13, 1897. The coroner's jury ruled that it was an accidental death from an overdose of morphine administered by Creede's own hands. Creede occasionally took morphine to allay the pain of neuralgia of the stomach and rheumatism of the heart, and on this occasion unintentionally took an overdose that caused his death, according to the article.

There were rumors at the time that Creede had taken his own life. *The Denver Republican* article dated July 14, 1897, had this to say:

> *"Must the biography of Nicholas C. Creede, replete up to its last chapter with stirring incidents, his struggles against the Indians of the plains, his weary years of poverty and hardships, seeking the sesame to the treasure chambers of the Rocky Mountains, his splendid triumph over circumstance when he founded the great silver camp which bears his name, and all the other phases of a career that was useful to mankind, if nothing more commendatory can be said of it, be closed with the ugly word 'suicide'? One of the dead prospector's earliest patrons and closest acquaintances, Major L.E. Campbell of Denver, says not.*
>
> *"'He never killed himself,' said Major Campbell yesterday, 'and I said so when I read the dispatch from Los Angeles this morning. Creede was too brave a man to die that way. I do not doubt the statement about his having died of morphine poisoning. In fact I knew of two or three occasions when he came very near dying from the same.*
>
> *'The fact is not very widely known but Mr. Creede had for several years been hopelessly addicted to the morphine*

habit. He acquired it early in 1892, when he was living in Creede. As he is dead now it can do no great harm to tell the story. For some time then Creede had been drinking heavily, always whisky, and finally he got into such a condition that it was deemed necessary to call in a physician. His friends in Creede called in a doctor from Del Norte — never mind his name, its publication would not benefit him — and this doctor put Creede under treatment. His method of curing the whisky habit was to furnish the patient with a substitute stimulant — and he chose opium.

'The opium prescribed for him then started Mr. Creede in the morphine habit, and he continued to use morphine afterwards. Whenever he was worried or anything went wrong with him, the regular dose did not have the desired effect, so he used to take a second and a heavier dose. Three times when this occurred, while he was still fresh in the habit, he went into a sleep from which he could be aroused only by medical treatment. The third instance of this kind that I remember occurred in Galveston, Texas, where Mr. Creede was visiting me.'"

The same *Denver Republican* article described Creede's life after his discovery of the Holy Moses:

"While the Holy Moses was being operated by Moffat, Campbell, and Smith, Major Campbell, who was managing the property, engaged Creede to prospect the country around. Creede received $40 a month, and was to get a third interest in whatever he might find. His next find of value was the Amethyst vein from which $3,090,000 of ore has since been taken. On this vein, the discovery stake bore the names of L.E. Campbell, D.H. Moffat, and N.C. Creede.

"Development work was started at once by the Amethyst Mining Company, organized by Mr. Moffat and his associates, and N.C. Creede found himself in sudden opulence. The story of his rich strike went abroad. In a few weeks 'a thousand burdened burros filled the narrow, winding, wriggling trail' — and the rush to Creede was on. After much discussion among the inhabitants of the town that grew in a month about the Amethyst, it was named after its founder, the name also sticking to the camp.

"N.C. Creede's fortune was now assured and he decided to take unto himself a wife. Her he found in the town of Del Norte. She is the woman whose hankering for his society after they were parted last January, drove him to his death by morphine in Los Angeles on Monday.

"There is a bit of queer romance in the circumstances that caused Creede in the first bloom of his riches to marry Lou Patterson, the Del Norte danseuse and sometimes boarding house landlady. Miss Patterson was born in Paducah, Ky., and settled in Del Norte about 1875. She was then a woman with a history and slightly served as to beauty and graces of form.

"In Del Norte she starred, when times were flush, on a stage of Jud Calkins' dance hall. Between her engagements at acting she kept boarders. About '81 or '82 she married Frank Kyle, but to the inhabitants of Del Norte she still remained Lou Patterson.

"Before she married Kyle, or in the early '70s, Lou Patterson made the acquaintance of N.C. Creede, who was then a poor, unknown and friendless prospector, tramping the hills in search of good luck. They became quite intimate, and whenever Creede returned from his prospecting trips to Del Norte he put up at Lou Patterson's boarding house. Once when he contracted pneumonia and was without money to pay for medical attendance, she nursed him through his illness, which was very dangerous.

"This strengthened the tie that bound them. And later on there happened something which raised Lou Patterson still higher in the estimation of N.C. Creede. He wanted a partner to go with him on a long prospecting trip into La Garita Mountains, about the head waters of the Saguache, and as the journey was one which entailed great hardships and dangers, he could not find a man willing to accompany him.

"To his surprise, Lou Patterson offered to go along, sharing and sharing alike with him whatever the trip brought, whether it might be profit or loss. Creede accepted her for a partner and all one summer the man and woman prospected La Garita together. Creede's firearms furnishing them with the greater part of their

*food supply. These two incidents made for Lou Patterson
a warm corner in the heart of N.C. Creede.*

*"In 1892, when the dollars began to roll in upon him
from the Amethyst Mine, Creede hired carpenters to build
a log cottage for him at the head of West Willow creek.
When it was finished up he made a quiet visit to Del Norte,
had a private talk with Lou Patterson — then Mrs. Frank
Kyle — and soon afterwards she procured a divorce from
her husband, or he died, it is not clear which thing
occurred. Anyway, Mrs. Kyle became a single woman.
Then she and N.C. Creede took a train for Las Vegas,
N.M., where a justice of the peace made them husband and
wife.*

*"They remained in Creede that winter and in the spring
of 1892 moved to Pueblo, where Creede had already built
a residence more befitting his pocketbook than the log
cabin on West Willow creek. Nearly a year later, in 1893,
water being then hampering the operations at the Amethyst
Mine, Creede sold out his third interest in the property to
D.H. Moffat and L.E. Campbell. Directly afterwards he
and his wife moved to Los Angeles.*

*"During the two years Creede was connected with the
Amethyst Mine, his receipts from it totaled $340,000. He
was probably worth $30,000 at the time he married Mrs.
Kyle nee Patterson. The marriage was greatly opposed by
his friends. Creede's answer to one of them, a few days
before the wedding took place, when he was told that she
was not the kind of woman he ought to marry, was: 'Yes
she is. If Lou Patterson was good enough for me in my days
of poverty, I am not too good for her, now that I am rich.'*

*"'He married her from a strict sense of duty,' said an
acquaintance yesterday. 'Creede was one of the most hon-
orable men I ever met in his own way, and he believed it
was incumbent upon him to make the woman his wife.'*

*"The life of Mr. and Mrs. Creede in Los Angeles is
pretty well known through the press dispatches. They
did not get along well together, as they grew older, and
last January Creede paid his wife $50,000 upon her
agreeing to go away from him and stay away. Previous
to that time he had adopted Edith Walters Walker (Edith
Dorothy Creede), the baby daughter of an actress. She*

was still under his care when he died, and he is said to have announced several times that she would inherit his fortune.

"With a wife, an adopted daughter, several brothers, or half-brothers or whichever they are — and no will, N.C. Creede left the concomitants for a beautifully savage will contest behind him when he took his last dose of morphine."

The story of Creede's adoption of Edith Waters Walker was told in an article by Eleanor Fry in *The Pueblo Chieftain and Star Journal* of June 7, 1980. Edith Waters, whose father owned San Miguel Island off Santa Barbara, California, was little Edith's mother. Edith Waters had left the island determined to become an actress. She met an actor named Walker who married her only to abuse her and then abandon her after she became pregnant. Creede, for some reason, visited the county hospital where Edith and her baby girl had taken refuge. He was captivated by the child and he and his wife made frequent trips to visit her. He eventually offered to adopt the child, and Edith reluctantly accepted. Creede then renamed the girl Edith Dorothy. After Creede's death, the courts determined that the little girl should be returned to her natural mother who, in the meantime, had found a new husband from San Francisco.

The Denver Republican of July 15, 1897, ran the following article that completes the Nicholas C. Creede story:

Dorothy Creede Gets All
Creede's Will Found and It Is Ripe for Contesting
The Widow Was in Mississippi and
Full of Fight When He Died

"Contrary to the general belief, Mrs. Creede, widow of the famous mining man, is not in this vicinity. Today she left Iuka, Miss. for Los Angeles, and should arrive here by Monday. Meanwhile her attorney, G. Finlayson, is watching every move made by the attorneys of the estate. There is a will in existence in which Creede leaves his fortune to his adopted child, Dorothy, and John T. Jones, attorney for Creede, said this morning that document would be produced at the proper time. It will be offered for probate the early part of next week. Beyond this, however, Mr. Jones declined to make any statement.

"Creede seemed to be wrapped up in the future of the child and his sole hope was, apparently, for her welfare. He frequently talked of Dorothy and what he intended doing for her and how dearly he loved her. One reason for his hurried trip at Elsinore was the fear that Mrs. Creede might try to take the child away or else influence her against him.

"When Creede died last Monday search was immediately made for the widow and as she had been here three weeks before, it was naturally supposed that she was still in this city or vicinity on account of her intention of fighting her husband's action for divorce. Diligent search failed to secure any trace of her and for the time being the supposition was that she was in hiding in some lodging house or else had gone to one of the outside towns. Apparently Creede's fear of annoyance from her was needless, for she went away soon after her arrival.

"About two years ago Creede began action against his wife for divorce on the grounds of cruelty, alleging that she was addicted to the use of morphine and while under the influence of the drug abused and was very cruel toward him. Mrs. Creede had gone to Iuka, Miss., and notice of the action for divorce was served on her at that place. She engaged attorneys there and they in turn communicated with Mr. Finlayson of this city and asked him to look after her interests. He wrote to her and secured all the necessary facts of her side of the matter and filed a cross-complaint asking for half of the property.

"It appears, according to the claims of Mrs. Creede, that she had gone prospecting with her husband and his nephew. She remained with them and had borne her share of the hardships of the trip; had cooked and washed for them, and as a partner in their trip was entitled to her share of the fortune discovered by Creede, who soon after returned from the trip and married her. The estate is worth something less than $500,000 and the heirs besides Mrs. Creede are: Jerome L. Creede of Colorado, J.W. Creede of Iowa, McConnell Creede of Texas, Mrs. William Phifer, a sister, and Edith Dorothy Creede, 3 years old, of this city."

RALPH GRANGER

Ralph Granger, the Del Norte butcher who grubstaked Haase and Renniger, discoverers of the Last Chance Mine, retained his one-third interest in the Last Chance even after being offered $100,000 for it.[6] The July 13, 1897, issue of *The Denver Republican* reported that: "It was closely computed that Granger's income was $3,000 a week for a long time from the Last Chance." A fantastic "return on investment" for a $13 grubstake!! Granger was a millionaire before he left for California.

Granger, his wife, and small son left Del Norte and moved to California. Mrs. Irene Phillips, in an article, "A Silver Baron Who Built a House of Golden Music," in the June 6, 1965 issue of the *San Diego Union*, wrote about Granger's life in California:

> "It is known that he [Granger] arrived in San Diego, April 28, 1892 and soon bought, for $40,000, the new home of Charles Joselyn in Paradise Valley east of National City. He also paid half a million dollars for lemon and orange orchards.
>
> "Though the prices he paid would not indicate it, the home undoubtedly was more important to Granger than his citrus interest. For, nine years later, Granger sold his orchards and they became home sites; he kept the house, which with its surroundings was to make local history.
>
> "The home was set in the center of a sweeping lawn, and it had a magnificent view. In the lawn's center was a 100-foot square full of tropical plants sprayed by a fountain supplied with water from a newly-bored well.
>
> "Granger's first few years in National City were spent tending his citrus groves, enjoying his new home, building Sweetwater Race Track, and sailing his 40-foot yacht, often in competition with John D. Spreckels and his yacht, Lurline.
>
> "He then turned his interest to fine music. What sparked this interest in the National City of the 1890s is not known, but it undoubtedly stemmed from his New England heritage and the dearth of such cultural activity in the Colorado silver mine district.
>
> "On August 2, 1896 Granger purchased the Hawley collection of 12 fine violins, which included the King Joseph violin, known as 'dei Jesu'. It was the gem of the

collection and was said to be the finest violin created by Joseph Guernerlus, master-builder of Stradivarius violins.

"To house the collection, Granger built a room east of his home, and installed a safe. This room soon became inadequate for his musical plans, so he built an 80-by-30 foot addition, and the smaller, earlier room was used as a reception room.

"In the larger room, he commissioned one D. Samaan to paint murals on the ceiling, the motif of which is Euterpe, goddess of music. He covered the floor with an Oriental rug.

"He bought a piano that had a 13-foot sounding board, said to have been the largest in a private home in those days.

"And he bought, with gold coins, a pipe organ — a duplicate of the organ in the Mormon Tabernacle at Salt Lake City. 'The swell organ has 574 pipes and 10 stops, the great organ 366 pipes and six stops and the pedal organ has 60 pipes and two stops,' reported the National City Record with a certain degree of local pride. 'It is set behind a grill-work panel of an intricate design. All woodwork is California sugar pine.'

"The Conservatory, as it first was called, became a mecca for artists. Few forgot the visit of Belgian violinist Eugene Ysaye, when he took the famous 'dei Jesu' in his arms with a feeling of reverence. The sounds he brought forth from it were of such a divine nature that has fallen to few human beings to hear. That was on June 9, 1898.

"Granger sought to be modern, so he installed an 'electric factory' and the Music Hall and his home were flooded with light. Granger also installed a large clock on the west tower of his home.

"At first, the artists who came to the Music Hall performed only for Granger and his friends. But, as word of their performances spread, Granger invited the public to some concerts. One, on May 11, 1899 was promoted this way by the local press: 'Ralph Granger has again assumed the cost of bringing the famous Kneisel Quartet of Boston to San Diego and his guarantee will enable the people of San Diego to enjoy the fine concert.'

"Though such artists as Polish pianist I.J. Paderewski, actress Helena Modjeska, and the female violinist Sada were engaged for private performances after their San

Diego appearances, large groups often enjoyed the Granger hospitality.

"There was so much travel to the Granger home that the City of National City graded the road from Baird's Hill at the head of 8th Street to the entrance to the Granger home and planted olive trees on each side of the road.

"Despite a safe in which to store the violin collection, moisture was a constant problem. Finally, fearing that excessive moisture might destroy the violins, Granger, in March, 1902 sold the collection to a Chicago firm, retaining only the famous King Joseph.

"Eighteen months later, he bought the first automobile in National City, creating great interest. Having sold his orchards in 1901, he turned his attention to real estate. In National City, he built a structure at 8th Street and National Avenue that later became Pythian Hall (it burned in 1949). In San Diego, he bought a block on Laurel Street and constructed the Granger office building, completed in 1904.

"Tragedy struck on July 4, 1906: The ornate Granger home burned to the ground — but the Music Hall escaped damage. There were newspaper reports that mice chewing on matches had started the fire, but it more likely was caused by electrical wiring. The Granger family then moved to a home on Laurel Street in San Diego.

"In San Diego, the family — Granger, wife, son Paul, and daughter Rachel — continued their interest in music, often having small groups into their home for a concert.

"As the years passed by, the Music Hall in National City, virtually abandoned when the family moved to San Diego, became a place of mystery and was known as 'The Sleeping Beauty of Paradise Valley'. The hall, still is owned by Granger's son, of Los Angeles. The daughter, Mrs. Henry Wegeforth, still lives in San Diego.

"As Granger aged, neighbors in San Diego recalled seeing him in the yard, carrying a violin and holding it close as though to keep it warm. One day, he dropped it on cement and the brittle wood shattered. He spent hours trying to glue the pieces in place but the prized King Joseph was beyond repair.

"Ralph Granger died in 1938, but his musical interest lives on. A few years later, Lester Wegeforth, a Granger grandson, did considerable restorative work in the Music Hall and it has been opened several times to the public. Weddings have been held there, and the hall has been the site of an annual musicale sponsored by the Altrusa Club of National City.

"The pipe organ is still there, although it's not always in playable condition; so is Euterpe, the goddess of music — preserved on the ceiling all these years on a linen cloth.

"These are among the things San Diegans are seeing this weekend as they attend the Music Hall's open house. They are learning that Ralph Granger was not only a mining pioneer in Creede, Colorado, but he also was a pioneer in bringing good music to the San Diego area. The little Music Hall remains as a shrine to his memory."

CHARLES F. NELSON

Charles F. Nelson, one of the founders of Creede, died in Copenhagen, Denmark, on November 3, 1919. *The Creede Candle* printed his obituary in the February 21, 1920, issue:

ONE OF THE DISCOVERERS OF
CREEDE IS DEAD

"Charles F. Nelson, for whom the big tunnel was named dies in Copenhagen, Denmark — Through the kindness of Horace G. Lunt of Colorado Springs, the Candle is informed of the death, at Copenhagen, Denmark, of Charles F. Nelson, one of the first two men to discover the rich silver lodes in this district. He died from the result of undergoing a major operation on the 3rd day of November 1919. He was 74 years old.

"Charles F. Nelson came to this district with N.C. Creede, for whom this city was afterwards named, in 1890. They located the Nelson Gulch, above where the Amethyst Mill now stands and built a cabin. Shortly after this, N.C. Creede located the famous 'Holy Moses' Mine and Nelson located the Ridge and Solomon Mines.

"In the winter of 1890 and '91 Nelson moved over into East Willow Creek canyon and built a cabin which is still standing in North Creede today. The first church

services in the new camp were held in this cabin by the Reverend Sanderson of Denver in the summer of '91, that being the only available place. Nelson, upon hearing that there was a preacher in camp who could not find any place to preach, insisted that he use his cabin whenever he wished to.

"In the summer of '91 Nelson located the Del Monte and several other claims on Bachelor Mountain and in the winter of '92 he located the Nelson Tunnel and several other claims along it. All the ore from the 'big vein' (Amethyst Vein) had for years been taken out through this tunnel.

"Nelson sold the Ridge Mine to Senator Bowen for $20,000. Later he sold the Solomon to Abbott & Naylor and the Del Monte to Colorado Springs parties. During the summers of 1892 and 1893 he did a lot of prospecting at Bear Creek and located a lot of claims.

"Nelson must have realized over $100,000 from the sale of his various claims. At the time of his death he still retained stock in the Nelson Tunnel and the Byron Shear Mining Company at Bear Creek. He located altogether more than twenty claims in the Creede district and was tangled up in a number of early day lawsuits between the New York and Last Chance and Del Monte companies.

"Mr. Nelson was a quiet unassuming man and his judgment was much sought after in mining matters. He at one time had offices in both Denver and Cripple Creek as a mining promoter.

"In 1895 he left Colorado going to his old home in Copenhagen, Denmark, where he died.

"He made few enemies and many friends, to whom he was always loyal, standing by them to the finish. His death marks the passing of another one of those boom-day characters who did so much to make the state of Colorado famous. There are many old-timers here yet, in the camp he helped to discover, who remember the things he did, and who will regret to learn of his death."

DAVID H. MOFFAT

David Halliday Moffat was, without a doubt, the most influential of those who invested in the Creede mines. He personally was responsible for extending the railroad from Wagon Wheel Gap to Creede — one of the most important factors in the success of mining in the Creede district throughout its history. Moffat's story, particularly the extension of the railroad to Creede, was begun in Chapter Three. The following paragraphs "flesh out" the Moffat story.

Moffat, born in Washingtonville, New York, on July 22, 1839, went to work at the age of twelve in New York City as a messenger boy for the New York Exchange Bank.[7] In 1855 he moved to Des Moines, Iowa, and in 1857 he was employed in Omaha, Nebraska, as a cashier at the Bank of Nebraska. While in Omaha, Moffat speculated in land but lost his "paper" fortune when the land boom went bust and the Bank of Nebraska closed its doors in 1860. Moffat liquidated the bank without loss to anyone.[8]

Moffat then joined a wagon train to the new town of Denver where he started a successful stationery and book store that he expanded to sell groceries and other goods. He also was the postmaster and Denver's first telegraph operator. Moffat returned to the East and married his childhood sweetheart, Frances A. Buckhout, of Mechanicsville, New York, in 1861. The couple made their home in Denver and had a son. Moffat was made the adjutant general of the Colorado Militia in the 1860s, became the cashier of the First National Bank in Denver in 1866, and gave up his stationery and book store in 1870.

Moffat was convinced that if Denver and Colorado were to thrive, rail transportation to the rest of the country was of the greatest importance. To this end, he invested in the Denver Pacific, built in 1870 to connect Denver to the Union Pacific in Cheyenne. The trans-continental Union Pacific Railroad had bypassed Denver to take advantage of a lower and much easier crossing of the Continental Divide in Wyoming, rather than cross the Rocky Mountains in Colorado. Moffat was treasurer of the Denver Pacific.

Moffat and Jerome B. Chaffee, future Colorado senator, invested in Colorado mines starting in the early 1870s. Moffat reportedly invested in more than a hundred mines, some located in Leadville, Aspen, Cripple Creek, and, of course, Creede. Through his mining investments, he became a millionaire.[9] He was an astute businessman who understood efficient, cost-effective mining as evidenced by his Creede mines, equipped with aerial tramways to cheaply transport the ore from the mines to the rail head.

Moffat became president of the First National Bank in 1880 and held the position until his death. He was one of the owners of *The Denver Times* and was a director and president of the Denver Water

Company, where he was associated with another Creede investor, Walter S. Cheesman.

Moffat's greatest passion was the construction and operation of railroads to serve Denver and Colorado, particularly the mining areas of the state. His presidency of the Denver and Rio Grande Railway was described in Chapter Two. Previous to his tenure as president of the D&RG, he helped finance the short Boulder Valley Railroad and had a major interest in the Denver, South Park & Pacific Railroad that started operations in 1872. Control of the DSP&P passed to Jay Gould's railroad properties in 1880 and a year later to the Union Pacific.[10]

After Moffat's resignation as President of the Denver and Rio Grande, he built not only the Creede line but was the moving spirit behind the construction of the forty-mile Florence & Cripple Creek Railroad connecting the Cripple Creek gold mines — including the mine he purchased in the early 1890s — to the Denver and Rio Grande tracks at Florence, Colorado. Railroad construction started in 1893.[11]

At the beginning of the twentieth century, Moffat was a multimillionaire, a power in the Republican party, and a railroad and mining tycoon. He still had one dream left — building a railroad across the rugged Colorado Rocky Mountains to Salt Lake City and on to the Pacific Coast, so that Denver would be on a direct transcontinental railroad route and would reduce the distance to Salt Lake City by about 200 miles. Moffat organized the Denver Northwestern & Pacific Railroad, the "Moffat Road," in 1902.[12] He was opposed by the Denver & Rio Grande and was blocked from eastern investment funds by E.H. Harriman and James J. Hill, who did not want any competition for their railroads serving the West.

As a result, Moffat spent his personal fortune building the route that crossed the Continental Divide at Corona Pass at an elevation of 11,600 feet. Construction across the mountains to Steamboat Springs, Colorado, was completed in 1908. Because of steep grades, sharp curves, and ferocious winter storms, the line was not successful. Moffat determined that a tunnel under the Continental Divide was necessary if the railroad was to succeed. To that end he made a trip to New York City to find money to finance the tunnel. He died on March 18, 1911, while on that trip. After Moffat's death the six-mile tunnel under the Continental Divide, named the Moffat Tunnel in his honor, was completed in 1920. The Moffat Road ultimately merged with the Denver & Rio Grande and is, to this day, the most important east-west route connecting Denver and Colorado to the rest of the country.

WALTER S. CHEESMAN

Walter Scott Cheesman, like David Moffat, had migrated from New York state to Denver during the "Pikes Peak or Bust" gold rush. He opened a drugstore at Fifteenth and Blake Streets, the first in the Pikes Peak region.[13] Cheesman went into real estate development, buying land that would increase in value. The Colorado State Capitol Building was built on one of his properties, where Cheesman and his neighbors grazed their cows. It was called "Cheesman's million-dollar cow pasture." He organized the Denver Union Depot Company to service the railroads in Denver with side tracks and a depot, promoted city parks, and started Denver's water works. Denver's Cheesman Park was named after him. Cheesman was the prime mover for the Denver Water Board's construction of a dam west of Denver to store sufficient water for a city of one-half million people. No one at that time, except Walter Cheesman, had the foresight to visualize Denver growing into a city of that size. The resulting reservoir was named Cheesman Lake in his honor.

LAFAYETTE E. CAMPBELL

Lafayette E. Campbell, an old army acquaintance of N.C. Creede, was contacted by Creede after he discovered the Holy Moses Mine for assistance in financing its development. In turn, Campbell contacted David Moffat. A partial Campbell biography was included in Paul Berteloop's University of Denver Thesis:[14]

> "Captain Campbell joined the U.S. Army during the Civil War at the age of fifteen and was eventually appointed a Second Lieutenant. He also served in the Indian campaign and was with General David S. Stanley's expedition to relieve General Custer at his last stand. He served as Quartermaster at Fort Monroe, Virginia, Fort Sheridan, Illinois, and at Fort Logan, Colorado. Campbell married the only daughter of Colonel Fred Dent, brother-in-law and confidential friend of General U.S. Grant. Captain Campbell was granted a leave of absence from the Army to engage in mining activities."

Campbell not only invested in the Holy Moses and Amethyst Mines but was appointed general manager for both. He spent several years in Creede, and Campbell Mountain was named after him. He filed on a 160-acre homestead on February 20, 1894. His homestead and an adjoining quarter section, homesteaded by Frederick T. Dent, Campbell's father-in-law, were jointly called the Campbell Ranch. Campbell's ranch was his "country estate" where he entertained visiting celebrities and leading actors in stock companies that played in Creede.[16] The ranch was ultimately sold to Silas Frank.[15] Frederick Dent was a general under U.S. Grant's command during the Civil War. After the war he served as President Grant's military secretary.[17]

The *Del Norte Prospector* in its June 2, 1942, edition, "Creede's 50th Anniversary Edition," had the following article about Captain Campbell: "July 25, 1891 — L.E. Campbell of the Holy Moses came in last Sunday with a gripsack full of gold and silver and paid the boys off to the tune of $3,000. And that night the band played and all waltzed."

L.E. Campbell's obituary was published on May 7, 1919:

> *"The funeral of Lafayette E. Campbell, Colonel, U.S.A., retired, Colorado mining operator, and for thirty-two years a resident of Denver, will be held at 4 o'clock Monday from the residence, 950 Logan Street. Colonel Campbell died Saturday night following an illness extending thru several years. The body will be taken to Washington, D.C., where interment will be in the Arlington National Cemetery.*
>
> *"Colonel Campbell was 66 years old. His military career began at the outbreak of the Civil War when he left Miami University and enlisted in the Union Army, rising from the rank of private to first lieutenant. In 1866 he re-enlisted in the Regular Army as a second lieutenant and served five years in the Dakotas. In 1874 he was transferred to Fortress Monroe, Va., and was closely associated with General Grant. Later he was sent to Fort Sam Houston, Texas, where he built the post, the second largest in the United States.*
>
> *"In 1902 he retired from active service and became interested in the Creede mining district with David H. Moffat, Sylvester Smith, and other prominent men of the state [in 1890]. When his health failed he retired from business, devoting his entire effort to the management of St. Luke's Hospital."*[18]

THOMAS M. BOWEN

Thomas Meade Bowen's purchase of mining properties on East Willow Creek created confidence in the Creede district since he was a well-known mining entrepreneur. Bowen, born on October 26, 1835, in Burlington, Iowa, was educated at Mount Pleasant, Iowa, and began practicing law at the age of eighteen.[19] He served one term in the Iowa House of Representatives before moving to Kansas. He fought with the Union Army during the Civil War where he advanced to the rank of brigadier general in 1863. After the war Bowen settled in Little Rock, Arkansas, where he married Margarette Thurston. He established himself as a lawyer and was involved in the turbulent politics in the period of Reconstruction after the Civil War. He served as a member of the Arkansas Supreme Court for four years until President Grant appointed him the governor of the Territory of Idaho in 1871 for a short tenure. He returned to Arkansas the same year. He ran but lost a bid to become a U.S. Senator from Arkansas. Bowen then moved his family to Del Norte, Colorado, in 1875 where he started a law practice.

Bowen's Del Norte law practice was successful and he became involved in mining ventures in the San Juans. He again became active in politics and was elected Judge of the Fourth Judicial District on October 3, 1876, serving until May 25, 1880, when he resigned in order to devote full time to his mining ventures.[20] He was secretary of the San Juan Consolidated Mining Company at Summitville in 1876. The company owned a large number of claims and had a capital stock of $3,000,000 and offices in Del Norte.[21] Bowen's Summitville, Colorado, investments made him a wealthy man and established his reputation as one of the state's prominent mining investors.

In 1882, Bowen was elected to the Colorado House of Representatives and a year later was elected to the U.S. Senate from the state of Colorado. Bowen served one term of six years in the Senate and chaired the Committee on Mines and Mining. He was a champion of the free coinage of silver, federal irrigation projects in the West, and federal aid for public schools.[22] He returned to Colorado in 1889 and continued his involvement in mining, including the purchase of mining properties in the Creede district. Edward O. Wolcott, another Creede investor, replaced Bowen as a U.S. Senator from Colorado on March 4, 1889.

Bowen and his wife built a mansion in Pueblo, Colorado, now listed in the National Register of Historic Places. He died in Pueblo on December 30, 1906. This story was told about Bowen:[23]

"According to a fantastic ballad, 'Tom Bowen's Ride,' first published in the Denver Inter-Ocean Press *in 1882, he had problems traveling from Summitville to the Convention of the Colorado General Assembly one late fall day. Hurrying down the twenty miles to Del Norte, he missed his train by three minutes. He hired some men to race the train to Alamosa by handcar and helped to pump it himself. Only they missed that connection too! He plied an engineer with cash to catch up to the Denver train some fifteen miles over LaVeta Pass and, pinch-hitting as fireman, shoveled coal to the steam engine. Credulity of the verse aside, he did succeed in the ascendency to the U.S. Senate within three months!"*

Frank Hall, Colorado's historian, had this to say about Bowen: "He is of the type who leaves the imprints of their feet and deeds upon the times and places in which their lives are cast; one of the sprightliest, most winning, most interesting and companionable fellows." [24]

ALBERT E. REYNOLDS

Albert Eugene Reynolds was born on February 13, 1840, in Niagara County, New York, one of ten children. [25] Reynolds attended the Fort Edward Collegiate Institute and Madison University that later was named Colgate University. At the close of the Civil War, he left home for Kansas with $80 in his pocket and worked for a mercantile firm near Leavenworth. He then joined his brother in establishing a store in Richmond, Missouri, and shortly thereafter went further west to Fort Lyon, Colorado, as the "sutler," or trader, who sold goods to the soldiers at the post store.

In 1869, Reynolds and W.M.D. Lee formed a partnership to sell merchandise to the Arapaho and Cheyenne tribes. The business was very successful while the Indians had buffalo hides to trade for goods. When their Indian trade fell off after the slaughter of the buffalo herds, the partners sold merchandise to the military and cattlemen from stores in Fort Supply, 100 miles south of Dodge City, Kansas, and Fort Elliott in the Texas Panhandle. They branched out into freighting and ranching. The partnership was terminated in 1882 and thereafter each man pursued his own interests.

Reynolds married Dora Earll in Columbus, Wisconsin, on April 25, 1883. They lived in Lake City, Colorado, for a short time and then relocated to Denver after their only child, Anna Earll Reynolds, was born in Columbus. The Reynolds were long-time residents of Denver.

Reynolds continued merchandising and freighting for several years until he devoted his efforts to invest in mining ventures full time. He first involved himself in mining operations at Lake City, where Enos Hotchkiss had located a rich vein of ore in August 1874. News of the strike spread rapidly and Lake City soon became a center of prospecting and mining activity. Evidently Reynolds didn't find any mining properties at Lake City that suited him, but the experience started him on a lifetime of acquiring mining properties in most of the western states.

After Lake City he directed his attention to the mining districts near Ouray, Colorado. There, like Tom Walsh, he struck it rich! He and Hubbell Reed developed the Virginius Mine by driving the Revenue Tunnel, started in 1888 and completed in 1893, into the ore body at a depth of 3,000 feet below its outcrop. The ore was then dropped to the tunnel level by gravity for haulage out of the mine instead of being hoisted to the surface through a shaft. This method dramatically reduced the cost of mining, provided good ventilation and easy access to the workings, and eliminated the cost of pumping water to the surface through shafts. The Virginius Mine was the first all-electric powered mining operation in Colorado. Electrical power for the mine was generated by a hydroelectric plant built by Reynolds. Mules used to haul ore through the Revenue Tunnel were replaced by electric locomotives in 1896.

Reynold's revolutionary approach to low-cost mining was very successful and he convinced mining investors, particularly from the East, to fund his mining projects throughout the mining districts of Colorado, including Creede. He maintained control of his mining companies by holding a majority of the stock. His principle mines were the Virginius at Ouray and the Commodore at Creede.

The repeal of the Sherman Silver Purchase Act in 1893 started the precipitous decline in the value of Reynold's mining properties. A millionaire at the age of fifty, he was approaching insolvency when he died. Even though he was still worth $2,000,000 on paper, his mine holdings could not be liquidated. Reynolds passed away at his daughter's home in Hickory, Tennessee, on March 21, 1921.

An interesting bit of information about Reynolds was in *The Arizona Daily Star's* travel section of December 6, 2002. A.E. Reynolds purchased the site of Bent's Fort in Colorado and deeded the property to the La Junta, Colorado, chapter of the Daughters of

the American Revolution to save the historic site for future genera-
tions. Bent's Fort, located near La Junta, was built by William Bent
in 1883. It served as a major wagon-train stop and Indian trading
post, was a haven for early westerners, and occupied a strategic
location along the old Santa Fe Trail.

ALBERT E. HUMPHREYS

Albert Edmund Humphreys was the last and probably the most
important of the early Creede investors who had a major impact on
the district. He became a principal stockholder in the United Mines
Company in 1896.

Humphreys was born on January 11, 1860, in Sissonville,
Kanawha County, Virginia, later part of West Virginia.[26] His father,
Ira, was a millwright and owned a store and grist mill. Humphreys
spent a term at Marshall College where he was granted a teaching
certificate. He didn't spend much time teaching as, at the age of sixteen, he first went to work for his father and then became his partner in a logging operation. The logs were floated down the
Pocataglio and Kanawha Rivers to saw mills along the Ohio River.
The partnership failed in 1887 when their major log purchasers
went out of business, leaving Humphreys in debt for $200,000.

Humphreys left West Virginia for the iron ore country north of
Duluth, Minnesota, where he took options on 480 acres of land containing iron ore. He returned to West Virginia to successfully raise
money to develop his property. He commenced iron ore mining operations and the town of Virginia was platted and developed near
Humphrey's mine. His mine made enough money so that Humphreys
was able to pay off his logging business debts within two years. Two
sons were born to Humphreys and his wife while they lived in Duluth
— Ira Boyd in 1890 and Albert Edmund, Jr., in 1893.

Competition and the Panic of 1893 ended Humphrey's iron mining venture. John D. Rockefeller controlled the Lake Superior
Consolidated Mining Company and the railroads that linked the
mines to the Great Lakes ports. Rockefeller was able to put his competition out of business by selling iron ore to the steel makers at low
prices and raising transportation costs of his competitors.
Humphreys sold his Minnesota property for a fraction of its value
to the Rockefeller interests and again was $1,200,000 in debt.

Humphreys' next mining venture was in British Columbia,
where he invested in precious metals and lead mines and built a
concentrating mill. He sold his properties to a Scottish syndicate in

1895 and was involved in the development of Trail, British Columbia, along with Augustus Heinze, one of the Butte, Montana, copper barons. He returned home to West Virginia in 1897 after examining Colorado gold and silver mines. According to *The Creede Candle*'s Mining Edition of January 1, 1927, "Early in 1897 Colonel A.E. Humphreys visited Creede for the purpose of inspecting the Creede Mines (successor to the United Mines Company) property and secured a lease upon the same."

After returning to West Virginia, he invested in coal mines in eastern Kentucky but a disagreement among the investors induced Humphreys to sell out. He moved to Denver in 1898 and made sizeable investments in Colorado's leading gold and silver camps. Creede was the center of his business activities, but he also owned mines in Leadville and Cripple Creek. His Creede investments yielded profits for many years, but by 1911 low prices for metals ruled out profitable operations at his precious metals mines, so Humphreys turned his attention to petroleum exploration. His exploration efforts were successful in finding large reserves of oil and he was finally able to pay off his Mesabi Range debts in 1916. About the time of his Colorado mining investments, he acquired the title "Colonel," a non-military title given in some southern and western states.

Humphreys' successes in petroleum made him a very wealthy man, and at that point he decided to devote much of his wealth to benevolent activities. To that end, he incorporated the Humphreys Foundation in 1922. He had an opulent lifestyle that included Rolls-Royce automobiles, steamship trips to Europe, polo ponies, and race horses.

Colonel Humphreys purchased land on Goose Creek, a stream that enters the Rio Grande River near Wagon Wheel Gap, about ten miles east of Creede. The quarter section tract was originally homesteaded in 1919 by Colonel Albert H. Pfieffer, Indian fighter and Kit Carson's confidant.[27] Humphreys had a concrete arch dam, the highest in Colorado at the time, built across Goose Creek to form Humphreys Lake. Earthen dams were constructed above Humphreys Lake to form Haypress and Hatchery Lakes. He built a log lodge and guest houses on the property to serve as his extended family's summer home. During the early years, a fish hatchery was operated but was not commercially successful. The Wagon Wheel Gap Estate is now owned by Ms. D.R.C. Brown, daughter of A.E. Humphreys, Jr. Colonel Humphreys died in May 1927.

THE WALLACES

Dr. J.P. Wallace of Creede and Robert B. Wallace and John T. Wallace, both of Monte Vista, Colorado, were, among others, investors in the Nelson Tunnel & Mining Company. Very little is known about Dr. Wallace, except that he was one of the incorporators of the Nelson Tunnel & Mining Company in 1892, that he served as treasurer, and was on the board of directors in 1894. He also served as treasurer of the Amethyst Electric Power and Light Company.

Robert B. and John T. Wallace were brothers who established the first bank in Monte Vista, Colorado, in 1886 as reported in *The Monte Vista Journal* on April 17, 1925. The Wallace brothers also engaged in hardware and lumber businesses and financed the construction of Monte Vista's first flour mill, as well as investing in the Nelson Tunnel venture.

Robert B. Wallace's obituary in the *San Luis Valley Graphic*, June 9, 1911, stated that he was born at Wooster, Ohio, on October 15, 1854. After graduating from Wooster University he went to Coin, Iowa, where he was in the lumber business with his brother, John T. Wallace. From there, the brothers came to Monte Vista in 1886 and organized the firm of Wallace Bros. & Clark. In December of 1886 the Bank of Monte Vista was organized, and Wallace was actively engaged in managing the bank thereafter. In addition to his business duties, he was involved in community affairs. He served one term in the state legislature representing Rio Grande County and was active in securing the Soldiers' and Sailors' Home for Monte Vista. Robert B. Wallace died in early June 1911.

John T. Wallace was born in Wooster, Ohio, and, with his brother, was identified with the early history of Monte Vista. John Wallace always retained his interest in the bank he and his brother started but devoted much of his energy to the lumber business and established lumber yards at other San Luis Valley towns. He was the president of Amethyst Power and Light, a Creede utility company. In 1903 he moved to Denver and established the Wallace Lumber Company in south Denver.

John Wallace's obituary in *The Monte Vista Journal* of April 17, 1925, states that he died April 10, 1925, at his home in Denver and was survived by two brothers, Boyd of Monte Vista and James of St. Paul, Minnesota. James' son, DeWitt Wallace, worked his uncles' Bank of Monte Vista for a year.[28] DeWitt Wallace and his wife, Lila (Acheson) Wallace, founded the *Readers' Digest* magazine in January 1922.[29]

CHAPTER 6

BOOM TIMES

THE CREEDE "BOOM" WAS SHORT-LIVED, lasting from the discovery of the Holy Moses Mine in August 1889, until the precipitous drop in the price of silver and the collapse of the silver market in 1893.

The intent of this history of the Creede boom times is not to describe the "hell-roaring" aspects of the camp, but to describe the lives and times of the those inhabitants who worked in the mines and those who provided services. The story will be told, whenever possible, in the words of those who saw Creede Camp in its hey day.

The U.S. Geological Survey, in their annual report for 1891, stated that the only surprise in gold and silver mining was the great development at Creede, Colorado. With this exception, no especially important mining districts were developed.

The *Report of the Colorado State Bureau of Mines for 1897* had this to say about Creede's early history:

> "The early history of this region may be epitomized as follows: An unknown section prior to 1890; a producing camp equipped with a railroad in 1891; created a county in 1893. This growth and development exceeds in point of time that of any other portion of the state, and was considered phenomenal even in Colorado. Its achievement was possible on account of a combination of most favorable conditions. No winter campaign of 'future possibilities in a newly discovered district' was made by the newspapers. The district was entered quietly and the first news to reach the public though the press was 'large and regular shipments of high grade ores from Creede.' The rush that followed this announcement was second to none in the history of the state, and constantly increasing production gave credence to a common belief in a section 'greater than Leadville.' Thousands of men flocked to the new fields in the winter of 1891-92, the 'boom' reaching its height in February. Accommodations were inadequate

and much hardship was encountered. One of the memorable events connected with this district was the scramble for town lots. Creede, the original center, was located on Willow Creek, in a narrow gulch with almost vertical walls, and eligible building sites commanded fabulous prices. Later Jimtown [present-day town of Creede] was located a little further down where the valley was somewhat wider, grew to a town of considerable importance and was almost entirely destroyed by fire. Notwithstanding hardships and back-sets, the year 1892 was one of great development in the mines and a large amount of prospecting throughout the county. The year 1893 opened under the most favorable auspices, but before its close the outgoing passenger traffic far exceeded the incoming."

A journalist from *The Denver Republican* wrote this about Creede on December 12, 1891:

"With the rush of prospectors to the camp came the building of a town. The camp was first made in Saguache County and called Creede. This was all the town in existence until three months ago, when the building of the railroad from Wagon Wheel Gap soon brought more merchants, families, ore haulers, and miners than could find lodgment in the narrow gulch in which the original location was made.

"This led to the building of an overflow town in a widening of the gulch about one mile down Willow Creek. Here, across the line into Hinsdale county, about the 1st of October was started a town that has since grown into a collection of about 150 shanties crowded into the creek bottom and up the mountainside. This place has been known locally as Gintown, Jimtown, Creedemore, Willow Glen and later as Amethyst, and no one yet seems to know in which one of these towns he is living today. It is here that the state school land, which is just now a bone of contention, is situated. M.V.B. Wason has a lease on a large section of school land which reaches over and includes about half of the territory which might otherwise be available to the newcomers for the building of their homes and the platting of a town. Mr. Wason has

a cattle ranch three miles below Jimtown and uses the land for pasture. On his own land he has laid out the town site of Wason and the railroad company will erect a depot there.

"The camps are alive with business and are typical booming mountain towns. Dozens of log and board shanties are being thrown up: the gambler, the tent saloon, the bad man with a gun are all to be seen in great number. Wages at the mines are $3 to $3.50 a day, and the operators find it difficult to keep a sufficient number of men on hand.

"The weather for the past week has been intensely cold, and the snow fell to the depth of about six inches in the gulches and twice that depth on the summits. The ore-hauling and town building has gone on uninterruptedly in spite of it all.

"Everybody here is anticipating and preparing for a great boom in the spring, and there is certainly reason to expect that they will not be disappointed, for as an old prospector said yesterday: 'Creede is either the biggest thing I ever saw or it is nothing, and from the way the ore is coming down from the hills, I am inclined to believe there is something here.'

"Before the first of the year Creede will be sending out thirty cars of ore a day, and it is to be remembered that the greatest half of her mines are only six months old."

The Engineering and Mining Journal, the most prestigious of the mining industry periodicals, sent journalists and well-known mining engineers to the new camp to investigate and write about their impressions and opinions of Creede Camp:

February 13, 1892:

"The new mining camp, Creede, situated in the southern part of Colorado, is now the center of attraction in the state, where it is heralded as a second Leadville. For the past six or eight weeks there has been a rush thither, and already the population of the place is said to exceed 2,000 — this is in the midst of winter, when the ground is covered deep with snow and prospecting is almost impossible on that account. There is evidently a solid foundation for the boom, however, as the mines which have been opened are already producing from ten to twelve cars of ore, or

from 100 to 120 tons, daily. The excitement reminds some old timers of Leadville in '78 and '79; yet the scenes of the Leadville boom can never be repeated, such a difference has thirteen years wrought in conditions in Colorado. Those who trudged wearily and heavily laden down through the snow of Mosquito Pass in 1879 can now ride to Creede in a Pullman sleeping car. The papers which reach us from Creede give the usual accounts of new strikes and sales of mines and prospects, speculation in town lots, notices of the opening of shops of various kinds, liquor saloons, gambling rooms, and dance houses — all typical accompaniments of the typical mining boom, from that of Virginia City in 1859 to Leadville in 1879. Creede, variously known as Amethyst, Jimtown, and Creedmore up to a fortnight ago, has now been christened formally after the prospector who discovered the mines. Two daily papers, the News and the Amethyst, have been established and the map of the camp published by the latter in its second issue, January 23rd, shows almost as intricate a checkerboard of rectangular claims as a map of Fryer Hill, Leadville, or Aspen Mountain. Will the new camp prove to be such a bonanza as either of those or will the bubble burst like that of Robinson and Kokomo, in the Ten Mile, time only can tell."

Thomas R. MacMechem, in an article, "The Ore Deposits of Creede, Colorado," wrote the following:

March 12, 1892:

"In presenting a totally disinterested and impartial report of Creede Camp, Colo., the present cynosure (i.e. center of attention) of all eyes in the West and the center of vague hopes, one is constantly reminded, if truthful, that the instinct of such an article is persistently antagonistic to insincere estimate and undue popularity, on which the fame of that remarkable camp has thus far been based. Nevertheless, the utmost veracity cannot injure it, for while it has certainly not yet attained, in the estimate of the critical and careful, the distinction of a bonanza camp, and its present development will never justify such a classification, the results, even at this early date, are indicative of a permanency that will make it important in the mining world.

"The excitement incidental to the opening of a new camp has been the reason of many a financial delusion, but it is only just to state that the 'booming' method by which Creede has been advertised meets with the sincere disapproval of the original discoverers and locators. Colored and feverish statements of the camp's magnitude are exceedingly deplored by them. This success was, as usual, introduced by schemers and speculators, who, suspicious and timid about exploring the earth for real value, stake their chances on the surface and remain there until the last lot is gone. Creede's future depends entirely upon the unlocking of her own resources.

"The enormous quantity of snow prevents all work of this sort at this time of the year. Prospectors are leaving the camp daily for the south and east with a view to examining the country lying 20 and 30 miles from Creede. As far as the town itself is concerned, the excitement can hardly be overdrawn. About 6,000 people form its shifting population, and the usual sensations of a new western camp are ever present. Many improvements have been introduced since the Rio Grande Railway advanced its road from Wagon Wheel Gap, a distance of 10 miles below Jimtown or Lower Creede. Electric lights, banks and other metropolitan equipments have been established. This is a brief description of Creede as it is today: as for the future, patience."

March 19, 1892:

"Our warning to investors with respect to the boom in the iron lands of the Mesaba Range of Minnesota is equally pertinent with respect to the boom at the silver camp of Creede in Colorado. The mines that have so far been opened there are rich and their record during the few months that they have been producing is wonderful, but as yet there are only four shippers, and it is evident that these cannot support a population of 6,000 or 7,000 men, as Mr. Edward R. Kirby, in a very conservative article, which we print in this issue, remarks. It is extremely likely that other mines will be discovered as soon as the snow melts and prospecting, stimulated by the rich discoveries of last autumn, is resumed, but unless the district proves

to be another Leadville or Aspen, which no experienced mining man expects, the chances are that those who invest in town lots at inflated prices will lose their money, just as has been the case in the majority of boomed mining camps. The men who are actually engaged in developing the resources of Creede deprecate the wild speculation in its mining claims and town lots, which they realize is bound to result in the injury of legitimate interests."

March 19, 1892:

THE ORE DEPOSITS OF CREEDE AND THEIR POSSIBILITIES

Written for the Engineering and Mining Journal by Edmund B. Kirby, M.E.

"The main town of Creede, formerly known as Jimtown, and now the scene of wild real estate excitement, is in Saguache County, twelve miles from Wagon Wheel Gap, and at a point where the canyon of Willow Creek, a northern tributary of the Rio Grande, opens out into the broad valley of that river. Following the stream about three-quarters of a mile up the narrow canyon it forks into East and West Willow. Moses Mountain, the scene of the first discoveries, is the lower extremity of a spur-like ridge from the main range on the north, and stands between the two forks. It rises with sharp precipitous sides 1,000 ft. to 2,000 ft. above the streams, while on the west side of West Willow fork is the slope of Bachelor Mountain, the present center of excitement. The Bachelor Mountain mines are 4,200 ft. west of those on Moses Mountain, and both groups are about two and a half miles north of the town and 1,500 ft. to 2,000 ft. above it.

"The short period of five months, in a winter with heavy snowfall, has seen the advent of the railroad, the shipment of some 8,300 tons of high grade ore, and a rush to the district that has changed the population from two or three hundred to six or seven thousand men. No new discovery of pay ore has been proven in this time, but under the efforts of boomers real estate speculation in the town has reached fantastic proportions. Lots worth $10 to $25 last summer are now selling for $2,500 cash, while town lots are being sold over an area sufficient for a city *and reaching from the mouth of Willow Canyon well over the broad valley of the Rio Grande, here some two miles wide. Only a remarkable and improbable number of genuine new discoveries this summer can prevent a speedy collapse of this insane inflation. The loss will fall chiefly upon the Eastern investors and "tenderfeet" who will become the final lot owners; but it will none the less react in inevitable injury to the genuine mining and real estate interests of Colorado."*

The *Rocky Mountain News* published a booklet, "Creede Camp," in March of 1892 that described life in the new silver camp:

"Chaos come again is the way to describe Creede. It is not quite chaos, but the ordering divinity seems to have taken a day off. Six thousand rustlers are in the camp, and before June the chances are that 10,000 will be seeking wealth in and about the narrow gulch of Willow Creek. Last week there were 100 on every train that puffed and snorted up through the gap. It's the old story over again — a flock of sheep scurrying after a leader. The camp is about 8,500 feet high, and the mountains stick up anywhere from 1,000 to 3,000 higher.

"Upper Creede lies in a basin with walls of granite, absolutely precipitous in places and 1,000 feet high. Should one of these great cliffs topple over, it would reach clear across the basin and smash against the opposite side. Consequently the sun at this season does not have an opportunity to look in and see what is going on during more than six hours or thereabouts. At Jimtown they are better off, because the gulch widens out.

"For six miles up and down Willow Creek there is scarcely a foot of land that has not been staked by somebody as a lot. Away up above the end of the railway, where the gulch is often so narrow that there is not room for a house, they have thrown up log cabins and board shanties. Here and there a man with a pick and a long-handled shovel is chiseling away the partly disintegrated granite of the steep mountain side to make a shelf whereon to put a hut. Often a woman sits on a boulder and watches him at work. It is home-seeking under difficulty. Others have calmly cut down poles, laid them

across from bank to bank of the creek and put up such shelter as a painful lack of mechanical ability alone could make possible. The log cabins away up the gulch are mainly those of old-time prospectors who have come with their wives and families, when they have any, to settle down and do systematic work in the hills.

"Now and then a big ten-ton load of ore in a ponderous sled comes thundering down the steep road with the driver pounding his horses lustily and shouting at the top of his lungs. He is more afraid of sticking somewhere than of smashing all creation by colliding with it. Behind him come two or three more in the same style. A vehicle going up that road needs a scout ahead, because the ore sleds could no more stop than an avalanche could handle a razor. Dirty-faced youngsters spend their lives in shrilly shrieking from safe eminences at this performance, awaiting meanwhile with gleeful expectancy the inevitable catastrophe.

"The sleighs whirl around with a tremendous swing when they reach the depot and unload into the cars. Down the trail from another direction has come maybe a train of fifty burros, each with 150 to 200 pounds of sacked ore on his back. Now and then there is a new burro. An old one leaned over too far on some precipice and was overbalanced by his load, that's all. The last that was seen of him he looked like a pinwheel with calliope attachment, as he went down a couple of thousand feet.

"The first depot at Upper Creede was soon found insufficient, and the Rio Grande promptly built another in the lower part of the young city. Such a sight as they are! Bags, barrels, boxes, beer kegs, stoves, blankets, packing cases, and furniture are heaped about them. Men and animals swarm around. Every living thing is busy shoving around every inanimate thing. A continuous coming and going occasions jostling and pushing.

"Old Creede consisted of a street about three quarters of a mile long with side extensions here and there, where the cliffs fell back a few feet. There is scarcely a foot of ground left whereon to plant a post, for it is an old settled locality nearly a year — and real estate is valuable. The street is rather straighter than a corkscrew.

"But Creede, months ago, outgrew the narrow limits of a street and surged and flowed out into the wider ground lower down the gulch, bring into life what became known as Jimtown. That prosaic appellation didn't last too long, for who of the great would know of any other name than Creede, and Creede it is now, the whole of it, as it should be. And lo! It is at Jimtown, the Mighty, that the nations of the earth meet, and great is the mingling of the peoples thereat.

"Five months ago there was nothing, now there are a thousand or more buildings. Boards are heaped everywhere, men are rushing around with them. Probably seven hundred houses are completed. The remainder present an array of every conceivable way of projecting scantlings (i.e. a small beam or timber such as a 2" x 4") into the air. Tin cans, old boots, and shavings are thrown everywhere with reckless profusion. The hills to the west slope gradually up to the mesa. Their top is crowned with a long row of gaunt silhouettes against the sky. More scantling! If a man drives a stake into a lot it holds the ground a short time, but if he wants to keep it he must lay a foundation. This is a foundation: Take a tree trunk and saw off six round pieces, like small butcher blocks, run boards from one to the other; at each corner nail two upright planks, so as to form two sides of a square. There you are; that is a valid foundation and a tangible evidence of good faith. These things are everywhere — dozens of them. Down on the flat, far below the town, where the ground is even more overflowed and is covered with six inches of ice, you see them. They look like no other thing on earth. Perhaps the owner became disheartened and went away, concluding that the whole business was a fraud. Just go over and start to fool with the structure, pull off the boards, and kick over the butcher blocks. You'll find out all the particulars you wish to learn immediately.

"There is a clangor of hammers and saws, a slamming of planks, a calling of men to one another, a din as of war. That is the way they make mining camps in Colorado at places where there are millions in sight. Now and then a man shoots out of a saloon door or a barber shop — for there are barber shops — with a foot or a fist behind him.

The man from the barber shop at once goes into the saloon, the man from the saloon hunts another. The shanty on poles across the creek flourishes in rankness here, as does the smoke-begrimed tent.

"But it didn't take long for the town to get beyond the mere shanty epoch. Excellent two-story buildings have become numerous in the past couple of months. Half a dozen hotels that have real beds, with springs in them, have been built, and the man who last January slept on the floor of a saloon and was glad to have it, now slumbers in comfort beneath quilts.

"Water is obtained from Willow Creek, and two companies have been formed to pipe pure fluid from above the town. There has been more lumber and other material and supplies shipped into Creede than into any other camp in the world, during the same time.

"Municipal affairs are regulated by committees appointed by mass meetings of the citizens. Officers of the three counties which corner near the town, are present, and marshals have been appointed.

"There is not any undue interference with the vested right of each citizen to raise a moderate amount of Cain, and it is safe to say that fully half the population is of the kind which does see fit and loves to imagine itself a sportive whale.

"The saloons and dance-houses are in full blast. And such dance-houses as they are, and such dances, and such discarded remnants as the old fairies who flaunt around in there, never were seen before! The aforesaid fairies are not of the young and charming kind, with stars on their brows, long wands and shapely pink limbs, delicately displayed amid gauzy drapery. They are a job lot of weazened witches, but they make the night groan just the same. Along in the morning, when the wheezy accordion lets up, the time is occupied by a riot! Nobody bothers.

"Drunken men come out occasionally and empty their guns into the air or somebody's legs. The latter process indicates a cultivated softening of old brutal habits. There are a few 'bad' men in Creede and many who are reckless, but thus far there has not been a murder. This is a source of constant amazement, but it is true.

"*Creede to-day is passing through that period which is inseparable from the founding of a city in a day. It is the only place of true frontier type in Colorado, and it is doing its best to keep up its end. A year from now it will have changed, and the sober-minded citizens will have shaped and molded it into an orderly town. But it will have experiences before that comes to pass.*

"*Lots are worth money. Everyone has read of the remarkable scenes at the recent sale of school land which was necessitated by the incoming of thousands. From a little over sixty acres the state realized nearly $250,000. The sum would have been much larger, were it not that chivalry withdrew all opposition when a woman bid and cheered her when she obtained a lot for a quarter of its value. The claims in equity, which had no legal status, of those who had made improvements, were also respected. It was a strange sight in a community supposed to be turbulent, to see one lot bid in for a nominal sum by a little woman, while the lot next to it was run up to thousands by roughly dressed and bearded men, wild with the excitement of a contest. Then came the building and the tumult of creating a city in a week.*

"*Three miles below the creek junction, the gulch spreads out into a little park beautifully level. Here Wason (M.V.B. Wason) has a fine 1,500-acre ranch, and here he believes is the natural location of the town. Several streams have their confluences, and the roads which follow them meet at this point, which thus becomes the center of the country for fifty miles above. Wason points out that there is no danger from washouts, and says that he will put in a system of pipes to bring pure water from the springs above the proposed town, thus doing away with the necessity for drinking the sewage-poisoned fluid which flows down Willow Creek. He also says that he will build an electric line up the gulch to the mines. Quite a number of houses have been built and many lots sold.*

"*The doubt as to what county the camp is in is a nuisance of the first water, but it shows what a wilderness this region was until recently. There wasn't anything there to be taxed, and none of the counties cared anything about the place. The whole business is a snarl! The lines of Hinsdale county as laid down by law are impossible, because they do not join. The line of Saguache is said in the statute to run westerly from the joint meeting place to Hinsdale, Saguache, and Rio Grande. What is westerly? Does it mean due west? The maps show the line running almost north. Rio Grande County's interest is in the school land, which may be within its borders.*

"Post-office facilities were fearfully bad but have been improved. Two telegraph offices, one at Creede and one at Jimtown, are busy night and day.

"Supplies at Creede cost but little more than in the San Luis Valley. The prices are practically those of Del Norte, with something more than freight added. This state of affairs is rather unusual in a new camp which has a veritable boom, but the easiness of communication accounts for it. In car-load lots, the freight rates from Alamosa are 37 cents a hundred, from Monte Vista, 27 cents, and from Del Norte, 22 cents. Merchandise from Denver ranges from $1.35 to $1.80 per hundred, according to class. Freight on ore to Denver, where all the product is shipped, is $7 a ton, which is pronounced to be very reasonable.

"Wages are not especially high. Miners obtain $2 a day and board. Carpenters, who are more in demand than any other class of mechanics, are paid $4 to $4.50 a day. Really expert men with the saw and plane are very few in the camp, and such can easily command more. Anyone who can make a straight line through a board, and a good many who can not, are pressed into service.

"A man with a team is also in great luck. He can get all the work he can possibly attend to, either in freighting or in jobs around the camp. The press in this direction is not so great as it was a short time ago. For handling ore by four-horse teams for two miles, the mines were paying $10 at first and then $5. The rate is now down to $2.50, and is expected to reach $1. As the teams are able to pull ten tons in heavy sleds down the snow road, the rate of even $2.50 a ton is a perfect bonanza. Working by tramway, the cost of bringing down ore is less than $1 a ton, so that the halcyon days of the freighters will be over when the two additional trams projected have been built. This, however, cannot be before the summer. One firm of

freighters, W.A.[D.W.] Hoover & Co., employs thirty-five men, forty-five mules and one hundred and ten jacks (burros) and several others have large outfits.

"Blacksmiths are needed, and the better the man the worse he is wanted. Painters are not called for, because the decorative taste of the camp runs almost altogether to a severe style of plain board with nail-head dottings.

"Flour, bread, pork, etc., are twenty-five percent higher than in Denver. Necessaries of life, such as whisky, are not much dearer if you are content to risk corrosion by drinking the ordinary article retailed under the name of whisky. Fifty cents, or four bits, is about the rule for meals or bed. Four newspapers, one of which is a daily, are published. Denver men have equipped the town with electric lights, and the building of the plant by John H. Poole, was the most rapid piece of construction on record in this line."

THE TOWNS

The Creede Mining District contained not one but five towns that existed during the boom times. Creede is the only survivor. The others became ghost towns early in the district's history. Sunnyside was in existence before the boom and Weaver, Bachelor, and Stumptown came into being when the mines on the Amethyst fault system were developed. Creede was several miles south of these mines and a thousand feet lower. Thus, Weaver, Bachelor, and Stumptown gave the miners and their families places to live within reasonable walking distances of the mines. In addition to the five, M.V.B. Wason platted a town site on his ranch about three miles south of Creede, but it never became a town in reality, even though the Colorado legislature made it the county seat when Mineral County was formed.

Creede

In June 1891, the only producing mine in the Creede district was the Holy Moses Mine about 1.5 miles above Ryderville, located in the East Willow Creek Canyon.[1] In 1887, Haskell Ryder built a cabin on Willow Creek where the town of Creede was later founded. It is considered to be the first structure erected in Creede.[2] The town site was called "Willow" in 1890 when prospectors and miners were attracted to the area after the Holy Moses Mine was purchased by David Moffat and his partners. The name of the camp was changed at a miners' meeting held on October 22, 1890, to "Creede" in honor of the man who located the Holy Moses Mine.[3] By the end of the year a number of houses and stores had been built in the narrow gulch of East Willow Creek. Construction continued all winter in spite of snow and bitterly cold weather.

The migration of people into the Creede area continued unabated through 1891 and dramatically increased after the rich

First House Built in Creede in the Fall of 1885 by Haskell Ryder
Al Birdsey Collection, Courtesy of the Creede Historical Society

Upper Creede, Photo by W.H. Jackson — 1891
Courtesy of the Colorado Historical Society

Creede Near Willow Creek Junction,
Photo by W.H. Jackson — circa 1891
Courtesy of the Colorado Historical Society

Upper Creede, Photo by W.H. Jackson — 1892
Courtesy of the Colorado Historical Society

strikes were made on the Amethyst vein and after the railroad's arrival in December. The camp's population at the end of 1891 was 1,200 and in February 1892 exceeded 2,000 individuals.[4] At the peak of the boom, the district's population was reported as 6,000 in one estimate[5] and as many as 10,000 in another.[6] As fast as people came into and then left the area, the actual maximum population is, at best, a guess. Many of the camp's inhabitants lived in Sunnyside, Weaver, or Bachelor.

The overflow of people could not be accommodated in the narrow gulch of East Willow Creek, bounded by steep cliffs, so the town expanded south toward the mouth of the gulch. The towns of Amethyst, Jimtown — also known as Gintown, New Town, or Creedmoor — and South Creede were formed. The name "Gintown" was either a corruption of "Jimtown" or, more likely, so named because of the cheap gin that was sold in the town. According to some, the name "Jimtown" was taken from "Jamestown," a gold mining camp in Boulder County, Colorado. At the peak of the boom, the Creede towns along the gulch were called "Stringtown," because there were tents, frame buildings, and residences "stringing" from North Creede to South Creede.

Creede's first newspapers, the *News* and *Amethyst*, did not survive. Lute Johnson arrived with a hatful of type, a hand press, and brains and started *The Creede Candle* as a weekly paper. Its first edition was published on January 7, 1892, in which Johnson had this to say:

> *"Of course if you are a miner or in any way interested in mining you will want the Candle. For two silver discs you can have a new one every week for a year and may be lighted to a prospect that will return you thousands for one. It is supposed that you understand that it takes 'tallow' to keep a Candle going and that is what I'm here for."*
> Lute H. Johnson, Boss Trimmer

The Creede Candle was a permanent fixture in Creede and faithfully chronicled the camp's history until its last edition on December 27, 1930. One of Johnson's most pithy comments about some of the citizens of Creede was in the April 29, 1892, edition:

> *"Creede is unfortunate in getting more of the flotsam of the state than usually falls to the lot of mining camps. . . . some of her citizens would take sweepstake prizes at a hog show."*

Cy Warman started the daily *Creede Chronicle* and published the first issue on March 22, 1892. The *Chronicle* lasted until 1895. Warman wrote his famous poem about Creede ending with the lines: "It's day all day, in the day-time and there is no night in Creede."[7]

The boundaries of these towns were not well defined and questions about their locations exist even today. Chuck Barnes describes the towns' locations:

> "*Creede, no doubt, was the community that developed within the East Willow Creek gulch, now known as 'Old North Creede,' closest to the Holy Moses and other early operating mines. Jimtown seems to have been the community that developed south of the confluence of the east and west Willow Creek drainages, and matriculated down the Willow Creek canyon past Windy Gulch.*
>
> "*According to what is found in the copies of the Candle, 80 acres of school section land, taken over by the state, subdivided and sold at auction, fills in the area as far south as today's Wall Street, the east-west street just north of the present day post office. Another part of the school section land, south of First Street formed South Creede, and extended to somewhere further south, possibly even to where State Highway 149 crosses the railroad tracks in the very lower part of Creede today.*"[8]

The school land issue is an important facet of Creede's history. Sections 16 and 36 of all townships in the state had been set aside as school lands and could be sold by the state. The northeast quarter of section 36 joined the Jimtown site on the south. Governor Routt and a party of state officials visited Creede in January 1892 to decide whether or not the school land should be sold as town lots. On January 14, 1892, while at Creede, the state officials decided to survey eighty acres of school land into town blocks and lots. In conversation with *The Creede Candle*'s reporter, the governor stated his position on the case:

> "'It is but just,' he said, 'that the land be thrown on the market and it seems to me that the board could not do better than in the settlement arrived at. The land at once required will be surveyed and sold at once and after the snow goes off and the engineers can do their work, then the mesa land to the west will be treated in the same way. The mesa land is a beautiful place for the town to build

up to. It is high, dry, and sightly. The residences, school houses, public buildings, and many business houses will eventually be on the high ground. We have reached an agreement with the railroad company. They are not inclined to act hoggish. They will put their depot near the present town and go down below for side tracks, round houses, and the Y."[9]

M.V.B. Wason, who held a lease on the school land, gave notice that he would fight the right of the land board to set aside his lease. The lease was in force for three more years and the state had been paid its rental fee for a year in advance.

On February 4th the State Board of Land Commissioners canceled M.V.B Wason's grazing lease on the school lands. *The Creede Candle* reported on the sale of the lots in the March 3, 1892, edition:

"The topic of chief interest in Creede camp for the past week has been the sale of lots in South Creede by the state board of land commissioners. Governor Routt and party reached the camp Thursday afternoon in a special train, and with them came, in four sections, over 1,200 lot buyers and people who came to see.

"That evening there was a meeting of the squatters on the land held in the show tent, at which a number of resolutions were passed declaring the rights of the settlers to preference in bidding. A committee requested the presence of the Governor, but he being unwell, Secretary of State Easton and ex-Treasurer Brisbane appeared and explained the position of the bard and its inability to do more than offer the lots at auction as the law requires. He stated that the board did not wish to see the price run up on the lots, but if others chose to bid them up, it was impossible for the state to prevent it. Mr. Brisbane said that if any speculator tried to bid above the settler he would be hissed down. They would all assist in hissing him down. The statement was received with great cheering. The state had no right to hold a lot on its speculative value, Mr. Brisbane said, and the governor agreed with him. The meeting was adjourned after a number of rousing speeches were made urging squatters to stand together and demand their rights.

"Throughout the sale the feeling between squatter and speculator was most intense. In his sense of judgement,

*every squatter knew the state's rights in the matter, but did
not propose to get left if he could help it. Therefore, while
they made a good showing to get the lots cheap when the
bluff did not work their sense of right prevented them
from making any disturbance.*

*"The element of lawlessness manifest at the sale in the
picking of pockets, the plot to rob the cash box and similar deeds, were not, we are happy to say, the work of
squatters, but of floaters who came in with the lot buyers.
The squatters acted the part of noblemen, and the guard
of honor came from them.*

*"It was a great event in the camp's history and the
opening of a new era in the boom. Buildings are being
contracted for by the hundreds, and the rush has broken
out again."*

The Engineering and Mining Journal had this to say about the
school lands and claims:

March 5, 1892:

*"Nothing could show more conclusively the progress
of civilization in the West than the sale of school lands at
Creede, belonging to the State of Colorado, which took
place last week. These lands, which are located in the
heart of that new and promising camp, had been advertised for sale at auction on the 26th ult. (i.e. ultimo, in the
last month) but had been previously taken up, for the past
part by squatters. As prospecting at Creede is now practically at a standstill on account of the snow, the boom in
the town has been so far principally in real estate and the
disposition of the school lands has been the common topic
of discussion. For weeks proceeding the sale there have
been rumors of trouble when the real estate speculators
should attempt to bid up the price of the lots already
occupied by squatters. One day last week the press dispatches brought eastward accounts of a general pistol fir-
ing at Creede for the purpose of frightening prospective
purchasers of the lots and ghastly predictions of gore on
the auction day were confidently made. The auction day
came and went, however, as peacefully as if it had been in
New England, being distinguished only by the natural
exuberance which marks men in affairs in the West. But*

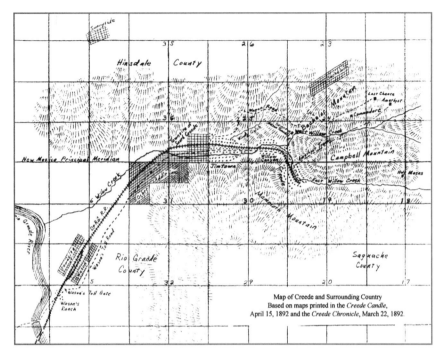

Map of Creede and Surrounding Country
Based on maps printed in the *Creede Candle*,
April 15, 1892 and the *Creede Chronicle*, March 22, 1892.

as for 'trouble' and 'gore' there was none. The fact is that the law is just as paramount now in Colorado as in New England, as this and the railway and the telegraph have put a repetition of the disorderly and exciting times of Virginia City, Deadwood, Leadville, and Tombstone entirely out of the question."

March 12, 1892:

"A committee of citizens of Creede appointed at a mass meeting on the 2d inst. [i.,e. Instant or this month], met on the following day with J.P. Kinneavy as chairman and Clint T. Brainard as secretary. This committee was appointed to arbitrate disputes about claims in lots of the unsold school sections and land lying west of that portion of the school land recently sold. The committee will decide who shall be entitled to the claims the contestants make and if their decision is not satisfactory to the disputing claimants then the matter is to go before a mass meeting of citizens for hearing. This committee is composed of J.P. Kinneavey, Clint T. Brainard, John Lord, J.L. Jones, John Kirwin, James O'Connor, E.C. Burton, J. Miller, W.J. Allen; The following resolutions to cover

disputes that may arise on lands designated were unanimously accepted:

"Resolved, 1. That a stake or foundation shall hold good for 30 days.

2. No man can hold more than three lots by stake or foundation.

3. Priority of location shall always hold good.

4. That after the expiration of 30 days the locator shall do continuous improvement work.

5. Every claimant shall have the privilege of putting his proof of claim before the committee on arbitration.

"Clint T. Brainard, as attorney, was instructed to communicate with the county commissioners of Saguache, Rio Grande, and Hinsdale counties concerning the appointment of five deputy sheriffs to preserve the peace, and the following were recommended as appointees: Deputy Sheriff Delany of Hinsdale County, W.J. Allen, Capt. Light, John Kirwin, and Mr. Plunkett."

John W. Flintham, General Manager of The Denver Consolidated Electric Company, formed the Creede Electric Light and Power Company on February 1, 1892. Work on the electrical system started that very day and continued around the clock, through cold and snowy weather, to completion at 10:00 P.M. on February 6th, and the lights were miraculously turned on for the first time. Creede was lit up until the June 1892 fire and then experienced several months of darkness. On January 1, 1893, the power system was sold to Amethyst Electric Power and Light, a company headed by John T. Wallace of Monte Vista as president; J.P. Wallace of Creede as secretary and treasurer; and Ed. M. Wagner as superintendent.[10] *The Creede Candle*, December 9, 1892, reported:

"The Amethyst Company is making its electric light plant first-class in every particular and giving good service. Poles and wires have been stretched into upper Creede this week, and both the incandescent and arc lights will be supplied to all parts of the gulch. The supplies for the incandescents are not all here yet, but Dr. Wallace thinks the time will not be long before customers who signed for the lights can be accommodated. In the meantime, the plant will be shut down for ten days to permit a thorough overhauling of the old machinery."

Lower Creede, Photo by W.H. Jackson — 1892
Courtesy of the Colorado Historical Society

The Denver Times carried a story about one of the early women (there weren't many) in the July 15, 1898, issue:

> *"The first restaurant opened in Creede, Colorado was owned and conducted by a woman. She is a widow and her name is Mrs. Reid Miller. On April 1, 1891 she reached Creede, too poor to pay the freighter who took her there. In exactly one year to a day she was in receipt of an income of $500 a month and had a snug sum in the bank. She is now worth $50,000. Several other plucky women also made fortunes in the early days of Creede."*

Before the coming of the railroad, the mail was dropped off at the Wagon Wheel Gap Post Office and delivered to Creede the next day. After its arrival it was placed on the floor of a pine board shanty to be sorted. In the shanty were about a dozen private letter boxes and a counter; behind this stood the postmaster knee-deep in mail.[11] Creede was served by two post offices at first. The Creede Post Office was in the upper gulch and the Amethyst Post Office was in Jimtown. A.H. Major was the Creede postmaster and Silas Frank was commissioned as the Amethyst postmaster on March 1, 1892, at the post office on Cliff Street. Frank owned property on the lower

Mrs. Reid Miller, Son, and Restaurant — 1892
Courtesy of the Denver Public Library Western History Collection

end of Willow Creek above its confluence with the Rio Grande River. He ran a hack service from Creede down to Wagon Wheel Gap.[12] Another Frank, named Anton, will appear in Creede's history as the plaintiff in a landmark stream pollution court case.[13]

On June 5, 1892, a disastrous fire destroyed all of the upper business section of Jimtown. About six o'clock in the morning a fire broke out in Kinneavy's Saloon in downtown Jimtown. The flames quickly spread, jumping from building to building and crossing streets, fanned by the draft created by the narrow canyon that acted as a flue. By eight o'clock that morning Jimtown's business district was smoldering ashes. The fire burned eight city blocks before it was brought under control. The Rio Grande tracks were buckled and trains stopped south of town. Many businesses and over a hundred houses were destroyed. Rebuilding of the destroyed section commenced within a few days, attesting to the faith the citizens had in the future of Creede. As an example, The Tompkins Hardware was reopened for business in a tent five blocks from their destroyed building two hours after the fire was put out! Unfortunately, the drop of the price of silver in 1893 effectively finished the rebuilding effort.

Mrs. A.H. Major gave her remembrances of the fire in an article in the *Colorado Magazine*, Vol. XXII, No. 6, 1945:

"A two story building, a short distance down the street, was in flames and the breeze sweeping up the narrow canyon frightened us. In a few minutes a bucket brigade was formed — the only means of fighting fire at that time. Men and women, too, quickly responded to the fire call, and in a short time a long line was formed, and pails and even cooking kettles were pressed into service to carry water to the flames. But the fire jumped from one building to another — all dry wood and built close together — so it seemed for a time that nothing would be left of the camp but the ashes.

"My husband ran upstairs and called me that our time had come to save what I could. First our young son dressed and carrying a new book was in one corner quietly watching. Two trunks, a satchel, a basket, a dishpan, some warm bedding, and some favorite books were placed on a flat car. Three women of questionable character came to help me. They carried our belongings to the car and guarded them. The street was filled with weeping women and swearing men. I noticed Mrs. Stephenson clad in her best and wearing a hat and veil at the station. Finally the fire was brought under control and the women helped me carry our belongings back into the house.

"In March of 1891, A.H. Major and his brother-in-law, Finley Frazee, came to Creede from Crestone to look the place over and ordered logs out for a store building. In May, they moved over and started a store. In 1892, their building was completed and, occupied at the site, it remained until destroyed, some forty or fifty feet below the first cabin in Creede, built by Haskell Ryder, several years before. In addition to their line of dry goods and groceries, they handled a variety of other products, as is indicated that they paid just a dollar or two less than a thousand dollars on one shipment of blasting powder."

After earlier incorporations of North Creede and Jimtown, the whole of Creede was incorporated as a city on June 16, 1892. Mr. V.V. Clark makes reference to a report by Frank E. Wheeler in which Mr. Wheeler tells the following story:[14]

"The Creede District is often referred to as 'No Man's Land.' Hinsdale, Saguache and Rio Grande Counties all

After the Fire, Jimtown, June 6, 1892

Courtesy of Dave Bunk

*claimed the territory but not one of them would assume
jurisdiction or furnish the necessary police protection,
which condition resulted in the creation by legislation of
the County of Mineral and the organization of a provi-
sional city government. Edward Morton was designated
mayor and a complete set of city officials was appointed.
In order to raise the social and moral standard of the
community a Committee of Safety was chosen. This committee made a survey of the city and found a great many
undesirables. Mr. John McDonough, president of the First
National Bank of Creede, was selected by lot to advise
some thirty odd individuals that their presence was a men-
ace to the constructive advancement of the city and they
were given twelve hours in which to leave and never
return. A careful check was made on the effect of this
order and it was found that the last to comply with the
order had thirty minutes grace."*

The Colorado Sun, June 19, 1892, article reported that:

*"Building in Jimtown still goes steadily on. The
stone foundations for the First National Bank building
are now being laid. Tomkins & Bro. Hardware dealers
will erect a brick structure, from front and fifty feet in
width. Ex-Governor Adams will erect a similar building,
as well as Levy & Benedict. One block of seven two-story*

1. Water tank, northern limit
2. Kinneavy's Saloon, where the fire started
3. The big bridge, 500 ft. long
4. The Orleans Club
5. Brainard & Beebe's Hotel
6. Governor Cooper's Block
7. Western Union Telegraph
8. Miners Bank
9. Jimtown Depot (Creede)
10. First National Bank
11. Frank J. Hard's row
12. Post office
13. Wall Street Bridge
14. South Creede Depot
15. Electric Light Works
16. D. Mitchell
17. Bank of Creede
18. Levy & Lewin's Store
19. Hoover's Barns, covering four acres
20. Emlick's Store
21. Denver Hardware Company
22. H.H. Tompkins
23. Raab Brothers
24. The Albany
25. Boston's Cafe
26. Sponsillers Theater
27. D. Long
28. Watrous & Bannigan
29. Alexander and Heitler
30. San Juan Hardware Co.

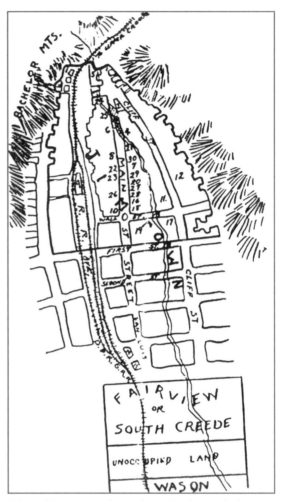

Note: The heavy lines show the burned district

Map of the Creede Fire of June 5, 1892
The Rocky Mountain News, June 6, 1892

*frame buildings substantially constructed, is being figured
on and also a three-story brick hotel. Considerable building is still going on on the school section."*

The Denver Republican reported on July 17, 1892, that property owners in Jimtown were awaiting action by the new city council to adopt ordinances providing a fire limit and regulating the
construction of buildings within it, channeling the creek, and estab-
lishing building lines and grades.

The September 16, 1892, edition of *The Creede Candle* reported
that the Creede schools would open the following Monday with a
total of 175 pupils enrolled. Schools were located in lower Creede
and upper Creede.

The Creede Candle of September 30, 1892, reported the creation
of a city water system that, unfortunately, was not installed prior to
the June fire. Earlier attempts had failed.

> *"An ordinance providing for the issue of $25,000 in
> city bonds and for the putting in, owning, and operating of
> a system of water works by the city was passed. It is pro-
> posed to sell the bonds at once. A line of 12-inch wood pipe
> is to be laid from a reservoir site up Willow creek, and a
> sufficient system of supply pipe put in to fully cover the city
> and supply all with pure water by gravity pressure."*

A second serious fire broke out on November 26, 1892. The fire
was caused by an overheated stove in the Holy Moses building owned
by Captain L.E. Campbell in Upper Creede. A.H. Major directed the
efforts of the firemen and a second disastrous fire was thwarted.
Dynamite was used on the Moses building to contain the fire.

In the first anniversary edition of *The Creede Candle* on January
6, 1893, a summary of Creede in the year of 1892 is given:

> *"Creede has good public schools and two church
> organizations. There need be no alarm over the social and
> moral status of the citizens. The day of the six shooter and
> the gambler is past and the camp has settled down to a
> well-ordained, decent, reading, visiting, and praying com-
> munity. Not that everybody in the camp reads, not that
> everybody prays, and not necessarily that everybody is
> decent, but the general run of people will stand compari-
> son with those in any mining camp in the West."*

The *Colorado Business Directory* listed Creede as having a population of 6,000 in 1892, of which 181 were business and professional people. The *Directory* also listed the following businesses in Creede: banks, hotels, restaurants and saloons, groceries, meats, bakery, hardware, real estate, mines, insurance, contractors, builders, lumber, hay grain, druggist, attorney, shoemakers, mining-civil engineers, livery, blacksmith, assayers, laundry, barbers, physicians, jewelry, and watch repair.

Lower Creede, Photo by W.H. Jackson — 1893
Courtesy of the Colorado Historical Society

The *Directory* stated that Creede had a population of 6,000 in 1893, of which 212 were business and professional people. Businesses listed in the *Directory* included: groceries and meat markets, 8; men's clothing and furnishings, 6; boots and shoes, 7; coal, 4; restaurants, 6; dry goods, 3; hay and grain, 3; hardware, 3; drugs, 2; jewelers, 2; furniture, 3; master carpenters and builders, 10; lumber yards, 5; planing mill, 1; transportation, 5; livery, 5; real estate, 4; milk ranches, 3; blacksmiths, 5; harness maker, 1; brokers, 2; tinsmiths, 2; barbers, 3; dentist, 1; shoemakers, 2; bakers, 4; fruit and confectionary, 3; news stands and stationery, 3; tailors, 2; wholesale meat companies, 1; ticket brokers, 2; banks, 2; hotels, 8; assayers, 4; civil engineers, 7; U.S. Deputy mineral surveyors, 5; lawyers, 10; doctors, 4; undertakers, 1; saloons, 8; newspapers,

1 daily (*Chronicle*) and 2 weeklies (*News* and *Candle*); telegraph office, 1; depots, 2; churches, 3; school, 1; lodges 4 (Odd Fellows, Masons, Knights of Pythias, and Red Men).

Sunnyside

Sunnyside, about two miles west of Creede, probably dates back to the 1870s when mineral locations were made and allowed to lapse. Some mining occurred in the late 1880s that was unsuccessful and the town was all but abandoned for a time, even though a post office had been established by 1887.[15] The town was reactivated during the 1890s, but it gradually declined over the years to the status of a ghost town as the adjacent mines shut down.

Bachelor

The town was established in 1892 to serve the Bachelor, Last Chance, Amethyst, and other operating mines on Bachelor Mountain and is located about three miles northwest of Creede at the head of Windy Gulch at an elevation of 10,500 feet, 1,500 feet above Creede. The mines were located a short walking distance across a gentle saddle from the town.

According to *The Colorado Sun* of September 11, 1892, the first buildings in Bachelor were one home and a boarding house erected by C.L. Calvin and his wife on September 6, 1891, near two springs. Development of the Last Chance Mine created the need to house miners and the company built a second boarding house near the springs.

The Creede Candle edition of January 21, 1892, commented that:

> "The latest town site excitement is in a park on Bachelor Hill, around the Last Chance boarding house. Yesterday there was a stake raid for lots and it is proposed to plat an 80 acre government town site to include the territory of the Last Chance mill site, portions of the Quakenasp and Greenback claims and some vacant ground. Two saloons and a female seminary [houses of prostitution] are already in operation and other business houses are expected soon. It is to be called Bachelor."

Several claims had been filed on the land covered by the application for the town site patent. The owners of the claims crossing the town site proposed to fight the issuance of the patent to the bitter end. Evidently they did not succeed because in January, 1892,

S.D. Coffin, the discoverer of the New York claim that was embroiled in controversy and litigation, G.C. Martindale, and Newt. J. Thatcher had a town site survey made for eighty acres platted into twenty-four blocks, with three main streets and nine cross streets. Coffin built the second house in Bachelor. By March of that year, the town had 100 houses with additional houses being built. Approximately 1,000 men were engaged in mining and prospecting within a three-mile radius of Bachelor.[16]

The Creede Candle summed up Bachelor's progress in its April 1, 1892, issue:

> *"Bachelor is one of the liveliest of the many towns in the camp. Many new buildings are going up and the merchants are having a good trade. There are eight stores, about a dozen saloons, several assay offices, boarding houses, hotels, and restaurants in operation and more going up. Some large and substantial two story buildings are in the course of erection, and the town has all the appearances of permanency. The order for a resurvey of the township and some technicalities in the town site papers have delayed getting titles to lots, and the fact that the town is on mineral ground will operate against, but there is no doubt but that Bachelor will be one of the best suburbs of Creede."*

Bachelor was incorporated and the first election of town officers was held in June 1892. The *Colorado Business Directory* for 1893 listed seventy-two businesses in the town. The community had a good school and an active miners' union. A post office was opened in April 1892, but it was called "Teller" to eliminate conflicts with a then-existing Bachelor, California. The *Teller Topics* commenced publication in July of 1892. Bachelor was known as a rowdy, rather crude settlement with a peak population of between twelve and fifteen hundred people. The *Colorado Business Directory* records indicate that the population of Bachelor dropped to 800 in 1896 and was only 200 in 1900.

The first anniversary issue of *The Creede Candle*, January 6, 1893, had this to say about Bachelor:

> *"Bachelor, Teller Post Office, has grown in a year on top of Bachelor into a bustling business center of 1,200 population. It is one of the liveliest divisions of the camp and furnishes a trading place for 1,200 or more miners employed on the hill."*

Bachelor — circa 1892

John Gary Brown Collection,
Courtesy of the Creede Historical Society

A tragedy involving three of the town's citizens is often narrated:
A minister, whose desire was to reform Bachelor, was forced to leave
his ill daughter alone while making a call. When he returned he
found a man in the cabin. Thinking that he was a molesting miner,
the minister shot him. His daughter revealed that the man had been
a doctor and then she, too, died. The minister shot himself as a
result of his remorse. All three bodies were buried in the same grave
because of the difficulty of digging in the frozen ground.

Fires were a problem at Bachelor. The oldest cabin in town used
as the Bachelor Mine bunkhouse burned down in January 1893. A
major forest fire that extended from Shallow Creek and Sunnyside
to the forks of Willow Creek threatened the town of Bachelor during June of 1893. It burned to the edge of town but destroyed only
one or two cabins. Almost the entire population of Bachelor spent
days combating the fire that burned all the timber surrounding the
town. *The Creede Candle,* June 23, 1892, reported "that half the
population of Jimtown was headed up the hill to lend our neighbors
all the assistance possible."

The first saw mill in the Creede district was located in Windy
Gulch near Bachelor. It was owned by A.S. Crawford and commenced
operations in November of 1891 and continued until 1892, when it
was moved onto West Willow Creek where it operated until 1898.

Harold Wheeler reminisced about Bachelor in the history of his
life that he wrote for his grandchildren:[17]

"I was born in Monte Vista, Colo., June 7, 1897. My father was Horace W. Wheeler, who was raised in Missouri on a farm. My mother was Nellie French, daughter of Col. S.M. French of the G.A.R. who fought on the Union side in the Civil War. At the time of my birth, Col. French was Commander of the Soldiers Home in Monte Vista.

"Needless to say, the first few years of my life are a complete blank. I have heard that I once pulled a table-cloth full of dishes onto the floor after a banquet at the Home, but I don't remember it.

"I really came to life in Bachelor, a small town in Mineral County, Colo. Bachelor was closer to the mines than Creede, and was named because many bachelors settled there to be closer to their work. It is now a ghost town. Only parts of 2 or 3 buildings remaining.

"Bachelor, as I remember it, had a population of 5 or 6 hundred people. We had three saloons, two grocery stores, one dry goods store, five boarding houses, one bowling alley, one barber shop, two churches (one Catholic, one Protestant), many barns, and one doctor's office. Oh yes, and there was Madam Pom Pom's establishment. (More about her later, bless her heart.) A school house and town hall. We even had a telephone in Bachelor, and of course a cemetery. The wooden sidewalks were a real treasure trove. We crawled under them and found nickels, dimes, quarters galore. We were never broke, but there was nothing to spend it on but candy.

"In the center of town was the pump, where everyone got their water. What a job it was packing water and keeping the horse trough full. I used to envy the Cummings kids. They had a barrel mounted on a burro cart. Many had kind of a neck yolk so one man could carry 2 five gallon cans.

"Our water bucket and wood box were always dry, and we lived about 1/4 mile from the pump. Saturdays and Mondays were the worst days (bath night and wash day).

"In case of fire, the pump always went dry, so we just moved out the piano and let her burn. (I could never understand why, but they always saved the piano or something heavy and let everything else go.)

"Bachelor was right at timberline, 10,000 feet. A new-comer once asked a Swede miner: 'When do they ever have summer in this Godforsaken place?' The Swede replied, 'I don't know, I've only bane here eighteen months.'

"It snowed anytime, at any month. The summers weren't long enough to store up wood for the really bad months, so we just froze. The kitchen stove was the only heat. In a real heavy snowstorm, we literally had to dig out from under it.

"The mines were over the top of the hill in Stump Town, about 1 mile away. The main mines were the Last Chance, the Happy Thought, the Amethyst, the Del Monte, the Winchester, the Commodore (No. 3, 4, 5. Don't know where No. 1 and 2 were), the Park Regent, the Bachelor. There were many more, but these were the main producers. Silver was the main ore, though there was lead, zinc, and a little gold.

"Most of the mines were shafts, and each had a steam operated hoist. Whistles blew at the start of each shift. Amethyst time was always 10 minutes ahead of the rest.

"Ore was hoisted to the surface and then hauled in wagons to Creede and the railroad. Later on the Nelson tunnel was driven to connect the bottoms of the shafts and the ore was taken out through the tunnel, to a point just above Creede. This tunnel was about 4 miles long."

The Congregational Church — Bachelor, 1894
Courtesy of the Colorado Historical Society

According to John Jackson and other sources, Jack Dempsey, heavy-weight boxing champion of the world and nicknamed the "Manassa Mauler," spent part of his childhood in Bachelor. John Jackson's grandparents journeyed to Bachelor from Leadville with two toddlers born in 1888 and 1889. In 1893 a daughter was born to their family in Bachelor. The Dempsey family moved from Manassa, Colorado, to a cabin near the Jackson home in Bachelor in 1900. John's father, William T. Jackson, Jr., and five-year-old Jack Dempsey, became playmates until the Dempsey family moved on to the Ouray and Montrose, Colorado, areas. There Jack first put on boxing gloves and began a career that would lead to his fame and fortune.[18]

The author, while on a business trip to New York City in the 1970s, happened to stop at Jack Dempsey's Broadway Bar the last evening of its existence. Dempsey was there, shaking hands with well-wishers. I joined the line and, when I stood face-to-face with him, said, "Mr. Dempsey, there are at least two good men who came out of southern Colorado." He replied, "Who are they?" and I replied, "You and me." We talked about southern Colorado and our discussion turned to Creede. He mentioned several family names that were familiar to me, particularly "Jackson." He remembered his playmate of many years ago!

Life in Bachelor was not easy. According to John Jackson, "Bachelor sat in a defile with only one well at the southerly end which served all above it. The youngsters carried buckets of water to their cabins on neck yokes from this community well. Everyone had an 'outhouse' and refuse pile, so you can be sure that the water was almost always contaminated. A little cemetery sits in an aspen grove at the southeast end of the Bachelor town site and most of the graves contain children, including two of my grandparents' children."[19]

Weaver

Little is known about the town of Weaver, except that the name came from the fact that most of the people in the town were named Weaver. The September 30, 1892, issue of *The Creede Candle* had this comment: "The new town of Weaver, tributary to upper Creede, is booming right along, and has appearances of permanency. The wagon road up West Willow is still being agitated."

Weaver attained the status of a "ghost town" shortly after the 1890s. The site is located in a narrow valley along West Willow Creek about two miles north of Creede, within walking distance of the Amethyst and Last Chance Mines and just downstream from the Amethyst Mill site. The town was largely abandoned by 1915.

Stump Town

The Creede Candle, December 23, 1892, had this comment: "The Amethyst Company no longer asks its men to board at the company house, and as a consequence quite a town of dwellings and small boarding houses is being built on the hill, close about the mine."

This was most likely the beginning of Stump Town for which there is no recorded history. It was an unplatted community that grew up north of the Amethyst and Last Chance Mines on Bachelor Mountain in the West Willow Creek drainage, north and across the ridge from Bachelor. It grew in an area of extensive logging where high stumps remained, thus the name "Stump Town." Again, the town provided a place where miners could easily walk to their work in the mines.

MINERAL COUNTY

Mineral County was created from Saguache, Rio Grande, and Hinsdale Counties and has an area of about 860 square miles. The adjoining counties are Hinsdale and Saguache on the north and Rio Grande on the east, Archuleta on the south, and Hinsdale on the west. The county has an extreme length north and south of forty miles and is twenty-four miles wide. The east, south, and west boundaries follow the cardinal points of the compass; the north is outlined by the Continental Divide.

At the beginning of the boom, the Creede district was a "no man's land." Rio Grande, Saguache, and Hinsdale Counties all claimed the area but none of them would assume responsibility for government functions such as police protection, land records, and so forth. Many miners had their claims recorded in Rio Grande, Saguache, and Hinsdale Counties to be sure of their legality.

Paul Davis, a mining engineer who started working at Creede in 1940, remembers a stone marker on the mesa west of Deep Creek on the north side of the road. On one side was chiseled "Rio Grande County" and on the other "Hinsdale County." The stone disappeared many years ago.[20]

The Creede Candle in its March 17, 1892, issue had this comment:

> *"Creede wants a county government badly enough but is content to wait until the setting of the legislature in January 1893 before asking for a county of its own. The state is not in a position to stand the cost of an extra session and the talk of the people here paying half the expense is kiddish rot."*

The Engineering and Mining Journal, April 2, 1892, stated that:

> *"State Engineer James P. Maxwell, George D. Nickel, deputy surveyor of Rio Grande County, W. McCree, county surveyor of Saguache, and J.J. Abbott, county surveyor from Hinsdale, held a meeting at Creede recently to determine the county lines at that place. The lines decided upon place Jimtown and the school land in Hinsdale, and leaves only a small portion of Upper Creede, together with the Holy Moses Mine and its immediate vicinity, in Rio Grande County. The decision was satisfactory, save to the representatives of Saguache County. Proofs of title to the land in Jimtown were made in Saguache, and nearly all the recording has been done in the wrong county."*

The Creede Candle, April 1, 1892, gave Saguache County's opinion on the county line decision:

> *"The officials of Saguache County are wrathy over the decision of the state and county engineers which places Jimtown in Hinsdale and Creede and Moses Mountain in Rio Grande. They are preparing to fight for a slice of the big camp in the courts. Creede isn't very particular. It is more convenient to do business at Del Norte, but in ten months the legislature will settle all disputes by forming a new county."*

Mineral County was created by an act of the Colorado legislature, approved March 27, 1893. This act resolved the problems created by having the district split up among three competing county governments, but, unfortunately, the legislature selected the town site at Wason as the county seat.

M.V.B. Wason had built a one-story frame building with a brick vault at Wason that was rented to the county as a courthouse. A special election was held in Mineral County on November 7, 1893, and the voters legally changed the county seat from Wason to Creede.[21]

The Creede Candle printed the following story in its November 10, 1893, edition:

WASON COLD-DECKED
> *"While the county seat is down in the cow pasture at Wason, business is conducted in the 'Heart of the City' of Creede. — At the election Tuesday the voters of Mineral County decided in favor of a removal of the county seat*

from Wason to the City of Creede. Thursday morning the county officers opened up in the Wilcox building, and Creede is now the county seat.

"Wednesday afternoon rumors were current that Major Wason intended to take advantage of some technicalities and prevent the speedy consummation of the expressed desire of the voters. There was talk of injunction proceedings to effect delay; the courthouse matter was in dispute; it seemed uncertain what might happen, so it was concluded to take the bull by the horns and move.

"Darkness had hardly settled down before heavy transfer wagons began to rumble down the Wason Road. Faces could not be identified in the darkness.

"At 10 o'clock the wagons came back. They were piled up with huge docket books, records, canvas-backed volumes of all sizes and kinds. The vaults of the First National Bank were unlocked; likewise the unoccupied rooms in the Wilcox pueblo. Into these were piled the archives of the county and later came the furniture. By midnight not a vestige of the properties of Mineral County remained at the old county seat.

"But a few knew what was going on and the flags flying from the improvised court house in Creede and from the staff of The Creede Candle office created not a little curiosity in town. People strolled around to see what had happened; saw the county officers indoors straightening about desks and blank cabinets, arranging records in the narrow quarters, tumbled, grinned, and went away to say that a march had been stolen on those who had stolen on those who planned delay and chuckled over 'a good job.'

"Some said it was not legal and could not be done. The officials did not argue with the first proposition, but pointed to the completed job as a denial of the last.

"One thing is settled; Creede is the county seat of Mineral County."

The Mineral County Commissioners purchased the Wason building, originally used as the county courthouse, on January 10, 1895, and had it moved to Creede where it remained in use until its destruction by fire on December 12, 1946.[22]

WASON TOLL ROAD

Martin Van Buren, Harriet L., and Edith Wason formed the Wason Toll Road Company on December 30, 1890. The road began at the bridge over the Rio Grande near the Wason ranch house below Creede and terminated at the Holy Moses mining claim on East Willow Creek. Wason constructed his toll road in 1891 and 1892 to the junction of East and West Willow Creeks. He collected a toll of $0.75 a team for everything that traveled over his road. This, of course, infuriated the citizens of Creede Camp. In fact, he was hung in effigy in August of 1892 and thereafter Wason hired bodyguards for protection.

In September of 1892 a delegation of Creede citizens traveled to Lake City to discuss the situation with the Hinsdale County Commissioners. The delegation found that Wason had promised them to charge a toll only on ore hauled over the road. However by this time rails had been laid into Willow Creek Gulch and ore was loaded into rail cars without traveling on Wason's road. In September 1892, the toll gates were taken down after two toll collectors were charged and fined for unlawfully obstructing a public highway. *The Creede Candle* reported on November 3, 1893, that Captain L.E. Campbell of the Amethyst Mining Company had the company's lawyers, O.P. Arthur of Creede and Charles J. Hughes of Denver, prepare an opinion that stated the Wason Toll Road had been abandoned by the Wasons and tolls could no longer be collected.

The saga of the Wason Toll Road continued in the courts until the General Assembly of Colorado passed a bill that was signed by the governor on April 3, 1899. The bill appropriated $10,000 for the purchase of the Wason Toll Road to ensure the route's use as a public highway.[23]

CHAPTER 7

CONFLICTS AND LITIGATION

CONFLICTS OVER MINING PROPERTIES and litigation to resolve those conflicts created serious obstacles to the development of the mineral resources of Creede Camp. Most, but not all, of the conflicts were created by the application of the Mining Act of 1872, particularly the Apex Law and extralateral rights. There were cases of claim jumping and the moving of boundary stakes. Many conflicts were settled without serious litigation by consolidating mining claims into mining companies jointly owned by those owners of the claims in conflict. The New York Chance Mining Company, the Bristol Head Mining Company, and the United Mines Company were the major consolidated companies. A conflict between the Del Monte Mining Company and the Last Chance Mining Company was taken all the way to the U.S. Supreme Court, where a landmark ruling concerning the mining law was made in 1898. This particular conflict was not completely settled for years and seriously impacted the timely development of the ore bodies in the Last Chance, New York, and Del Monte claims.

When the owners of the Last Chance lode claimed some of the ground of the New York lode, A.E. Reynolds took the lead in working out a compromise between the owners of the two mining claims. In early 1892 Reynolds had acquired a controlling interest in the New York lode from George K. Smith, Samuel D. Coffin, and his wife, Mary A. Coffin. Reynolds was represented by Colin Timmons, an engineer, and Byron L. Shear and Isaac L. Johnson, two lawyers he had retained during apex suits at Aspen. After Reynolds' purchase, the New York lode was proved to be on the Amethyst vein apex. The New York Chance Mining Company was organized to combine both sets of owners to mine the disputed ground. Reynolds was made vice president and general manager of the joint company. It yielded large returns to its investors. Reynolds invested his profits in other Creede mining properties, particularly the Commodore Mine.[1]

The Engineering and Mining Journal had these comments about the compromise:

March 12, 1892:
"The presence of the Last Chance-Amethyst vein in the New York extension has been demonstrated, but no ore is being shipped at this time owing to a dispute about the ground, the north end of the New York overlapping the Last Chance. Alleged illegal changing of the boundary stakes upon the part of the Last Chance people, after location, forms the basis of an action against them. The same mine is in a like predicament upon its south end, where the Del Monte overlaps it for 100 ft. This is the first litigation in the camp. The exploration of the New York is interesting because it promises to be the most extensive development of the big veins outside of the producers."

July 2, 1892, Saguache County:
"New York Chance Mining Company, Creede — To avoid the long litigation, heavy court expenses and the delay in working certain portions of the properties, the owners of the Last Chance and New York Mines have compromised and consolidated. The owners of the Annie Rooney were bought out for $8,000 cash. The new organization will be incorporated as the New York Chance Mining Company. The present owners of the mines who share in the combination are; on the Last Chance side, Ralph Granger, J.F. Sanders, L.Z. Dickson, H.R. and E.O. Wolcott; on the New York side, A.E. Reynolds, O.E. LeFevre, S.D. Coffin, Colin Timmons, and others. The Willow Mining Company, selling the Annie Rooney, is composed of J.B. Moore, M.H. Rogers, Butler & McKinley, and others."

Mary A. Coffin, after the incorporation of the New York Chance Mining Company and its financial success, sued Reynolds, Timmons, and Johnson, charging that they knew the New York claim was on the apex of the Amethyst Vein when she sold them the claim for $15,000. This became one of the celebrated lawsuits of the time. The suit was settled in 1899 in favor of the defendants with a decision that denied Mrs. Coffin's claim. *The Denver Times* ran this story about the suit in its May 25, 1899, issue:

Coffins [Mary A. and S.D. Coffin] Lose The Big Suit —
Plaintiffs Had No Standing
    "*Story of the New York Mine; how the camp of Creede*
was established and the litigation just decided was brought
to court. A mining suit, the most extensive and one of the
most important ever brought in Colorado and involving the
greatest amount of money, was decided this morning by
Judge Charles Y. Butler in favor of the defendants. The
amount involved was over $3,000,000 and land above the
famous New York Mine at Creede. The suit was brought by
Mrs. Mary A. Coffin, one of the original owners of the
property, against I.L. Johnson of Culpepper, Va. and A.E.
Reynolds of Denver, to recover the property after having
disposed of it nine years ago at her own price."

    The June 17, 1897, issue of *The Engineering and Mining Journal*
best describes the settlement of a conflict over mining property that
was settled by the organization of the Bristol Head Mining Company:

    "*Bristol Head Mining Company — The long-standing*
dispute between the Amethyst Mining Company and the
Commodore Mining Company of Creede, over the
Sunnyside Mine, has been amicably adjusted. The settle-
ment arrived at results in the organization of the Bristol
Head Mining company, with David H. Moffat as president;
A.E. Reynolds, vice-president; and James A. McClurg, gen-
eral manager. The territory in dispute, known as the
Sunnyside Mine, embraces 517 ft. in the center of the min-
ing property owned by the Amethyst and the Commodore
Company. Four years ago when it was not supposed that
this little strip of vacant territory had any particular value,
the two companies each secured a half interest in it by pur-
chase. The purchase was made solely to protect themselves
from any possible interference from outside parties. But as
the Amethyst and the Commodore workings progressed it
soon became evident that the small extent of territory was
the most valuable of all and that it contained the principal
ore chute of the veins being exploited by the two compa-
nies. This discovery immediately threatened expensive liti-
gation to determine which of the two should have the ore.
Almost one year ago both companies began to develop the
disputed territory, and it was this that made more imminent

a legal fight. But six months ago an understanding was reached whereby the development of the disputed strip has been prosecuted along certain lines for the purpose of ascertaining what rights each of the two companies had. This work was recently completed, and the settlement that has been reached was based on the determination shown by the development work."

The enriched zone of the Amethyst Vein was exposed only in the Last Chance and Amethyst lodes. To the north of the Amethyst a great amount of costly exploration work was necessary to disclose the course of the vein due for several reasons: 1) the vein's apex was masked by overlying erosional debris; 2) the vein at its uppermost reaches was leached and of a lower grade of mineralization than that in the Amethyst and Last Chance lodes; and 3) an unforeseen bend, or change in strike, the direction of the Amethyst vein's intersection with the horizontal, made exploration uncertain. *The Creede Candle*, January 6, 1893, commented that: "In the vicinity [the unforeseen bend], opening like a fan from the Amethyst shaft house, the mountains were dotted with deep shafts that have been sunk through the wash or on faint hints of leads, in the hopes of discovering the vein. With steam plants are the Little Main, the New Discovery, the Argenta, Happy Thought, Stanhope, and True Friend all hunting the lead." Ultimately the strike and the apex of the Amethyst vein north of the Amethyst lode was determined at considerable expense for at least 2,000 feet by the involved companies through exploration shafts and tunnels.

The determination of the actual location of the vein's apex created property conflicts between the claims located with less than perfect information. The mining companies who had purchased the claims spent considerable time and money in their exploration and were perfectly willing to protect their investments. *The Creede Candle* in its January 6, 1893, issue stated that: "Litigation will have to be settled and the question of ownership decided, but this should be done and the properties all shipping before the end of another year." *The Candle* reported on the conflicts and cited instances when they became heated:

> *November 25, 1892:*
> "Small war precipitated on Bachelor Mountain in consequence of the Moran Park Regency controversy. Both sides armed with Winchesters, but luckily no shooting was done, and a compromise has been effected."

December 23, 1892:

"*Following the publication of the facts regarding the location of the Ironclad on the Happy Thought ground in last week's Candle, the camp was treated to another of those bloodless gun plays which are becoming the fashion up in the vicinity of the switched Amethyst vein.*

"*Saturday evening Arthur Miller got a tip that there would be an attempt to drive his men from the work. He took an ounce of precaution and sent two armed men up to be ready in case the Happy Thought should do so. Manager Dewey asserts that he never contemplated such a move but other parties in the property did go up with Winchesters and a great display of war and they attempted to gain entrance into the Mary Taylor shaft. On Saturday Phil Flynn set a force of men to work on the Golden Eagle and these were driven away by armed men from the Happy Thought. Flynn then came to the rescue and put his men back to work prepared for a second attack.*

"*Sunday a general treaty was agreed to, all factions disarmed, their men and work settled down on a peaceful basis.*

"*The courts will be called upon to settle the dispute of ownership and the litigation promised to be long. A compromise may be effected.*

"*In such cases there always arises such a conflict between right and law that it is hard for those who wish to render honest judgment to decide which side his sympathies are with.*

"*The Golden Eagle is effected very much in this case, and no one can count but that the Golden Eagle was located in all honesty, and that the owners have put out much money upon it to make a mine. It was located before any kind of a claim was supposed to have a market price, and for this reason was legitimate. There has been talk of claim jumping, two words which are pronounced with greater contempt in this country than any other two. Yet it is a fact that the Happy Thought jumped the Golden Eagle, and if any odium attaches to the transaction, it should begin there. The Eagle was located October 26, 1891 before the boom. Gray and Mann located the Happy Thought January 19, 1892, and sunk their discovery hole thirteen feet in the wash on the Golden Eagle, with the semblance of a lead.*

"There are two Happy Thoughts. The one of Gray & Mann and the one on which the Norton-Dewey company found the lead. The latter are the sufferers in this difficulty, but it is a question whether they should not have made a new location then and not waited until after Miller had taught them law and then attempted to make good the defects in their location by the filing of a new claim with their deep shaft for a discovery hole.

"The new owners of the Happy Thought seem to be unfortunate in their advisers, and if they lose their claim through playing in Miller's hand by holding off too long in filing on their lead, it will be due largely to ignorance of the mining laws and the insufficiency of their counsel."

March 3, 1893:

"Happy Thought-Golden Eagle Litigation — There is still plenty of trouble over the illegal location of the Happy Thought as it overlaps on other discoverers. The president of the Golden Eagle is a fighter and this controversy will no doubt mean a bitter court fight. Later, it is learned from Denver papers that a compromise has been effected which is satisfactory to all."

The claims owned by five separate companies along the Amethyst vein north of the Amethyst Mine were consolidated into the United Mines Company in 1894. This consolidation resolved conflicts between these companies that had the potential of becoming violent, as evidenced by the display of Winchesters at several confrontations. *The Engineering and Mining Journal* in its March 3, 1894, edition had this article that clearly indicated that most, but not all, conflicts in mining rights on the Amethyst vein north of the Amethyst lode had essentially been resolved without court action:

"United Mines Company — Announcement is made that the Cleopatra Company has put its New Discovery claim into the United Mines Company. This is as was expected when the combination was formed and a place has been held open for the Cleopatra to come into. There had been several hitches and disagreements between the stockholders of that company, owing to a belief held that the biggest and richest part of the switched vein was

within the New Discovery ground. Development made since the United was incorporated have convinced the Cleopatra people that the interest they secure in the combine is as favorable to them as it would be to stay out and hold their own ground, and since this was decided they concluded to join with the combine and get rid of litigation. This gives the United between 1,800 and 2,000 ft. of the big lead, free from conflicts of any nature, about 50 acres of patented ground, three complete machinery plants and gets rid of several suits between the parties to the combine."

Several ongoing court cases were resolved by the incorporation of the United Mines Company. The May 26, 1894, edition of *The Engineering and Mining Journal* stated that the suits of *Shear vs. the Great Republic Mining and Milling Company; Mary Taylor vs. the Happy Thought Mining Company;* and *Ironclad No.2 vs. Happy Thought* were all dismissed by stipulation in the United States Court at Denver.

However, not all conflicts and litigation were resolved by the formation of the United Mines Company, and it was not until 1909 that litigation between mining property owners north of the Amethyst lode was essentially resolved. In the meantime, much had been lost in the efficient and timely development of the ore bodies.

The Denver Times reported on May 3, 1900, that: "C. J. Hughes of Denver has purchased the Grab Root lode on Bachelor Mountain. Messrs. Born, Long, and O'Laughlin, who each owned one-tenth interest in the property over which so much litigation has been going on with the Antlers Park Regent."

The Denver Times also reported on January 15, 1901:

Compromise Between Mines in Litigation
    "Litigation which has lasted more than eight years between the White Star Mining company, the Mary Taylor Company and the Antlers Park Regent Company of Creede has been compromised and the result will be the opening of a large area of valuable territory that has been tied up."

The *Mining Reporter*, April 28, 1904, commented that:

    "A deal was recently consummated whereby this company (the United Mines Company) acquired the properties

of the Winchester Mining Company and the Sewell Mining Company, consisting of nine claims lying west of the United Mines property. Negotiations to this end have been pending for some time, and the consolidation will settle any apex questions which might arise regarding extralateral rights."

Mining Science carried the following story on September 16, 1909:

> *"The renewal of work in the United Mines properties and the continuation of the Wooster tunnel and the re-opening of the Humphreys mill means much for Creede. Litigation which has for years handicapped development is now out of the way and the contending interests have been consolidated. The resumption of work on the United, Park Regent, Grab Root, and other properties on the great contact, will be started in the very near future."*

Most of the conflicts in ownership of mining properties occurred on the Amethyst vein; however, not all. *The Engineering and Mining Journal*, March 3, 1894, had this to say:

> *"Compromises are clearing the court dockets of mining suits at a rapid rate. Last week settlements were made between the Mother and Ramey properties, the Spar, Eclat, Rio Grande, and Nancy Hanks, on Mammoth (Mountain), and between the Ellen and German National No. 2, on South Bachelor. A division of surface grounds and right to follow the lead located is the basis of settlement in nearly every case."*

As indicated in *The Engineering and Mining Journal's* March 12, 1892, article, the Del Monte lode overlapped the Last Chance lode by 100 feet. This conflict over mining rights ended up in litigation between the Del Monte and the Last Chance mining companies in the U.S. Circuit Court of Appeals in Denver, as reported by *The Engineering and Mining Journal*.[2] Judge Hallet denied Del Monte's claim:

> *"Del Monte Mining Company, versus Last Chance Mining Company — At Denver, on March 29th, Judge Hallett denied the application of the Del Monte for an injunction to restrain the Last Chance Company at Creede from working below the point in its shaft where*

*the vein on its dip crosses the east side line of the Del
Monte. The injunction had been asked for on the grounds
that the southerly end line of the Last Chance claim was
identical with the northeasterly side line of the New York
and consequently not parallel to the north end line of its
claim, as the law exacts, and because of the defect the Last
Chance was not entitled to follow the ore beyond its side
line. There are several interesting points in the decision,
which was rendered orally by Judge Hallett, says the
Denver Republican. It is held that for the purpose of apex
rights a party can place an end line over another claim,
that the lines of a claim may be located wholly or partly
upon other territory which is not open for location for the
purpose of determining the extra-lateral question.*

*"The court advanced that the locator in order to make
a valid location is required by the statute to locate his lines
so as to make a rectangular form, and holds that if in so
locating it the claim gets upon territory of other claimants,
even though the patent has been secured, the lines are well
laid with reference to the territory actually open to location. In effect, that if the territory open for location by the
Last Chance had been triangular in shape, the location
would have had to be made rectangular, even if the surplus of the claim so located should have lapped onto the
New York after it was patented, so that the fact that parts
of each of the side lines and of the southern end line of the
Last Chance being upon the New York is not controlling
in the determination of the question. Extra lateral right
upon the course of the end lines is allowed the Last
Chance within the principle announced in the case of Del
Monte vs. The New York and Chance, decided by the
court on March 13th. The north end line being properly
located, the other is to be placed where the vein leaves the
Last Chance and enters the New York on its strike, and
the fact that the end line located in originally laying out
the rectangular claim lies a considerable distance on the
south and on another claim does not affect the question of
its force and effect as an end line. The Last Chance end
line on the south must be drawn parallel to that of the
north at the point where the apex departs from the claim,
and this being identical to the 'north compromise line'*

between the Last Chance and New York, the court could allow the Del Monte no claim to the territory north of that line, which was the claim it had sought to establish."

The case was appealed to the U.S. Supreme Court in 1898, Docket No. 171 U.S. 55,43 L. ed. 72, 18 Sup. Ct. 895. The following facts were presented in the case of the *Del Monte Mining & Milling Co. vs. Last Chance Mining & Milling Co.:*[3]

"On a Certificate of the United States Circuit Court of Appeals for the Eighth Circuit.

This case is before this court on questions certified by the court of appeals for the Eighth Circuit. The facts stated are as follows: The appellant is the owner in fee of the Del Monte lode mining claim, located in the Sunnyside mining district, Mineral County, Colo., for which it holds a patent bearing date February 3, 1894, pursuant to an entry made at the local land office on February 27, 1893. The appellee is the owner of the Last Chance Lode mining claim, under patent dated July 5, 1894, based on an entry of March 1, 1894. The New York lode mining claim, which is not owned by either of the parties, was patented on April 5, 1894, upon an entry of August 26, 1893. The relative situation of these claims, as well as the course and dip of the vein, which is the subject of controversy, is shown on the following diagram:

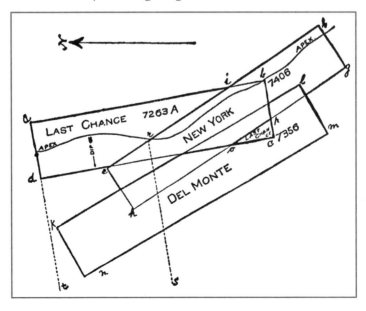

"*Both in location and patent the Del Monte claim is first in time, the New York second, and the Last Chance third. When the owners of the Last Chance claim applied for their patent, proceedings in adverse were instituted against them by the owners of the New York claim, and an action in support of such adverse was brought in the United States circuit court for the district of Colorado. This action terminated in favor of the owners of the New York and against the owners of the Last Chance, and awarded the territory in conflict between the two locations to the New York claim. The ground in conflict between the New York and Del Monte, except so much thereof as was also in conflict between the Del Monte and Last Chance locations, is included in the patent to the Del Monte claim. The New York secured a patent to all of its territory except that in conflict with the Del Monte, and the Last Chance in turn secured a patent to all of its territory except that in conflict with the New York, in which last-named patent was included the triangular surface conflict between the Del Monte and Last Chance, which, by agreement, was patented to the latter. The Last Chance claim was located upon a vein, lode, or ledge of silver and lead bearing ore, which crosses its north end line, and continues southerly from that point through the Last Chance location until it reaches the eastern side line of the New York, into which latter territory it enters, continuing thence southerly with a southeasterly course on the New York claim until it crosses its south end line. No part of the apex of the vein is embraced within the small triangular parcel of ground in the southwest corner of the Last Chance location which was patented to the Last Chance as aforesaid, and no part of the apex is within the surface boundaries of the Del Monte mining claim. The portion of the vein in controversy is that lying under the surface of the Del Monte claim and between two vertical planes; one drawn through the north end line of the Last Chance claim extending westerly, and the other parallel thereto, and starting at the point where the vein leaves the Last Chance and enters the New York claim as shown on the foregoing diagram. Upon these facts the following questions have been certified to us:*

(1) May any of the lines of a junior lode location be laid within, upon or across the surface of a valid senior location for the purpose of defining for or securing to such junior location underground or extralateral rights not in conflict with any rights of the senior location?

(2) Does the patent of the Last Chance lode mining claim, which first describes the rectangular claim by metes and bounds, and then excepts and excludes therefrom the premises previously granted to the New York lode mining claim, convey to the patentee anything more than he would take by a grant specifically describing only the two irregular tracts which constitute the granted surface of the Last Chance claim?

(3) Is the easterly side of the New York lode mining claim an 'end line' of the Last Chance lode mining claim, within the meaning of sections 2320 and 2322 of the Revised Statutes of the United States?

(4) If the apex of a vein crosses one end line and one side line of a lode mining claim, as located thereon, can the locator of such vein follow it upon its dip beyond the vertical side line of his location?

(5) On the facts presented by the record herein, has the appellee the right to follow its vein downward beyond its west side line, and under the surface of the premises of the appellant?"

Justice Brewer delivered the opinion of the Court. It was certified to the Court of Appeals for the Eighth Circuit that the Supreme Court answered the first question in the affirmative; the second was not answered; the third in the negative; the fourth in the affirmative; and the fifth was not answered.

The decision in the case of Del Monte vs. Last Chance mining companies established one of the defining principles of the mining law. The basis of extralateral rights is the existence of the apex of the vein within surface boundaries of the location dropped downward perpendicularly, and therefore their extent along the vein should always be limited by the extent of the apex within the claim.[4]

Even though the U.S. Supreme Court ruled on apex and extralateral rights, the case was remanded to the lower courts. A compromise settlement was effected years later by the parties to the litigation. The *Mining Reporter* had the following comments:

March 15, 1902:

"Del Monte Leasing Company — The long-delayed settlement of claims between the New York Chance and the Del Monte Mines at Creede has been arranged, and this company will direct future development. The ground set free for exploration is said to be of great richness."

April 5, 1902:

"Last Chance — The troubles of this mine at Creede and of the New York & Chance Mine, which began in 1894 have been adjusted. In 1890 the Del Monte Company claimed the mine, alleging apex rights. The case was carried into the United States courts, where last winter a compromise was proposed, and this has been approved. The Last Chance is given the ownership of the mines, the Del Monte to have a lease for 20 years."

A memorandum of preliminary agreement, dated February 7, 1902, gives a description of the final resolution of the conflict. The agreement was between the New York & Chance Mining Company, Volunteer Mining Company, Del Monte Mining and Milling Company, and the Del Monte Leasing Company:

"Whereas there is and for many years has been pending in U. S. Circuit Court for Colorado certain litigation between parties wherein there is involved the rights to certain ores, veins, and mineral deposits lying within the external boundaries and beneath the surface of the New York lode and the Del Monte and Aspen lodes, which said ores and mineral deposits are claimed by the parties of the first part as belonging to and being parts of a certain vein supposed to have its apex upon said New York mining claim, and the same are also claimed by the said parties of the second part by virtue of certain supposed extralateral rights, and further by virtue of certain veins and deposits claimed to have their apex and existing on and within the boundaries of the said Del Monte mining claim and whereas said Volunteer Mining Company is now the owner of title of the Del Monte and Aspen claims. Del Monte Leasing Company (A.E. Humphries, President) has a lease on the Del Monte and Aspen lodes.

"Del Monte Mining and Milling Company claims damages against the first party for ores extracted from the Del Monte lode.

"Litigation has been settled on all that portion of the New York, Last Chance, Del Monte, and Aspen lode claims lying to south of a certain fixed line known as the 'north compromise line' which crosses claims in an east-west course parallel to the north end line of the Last Chance claim and intersecting the west side line of the Last Chance claim at a point about 15 feet northerly from what is known as the New Reynolds Shaft upon the New York claim." [5]

This final settlement eliminated litigation as an impediment to mining the Amethyst vein. *The Denver Times,* February 21, 1902, reported that:

"The settlement of the long-standing suit between the New York and Del Monte people (accomplished a few days since) means a resumption of operations on these properties, which contain great bodies of high grade silver and lead ores. It is reported that the management of the great tunnel will also secure the New York and Del Monte, which means that they will have between 7,000 and 8,000 feet of the Bachelor Vein. When once all these properties along the way of the tunnel get into working shape, and it is believed they will be by this summer, nearly 1,000 men will be employed on Bachelor Mountain. The other properties working are the Commodore and the Bachelor, the latter leased to local people."

On March 21, 1902, the stock holders of the Last Chance Mining and Milling Company ratified the action of the directors in giving a lease on their property in the Creede Mining District to the Del Monte Leasing Company, thus formally ending the extensive litigation in which the Last Chance and Del Monte Companies had been involved for eight years. [6]

CHAPTER 8

THE EARLY MINES
AND MINING
COMPANIES
1884-1899

THE CREEDE CANDLE in its first anniversary issue of January 6, 1893, reported that: "Prior to the regular operation of the railroad from Creede seventy-nine cars containing 675 tons were shipped from Wagon Wheel Gap and 110 tons were shipped from the Wason station. The first recorded ore shipment from Creede Camp was from the Bachelor Mine in 1884. An estimated 350 tons were packed to Sunnyside by horses by J.C. McKenzie, treated in an arrastre and then transported to the railroad by wagons." The Irwin brothers mined ore from their Sunnyside properties as early as 1885 and continuing until 1890.[1] Their ore was also concentrated in an arrastre and shipped to Del Norte by ox team. *The Candle* also reported the following statistics on the mines and their production up to the end of 1892:

> *"The first shipment from the Amethyst Mine was made Dec. 4, 1891; the Last Chance, same date; Holy Moses, Dec. 21, 1891; Ethel, in same month; Ridge, March 3, 1892. The more recent shippers are the New York, which commenced the latter part of September last; the Yellow Jacket, in October; the Solomon, Nov. 30; and they bid fair to make up for lost time by the end of the present year.*
>
> *"The total output from each shipping mine in the Creede district up to December 31, 1892:*

Name	Cars	Tons of Ore	Estimated Value
Amethyst	1,680	22,500	$2,200,000
Last Chance	1,427	19,000	1,600,000
New York	182	2,000	170,000
Holy Moses	86	1,065	100,000

Ethel	85	1,050	100,000
Bachelor	35	350	30,000
Yellow Jacket	10	100	10,000
Ridge	3	50	4,000
Solomon	1	10	500
Del Monte	1	10	500
Bondholder	1	10	500
World	1	10	500
Total	3,512	46,155	$4,215,800

The Bondholder and World Mines are not in the Creede district. The Bondholder is located on Spring Creek, a tributary of Cebolla Creek, where N.C. Creede was prospecting prior to his discovery of the Holy Moses. The World Mine is located at Spar City, ten miles southwest of Creede.

Charles W. Henderson in *Mining in Colorado*[2] gave mineral production from Mineral County based on reports of the agents of the mint in annual reports of the Director of the Mint as follows:

	GOLD	SILVER			LEAD			
Year	Value	Ounces	Price Per Oz.	Value	Pounds	Price Per Lb.	Value	Total Value
1891	$ 10,055	378,889	$0.99	$ 374,382	354,854	$0.04	$ 15,259	$ 399,696
1892	87,219	2,391,514	0.87	2,080,617	3,000,000	0.04	120,000	2,287,836
1893	53,252	4,897,684	0.78	3,820,194	7,500,000	0.04	277,500	4,150,946
1894	40,336	1,866,927	0.63	1,176,164	6,500,000	0.03	214,500	1,431,000
1895	114,482	1,423,038	0.65	924,975	8,220,870	0.03	263,068	1,302,525
1896	52,238	1,560,865	0.68	1,061,388	6,021,109	0.03	180,633	1,294,259
1897	61,328	3,070,576	0.60	1,842,346	6,080,673	0.04	218,904	2,122,758 *
1898	46,383	4,177,184	0.59	2,464,539	5,453,104	0.04	207,218	2,729,166 **
1899	91,671	3,796,899	0.60	2,278,139	5,677,162	0.04	255,472	2,634,540 ***
1900	209,387	2,280,038	0.62	1,413,623	4,951,956	0.04	657,886	2,301,130 ****

* Total Value includes $180 value for copper produced.
** Total Value includes $1,826 value for copper and $9,200 value for zinc produced.
*** Total Value includes $3,458 value for copper and $5,800 value for zinc produced.
**** Total Value includes $434 value for copper and $19,800 value for zinc produced.

The Creede Candle's value of production through the end of 1892 is considerably more than Henderson's value of mineral production for 1891 and 1892. This difference is probably explained by the fact that *The Candle*'s figures are based on an approximation of the value per ton shipped to the smelters and Henderson's are based upon receipt of the finished products after the smelting process. Henderson, however, quotes the U.S. Geological Survey Mineral Resources, 1892:[3]

> "Creede credited by mint authorities with $3,500,000 (at a coining rate of $1.29 plus) of silver in 1892, other estimates giving even a larger amount."

Obviously, there were discrepancies in early reporting of Creede's mineral production. The dramatic drop in production of metals and, in particular, their values between 1893 and 1894 show that Creede Camp was seriously affected by the drop of silver prices in 1893 after the repeal of the Sherman Act, but mining continued in 1894 on a reduced scale of approximately one-third of that of 1893. Several newspaper articles described the situation at Creede. *The Denver Republican* on June 30, 1893, carried the following item:

> *"All the producing camps have practically stopped shipping, the owners preferring to let the silver lie in the ground rather than sell it at the present low price. The Amethyst was the first to reduce force and did so early in the week. The New York and Chance and Bachelor will ship no more after tomorrow until the price goes up. Development is going ahead in all the big mines without intermission, and all are working small forces to keep out the water, protect the properties, and open new ground."*

The Creede Candle reported on July 7, 1893, that:

> *"Last Chance Cuts Working Forces — The Last Chance which has been running full handed up to that time, cuts its force in half yesterday, letting out seventy-five men and continuing that number at work. They were the last to close for the reason that their contract with the Leadville smelter kept them up. The New York and Chance is completely shut down but the Amethyst continues to give employment to about forty in developing and protecting the property."*

The Engineering and Mining Journal had the following comments:

September 16, 1893:

> *"The mining industry of the State of Colorado is slowly recovering from the collapse caused by the sudden fall in the price of silver. At Creede some of the most important mines, such as the Amethyst, Last Chance, and New York, have recently resumed operations. There are symptoms of revival at Leadville, and Aspen will not remain quiet long. At the Denver smelters the stocks of ore have been considerably reduced and more ore is now being purchased than has been the case since the end of June.*

"The southwestern portion of the state — the 'Silvery San Juans' — is still in a woeful condition, owing to the closing down of the mines. How severe has been the blow to business of this particular section is best indicated by the falling off in the earnings of the Rio Grande Railway, which for August were $469,300, as compared with $931,000 for the corresponding month last year."

October 28, 1893, Saguache County:

"Late news from Creede is of a more encouraging nature since the agreement between miners and mine owners went into operation in the camp. The output, while less in actual value than formerly, is nearly the old quantity in tonnage, and the mines are employing about as many men. Development work is being gradually resumed in all divisions of the camp."

The Engineering and Mining Journal, March 10, 1894, gave the number of miners working in the Creede mines:

"Advices from Creede disprove the report that only 200 men were at work in the mines of that once lively camp. The New York, Last Chance, and Amethyst Mines are employing 325 men alone, and added to these are the men at work on the Park Regent, Ridge, Bachelor, Ethel, Nancy Hanks, Mammoth, Mother and Ramey tunnels, Monon, Red Top, Sundown, Ballarac tunnel, Eureka extension, Yellow Jacket, Alpha, Judson tunnel, Corsair tunnel, Kruetzer Sonata, Schuylkill tunnel, Lafe Pence, Jumbo, Yankee Girl and Yankee Girl extension, Sunnyside and Sunnyside extension, Manhattan, Nelson tunnel, Emma, and the properties of the United Mines Company, making a total of over 500 men who are kept steadily at work developing the respective properties."

The Engineering and Mining Journal discussed the Creede situation in its August 28, 1897, issue:

"It is probable that the great silver mines of Creede, Colorado will be closed down on account of the low price of silver unless the railroad and smelting rates are reduced. Several conferences have been held between the mine owners and the smelter and railroad officials, and it is said the latter evinced a disposition to make every

concession possible in order to keep the mines in opera-
tion, but the smelters having already suffered heavy losses
by the sudden fall in the value of silver, can hardly afford
to reduce smelting charges to keep a few mines in opera-
tion. The most important shipper is the Commodore
which until lately has been paying large dividends."

Evidently an accommodation was made with the railroad to
reduce shipping rates as silver production dramatically increased in
1897, even though the price of silver had dropped. The mine operators and miners agreed to a twenty-five cent per day reduction in
wages in August 1897. In March 1899 miners were paid $3 a day
for a ten-hour day.[4] Silver production in 1898 and 1899 approached
that of 1892-93. In 1900 silver production again dropped significantly but the value of lead production greatly increased.

The Engineering and Mining Journal, July 9, 1898, reported that
481 men were employed in the Creede mines:

"The Commodore Mining Company is working 250
men, the Last Chance 50, the Amethyst 30, Ridge 30,
Antlers' Park Regent 25, Solomon 25, Nelson Tunnel 25,
Creede Co-operative Leasing, Milling and Mining
Company 20, Bachelor 8, Rio Grande 6, Monte Carlo 6,
Mollie S. and Eunice 6."

A strike against all the major smelters began in June 1899 and
was not settled until August. The smelter operators had been
through several lean years and were not about to increase wages for
their workers. In late July the state set up a Board of Arbitration
with power to bring the two sides together. In the meantime, the
strike seriously impacted Colorado mining operations, particularly
those in the San Juans. The Miners' Bank at Creede failed during
the smelter strike.[5] *The Engineering and Mining Journal* reported on
the strike:

August 12, 1899, Colorado:
"Smelter situation — There is as yet no change in the
situation at the Denver, Pueblo, and Durango plants of
the American Smelting and Refining Company. During
last week more mines were forced to shut down from an
over-supply of ore at the furnaces in blast and many small
mine owners are having to give up development work, as
they have no surplus funds on hand. The situation is

particularly gloomy in Mineral County and in the San Juan Region. The managers of the smelters state that they cannot afford to pay the wages demanded by the employees or even those recommended by the State Board of Arbitration, without increasing treatment charges."

August 31, 1899, Mineral County:

"There is a notable improvement in all branches of business at Creede since the resumption of the smelter. Ore is now being shipped at the rate of 15 to 20 cars a day, though but few of the larger producers are mining with full force."

The Denver Times carried this story on August 2, 1899, that overstates the facts and deals in exaggerations but relays the seriousness of the situation:

"Miners out of work are leaving that once busy camp — 'The smelter strike is killing Creede,' said C.P. Brooks, editor of the Creede Miner, who was at the capital building to mingle with friends. 'The town has lost 500 of its population and if this strike keeps up until fall I dare say many more will leave the place. There is practically not a dollar in circulation, and indications are for the worst time the camp has ever had if the smeltermen do not return to work in the very near future.'

"The Commodore Mine closed down last Friday afternoon, throwing about 600 men out of employment. The district ordinarily employs about 1500 men, but only a few of the properties are working now. They are those which handle concentrating ores or zinc. Some ore containing zinc is being shipped to Missouri points for reduction.

"When the Commodore mine closed down about 500 men packed their clothes and left the place at once. Men in large numbers, some walking, some riding, were seen leaving Creede for other parts. Most of them, however, are the young ranchmen or others from the San Luis Valley, and have returned to their homes to wait the resumption of work in the mines. Some went prospecting, while some scattered in all directions. The town is like a graveyard now. No one is doing any business and it is simply as if we were besieged, with nothing to look forward to but desolation, living with hope and anticipation."

Early day mining operations took place on three of the four major vein systems described in Chapter One — the Amethyst, Solomon-Holy Moses, and Alpha-Corsair Veins and the Creede Formation at Monon Hill. Development and exploitation of the rich mineral bodies of the Bulldog Mountain Vein did not occur until a half century later, the second boom at Creede. The Amethyst Vein produced ninety-five per cent of the estimated value of the Creede district through 1892. The Solomon-Holy Moses Vein produced 4.75 per cent and the Alpha-Corsair 0.25 percent for the same period of time. In general these ratios held throughout the history of the district until the Bulldog Mountain Vein was mined in the 1960s. Of the mines operating at the end of 1892, six were on the Amethyst Vein. They were the Bachelor, Commodore, Amethyst, Last Chance, New York, and Del Monte. The mines on the Solomon-Holy Moses Vein included the Holy Moses, Ethel, Ridge, and Solomon. Only one producing mine, the Yellow Jacket, was on the Alpha-Corsair Vein. The history of these and other mines are described on the following pages.

AMETHYST VEIN SYSTEM

The mines along the Amethyst or "Big" Vein, as it was called in the early days, had, in fact, the greatest impact on the history of the Creede district until the development of the Bulldog Mountain Vein. Most of the district's production from 1891 through 1899 came from high grade oxidized ores in the southern part of the Amethyst Vein — the Amethyst, Last Chance, New York and Chance, and Commodore Mines. Silver accounted for most of the value. Mine production along the Amethyst Vein dropped drastically in 1900 after successfully rebounding from the repeal of the Sherman Act in 1893. Three factors created a "triple whammy" effect that seriously affected mining on the Amethyst Vein. First, the lack of consolidation of mining rights along the vein hindered efficient mining; second, water flows increased as the mines deepened; and third, sulfide ore was encountered instead of high grade oxidized silver ore.

Originally the mining enterprises were organized to mine the ore contained on one lode claim, a distance of no more than 1,500 feet along the strike of the vein, including extralateral rights. In the case of the Del Monte, New York, and Last Chance, claims that caused considerable conflict and litigation that lasted for many years, three mining companies were organized to exploit the strike length equivalent of one claim. The litigation delayed the development of a very rich ore body for years. This lack of consolidation of claims resulted in the non-systematic and inefficient development of the ore bodies; duplication of facilities such as shafts, power plants, shops, and other ancillaries; and increased hoisting, ventilation, and pumping costs. This condition is illustrated by a report in *The Creede Candle*'s first anniversary issue of January 6, 1893:

> *"Fifteen steam plants in operation on Bachelor Hill are divided among the following properties: Amethyst, Last Chance, and Transfer, two each; and one each to the New York, Ella C., Happy Thought, Park Regent, Stanhope, Diamond Drill, Nelson Tunnel, Del Monte, and Little Maid."*

Water was encountered in the Amethyst Mine workings as early as late 1892. A pump was installed in the Number 3 Shaft in January, 1893, to drain the mine.[6] As the workings along the Amethyst Vein deepened, the water problem continually worsened until the cost of pumping became so great as to threaten to put an end to profitable mining. The Amethyst Mine was making 700 gallons per minute in August 1894.[7]

The gravity of the situation was reported in the April 14, 1894, issue of *The Engineering and Mining Journal*:

> *"Amethyst reports from Creede are to the effect that the producing mines of Bachelor Hill are having a hard fight to keep the levels from filling up with water. The Amethyst is full to the top of the sixth level and still rising. Superintendent Allenby is borrowing all the idle pumps in camp and putting them in so as to keep the water down and the mine working. If the water rises 50 ft. more the pumps in the Last Chance will force the property to shut down. In three days more, had not the water started, the big Duplex pump of the Amethyst, one of the largest in the State, would have been in place. Two pumps of 500 gals. [gallons per minute] capacity arrived on April 3rd for the Amethyst and Last Chance shafts. The Amethyst is so situated that it drains all the mines and its pumps keep the others dry."*

The Engineering and Mining Journal on August 31, 1895, had this report:

> *"The Happy Thought, at the 600-ft. level, and the Park Regent, at the 700-ft. level, have been having*

considerable trouble with water. Both mines, it is believed, would be heavy shippers were they free from water. The water can only be handled by expensive pumps and machinery, or through a tunnel, the latter being the cheapest, best, and most convenient."

The Nelson Tunnel tapped the water in the Last Chance Mine in May, 1899, and that in the Amethyst in the fall of 1899.[8] The Nelson Tunnel is the subject of Chapter Nine.

Encountering water in the mines also signaled the end of the high grade "supergene" ores. These ores form by a process called "supergene enrichment" in which "meteoric" water (i.e. rain and snowmelt) leach silver, other minerals, and sulfur from the upper parts of the vein, leaving behind leached cavities of former sulfide minerals and iron oxides. The metal-charged meteoric water percolates down along the vein until it hits the water table. At this point, silver and some other metals precipitate out of the meteoric water to enrich the vein at the water table. Below this supergene-enriched zone, the vein is dominated by lower-grade, more difficult to treat sulfide, or "hypogene" ore. This process of supergene enrichment has continued since the start of the canyon cycle of erosion. As the tops of the veins have been eroded and the water table lowered, silver and other minerals continually have been enriched near the water table.

Simply stated, the Amethyst Vein could be divided into four ore zones, as could the other veins in the Creede district: 1) an oxidized leached zone at or near the surface; 2) an oxidized zone or partly oxidized zone of richer (supergene) ore below the leached zone; 3) a zone of rich (supergene) ore below the rich oxidized zone; and 4) lower grade primary sulfide (hypogene) ore below the rich sulfide.[9]

The elements oxidized the exposed tops of the veins over geologic time, forming native silver and other easily smelted minerals from the original sulfide minerals. The richest part of the vein was exposed at the surface only in the Last Chance and Amethyst Mines. Other mines along the Amethyst Vein commenced work in the leached portion of the vein and had to do development work before getting to the enriched ore. All the early mines extracted high-grade oxidized silver ore that could be shipped directly to the smelters without sorting at the mine site. One characteristic of the ores of the Amethyst, Last Chance, and Bachelor was that there were no mine dumps, because there was no waste rock to be "dumped."

The *Colorado Bureau of Mines Report for 1897* stated:

> *"The characteristic ore of this region is a fine-grained amethystine quartz, carrying silver, gold, lead, and zinc. The bulk of the ore marketed has been an oxidized product carrying an excess of silica, with little gold, silver in its native form or as a bromide or chloride, lead in form of carbonate, oxide or sulphate, and zinc in oxidized form. Oxidized ores are found to extend in places to a depth of 900 feet and may be noted as one of the remarkable features of the district."*

Unfortunately, the oxidized bonanza ores in the mines north of the Commodore gave way to sulfide mineralization in depth. In order to economically mine the sulfide ore, concentration before shipment to the smelters became necessary, adding additional costs for both the construction and operation of concentrating mills. Oxidized ore that could be shipped direct to the smelters was mined in the Bachelor and Commodore Mines well into the next century.

Thus, the "triple-whammy" effect meant the end of mining's heyday of the Amethyst Vein. This brought in a new era where long tunnels and ore processing plants not only changed mining techniques but dramatically impacted the communities of Creede Camp.

Seven early mining companies controlled the Amethyst Vein after mining rights conflicts were resolved by consolidations and litigations, except that between the New York and Del Monte Companies. They were, from the south end of the vein toward the north: Bachelor Mining Company, Commodore Mining Company, New York and Chance Mining Company, Last Chance Mining & Milling Company, Del Monte Mining Company, Amethyst Mining Company, United Mines Company, and the Park Regent Consolidated Mining Company.

BACHELOR MINE

The inaugural issue of *The Creede Candle* on January 7, 1892, stated that the Bachelor claim was located by John C. MacKenzie, H.M. Bennet, and James A. Wilson about July 1884, and an estimated 350 tons of ore were mined, processed, and sold, the first recorded mine production from the Creede district. The inaugural issue also described the formation of the Bachelor Mining Company:

> *"The Bachelor, an old location, was discovered several years ago by J.P. Barnett and passed into the hands of*

J.C. McKenzie [MacKenzie], Jas. Wilson, M.V.B. Wason, and others. Soon after the discovery of the Last Chance this property was purchased by parties interested in the Holy Moses Company for $20,000 and later the Bachelor Mining Company was incorporated with David H. Moffat, Sylvester T. Smith, Frederick F. Struby, Julius E. French, and John T. Herrick for directors and a capital stock of $100,000. The purchasers made extended development and have a mine of the property."

The apex of the Amethyst Vein on the Bachelor claim lies along the steep base of a high cliff that marks the western edge of a very prominent pinnacle to the west of West Willow Creek. This spire and the mines along its base have been photographed and sketched by many over the years and is a Creede landmark. Because of the steep topography traversed by the apex, the Bachelor Mine as well as the Commodore Mine were developed by a series of tunnels, not shafts, as were the mines further north on the Amethyst Vein. Companies other than the Bachelor Mining Company drove the tunnels used to develop and exploit the Bachelor Mine. The lowest tunnel that provided access to the Bachelor workings was the Nelson Tunnel. The highest point on the vein is about 1,375 feet above the Nelson Tunnel level.[10]

This, perhaps, is a good place to define the terms "tunnel" and "adit." A tunnel, by strict definition, is a horizontal or near-horizontal underground excavation with a tunnel-shaped cross section and openings to the atmosphere, or "portals," at both ends. An adit, on the other hand, is a mining term for a horizontal or near-horizontal underground excavation with a tunnel-shaped cross section and only one opening, or "portal." The other end connects with other underground excavations or workings. The term "tunnel" was used at Creede Camp throughout its history to describe what by a strict definition are adits.

The Engineering and Mining Journal carried several interesting news items about the Bachelor Mine during the 1890s:

March 5, 1892:
"The Bachelor has nearly reached the distinction of a pay mine. Its development consists of a 350-ft. tunnel run upon the course of the vein, which shows mineral of a marketable value for the entire distance."

March 3, 1894, Saguache County:

"Bachelor — This mine has recently cut in a body of rich rock, and a car shipped last week is expected to average 2,000 oz. to the ton."

January 19, 1895, Mineral County:

"Bachelor — This property has let a contract to continue the tunnel of the Manhattan Company to contact with its own vein, and it is expected that the work, when finished, will enable the mine to produce from the greater depth thus attained more extensively than ever in the past."

February 2, 1895, Mineral County:

"Bachelor — This property is running a 450-ft. tunnel from the Manhattan working and will drift north and south after the vein is cut. This will give them a much greater depth than has yet been attained."

[Note: A drift is a horizontal "tunnel" excavation parallel to the strike of a vein.]

December 14, 1895, Mineral County:

"Bachelor Mountain Tunnel Company — It is said that articles of incorporation have been prepared for this company, to operate in Mineral County, with D.H. Moffat as president. The company has it own tunnel and has leased the Manhattan Tunnel lower down. About 400 ft. still lower down is the Nelson Tunnel, and an arrangement has been made with the Nelson Tunnel Company to run a crosscut from their tunnel at some point to be determined from 1,000 to 1,500 ft. from the mouth, paying the Nelson Company a royalty for the use of the tunnel and working rights from the portion of the tunnel above the crosscut."

[Note: A crosscut is a horizontal "tunnel" excavation at an angle to the strike of a vein.]

The discovery of new ore bodies in the Bachelor Mine was partially responsible for the revival of the mining industry at Creede in the late 1890s.[11] *The Denver Times* of July 6, 1899, carried a story about the finding of a body of high-grade ore in the Bachelor:

"A big strike has been made in the Bachelor Mine. The strike was made in what is known as Intermediate Level No. 2 which is about 100 feet below track level No.

4 or the old Manhattan level. The vein is about five feet
wide and assays run from 348 to 400 ounces in silver."

COMMODORE MINE

The Commodore claim was located in April, 1891, by J.C.
McKenzie and W.V. Gilliard.[12] *The Creede Candle* reported in its
March 17, 1892, issue that:

> *"The chief topic of interest in the mines is the big strike*
> *made on Saturday last in the Commodore. It is by long odds*
> *the most important advance made in Creede mines since*
> *August when coupled with other developments that have*
> *been made on the big Amethyst vein within the week. W.A.*
> *Hadden of the firm of Hadden & Smith, assayers at*
> *Bachelor, came down with the news of the Commodore*
> *strike and brought with him the assayer's certificate. At the*
> *depth of 97 feet in the shaft a strong flow of water was*
> *encountered and directly after it the workmen came into a*
> *five-foot body of ore. Four feet of the mineral gave an assay*
> *of 158 ounces in silver and one foot run 655.1 ounces. The*
> *Commodore lies to the south of the Annie Rooney, along the*
> *course of the big vein is supposed to run, and east of and par-*
> *allel with the Sunnyside. It was located by W.P. McGilliard*
> *and J.C. MacKenzie and by them sold in December to I.L.*
> *Johnson for $10,000. The present owners are A.E. Reynolds*
> *and E.L. Shear of Aspen. Mr. Reynolds was here this week*
> *and investigated the strike and announces that immediately*
> *the mine will be put to shipping."*

The Commodore Mining Company was incorporated in the State
of Colorado on May 14, 1895, and capitalized for $1,200,000
divided into 1,200,000 shares of $1.00 per share of non-assessable
stock. A.E. Reynolds was president and C.F. McKenney secretary.[13]
The Commodore Mining Company owned the Commodore and the
Archimedes claims, a small fraction lying between the Commodore
and Bachelor claims. As a result, the Commodore Mining Company
controlled nearly 1,600 feet of the Amethyst vein apex.[14]

The Commodore was developed and mined by the use of tunnels
that pass through the Bachelor claim. One of these, the Commodore
No. 4 Tunnel, also known as the Manhattan Tunnel, was driven for
the Bachelor Mining Company. The Manhattan Tunnel portal was
on the north end of the Manhattan claim.

Bachelor and Commodore Mines — circa 1897
Mines from the Top — Commodore No. 3,
Bachelor (Commodore) No. 4, Commodore No. 5
Courtesy of the Creede Historical Society

The Engineering and Mining Journal printed the following items about the Commodore:

March 30, 1895, Mineral County:
"*Commodore Tunnel — The Commodore Tunnel [Commodore No. 4], located between the New York and Chance and Bachelor on Bachelor Mountain, owned principally by A.E. Reynolds, will resume operations with a good force of men at once. The vein was cut at a depth of 350 ft. and the first work will be drifting on the lead. Mr. D.G. Miller, mining engineer of Denver, has been appointed manager. The location of the Commodore Tunnel, adjoining two of the most famous mines in the district, would seem to promise that the ore is high grade,*

and it is generally believed that an intervening ore chute will be opened up in a few feet of work."

August 31, 1895, Mineral County:

"Commodore — The owners of this property have secured a perpetual right of way through all the tunnels belonging to the Bachelor Mining Company, and will take out all ore on the down-grade exit, which would otherwise have to be hoisted 1,000 ft. to reach the surface."

A contract between the Commodore and Bachelor Mining Companies was signed on November 11, 1895, to provide joint use and occupancy by the Commodore Mining Company of certain levels, workings, and other property of the Bachelor Mining Company.[15] The contract also provided for a tramway from Bachelor (Commodore) Tunnel No. 3 to the railroad with ore bins and other necessary appurtenances for the transportation of ore and waste from, and materials and supplies to, both mines with equal rights of use. The cost was to be born equally by both parties.

Reynolds had the Commodore No. 5 Tunnel constructed instead of signing a contract with the Wooster Tunnel Company, successor to the Nelson Tunnel Company, to provide ore and waste haulage, drainage, and access to the Commodore on a royalty basis. He felt that owning his own tunnel would be the most economical over time. The tunnel was driven about 2,200 feet to an intersection with the Amethyst vein and its portal is about forty-five feet higher in elevation than that of the Nelson Tunnel. It is at the same elevation as the 1,200-foot levels in the Last Chance and Amethyst Mines. The Commodore No. 5 Tunnel was slated to have a tremendous impact on mining at Creede.

Early in 1896 a claim, the Tunnel Lode, was located by the Bachelor and Commodore Mining Companies as a site for driving a tunnel (Commodore No. 5 Tunnel). The purpose of the tunnel was to provide access to the ore in the Bachelor and Commodore claims below the Commodore No. 4 Tunnel and for water drainage. The selected site was parallel to the Manhattan claim that was owned by Haskell Ryder. The area on the Tunnel lode available for shops and other facilities to drive the tunnel was found to be inadequate, so in August 1896, A.E. Reynolds authorized his manager, David G. Miller, to purchase the Manhattan claim.[16] Haskell Ryder, who built the first cabin in Creede, staked the Manhattan claim but thought so little of it that he did little development on it. Compared with the other mines around it, its production was small but its location made it a vital link in the tunnel system under the Bachelor and Commodore Mines. The portal of the Commodore No. 5 Tunnel was located in the southern end of the Manhattan claim. Haskell Ryder sold 51 per cent of his claim to the Commodore Mining Company in 1896. He gave his remaining interest to attorney Louis R. Smith as payment of an attorney's fee of $5,000. Smith was paid several hundred thousands in later years as his share of the royalties on the tunnel's use.[17]

A.E. Reynolds was a mining man known for his desire and ability to use the most modern techniques and technology in his mining operations. As an example, he electrified the Commodore Mine — a first at Creede. He was convinced that an adit into the bottom of an ore body was the only economical way to develop it, assuming that the topography permitted. He felt that an adit: 1) provided good access for haulage out and delivery of men and supplies to the mine; 2) allowed for the use of gravity to drop ore to the haulage way without the expense of hoisting; 3) provided drainage without the expense of pumping; and 4) enhanced updraft natural ventilation of the mine workings. It is believed by the author that the construction of the Commodore No. 5 Tunnel was on the cutting edge of technology at the time. It is very likely that an unsuccessful attempt to use a tunneling machine was made a half century before tunneling machines were perfected.

The Revenue Tunnel at the Virginius Mine at Ouray, Colorado, was part of a very successful mining venture of A.E. Reynolds. John P. Karns was construction superintendent at the Revenue Tunnel and in 1890 he developed a tunneling machine.[18] Karns built the machine in the blacksmith shop using twenty-four-inch water pipe for the band,

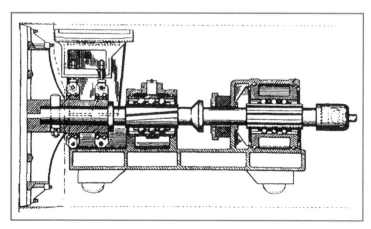

common steel for the cutters, and wrought iron for the support structure. The machine was powered by a conventional steam "slugger" rock drilling machine. Karns improved his design over the years and received a patent for his tunneling machine in 1903. He continued to improve his machine, and the previous sketch was part of his application for Patent No. 957,687, dated May 10, 1910.

It stands to reason that Reynolds, an individual who looked for the cheapest and best way to perform mining work, would at least try the tunneling machine at his Creede mining operations. John Jackson, in a letter to the author, described his discovery of evidence in the early 1940s of the use of the tunneling machine at the Commodore No. 5 Tunnel:

> *"In reopening Commodore 5 Tunnel, one of the first jobs was to replace rail with a switch from the main track to shuttle cars of waste rock south to be dumped in West Willow Canyon. My father and I were digging into the bank of a former waste dump to set a sill for timbers supporting rail when we happened on a treasure trove of old drills, books, and a mining magazine with an article and pictures of a continuous mining machine to be used in the driving of Commodore 5 Tunnel and touted as an invention that would revolutionize mining. It appeared to be a very large, heavy machine with a circular prow holding hundreds of drill bits and the prow rotated by steam. A steam locomotive was parked at the end of the tracks in Willow Creek near the Nelson Tunnel which would power this behemoth via steam pipes laid to the tunnel site. It proved to be unsuccessful in such hard rock and the first 1,000 feet of the tunnel was driven using conventional steam drills called 'sluggers' and explosives."*

John's father was a foreman for the mining company at the time, 1943 to 1945. John wanted to keep the mining magazine and a small pneumatic pin hole drill, but his father insisted that he turn his treasures over to the company office, which he did and regrets to this day.[19]

The Engineering and Mining Journal had these 1898 and 1899 news items about the Commodore:

July 9, 1898, Mineral County:
> *"The Commodore Mining Company is working 250 men."*

November 5, 1898, Mineral County:

"This Creede mine keeps up its regular shipments, and the mine is rapidly being put in shape for more extensive work. The electric system is completed and work is being pushed on the lower tunnel, which cuts the vein at the base of Bachelor Mountain."

March 18, 1899, Mineral County:

"Commodore — An explosion of several hundred pounds of powder in this company's No. 2 Tunnel at Creede did considerable damage to the mine and killed four men."

September 9, 1899, Mineral County:

"Commodore — This working force has been increased and about 150 tons are daily shipped."

September 23, 1899, Mineral County:

"Commodore — This Creede mine, owing to a lack of cars, has been shipping out 200 cars per day, but will soon make it 300. About 400 men are employed."

The Mining Reporter also reported on the Commodore Mine:

January 5, 1899:

"Mineral County — The principal producer is the Commodore, which company is a compromise combination. It produced about four-fifths of the value and tonnage during the year. With the exception of the Commodore every other property is worked by leasers, some of whom have grown wealthy during the past year or two.

"The Commodore is without doubt the greatest silver mine in the state. It is worked on a large scale, producing about 300 tons daily, worth about $40 per ton. It contains large ore reserves, and is good for years to come."

August 31, 1899, Mineral County:

"The working force on the Commodore has been materially increased and about 150 tons are daily shipped from that mine."

At the end of 1899 the Commodore Mine had been developed through five tunnels. The highest two were not being used. The others, about 400 feet apart vertically, were from 3,000 to 4,000 feet long, all being connected by raises. The ore was trammed to the tunnel portals where it was transported by aerial tramways to ore bins at the railroad. The power plant that provided power to the mine consisted of a five-foot water wheel driven by water through a twenty-six-inch pipeline; a five-drill air compressor; and a 135-horsepower electric generator.[20]

The Commodore's peak year of production was 1899 and, in that year, the Commodore Mining Company paid a sixty-two and a half cent dividend on each one dollar par value share.[21]

NEW YORK, LAST CHANCE, AND DEL MONTE MINES

The Last Chance, New York, and Del Monte claims overlapped one another in such a manner that the total rights of all three claims covered roughly those of a single full-length claim. The portion of the Amethyst vein in these three overlapping claims was much richer than any other equivalent length along the Amethyst.[22] The overlaps created ownership questions to a very rich ore body that took the courts years to settle, as previously discussed in Chapter Seven. More importantly, the lawsuits and court settlements took time, and this seriously impacted the efficient and timely development and mining of the ore under the three claims.

Since the three claims and the mining companies that mined them were so intimately connected, they will be described together.

New York Mine

Canfield, in *Mines and Mining Men of Colorado*,[23] described the New York Mine in 1893:

> "*The New York was located the first of June 1891 by Charles Born and G.K. Smith, the latter grubstaked by S.D. Coffin. Born, however, a few days later made known his dissatisfaction with the float to Smith and told him he could have the whole location. Smith accepted the offer and relocated it, destroying the first stake. A few months later Coffin succeeded in selling the property to A.E. Reynolds and I.L. Johnson of Denver for a nominal sum. The new owners were compelled to go into court in October 1891 to protect their interests, occasioned by the encroachments of the Last Chance people on their ground. The Last Chance people determined from underground surveys that this vein*

took a westerly turn and consequently changed their survey ten degrees into New York ground. The suit ended in a compromise [i.e., the formation of the New York-Chance Mining Company in mid-1892, as described in Chapter Eight]. As a consequence development has been going on vigorously since the latter part of September under the management of Alex Thorton from Summitville. This property is being opened up by three tunnels, the lowest being 300 feet down the hill below the discovery shaft. Work is gaining great headway by the air drills, and another tunnel will soon be started still further down the hill, which will be driven by electric drills. The plant is situated in the gulch about 1,000 feet below the discovery shaft. Both tunnels are in high grade ore, from which are now being shipped about fifty tons a day, beginning November 1 [1892]. The building improvements so far consist of an engine house, 20 x 30, enclosing the power for the drills, an office building, and an ore house, 14 x 30 x 40, having a capacity for 250 tons. Seventy-five men are at present working on the mining end of the property and twenty-five more engaged in building a road and other occupations. The property shipped 100 carloads of ore last fall averaging eighty ounces to the ton."

The Creede Candle, January 6, 1893, described two of the New York Mine tunnels:

"A tunnel to the vein was run from the vicinity of the Last Chance No. 2 Shaft. After passing through 500 feet of barren ground a new ore chute of great richness similar in character to that of the original discovery was encountered. The New York and Chance Tunnel being run from the water level will be 1,700 feet long."

The Creede Candle, July 7, 1893, reported that the New York and Chance completely shut down its operations as a result of the drop in the price of silver. *The Engineering and Mining Journal* on August 25, 1894, reported that the New York Chance was in good ore with a quantity of it, that there was stoping ground to keep up their shipments for three or four months, and that they are continually opening up new ground.

Perhaps this is the place to define more mining terms: 1) a stope is an excavation to remove ore from an ore body that has been "developed" by drifts, crosscuts, raises, and winzes; 2) "stoping ground" is a term used to define a section of an ore body that can be stoped, or excavated, at a profit; and 3) raises and winzes are vertical or near-vertical underground openings. A raise is driven upwards and a winze is sunk downward.

The mines at Creede were developed by a series of "levels," or horizontal drifts on or parallel to the vein and horizontal crosscuts at an angle to the vein. The levels were spaced at 100-foot intervals down the dip, or slope, of the vein. These levels were connected by raises and winzes and to the surface by shafts or adits, called tunnels at Creede. Most terms used in underground mining originated in the mines of Cornwall, England, and were brought to the United States by immigrant Cornish miners.

In June 1898, the New York Chance Mine started making shipments again, now that the litigation over the New York claim had been settled. The litigation referred to was Mary A. Coffin's suit against A.E. Reynolds and partners as described in Chapter Seven. The suit was first filed in November 1893 and ultimately settled in favor of the defendants in June 1899.[24]

Last Chance Mine

This is the story of a mine found by three obstinate burros that made a Del Norte butcher very wealthy. *The Creede Candle* issue of February 4, 1892, had this report:

> "*Mines and Prospects — Bonds on the interests of Theodore Renniger and Eric Von Bruddenbock in the Last Chance, $35,000 being paid to each for their third interest. Title of this two-thirds is now in the hands of Mr. Ward of New York, L.Z. Dickson of Denver, Jake Saunders [Sanders] of Leadville, Henry R. Wolcott and Senator E.O. Wolcott of Denver. The remaining one-third is held by Ralph Granger of Del Norte.*"

The first shipment of ore from the Last Chance Mine was on December 4, 1891, and by January 28, 1892, the Last Chance hoisting plant had arrived and was being installed at the upper workings where a shaft had been started. By February 1892 the mine employed seventy men under Superintendent E.H. Crawford.[25] Early development of the Last Chance Mine happened quickly simply because all development work was in shipping ore, and there was no need to mine barren rock.

No ore was shipped from the Last Chance in March 1892 because of the dispute over ownership of the north end of the New York claim where it overlapped the Last Chance.[26] This dispute was resolved and resulted in the formation of the New York Chance Mining Company, as reported in the July 2, 1892, issue of *The Engineering and Mining Journal*:

> *"New York Chance Mining Company, Creede — To avoid the long litigation, heavy court expenses and the delay in working certain portions of the properties, the owners of the Last Chance and New York Mines have compromised and consolidated. The owners of the Annie Rooney were bought out for $8,000 cash. The new organization will be incorporated as the New York Chance Mining Company. The present owners of the mines who share in the combination are, on the Last Chance side, Ralph Granger, J.F. Sanders, L.Z. Dickson, H.R., and E.O. Wolcott; on the New York side, A.E. Reynolds, O.E. LeFevre, S.D. Coffin, Colin Timmons, and others. The Willow Mining Company, selling the Annie Rooney, is composed of J.B. Moore, M.H. Rogers, Butler & McKinley, and others."*

A description of the Last Chance Mine in 1893 and its superintendent, E. H. Crawford, is included in Canfield's *Mines and Mining Men of Colorado:*[27]

> *"The Last Chance Mining and Milling Company was formed April 1, 1892. The company has expended $15,000 on buildings and $10,000 on roads during the past year. The development consists of two shafts. Number One, or the Granger Shaft, has gained a depth of 350 feet, and has four levels, showing a total of 1,000 feet of drifting. Shaft Number Two, 250 feet deep, has also four levels, and a total of 1,100 feet of drifting. The mineral carrying matter is a silicious quartz ore, also sulphides assaying 80 to 100 ounces of silver to the ton, the paying streak being from two to twelve feet wide. One hundred men are carried on the payroll. The Granger Shaft has just been equipped with a new double-hoist, 250-horsepower, which will lift 50 tons a day. The surface improvements consist of a shaft house, 32 x 100, at the Granger Shaft, and a boiler house, 22 x 32, a shaft house, 22 x 32, at*

Shaft Number Two, and boiler house, 16 x 20, also office building and two cottages.

"The output for the year 1892 was about 15,000 tons of ore valued at $1,400,000 — all silver. Under the skillful management of the superintendent, Mr. E.H. Crawford, everything about the mine is in excellent condition, the accommodations for the men being especially well conducted. The Last Chance Mining and Milling Company was incorporated under the laws of the state of Colorado, with a capital stock of $5,000,000, divided into 500,000 shares of the par value of $10 each. Ralph Granger is President, J.F. Sanders, Vice President, and Henry Wolcott, Secretary and Treasurer. The accounts of the company, at Creede, are under the charge of Mr. J. Rodman, who is the assayer as well as the bookkeeper at the Last Chance.*

"E.H. Crawford, superintendent of the Last Chance Mine, is a native of Maine, having been born at Gardner, in that state, October 15, 1852. He subsequently came to Colorado and engaged in mining, his first essay in that direction having been made about the first of September, 1873 at or near Georgetown, where at one time or another he owned or was interested in a number of prospects. None of these became producers, and he subsequently sold out all of them. Since then his experience has been wide and varied as superintendent or manager of various mines, among them the Bull Domingo at West Cliff, and others at Leadville. Besides the Last Chance, Mr. Crawford is at present interested in the Little Bear*

The Last Chance Mine — March 1893

Al Birdsey Collection, Courtesy of the Creede Historical Society

and American Boy. His wise and far-sighted management have contributed materially toward the splendid condition of the Last Chance Mine today."

The Creede Candle in its January 6, 1893, issue described the Last Chance Mine:

"The Last Chance has not been behind its big neighbor [i.e., the Amethyst Mine] in any feature, unless we except the advance of development. Its greatest depth is beyond 500 feet, but it has been practically stoped out or emptied of its riches above the fifth level. This has been made possible only with the employment of a large force and a first-class equipment. Two steam plants are in operation and a third, with skip attachment, is soon to be added. Two deep shafts and an equal number of tunnels furnish outlet from the maze of underground workings. E.H. Crawford is superintendent and Julius Rodman manager of the mine. A roomy boarding house for the men has been erected near at hand and this is in charge of Mr. Southworth.

"Ore from the Last Chance is taken down in wagons under contract by Humphrey & Morton. The output is kept steady at about five car loads a day. A peculiarity of these mines is that the ore from wall to wall is of remunerative quality. It requires no sorting, but is shipped as stoped.

"A spur track is being constructed up West Willow Gulch about 3,500 feet to permit the loading of the Chance ores with a shorter haul than is now necessary. Hoover and Marrow have the contract. Two ore hauling and transportation companies are kept busy with large forces of teams and men hauling the ore from the mines. D.W. Hoover & Company are the pioneers in the business. Humphrey and Morton have contracts from the New York and Last Chance. Twenty-four wagons are now running constantly."

The Last Chance cut its workforce in half to seventy-five men in July of 1893 because of the drastic drop in the price of silver after the repeal of the Sherman Act. The hoisting cables at its No. 1 shaft were increased to 1,200 feet each in 1894.[28]

The Engineering and Mining Journal reported on April 6, 1895, that the District Court at Denver, Judge Hallett presiding, denied the

Del Monte Mining Company's petition for an injunction to restrain the Last Chance Mining Company from mining the vein below the point where it crosses the east side line of the Del Monte. The Del Monte people ultimately appealed the decision to the U.S. Supreme Court, and the case was not settled until 1902. The case, discussed in detail in Chapter Seven, had a tremendous impact on Creede mining at the turn of the century since no mining occurred in the disputed area for seven years.

Probably the richest ore body found in the Last Chance and Del Monte Mines was known as the "Big Cave." Emmons and Larsen[29] described it as follows:

> "On levels 3, 4, and 5 there was a great body of ore known as the "big cave." This ore was so much fractured and the ground so unstable that it was mined by milling the dirt from the bottom on levels 5 and 6 and drawing it out by gravity from levels as high as No. 2. It is said that many thousand tons of ore was thus mined and, with little sorting, sent to the smelters. The cave left by drawing out the ore is inaccessible but is credibly reported to be in places about 100 feet wide."

Samples of fine ore from the Big Cave reportedly assayed between 90 and 110 ounces of silver per ton. The lawsuit between the Last Chance and Del Monte prevented mining operations in the area of the Big Cave for seven or eight years and, during that period of inactivity, the large opening did cave, preventing the extraction of adjacent ore.[30]

Water in the Last Chance Mine workings was a serious problem, so serious that the mine was essentially shut down for a period of time. *Mining Reporter*, May 25, 1899, reported that water was being drained from the Last Chance Mine:

> "The connection between the Nelson Tunnel and the great body of water in the Chance Mine was successfully made Tuesday the 23d. The prospective resumption of work at the Chance Mine at Creede, Colorado early in June, will add largely to the shipments from that district. The Chance is one of the very rich mines of the state, notwithstanding which fact it has been closed for more than two years because of the great volume of water encountered in its development which has reached a depth of 1200 feet."

In June 1899, the Last Chance workings were almost dry and the mining of stopes that had been under water for three years was underway; by September 1899 the mine was shipping fifty tons per day with plans to increase production to 150 tons per day. The water was below the eleventh level in December 1899 and pumping of water through the shaft had stopped.[31] What a Christmas present for Creede Camp!

A raise was driven up from the Nelson Tunnel to the Last Chance workings in late 1899 to connect it to the tunnel for drainage and ore haulage, thus eliminating the property's dependence on their shafts.

Del Monte Mine

Charles F. Nelson located the Del Monte claim in January 1891.[32] *The Creede Candle*'s inaugural issue, January 7, 1892, described the Del Monte Mine:

> *"The Del Monte was located by Chas. F. Nelson to the east from the Last Chance which it overlaps at the south end and takes in about 100 feet of the big lead. Mr. Nelson is sinking a shaft on the property in talc which is day by day becoming better mineralized. The work promises to be the most effective development of the big deposit which has been made outside of the mines directly on the lead and result is watched with a great deal of interest."*

The Colorado Sun, June 19, 1892, reported that the steam hoister for the Del Monte was in place and that large quantities of ore much resembling the Last Chance ore was being mined. Charles F. Nelson sold the Del Monte to a syndicate from the Colorado Springs, Colorado, vicinity in August 1892. Nelson retained an interest in the property and stayed on as general manager.[33]

The Del Monte shipped a little ore during 1892 and was listed as a mine. Machinery was put in place and the mine was in shape for active mining. All possibility of litigation had been removed by compromises effected, and the big engine was steamed up ready to go to work. Manager Hogan said that it was simply a question of the size of his force when shipments would begin.[34] The settlement referred to was between the Last Chance and Del Monte as reported in *The Creede Candle* of March 17, 1892. The settlement did not last long, as the conflict ended up in the courts, as discussed in Chapter Seven.

A.E. Reynolds injected himself into the controversy. He had a diamond drill hole drilled in a flat on top of Bachelor Mountain above the Del Monte claim in an attempt to locate the apex of the Del Monte (Amethyst) vein at that point. Apparently the hole showed silver values, and the Transfer Shaft was sunk by Reynolds at the site of the drill hole but failed to find any ore.[35]

The early history of the Del Monte Mine is included in Canfield's *Mines and Mining Men of Colorado:*[36]

> "*The Del Monte lies northwest of the Transfer and was located by Charles Nelson. It is believed to cover 300 feet of the Amethyst vein. The property is now owned by I.R. Ehrich, H.G. Lunt, and Mr. Hayes of Colorado Springs, Gen. Charles Adams of Manitou and Mr. Nelson. Over $7,000 have been invested in buildings and hoisting plant. The underground workings are quite extensive, consisting of a shaft 200 feet or more in depth and numerous drifts.*"

The Del Monte suspended operations in July 1893 after the repeal of the Sherman Act and the precipitous drop in the price of silver but resumed operations the following October.[37] The mine was shut down in 1894 pending settlement of litigation with the Last Chance and did not reopen until 1902, eight years later.[38] This must have been a real blow to the economy of Creede Camp!

AMETHYST MINE

Nicholas C. Creede located the Amethyst claim in the names of D.H. Moffat, L.E. Campbell, and himself in June 1891.[39] Creede, who was then engaged by Moffat and Campbell to prospect for them, visited the site of the discovery of the Last Chance claim and traced the outcrop for some distance. Impressed with the surface indications, Creede prevailed on Renniger to define the Last Chance claim, and he then located the Amethyst claim adjoining it.

The Creede Candle's inaugural issue of January 7, 1892, told about the Amethyst Mine, a mine only dreamed of by miners:

> "*The first shipment of ore from the Amethyst Mine was made on December 4, 1891. The Amethyst has a vein of ore about five feet wide between walls. It has been developed with two shafts located about two hundred feet apart on the vein, one 80 and the other 90 feet deep. In sinking these shafts, 778 car loads of ore which ran from $90 at the*

start and now $170 a ton, have been taken out and
shipped. They are now drifting between the two shafts and
are sending out from eight to ten cars a day. Not a pound
of ore has been taken out except in development. It is esti-
mated $1,000,000 worth of ore will be blocked out
between these two shafts. A third shaft is now being put
down and a steam hoisting plant is soon to be added."

The Amethyst Mining Company was incorporated on May 20, 1892. The company was organized under the laws of West Virginia with a capitalization of $5,000,000. D.H. Moffat, Walter S. Cheesman, William H. Baker of Denver, and Sylvester T. Smith of Kansas City were directors for the first year.[40] Officers of the company were: D.H. Moffat, president; N.C. Creede, vice-president; Walter S. Cheesman, secretary and treasurer; L.E. Campbell, general manager.

An excellent description of the Amethyst Mine at the end of 1892 is given in *Mines and Mining Men of Colorado:*[41]

"The Amethyst Mine, located by N.C. Creede, in June
1891 on a grub stake by David H. Moffat, has proven a
fortunate discovery in many ways. It is making money for
the investors, it is giving employment to hundreds of men,
and caused the opening up and development of new min-
eral territory in this the greatest mineral producing state in
the union, and has caused to be founded four towns, whose
aggregate population is now about 5,000, showing an
appraised valuation in building improvements of $350,000.

"The first shipment of ore from the mine occurred in
September [December 4, 1891 according to The Creede
Candle], following the location and at that time the aver-
age returns were seventy ounces to the ton. The working
condition and development in the property today is as fol-
lows: Two operating shaft houses, the first one erected in
June, now being used exclusively for air through the
underground workings. No. 2 Shaft, about 200 feet to the
north, is operated by a forty-horse power engine and hois-
ter, is down 450 feet, has five levels, each 800 feet long
and 75 to 100 feet apart, with intermediate levels between
the main levels. Still 500 feet more to the north and 700
feet from the west end of the property is No. 3 Shaft,
operated by a 120-horse power engine and hoister, down

Amethyst and Last Chance Mines — July, 1895
Courtesy of the Colorado Historical Society

260 feet, all the levels from No. 2 being extended through it. This shaft and drift work sums up a total of over two miles, all in ore, not a particle of stoping being resorted to until the first week in October last. In the southern end of the tunnels the vein is five feet wide, in the northern end twenty-three. No. 3 Shaft is all in ore for its entire depth and width, eight feet. There runs a shaft from the first to the second level off No. 2 Shaft, which has been sunk to the next level, and this also is all in ore. As depth is gained there is an increasing value in silver in the ore. At the bottom of No. 2 the rock is coated with large sized flakes of the pure stuff [native silver]. All the appurtenances for successful mining are in use, the best of buildings enclosing the best of machinery, the track between the two shaft houses under cover, an ore house with a capacity of 200 tons lying along the track, and from this ore house starts an automatic tramway which conveys the ore 8,200 feet down the hill to the Upper Creede depot, where it is loaded on the Denver & Rio Grande freight cars. This tram was set in full operation the latter part of June, one year from the location of the property, costing $38,000, is *running fifty-nine buckets, and is capable of running down 250 tons of ore a day. From the three shifts first put on, the company's payroll carries 150 men at the mine, twenty at the tram and contractors sinking shafts and driving drifts employ nearly seventy-five more men. The company's payroll averages $12,000 a month; that of the contractors about $5,000. The output of the property since the first shipment in September 1891 to December 31, 1891 is estimated at 1,720 cars, and as they load pretty heavy, averaging fifteen tons to the car, this gives a total weight of over 25,000 tons, of an approximate value of $2,000,000. This immense wealth has been taken out from development work alone, practically, and what will be put out when stoping is the order cannot be estimated. The property is controlled and operated by the Amethyst Mining and Milling Company, incorporated May 15, 1892 with the following officers, who also are the sole owners: D.H. Moffat, Denver, President; N.C. Creede, Pueblo, Vice-President; W.S. Cheesman, Denver, Secretary and Treasurer; Sylvester T. Smith and Lafayette E. Campbell of the Board of Directors. E.M. Rogers, of Aspen, was made General Manager November 1; prior to that time Mr. Campbell acted in that capacity, and Henry Allenby still holds the position of Superintendent of the properties of the company, which also includes the Holy Moses and Ethel, having been in that position since April 4, 1891. Mr. Allenby is an Englishman by birth, just forty years of age, and has spent most of his life underground. Mr. Moffat brought him here from Leadville, where he superintended the Maid of Erin Mine, and here he opened up the Amethyst to where she is, the best mine in the state. In Mr. Rogers the company has an able and experienced man, affable and courteous, and in conjunction with Mr. Allenby, has the confidence of employer and employees, harmoniously working to a successful issue."*

An efficient way to transport the ore from the mine high above Creede to the railroad was necessary for a successful mining operation. The company elected to construct an aerial tramway as a more efficient method than that of using wagons traveling on steep, difficult roads, as did the Last Chance Mine. The tramway was designed and constructed in short order as the following Creede newspaper articles indicate:

The Creede Candle, *January 14, 1892:*

"Engineer Sackett has completed the survey of the proposed Amethyst Tramway and sent his notes on to the Trenton Iron Works. The owners of the property are waiting for estimates on the cost to come from the company."

Creede Chronicle, *March 22, 1892:*

"Amethyst Tramway — Contract let and work started for its construction. Yesterday morning the owners of the Amethyst let a contract to the Trenton Iron Company [Works] for the construction of a tramway from the mine to Upper Creede. Seventeen men were put to work at once and the tram will be completed in a short time."

The Creede Candle, *June 17, 1892:*

"The buckets are now being strung of the long cable tramway from the Amethyst, and in a day or two ore will be coming down at a rate that will turn the heads of rival camps and make them giddy."

The hoisting plant installed at the Amethyst No. 2 Shaft is described in a *Creede Chronicle* article dated March 22, 1892:

"Steam in Use — The first steam appliances ever used in Creede for mining purposes were started on Saturday, March 12th when the new hoister for the Amethyst was put in motion. Capt. L.E. Campbell and N.C. Creede were present, and Mr. Campbell blew the whistle telling the surrounding hills that the Amethyst was now ready to take out all the ore there was in them."

The Engineering and Mining Journal, September 2, 1892, gave the following information on the Amethyst Mine and No. 3 Shaft:

"We extract the following items of Creede news from The Denver 'Times': 'The practicality of deep mining in this camp has been fully demonstrated in the results that have attended such work so far. The large new shaft house of the Amethyst is completed. It is 40 x 90 ft. The 80-HP boiler has been taken up. The hoister has 1,000 ft. of English crucible steel rope, and it is expected to sink a shaft its full length. During the month of July the

tramway brought down 1,650 tons of ore, and this month it is averaging 80 tons per day.'"

The Creede Candle, January 6, 1893, commented that: "The No. 3 Shaft of the Amethyst is down to the fifth level and has been run eight feet wide all that distance in ore without getting in sight of either wall. An immense pump arrived during the week and is now being put in place to drain the mine." This was the beginning of a serious water problem that was finally solved by gravity drainage into the Nelson Tunnel.

The Engineering and Mining Journal, December 16, 1893, had this to say about the Amethyst: "Some 300 ft. of the hanging wall in this mine caved in on No. 3 shaft December 5th. This compels the mine to shut down for two weeks to repair the damage. The cave-in extended from the surface to the third level."

Nicholas Creede declined to pay his share of the expense of fixing the damages caused by the cave-in and transferred his stock in the company to his partners, D.H. Moffat, Sylvester T. Smith, and L.E. Campbell. *The Engineering and Mining Journal* of September 15, 1894, confirmed that Creede had sold his remaining interest in mining property at Creede to Moffat and his associates. This event created a serious problem for the Amethyst Mining Company years later.

The Amethyst Mining Company was experiencing difficulty in finding ore as early as the first part of 1894. Seventy men were laid off in June and only fifteen men were working at sinking and stoping.[42] Captain Campbell, as general manager, was quoted in August 1894 as saying that unless shipping ore was found by the middle of next month, the mine would be closed down.[43] As if the predicament of no ore in sight was not enough, the water problem came to the front in a big way in 1894. *The Engineering and Mining Journal* of April 14, 1894, carried this report:

> *"Amethyst reports from Creede are to the effect that the producing mines of Bachelor Hill are having a hard fight to keep the levels from filling up with water. The Amethyst is full to the top of the sixth level and still rising. Superintendent Allenby is borrowing all the idle pumps in camp and putting them in so as to keep the water down and the mine working. If the water rises 50 ft. more the pumps in the Last Chance will force the property to shut down. In three days more, had not the water*

started, the big Duplex pump of the Amethyst, one of the largest in the State, would have been in place. Two pumps of 500 gals. capacity arrived on April 3rd for the Amethyst and Last Chance shafts. The Amethyst is so situated that it drains all the mines and its pumps keep the others dry."

To add to the mine's difficulties, a fire destroyed the shaft house and other buildings on August 24, 1894, for a loss estimated at $20,000. Far more serious was the deaths of four miners at the bottom of the shaft, killed by a falling skip, a "bucket" used to hoist ore through the shaft to the surface. *The Creede Candle* carried the story of the Amethyst disaster in its August 24, 1894, issue:

"The shaft house and outbuildings of the Amethyst Mine were destroyed by fire at about 4:30 o'clock this morning. Four miners who were working in Shaft No. 3 were killed by the skip falling upon and crushing them. The names of the killed are Chas. D. Proctor, Hugh Fay, Tom Eversole, and Archie McDowell.

"The fire broke out in the drying room adjoining No. 3 shaft house at 4:21 a.m. In fifteen minutes everything was consumed. The flames spread with a flash over the light and dry pine boards of the buildings and with such rapidity burned all that the men in and about the shaft house had no time to do anything but escape with their lives.

"J.W. Drake, engineer at the Happy Thought, says: 'I was on duty. Looking out of the window I saw a small blaze at the Amethyst and at first thought it was a cabin on fire. I ran up the lookout and saw the whole group of buildings flash into flame. Heard the whistle of the Amethyst toot; ran down and blew our whistle and by that time everything was burning beyond saving. It could not have been three minutes from the time I saw the first flame before it was all ablaze.'

"Just previous to the breaking out of the fire, August Olson, in dumping a car of waste, went down the bump with it and had his right leg fractured below the knee and the flesh badly torn from the bone. He had been picked up by Ike May, carried to the office building and May had bandaged the injured leg as best he could when the fire broke out. May got Olson out of the fire with difficulty,

waked up some men sleeping in the assay office and then started down the shaft to warn the five men working down there.

"Engineer H.E. Park says: 'It was 4:21 o'clock. The graveyard shift had been to lunch and gone back to work but a few minutes. I was hoisting the skip when I saw flames coming out from between the boards between the drying room and shaft. I brought the skip up, dumped it and left it standing on its nose, then hurried to the feed pipe and was getting out the hose to try to stop the fire when the flames burst out threateningly. Then I remembered a part of a box of powder in the candle room; went and got it and ran and threw it down the dump. I hurried back to the shaft room as quick as I could but it was all in flames and I had to get out. I had to fight my way through the fire and when I was more than 20 feet from the shaft house the main steam pipe bursted. It was all so quick there was no time for anything. I cannot tell when the skip went down.'

"Assistant Engineer Dan McAskell was in charge of the sinker and station pump. He was the only man in the mine at the time of the accident who escaped with his life. He says:

"'I was standing at the station pump at the seventh level when the steam played out. I, of course, knew nothing of what was going on at the surface but when the pumps stop the water comes up very rapidly and I went down the shaft ladder to the bottom where the men were working, about 125 feet below the station, and told them we had better get out. They were all getting out, going up the skip way, as by this time the station tank had overflowed and water was coming down the ladder way in a stream nearly as large as a man's body — about 700 gallons a minute. Proctor and Eversole had started ahead and were about twenty feet up the skip track, climbing on the timbers; Fay was standing on the timbers and McDowel was in the bottom of the shaft; I was standing holding to the ladder and off at the side of the skip track; Fay asked McDowel to hand him his jumper from off the pump and we were all just ready to start up when the crash came. The skip had struck them all, knocked my hat off and put out my light. I called but heard nothing but the rush of the water — none of the men made a moan. I

hurried up the ladder to the station, got a light and went back. By that time the water was over the skip. Blood, hair, flesh and brains were spattered all around. Then Ike May got down and told me the shaft house was on fire and Billy Crawford and Will Nash came through from the Last Chance. The water was rising and we concluded to get out, probably starting 15 minutes after the skip came down. I came up through the No. 2 shaft on the ladder, through the seventh level.'

"Dr. Lemke, assayer, was sleeping in the assay office. He says: *'I heard the car go over the dump with Olson and that woke me up. In a few minutes Ike May came and called to me the shaft house was on fire and I got out as quick as possible. Everything was burning like tinder, the snow shed was on fire and I had to go down the dump to get away.'*

"Everything from north of No. 2 shaft house was destroyed. It is thought possibly the boilers are sound and all morning Superintendent Allenby has been trying to get steam connections so as to start the pumps. From the minute the steam pipes busted the mine has been filling with water at the rate of 700 gallons a minute and the bodies of the four men are at the bottom of the shaft under the skip. They cannot be recovered until the water is pumped out. This may take several days, owing to how soon steam can be had and the pumps put to working.

"There was some disposition at first to attach blame for the accident in the shaft to the engineer, but it seems to have been one of those lamentable accidents which no human power could have prevented. The skip was in the safest position it probably could have been left unless the engineer could have had time to lower it to the bottom, but this it seems there was not time to do. The melting of the cable by the heat let the skip fall back into the shaft with the result as stated.

"How the fire originated will probably never be known. The drying room in which it started was a dressing room for the men in which they hung their wet clothing coming off shift and redressed on going on. Coils of steam pipe ran around the walls. It is likely that some one of the shift which had just gone on may have left a lighted

After The Fire at the Amethyst Mine — 1894
Courtesy of the Colorado Historical Society

candle about, its flame caught into inflammable garments or the dry wood of the building and gained such headway that when the fire broke from the drying room it had the strength to at once envelope the shaft house. The financial damage will reach $40,000 or $50,000 and is sustained entirely by the Amethyst Company.

"Tom Eversole was formerly of Del Norte and leaves a wife who is herself in a precarious condition brought on by the shock. Mrs. Eversole is a daughter of George Southey.

"County Coroner Dr. Simpson was called to the mine to attend to Olson's injuries. He kept on the lookout for witnesses to testify and will make close inquiry as to the cause and responsibility for the accident as soon as the recovery of the bodies make it possible to hold an inquest."

It took until November to repair the damage to the shaft house; to pump water out of the shaft; and for the company to start shipping ore again. The November 24, 1894, issue of *The Engineering and Mining Journal* carried this report on the accident:

"Amethyst Mine — The remains of Charles D. Proctor, Hugh Fay, Thomas Eversole, and Archie Dowell were last week taken from the shaft. It was 82 days since

*the burning of the shaft-house melted the strands of a
cable and let the heavy skip go crashing down 850 ft. of
incline to crush these four men, who were working in the
bottom of the shaft. At the time of the accident the mine
was making 700 gallons of water every minute and before
anything could be done among the debris at the surface
the mine was flooded through the stopping of the pumps
and no effort of the owners of the mine could avail to the
recovery of the victims of the disaster. With the boilers of
the mine ruined by the fire, the pumps flooded by their
own stoppage, new pumps and new boilers had to be
brought in from outside and put in place. By the time this
could be done the water was nearly 500 ft. in the shaft.
When the pumps were started, they could make but small
headway against the constant inflow and the immense
volume in the mine. Accidents intervened to aggravate the
work. One large pump got away and went to the bottom,
the water gained again before another could be procured,
and many causes worked delay until what promised to be
the work of a week has stretched out to that of nearly a
quarter of a year. The pumps accomplished their work
and the task of recovering the bodies was then begun. The
bodies were beyond recognition and could only be identified by the clothing and tools found with them."*

The water problem continued to be very serious, affecting the
profitability of the mine. In August 1895, the Amethyst Mining
Company completed a 900-foot tunnel to drain the Amethyst Mine
above the 500-foot level. The tunnel was completed in only 100
days.[44] The water problem was finally solved by connecting the mine
to the Nelson Tunnel for drainage. *The Engineering and Mining
Journal*, October 21, 1899, had this report:

*"Amethyst — The Sullivan Drill Company of Chicago
has a contract to drain this mine at Creede. Three holes
will be bored by diamond drills — one from the Nelson
Tunnel to tap the bottom of the Last Chance Shaft,
another from the 9th level of the Last Chance to the 10th
level of the Amethyst, and a third from the 10 fi level of
the Last Chance to the 9th level of the Amethyst. The bottom of the Amethyst is 800 ft. above the Nelson Tunnel,
and only 40 ft. above the bottom of the Last Chance."*

The Denver News reported on November 24, 1899, that the water in the Amethyst was being lowered at the rate of fifteen inches daily.

A final blow was dealt to the Amethyst Mining Company when the administrator of the estate of the late Nicholas C. Creede filed suit in the U.S. Court against Moffat, Cheesman, Smith, and Campbell, the only stockholders in the company, and the Amethyst Mining Company to recover a one-third interest in the mine, alleged to be worth $5,000,000.[45] The Amethyst Mine was essentially shut down from 1899 to 1904, according to *The Creede Candle* of March 5, 1904. The suit was finally dismissed in 1910.[46]

UNITED MINES

Five early mining companies, Cleopatra Mining Company, Baltimore-Creede Mining Company, 400 Acre Diamond Drill Consolidated Mining Company, Happy Thought, and Golden Eagle Consolidated Mining Company, were consolidated into one corporation, the United Mines Company, in 1894. These five companies controlled about 2,000 feet of the Amethyst Vein apex north of the Amethyst.

The Cleopatra claim was located in August 1891 by George Brewer, Sherman Phifer, and D.S. Cotton.[47] The Cleopatra and the New Discovery were purchased by Senator A.A. McGovney, A.L. Lawton, and Secretary of State Eaton. The Cleopatra Mining Company was incorporated on February 5, 1892, and capitalized at $2 million.

The Creede Candle described the Baltimore-Creede-Mining Company in its January 6, 1893, edition: "One of the best of the more recent companies organized in Creede — those for work and not the sale of stock — is the Baltimore-Creede Mining Company. It is a $1,000,000 capitalization, seven patented claims and over 400 feet of the Amethyst vein for a proposition. David H. Moffat had purchased half interest in three of the claims owned by Baltimore-Creede in 1892.[48]

The 400 Acre Consolidated Diamond Drill Mining Company was incorporated June 15, 1892, and capitalized for $3,000,000. Officers of the corporation were: Fine P. Ernest, President; George F. Coleman, Vice-President; Howard C. Chapin, Secretary; and George R. Swallow, Treasurer. The prospectus for the company stated: "The principal object however which led to the formation of this great enterprise was the favorable conditions existing on Bachelor Mountain for the successful operating of diamond drills to absolutely locate large bodies of mineral at a nominal cost."[49] The use of diamond drills for prospecting was a relatively new technique in 1892. The prospectus said that geologic evidence at the time (September 1892) suggested that some of the ore bodies were "flat veins" and could be easily located by diamond drilling. However, this early diamond drilling was most likely not too successful in delineating near-vertical veins on Bachelor Mountain. Diamond drilling was successfully used during the second Creede boom.

Gray and Mann located the Happy Thought claim on January 19, 1892, with a discovery pit sunk thirteen feet in the wash on the Golden Eagle claim without a semblance of mineralization, according to *The Creede Candle* of December 23, 1892. The claim was then sold to Major T.H. Norton, R.C. Ralphsnyder, and G.C. Dewey for $15,000. The Norton-Dewey company found mineralization on the Happy Thought claim, but then conflicts over ownership and mining rights on the north end of the Amethyst vein commenced, as was discussed in Chapter Seven.

The Golden Eagle claim was located on October 26, 1891.[50] The Golden Eagle Consolidated Mining Company was incorporated on December 2, 1892. The Directors were Roderic F. Kavanaugh, John H. Van Ness, L.N. McLane, Alex B. McKinley, and C.G. Worden.[51]

The January 6, 1894, edition of *The Engineering and Mining Journal* reported that "at a meeting of the directors of this company [United Mines Company] of Creede, held in Denver on December 29th, the following officers were elected: W.B. Felker, President; Byron E. Shear, Vice-President; D.H. Moffat, Treasurer; W.H. Bryant, Secretary; and L.N. McLane, Manager. The company owns the Golden Eagle, Happy Thought, Argenta, and Iron Clad properties. The manager was instructed to proceed with the active development of the mines, and contracts will be let at once." R.F. Kavanaugh, one of the principal shareholders in the United Mines Company, sold his holdings to A.E. Humphreys in 1896, giving Humphreys a strong voice in the company's affairs.[52]

The manager lost no time in proceeding with mine development, according to the February 17, 1894, issue of *The Engineering and Mining Journal*:

> "*United Mines Company — This company has let a contract for 300 ft. of shafting, and it intends to crowd the sinking of the Happy Thought shaft with all possible speed. This work, besides giving employment to 25 or 30*

*men, means much for the northern end of the Amethyst
Vein. It means that if there is any ore in the vein it has got
to give up. The company has ample capital, and its stockholders include the principal mining men of Colorado."*

Frank E. Wheeler wrote an article in *The Creede Candle*'s
Mining Edition of January 1, 1927, describing the beginning of the
United Mines:

> *"The first development work of importance was the
> sinking of a shaft upon the Happy Thought claim, under
> the supervision of Mr. James Collins, father of A.M. and
> S.B. Collins, and the first major ore north of the Amethyst
> Mine was discovered at the five hundred foot level, and a
> drift extending south produced considerable lead ore dur-
> ing the early work upon the property.*
>
> *"On account of the low price of silver and lead and
> the large amount of water encountered in the various
> mines operating along the Bachelor [Amethyst] Vein,
> there was a general suspension of work and during the
> winter of 1896 and 1897 there was not to exceed fifteen
> miners working in the Creede district.*
>
> *"All of the ores in the property were primary. Very lit-
> tle oxidized or secondary enrichment found north of the
> Amethyst mine."*

Wheeler, who was the superintendent for the United Mines in
1900, was born in Colorado territory and owned a farm at
Platteville, Colorado, inherited from his father. He told the story
that as a baby, when an Indian scare happened and everyone hurried
to the stockade, the young girl carrying him tired, put him in a ditch,
and ran on. He was retrieved afterwards in good condition.[53]

James Collins' biography was included in *Mines and Mining
Men of Colorado* in 1893. He was an officer in the Miners' Bank,
the first bank organized for business in Creede Camp.[54]

> *"James H. Collins, vice president of the bank [Miners'
> Bank], is a mining man of long experience, having followed
> the business for thirty-nine years. He was born in Guernsey
> County, Ohio, in 1837, and when 17 years of age went to
> California, meeting with all the incidents and experiences
> subject to that period while engaged in placer mining. From
> California he went to Idaho and Montana and was the first*

to introduce hydraulic mining in Idaho, at Elk River. Since 1878, Mr. Collins has been in Colorado engaged in super-intending mines and developing new properties. For nine years he was in the Gunnison country, seven of which he spent as superintendent of the Hiawatha and Legal Tender Mines, and still holds valuable interests in that county. Together with J.B. Maben he is interested in some of the best prospects in Creede. Among them are the Mary Taylor, Ironclad, Eureka, Stanley, Arion, Sunol, and others. He has retired from active superintendency of mines and only looks after his interests to which are added large ranches in the San Luis Valley, where he spends part of his time looking after the raising of wheat and fine horses on his 2,000 acres of land."

James Collins' two sons, Shrive B. and Albert M., were a part of the mining scene at Creede for many years. Both played important roles in the history of Creede Camp, as described in later chapters.

The Engineering and Mining Journal of March 3, 1894, reported:

"Work on the shaft is being prosecuted vigorously with good promises for pay ore in a short time. A streak of rich chloride ore, shotted with galena, is being followed in the shaft, now 335 ft. deep, and widening as develop-ment progresses. It is also known that the development made by the Cleopatra disclosed a good body of hard lead carbonates and the United management will follow up this discovery."

Sinking of the Happy Thought Shaft continued. The shaft had been sunk 500 feet by the end of April 1894. It was being sunk at the rate of four feet a day, and a station for a drift at the 500-foot level was being excavated for an exploration drift in the hope of showing an ore chute at that level.[55] At the end of June 1894 the shaft was idle, waiting for the arrival of a large pump.[56] Smelter returns of Happy Thought ore indicated that the gold content of the ore was increasing in depth and this information created consider-able excitement in Creede. By February 1895, the shaft had been sunk to the 700-foot level and the pump had arrived and was being installed at the 700-foot level pump station.[57] The following articles appeared in *The Engineering and Mining Journal:*

March 2, 1895:

"*United Mines Company — This company, of Creede, has decided to float a stockholders' loan of $25,000 to provide for future development and allow the work to go on undelayed until the property becomes self-supporting, says the Denver 'Republican.' The following report has been issued to shareholders: 'The end of the first 13 months of the company's existence find it not yet a paying proposition. The company has raised and expended the sum of $35,000, and it will require about $10,000 to liquidate bills falling due on March 10th next. The directors are satisfied that this money has been well expended and that the property will soon be placed upon a paying basis. We have our main working shaft 735 ft. deep, drifts extending there from a total distance of 890 ft.; a complete pumping plant, sufficient to raise 350 gals. of water per minute from our shaft for a distance of 1,000 ft.; three boilers, hoister, shaft house, ore bins, assay office and fixtures, boarding house, and all the necessary equipment to continue work. We have been greatly delayed and our expenses largely increased by reason of the quantities of water encountered. This has now been met and overcome. Our shaft for the last 50 ft. has been in ore running well in gold, silver, and lead, and both drifts from the 700 ft. station are in similar ore as far as they have been run. We commenced shipping in January and have realized over $1,000 net since that time. But little more depth must be gained before we can pay expenses, and to do this money must be borrowed.'*"

August 17, 1895:

"*United Leasing Company — A second issue of $25,000 of the capital stock of this company is to be made of August 19th. The company has a five-year lease on the property of the United Mines Company of Creede, and the new issue of the leasing stock will be divided among the shareholders in the original company. The sum arising from the new issue places the company out of debt, with the 800-ft. shaft widened and a full equipment of pumps and hoisting machinery. Several of the deep workings are in pay ore, and a great deal of development work has been done.*"

A drift was driven in late 1895 to connect the 500-foot level of the Amethyst Mine to the 700-foot level of the Happy Thought Mine to provide drainage above the 700-foot level.[58] The water was then conveyed from the Amethyst to West Willow Creek through the 900-foot tunnel that the Amethyst Mining Company had completed in August 1895.

Even after the expenditures for debt service and improvements in 1895, the cost of sinking the shaft deeper and the high costs of pumping water and hoisting ore made the mining operation unprofitable given the relatively low-grade ore that had been developed. Therefore, the United Mines operations were suspended. *The Engineering and Mining Journal*, January 25, 1896, carried the following story:

> *"United Mines Leasing Company — It is announced that this Creede company has decided to at once suspend operations on the United Mines property. No previous intimation had been given out of the company's intentions. Manager Ray is reported to have advised the miners and employees to secure their back pay by filing liens on the property. The miners, some 60 in number, went to town on January 15th to file their claims. Meantime, the Amethyst Mine, by its manager, sought to take possession of the mammoth compound pump, valued at $14,000, on the United Mines property. Hearing of this move, the United miners tried to secure an injunction to prevent the removal of the pump, but were unable to obtain it from either the county or district judge, and for this reason decided upon heroic action. They gathered some Winchesters and revolvers, and proceeding to the United Mines, prevented the removal of any kind of property, including the big pump, until they had been paid for their labor. Captain Campbell, manager of the Amethyst Mine, has notified his superiors in Denver that assistance is necessary if the pump is to be seized. Ray is said to have given the Amethyst an order for the pump previous to his leaving Creede. The United Mines Company and the United Mines Leasing Company are both comprised of Denver men. The owners of the property spent nearly $200,000 on the mine and then turned the property over to the Leasing Company, which, for the most part, consisted of*

the larger owners in the mine, for further development.
The Leasing Company is said to have spent $85,000 in
the past six months, and while there is plenty of ore
uncovered, its grade is too low to handle with a profit. Mr.
Eben Smith is the president of the Leasing Company."

Early in 1897, after the mine had been shut down, Colonel A.E. Humphreys secured a lease upon the United Mines property under the name of the Big Kanawha Leasing Company, a reference to his West Virginia upbringing. The Nelson Tunnel organization was bankrupt at that time. Humphreys was instrumental in organizing the Wooster Tunnel Company and securing a ninety-nine year lease upon the Nelson Tunnel. He let a contract to extend the tunnel (Humphreys Tunnel) to the south end line of the United Mines property. The Nelson-Wooster-Humphreys Tunnel is described in Chapter Nine. Humphreys also organized the Humphreys Mining and Milling Company in 1898 to construct and operate the Humphreys Mill at the mouth of the Nelson Tunnel.[59]

Colonel Humphreys' extension of the tunnel into the northern portion of the Amethyst vein and the construction of a modern mill to concentrate the sulfide ore before shipment to the smelters paved the way to essentially eliminate three serious problems facing mining at Creede Camp — a lack of consolidation of mining properties, increased water with depth, and sulfide instead of oxidized ore.

The United Mines property remained closed in 1898 but *The Mining Reporter* of July 20, 1899, stated that operations had re-commenced:

"Happy Thought — Another good strike was made last
week in the Happy Thought, Creede Camp. While doing
development work in the seventh level, a large body of ore
was uncovered that gives a high assay in silver, lead, and
zinc, and is said to be the most valuable section of the prop-
erty, but the workmen are much handicapped by the water
which the recent unwatering failed to entirely remove. This
mine is now taking out about 75 tons of ore daily, a large
increase over the best showing of last month."

The tunnel connection to the Amethyst Mine evidently drained most, but not all, of the water from the Happy Thought Mine. Sinking of the Happy Thought shaft re-commenced in 1899 with a connection to the Nelson-Wooster-Humphreys Tunnel for water drainage below the 700-foot level, as well as access, ventilation, and ore haulage as the ultimate target.

PARK REGENT MINE

The Park Regent Consolidated Mining Company was incorporated in March 1892; capitalized at $1,000,000; and controlled thirteen claims north of the Amethyst. Assays of the mineral are said to have run from $20 to $180 per ton. Directors were: O.P. Poole, A.W. Rucker, H.J. Sisty, W.J. Wolfe, D.C. Halcom, Chas. E. Noble, and A.H. Davis.[60] Evidently many changes were made in the organization and its name shortly after it was incorporated. Canfield[61] described the company's capitalization, officers, and operation in 1893:

> "The Antlers-Park Regent Mining Company is the largest mining corporation operating in Creede Camp. It is capitalized for $2,250,000, and among its directors are found some of the wealthiest men in the state. It is officered as follows: president, E. Barnett, proprietor of the Antlers Hotel, Colorado Springs; vice-president, C.E. Noble, treasurer of the Colorado Midland Railroad Company; secretary, John J. Minihan, commercial agent for the Rock Island Railroad Company; treasurer, Dr. G.W. Lawrence, one of the prominent physicians of Colorado Springs. The board comprises these gentlemen, all of Colorado Springs, and Louis R. Ehrich, mine operator, Colorado Springs; A.W. Rucker, attorney, Denver, and Mr. Poole.
>
> "Otho P. Poole, general manager for the Antlers-Park Regent Mining Company and the Coin Silver Mining Company, operating at Creede was born in Lexington, Mo., July 24, 1857. He was educated at Wentworth Academy and Masonic College, Lexington, and creditably passed through a fine course of the studies of those institutions. At the age of nineteen he entered his father's flouring mill, near Kansas City, as bookkeeper. Shortly, after gaining his majority, he arrived at Colorado Springs and engaged in sheep raising for a year and a half, when he went to Texas, and for two years made a success of cattle-raising. In 1878 Mr. Poole turned his attention to mining, his first experience being in Leadville, where he made a number of good locations, all of which subsequently passed into the hands of companies, and are today making money for the investors. His first visit to Creede was made in December, 1891, when he discovered the Park-Regent group on Bachelor Mountain, the locations

Park Regent Mine — Date Unknown
Courtesy of the Creede Historical Society

being made on a study of the formation and the judgment that the great Amethyst Vein took a north-westerly trend. Mr. Poole feels confident of the property being a producer in a very short time. The consummation of this end is being materially assisted by all the modern mining appliances and accommodations, showing an expenditure of $5,000, and including development work, $20,000 in all have been expended on the group. The machinery consists of a 30-horse power boiler, a 30-horse power hoisting engine, two Reynolds safety whims, and a No. 7 Cameron sinking pump. There are fourteen claims in this group, covering 130 acres. The other property owned by the company is the Antlers group of four claims [hence the name Antlers-Park Regent Mining Company], lying on the hill west of MacKenzie Mountain (on which the Alpha and Yellow Jacket are located). These are, as yet, prospects, but the indications are very encouraging for pay mines. Mr. Poole believes Creede will become the greatest silver producer in the state and that too, very soon. The nature of the ground leads to cheapness in development, and that there is a vast bed of mineral surrounding the camp that only needs time, energy and a little capital, compared with other parts of the state, to open up."

The Park Regent Shaft cut the vein on its dip and exposed ore of a low grade similar to that found in the Happy Thought.[62] The company had sunk the shaft into concentrating grade ore that carried gold values and installed equipment in 1895 to allow the shaft to be sunk 1,000 feet to find gold-bearing ore.[63]

A drift was driven in late 1895 to connect the 500-foot level of the Amethyst Mine to the 700-foot level of the Happy Thought Mine for drainage purposes. *The Engineering and Mining Journal* reported on September 21, 1895, that drainage had been provided above the 700-foot level, which allowed work to resume at the Park Regent:

> *"Park-Regent — Work has been resumed on this group, says the Creede Sentinel. A contract has been let for 300 ft. of drifting on the level southward to connect with the seventh of the Happy Thought, which is to connect with the fifth of the Amethyst, thereby making a complete drain from the Park-Regent out through the Amethyst into West Willow Gulch."*

The first serious attempt along the Amethyst Vein System to separate the commercially valuable minerals from the non-economic minerals, called "gangue" minerals, by concentration or "ore dressing" was made at the Park Regent. Concentration of the valuable minerals drastically reduced the amount of material that was shipped to the smelter, thus materially reducing freight and smelting charges. Concentration of the lower grade sulfide ores was nearly always mandatory for profitable mining. The history of early concentration mills at Creede Camp is the subject of Chapter Ten.

The Engineering and Mining Journal, August 29, 1896, carried the following story about the Park Regent Mill:

> *"This new mill, near Creede, built by the Colorado Iron Works of Denver, has been successfully put in operation and is now running to its full capacity, estimated to be 25 tons per day. Mr. Poole at present is having a trestle built, upon which will be placed the track to be used in conveying the ore from the dump to the mill which is built a short distance below the dump. Some 200 tons of ore is now on the dump, and so far the mill man in charge is more than pleased with the results."*

Unfortunately the story was wrong about the success of the Park Regent Mill. Its operation was not satisfactory and was shut down.[64]

On June 4, 1898, *The Engineering and Mining Journal* reported that "the Golden Link Mining and Leasing Company, headed by D.H. Moffat, has leased the Antlers-Park Regent group at Creede. The ore is a low grade gold proposition and will be handled by a mill to be erected." The project evidently did not work out as the mill was never built.

The Park Regent Mine did not produce any appreciable tonnage of ore until after 1900. Perhaps "Park Regent Shaft" would better describe the property prior to 1900.

MAMMOTH MOUNTAIN

The veins located on Mammoth Mountain by the early prospectors are thought to be extensions of the Amethyst fault system that breaks into a network of faults southeast of the Bachelor and Commodore Mines.[65] Much time and effort was spent on prospecting and exploring the veins, but no commercial ore bodies were ever found, even though some mineralization of commercial quality was seen as float on the surface or underground. The most extensive exploration occurred in the Mammoth, Nancy Hanks, Mother, and Eclat properties. One important reason that extensive prospecting on Mammoth Mountain occurred was the theory proposed in the early days of the district that blanket or "flat" veins similar to those at Leadville would be found. Some early geologists felt that the sediments formed in "Ancient Lake Creede" were an extension of the sedimentary strata that hosted ore deposits at Leadville. Unfortunately, this theory was not true. *The Creede Candle*'s inaugural issue of January 7, 1892, ran the following story:

> *"Back from the gulch on this mountain [Mammoth Mountain] there is an immense ledge of lime that seems to dip into the Mammoth. On this Herman Kruger is working on a shaft. He has sunk 46 feet through a carbonate of iron and expects to find blue lime beneath it. He is from Leadville and is of the opinion that the formation is similar to that of the great carbonate camp."*

Several of the early discoverers of Creede Camp located claims on Mammoth Mountain. These included N.C. Creede, who located the Mammoth claim; Charles Nelson, the Emily and Centaur claims; and S.D. Coffin, the Mary Anderson, Nancy Hanks, and other claims.[66] According to *The Creede Candle*, March 17, 1892, The King Solomon Mining Company was incorporated by N.C. Creede and

others and capitalized for $2,000,000. The company owned the Eclat
and King Solomon Mines. The directors included Creede (as president); S.K. Hooper, general passenger agent for D&RG Railroad; E.E.
Humphrey, surveyor general for Colorado: and George W. Robinson,
president of First National Bank of Pueblo, who was treasurer of the
company. *The Engineering and Mining Journal* reported on July 2,
1892, that assays of 230 ounces of silver per ton had been made, but
not enough ore to develop a mine was found.

SOLOMON-HOLY MOSES VEIN SYSTEM

The apex of the Solomon-Holy Moses Vein was first discovered on
what was to be the Holy Moses claim in August 1889 — the discovery that started the rush to Creede Camp. However, the
Solomon-Holy Moses Vein was quickly overshadowed by discoveries on the Amethyst Vein. The Solomon-Holy Moses Vein System
outcropped on the steep and, in some places, nearly vertical slopes
of Campbell Mountain on the west side of East Willow Creek
Canyon to the north and on Mammoth Mountain to the south. Due
to the precipitous topography, the early mines were generally developed through adits (tunnels at Creede) driven into the sides of the
mountains, not through shafts as used on the Amethyst Vein System.
This, of course, eliminated most of the water drainage problems, at
least for the early mines. The ore found in the Solomon-Holy Moses

Stock Certificate — The King Solomon Mining and
Milling Company

Courtesy of Dave Bunk

Vein System differed from that of the Amethyst Vein. Although some very rich silver ore was found near the surface and in thin seams, as was the case at the Champion and Mollie S. Mines, the tenor of the ore changed at a very shallow depth to lower-grade sulfide ore containing lead and zinc but little silver or quartz. This created the need to upgrade the ore sent to the smelters at a much earlier date than that at the Amethyst Vein mines. The earliest mills at Creede Camp were built along East Willow Creek to concentrate or "dress" the sulfide ores of the Solomon-Holy Moses Veins. Descriptions of these mills, the Ridge and Solomon Mills, are included in a later chapter. Ownership conflicts were not prevalent along East Willow Creek. Claims to the south of the Holy Moses Mine, excluding the Champion and Mollie S. Mines, were consolidated into the companies who owned and operated the Ridge and Solomon Mills.

The Holy Moses Mine is located on the west side of East Willow Creek about two miles north of Creede at an elevation of 10,500 feet above sea level. The Phoenix is located half a mile north of the Holy Moses. The Ridge Mine is located a half-mile south and the Solomon, three-quarters of a mile south. The Mollie S. and Eunice Mines are located high above East Willow Creek at the base of the cliffs on Mammoth Mountain, about 1.5 miles north of Creede. The Champion Mine is located high in the cliffs of Campbell Mountain across East Willow Creek from the Mollie S. Mine.

HOLY MOSES MINE

Nicholas C. Creede, E.R. Naylor, and G.L. Smith located the Holy Moses claim in August 1889. The discoverers did some development work the summer of 1889. In November, Creede built himself a cabin at a point on Nelson Gulch and spent the winter working on the Moses with two men, probably his partners.[67] They recognized that capital and better shipping facilities would be required for development of the mine. Creede and Smith interested David H. Moffat, Sylvester T. Smith, and Captain L.E. Campbell in the property and sold it to them for a sum of $70,000 in October 1890.[68] The Holy Moses Mining Company was organized in October 1890 with Moffat as president, Smith vice-president, and Campbell treasurer and general manager. *The Engineering and Mining Journal* commented on the company in its June 6, 1891, edition:

> *"Holy Moses Mining Company — This company owns*
> *the only producing mine in the Creede district, and it is the*

profits which it has been making in the past two years which has caused the present boom in the district. Ex-Senator T.M. Bowen is the principal stockholder in the company which owns the Holy Moses, Ethel, and Ridge Mines."

On January 7, 1892, *The Creede Candle* described the initial mining operation:

"The purchasers of the Moses at once put about thirty men to work upon the mine and since then has shipped a great quantity of ore [1065 tons with an estimated value of $100,000 by the end of 1892] to market. Soon after its purchase the owners saw the necessity for better facilities for getting the ore to market. With an immense body of pay mineral of comparatively low grade, it was important to reduce handling and operating expenses. Plans were laid for the construction of a wire tramway that would carry the ore to the valley below from where it could be loaded upon cars. Mr. Moffat was president of the Denver & Rio Grande Railroad which had a track to within ten miles of the mine and the easy grade and direct access, combined with the certainty of a regular output of the Holy Moses Mine, itself sufficient to pay operating expenses, made the extension of the track most natural.

"When the railroad was an assured fact, the Holy Moses company which had driven a tunnel about 300 feet on the lead and had stored over ten ton on the dump all but ceased development and turned all the men they could get to work on the building of the tramway.

"The properties of the Moses companies are all under the general management of Capt. Campbell. Harry Allenby is superintendent with James O'Brien and Samuel Billings foremen."

The Denver Republican reported on December 12, 1891, that the aerial tramway was essentially completed to the Holy Moses and, when completed, about twenty carloads of ore a day could be sent down to the railroad. *The Engineering and Mining Journal* commented on March 12, 1892, that three to five carloads of ore are shipped daily over the tramway and the average run of the ore is from $60 to $75 per ton — considerably less production than had been anticipated.

By August of 1891 the Holy Moses has developed 35,000 tons of ore. An estimated 30 per cent of the ore assayed 100 ounces to

125 ounces of silver per ton. The remainder of the reserves averaged $20 to $25 per ton.[69] In July 1891 a five-foot wide pocket of high grade ore was encountered, assaying $975 in silver per ton. Five tons of ore worth $40,000 were shipped to Denver in August.[70] The Ethel claim, located by Creede and Smith in July 1890 on the apex of the vein south of the Holy Moses and owned by the Holy Moses Mining Company, had 6,000 tons on the dump awaiting shipment and employed about twenty men underground in December 1891.[71]

The Engineering and Mining Journal reported on November 12, 1892, that a five-foot vein of good ore with an eighteen-inch streak said to run $1,000 a ton was found in the Holy Moses. Unfortunately, the good luck did not hold and shortly thereafter the high-grade oxidized silver ore was exhausted. Meeves and Darnell,[72] in their report on the Creede Mining District, determined that the rich ore came from a small ore body less than 100 feet in depth, 250 feet in length, and having a width of six feet.

The Holy Moses Mining Company built an office in Creede where General Manager Campbell made his headquarters for directing the company's operations, assisted by Van Fleet as bookkeeper; L.D. Sharp, time and store keeper; and O.A. Songer, assayer.[73] The office burned down in November 1892.

On January 28, 1892, *The Creede Candle* reported a rumor that D.H. Moffat had sold his interest in the Holy Moses for $1,000,000. At some point in time, the Holy Moses Mining Company was taken over by the Amethyst Mining Company. The Holy Moses was sold to Senator Charles H. Abbott of Salida, probably on December 31, 1892.[74]

The Holy Moses was an intermittent shipper in 1892 and little development work was done at the mine. The Holy Moses was idle

Office and Commissary of the Holy Moses Mine — 1892

Courtesy of the Denver Public Library Western History Collection

in 1893 and 1894 and was leased to others in 1895. Development and some production began again in 1895, as reported in *The Engineering and Mining Journal*:

February 23, 1895:
"*Holy Moses — This mine, at Creede, has recently been leased, and the shaft will be sunk 100 ft. to develop new ground. This mine, which was the original discovery in the camp, is now owned by C.H. Abbott & Co., into whose hands it came after D.H. Moffat surrendered his bond upon it. Being a silver proposition it has been idle for two years, but the impetus to development caused by the veins in other parts of the camp turned into lead and gold in their lower levels has decided a renewal of operations upon it. Possession of the cable train put on the property by its former lessees is being contested in the courts.*"

April 6, 1895:
"*The operators on the Holy Moses have reached a good ore body in the second level, 90 ft. below the surface, after driving but 5 ft. on from the breast where the company stopped when they gave up their lease two years ago. Two carloads were shipped last week.*"

December 14, 1895, Mineral County:
"*Holy Moses — The lessees of this mine have already advertised for bids to drive a 1,100 ft. tunnel to cut the vein on the property.*"

October 3, 1896:
"*Holy Moses Tunnel — It is reported that Senator Abbott has struck a 6-ft. vein in this tunnel after driving within 25 ft. of the distance of 1,100 ft., which the survey at the outset indicated would have to be driven.*"

Evidently little ore was found in the vein where it was intersected by the Holy Moses Tunnel. The mine was shut down in 1897 until October of 1898, when a crew was put to work cleaning out the mine in preparation to resume mining operations,[75] operations continued into 1899.

PHOENIX MINE
C.F. Nelson and N.C. Creede located the Phoenix claim jointly on October 2, 1890, while cutting a trail to get some horses up for a

hunting trip. In November, Nelson built himself a cabin at a point on Nelson Gulch and spent the winter sinking a shaft on the Phoenix with the help of one assistant.[76] The shaft ultimately was sunk 120 feet.[77] No ore of any consequence was found. *The Mining Reporter* commented on October 26, 1899, that W.G. Boyle & Company leased the Phoenix and that a contract had been let to re-timber the shaft and give the property a thorough cleaning. However, commercial mining at the Phoenix had to wait for another half century.

RIDGE MINE

Charles F. Nelson located the Ridge claim in August 1890. Ex-Senator Thomas M. Bowen purchased Ridge, Solomon, Hiram, Mexico, and other properties of Mr. Nelson for $21,000.[78] Although not mentioned in the press of the day, Bowen must have placed the Ridge claim with the Holy Moses Mining Company while he was a principal stockholder in 1891 and then regained control before selling it and other claims. *The Creede Candle* issue of January 7, 1892, stated:

> *"Ex-Senator Thomas M. Bowen purchased the Ridge and Solomon of C.F. Nelson and got a hold of a large group comprising the Mexico, Hiram, Senator Farwell, General Mahon, and the Ridge Nos. 2 and 3. After holding them a few months, developing them to some extent, and making important strikes in the Ridge and Solomon, he sold the group for a good sum to George Nichol [Nickle] and others, who added to it the purchase of the St. Peter, Wandering Jew, Rio Grande, Maggie, and Mammoth No. 2. Considerable development is not going on with occasional shipments. The Ethel lays in the center of this group."*

The Holy Moses Mining Company had owned the St. Peter, etc., group[79] and the Ethel. *The Engineering and Mining Journal*, March 12, 1892, described the Ridge Mine in a front page article about Creede:

> THE ORE DEPOSITS OF CREEDE, COLO.
> Written for The Engineering and Mining Journal *by*
> Thos. R. MacMechen, M.E.
> *"The Ridge and Ethel [Vein] is the only parallel vein on Campbell Mountain so far known. This group was sold by ex-United States Senator Thomas M. Bowen, of Colorado, to George Nichol [Nickle] and others. The*

Ethel occupies the center of the group and extensive explorations are being made upon its length. The vein's geology does not differ materially from that of the Holy Moses. The ore is a highly crystallized galena associated with considerable waxy blende [sphalerite or zinc sulfide]. Its average assay is about 75 percent lead and 25 ozs. silver per ton. Two or three cars are shipped daily."

The Creedmoor Mining Company was incorporated on October 7, 1892, by Senator Thomas Bowen, Lou Mercer, and George D. Nickel.[80] The company built the first concentrating mill in the Creede district at the Ridge Mine in 1893. By October 1893 the mine and mill had proved so successful that more ore was being developed in the mine, and the mill's capacity was increased.[81]

The repeal of the Sherman Silver Act did not affect the Ridge as seriously as it did the other mines dependent primarily on silver. The December 16, 1893, issue of *The Engineering and Mining Journal* gave this report:

"Ridge — Advices from Creede state that interest in the claims on Campbell Mountain was re-awakened last week by late developments in the Ridge, and there is now considerable demand for claims on the lead belt. Having been driven from work on the upraise to the right, the Ridge owners early in the week returned to the left drift, in which the first strike was made early in the summer, and from which the great flow of ore at first occurred. This had been timbered up during the attempt to work the vein through the upraise, but in this the lead widened out to 16 ft. and it was no longer possible to catch up the ore flow with the timbers, so the left drift was returned to the timbers knocked out and the ore allowed to flow again into the tunnel. The ore which comes from this portion of the mine is reported to be richer than that in the right drift and upraise, it running, it is said, from 300 to 3,000 oz. in silver, about 80 percent lead and a considerable quantity of gold. Although not to be reckoned as a new strike, since quantities of the high-grade were found in the flow and the presence of it in the mine has been known, it was not thought to be in any considerable quantity until the new development was started. As it is now, the Ridge promises to prove not only the largest vein yet opened in

the camp, but the richest as well, and this aside from its lead and zinc product. The new found high-grade ore will be shipped to the smelter as it comes from the mine, while the mill is kept steadily at work day and night concentrating the low-grade and separating the lead from the zinc. A car of zinc concentrates was shipped to Joplin, Mo. during the week."

The Creede district was one of the first in Colorado to produce zinc concentrates. Colorado's zinc production was not of consequence until 1902.[82] The Ridge Mine and Mill ran steadily during 1894 and in March, 1895, the mill was shut down and its capacity nearly doubled in order to treat increased production from the mine.[83] The Creedmore Mining Company that had been organized to mine and mill ore from the Ridge group of claims failed in July 1895. George D. Nickel, one of the original organizers of the company in 1892, was appointed receiver of the company.[84] Lessees of the Ridge property were reported to have struck a three-foot vein of ore running seventy per cent lead in 1898 and, in July of that year, thirty men were at work at the Ridge.[85] By September of 1899, the mine and mill were making shipments of 1,000 tons of lead and zinc concentrates per month.[86]

SOLOMON MINE

Charles F. Nelson located the Solomon claim in May 1890.[87] Ex-Senator Thomas M. Bowen purchased the Solomon claim from Nelson along with other claims. *The Creede Candle* carried a story in its January 7, 1892, issue about the Solomon:

"The Solomon has recently attracted attention because of the strike made last month. This was one of Nelson's first locations. It was tied up the greater part of the year under bond to Senator Bowen and after he allowed it to lapse, H.C. Rowley and George Dewey took hold of the property, did some work, and disclosed the Moses lead filled with ore of both the quartz and galena varieties. A test shipment was made and the returns being satisfactory, a tunnel was started to cut the vein at greater depth and furnish better shipping facilities."

Not much mining activity took place at the Solomon for several years after Rowley and Dewey purchased the property. *The Engineering and Mining Journal* reported on March 30, 1895, that:

"Harry Allenby, lessee on the Solomon, reports the tunnel is now in 30 ft. on the vein with a 2 fi foot pay streak. A shipment will be made in the near future. The ore carried from 15 to 60 percent lead and is increasing in value. Mr. Allenby is negotiating with Leadville parties to secure the erection of a mill at the mine." Additionally, *The Engineering and Mining Journal* carried the following article on August 31, 1895:

> *"Creede Leasing and Milling Company — This company will erect a concentrator on the Solomon mining claim for the purpose of treating the larger quantity of low grade ore. It is expected that the mill will be completed in 7 weeks, and will be able to treat 75 to 100 tons per day, under the superintendency of Harry Allenby."*

The Creede Leasing and Milling Company's Solomon mill, having a capacity of seventy-five tons of crude ore per day, began successful operations mid-November 1895.[88] In the spring of 1898, the Solomon and Ethel were leased to Charles H. Abbott of Chaffee County and H.C. Rowley of Creede, who placed both properties back into operation after making arrangements with the Solomon mill to treat their ore.[89] The Ethel and Solomon veins are adjoining branches of the Solomon-Holy Moses Vein System,[90] and the consolidation of both claims resulted in more efficient mine development and production in the following years.

As previously stated, the Ethel was owned by the Holy Moses Mining Company probably until December 1892. Shipments from the Ethel were about 450 tons up to March 1, 1892.[91] *The Engineering and Mining Journal* reported on August 25, 1894, that: "The lessees on the Ethel are shipping a car of lead ore this week from their new opening, and it will return about 4 oz. gold, 10 to 20 oz. silver and 60 percent lead to the ton."

MOLLIE S. AND EUNICE MINES

The Engineering and Mining Journal, April 23, 1892, described the organization of the Eunice Mining Company:

> *"A meeting of the stockholders of this company, operating at Creede [and] recently capitalized at $1,000,000, was held at Denver on the 14th inst. The following directors were elected: H.R. Henderson of Creede; W.H. Leves, Frank F. Mead, Frederick Robinson, Jr., W.R. Crowell of Denver; Ernest Riall, of Omaha; and Francis V. King of*

Mollie S. Mine from Campbell Mountain — June 2001

Photo by the Author

New York City. The property of the company lies on Mammoth Mountain, and assays taken from the ore body are said to run well in silver and gold. The shifts are being worked."

The Mollie S. Mine is high on the west slope of Mammoth Mountain, about 1.75 miles northeast of Creede at an elevation of 10,400 feet. The Eunice Mine is directly 125 feet south of the Mollie S. Mine. The October 28, 1893, issue of *The Engineering and Mining Journal* reported that the sale of the Mollie S. to David H. Moffat was not consummated as expected. The Mollie S. and Eunice Mines were not operating in 1894 and employed only six miners in 1898.[92]

The silver minerals occurred in narrow seams up to two inches thick that were dispersed through barren rock at two- to three-foot intervals. Even though the ore in the seams was very rich, considerable barren rock had to be mined along with the high-grade ore. The ore was hand sorted at the mine to eliminate the barren rock. The upgraded ore was packed by horses down the very steep and dangerous switchback trail from the mine to East Willow Creek, a vertical distance of about 1,200 feet. The miners had to hike from their homes in Creede to the mine. A day's work before work started! Serious mining at these mines did not begin until after the turn of the century, when a tramway was built to deliver ore to a station on the wagon road on East Willow Creek from the mine.

Service Cabin at
the Mollie S. Mine
— June, 2001
Photo by the Author

CHAMPION MINE

The Creede Candle's Mining Edition of Saturday, January 1, 1927, gave this description of the mine that is located about 1.75 miles north of Creede at an elevation of about 10,500 feet on the precipitous east slope of Campbell Mountain:

> *"The Champion Mine was the first located by J.W. White in 1892, in a crag in the rocks nearly 2000 feet above the level of the city of Creede. Owing to the difficulty in reaching it, development was naturally slow altho [sic] the vein showed a rich ore which in places assayed as high as 2000 ounces or more per ton.*
>
> *"The method by which Mr. White operated the mine was the sinking of a shaft from the top of the cliff to the vein and raising the ore to the surface in buckets by the use of a horse winch. After getting it to the surface it had to be conveyed to market on pack animals over a road a part of which was made over a rock slide along the side of the mountain where a mis-step would mean almost certain death to either man or beast, and it was nearly four miles to town by the shortest route over which it was possible to make the 2000 foot descent.*
>
> *"Under such a handicap, Mr. White, with limited capital, was unable to make much progress, so he leased it to a man by the name of Sisty who organized the Kentucky Belle Mining Co., and it was they who mined and shipped the first real high grade ore."*

The organization of the Kentucky Belle Mining Company was described in *The Engineering and Mining Journal* of November 3, 1894:

"This company has been organized with the following officers: S.W. Bradford, of Brookville, Ky., president; Thornton H. Thomas, of Creede, vice-president; W.H.R. Slate, of Colorado Springs, secretary; F.F. Horn, of Colorado Springs, treasurer; and H.J. Sisty, manager. The company has taken bonds on the Champion and Punxsutawney lodes at Creede, and intends to work them actively. Later this mine together with three properties in the same vicinity, became the property of the Champion Mining Company."

By the end of 1894, the Kentucky Belle Mining Company had transported four carloads of ore down the trail to the railroad by pack animals. The ore averaged 200 ounces of silver per ton.[93] By 1895, the company evidently had not been doing well as suggested by *The Engineering and Mining Journal* article in the March 30, 1895 issue:

"Kentucky Belle Extension Mining Company — The president of this company, who has for the past three weeks been arranging the financial matters of the company so as to pay off the men, has completed all arrangements and work will be resumed with a full force of men. The mine recently shipped a car of high grade ore and enough money was received from its sale to pay off all the men and start work again. The mine closed down about a month ago."

On June 15, 1895, *The Engineering and Mining Journal* reported that: "Work will be at once commenced on both the

Trail to the Champion Mine — September 2001
Photo by the Author

Kentucky Belle and Kentucky Belle Extension Company at Creede and a large force of men will be employed." However, there is no record of production from the Champion Mine until 1901.

ALPHA-CORSAIR VEIN SYSTEM

The Creede Candle described the early history of mining on the Alpha-Corsair Vein System in its January 6, 1893, issue:

> *"Dick Irwin's discoveries in 1872 first attracted attention to Sunnyside [a small camp about two miles west of Creede].*[94] *The district had been all but abandoned when Creede discovered the Holy Moses. When the rush for mines broke out the first of the year, Sunnyside came into notice. There had been a large amount of work done there in the past year. The most important result of it has been the opening of the Yellow Jacket Mine, which has from the first been a good property and is now beginning to be looked upon as a great one. Since A.S. Crawford took hold of it last September it has been a steady shipper and now has a four-foot body of high grade ore. Mr. Irwin came back to camp a short time since and is preparing to work the Alpha, one of his patented properties, in which he has considerable low grade ore. The Kreutzer Sonata is a stocked property that promises well, and Dr. Locke's Golden Buttes locations have produced some high grade ore. The hills along Rat and Miners Creeks are well-seamed with thin veins of rich mineral."*

YELLOW JACKET MINE

The Yellow Jacket claim's date of discovery and its discoverer are not known. The first car of ore from the Yellow Jacket Mine was shipped by July 1, 1892.[95] A *Denver Republican* article dated July 17, 1892, reported that: "Good progress is being made in this district. The Yellow Jacket bondholders are waiting for returns from the first car of ore sent out and doing a little work in the meantime." The Yellow Jacket shipped ten cars of ore in 1892, produced some ore in 1893, and was working in 1894.[96] *The Creede Candle*'s Mining Edition, January 1, 1927, had this to say:

> *"The Yellow Jacket Mine is one of the oldest producers of high grade silver ore in the county but has been closed down for a number of years, and the shaft, which is 200 feet deep, has filled with water."*

Yellow Jacket Mine — Sunnyside
Al Birdsey Collection, Courtesy of the Creede Historical Society

ALPHA AND CORSAIR MINES

John C. MacKenzie and H.M. Bennett located the Alpha claim on the Alpha-Corsair Vein System on April 24, 1883, at a point just above the confluence of Rat and Miners Creeks.[97] The claim was sold to Richard S. and J.N.H. Irwin in 1885. The Irwins actively prospected in the Sunnyside area and mined their claims until 1890. John C. MacKenzie and Richard Irwin's biographies are included in Chapter One as two of the discoverers of Creede Camp. Mining was not successful because of inefficient methods of concentrating the ore and the high cost of transportation, and it had been all but abandoned when Creede located the Holy Moses Mine. This, of course, renewed interest in the existing mines at Sunnyside and prospecting for new ones. Richard Irwin had left Sunnyside for British Columbia and then Cripple Creek, Colorado, when his mining operation proved unsuccessful. He returned to Sunnyside, probably in 1893, to reopen the Alpha. The June 1893 shipments of ore from Creede Camp included one car from the Alpha Mine.[98]

The January 19, 1894 *The Creede Candle* carried the story that Richard Irwin and his family would spend the winter in Colorado Springs and that he would do some mining at Cripple Creek. The June 2, 1894, issue of *The Engineering and Mining Journal* had this report on the Alpha Mine:

> "*A force of men at this mine has been doubled. The shifts are at work on the Alpha tunnel, which will cut the Alpha ore chute, one shift on a new tunnel to cut the*

Diamond I Vein, and one shift on the ore shaft on top of the hill. From the latter workings the men are now sacking the 50th carload of ore taken out since last December. Returns from the last car show a profit of $254."

The Alpha was closed in 1895. It was reopened by the Creede Cooperative Mining Company in 1899.[99] Irwin sold the Alpha to Motz & Peterson.[100]

Thomas A. Steven and James C. Ratté[101] stated in 1965 that: "Approximately one-half million dollars worth of metal, predominately silver, was produced from the Alpha-Corsair Vein prior to 1904. Most of this came from the Corsair Mine, and most probably was produced during the 1890s. "The one reference to the Corsair Mine prior to 1900 was found in the August 31, 1895, *Engineering and Mining Journal* that stated: "The Corsair Tunnel has resumed work, and in its breast is a strong lead, which indicates the near presence of a good ore body."

The three mines, the Yellow Jacket, Alpha, and Corsair, exploited the same ore body and were interconnected by mine workings. Separate companies mined the Alpha and Corsair but both were on the same ore body,[102] which was developed through three tunnels — two on the Alpha and one on the Corsair. The Corsair Tunnel intersected the Alpha-Corsair vein near the Yellow Jacket shaft.

KREUTZER SONATA MINE
John G. Canfield[103] described the Kreutzer Sonata in his book, *Mines and Mining Men of Colorado*:

"The Kreutzer Sonata Consolidated Mining Company was incorporated under the laws of the state of Colorado in March 1892, with Dr. Loui Weiss as President and General Manager, ex-Secretary of State James Rice, Vice-President, and Hon. D.O. House, Secretary. The capital stock is $1,000,000 in shares of $1 each. The property of the company consists of the following claims: Kreutzer Sonata, Emma, Xenia, Postmaster, Barrigan, Creedemore, Amended No. 1, Amended No. 2, and Amended No. 3. The Kreutzer Sonata was located in 1889 by J.C. Mackenzie and Richard Irwin, and re-located in 1891 by John Cleghorn Jr., S.E. Thomas, John Ewing Jr., and Dr. Loui Weiss, who, in order to be certain of getting all of the vein, located nine claims from the foot of the hill on one side across the top to the foot of the hill on the other side, three

abreast. The property is located between Miners and Rat Creeks on the continuation of the Alpha and Yellow Jacket vein. The ore is a chloride and sulphuret, and the first that was taken out, when treated, yielded a return of $250 to the ton. The development consists of a cross-cut tunnel, at present over 235 feet into the hill, which will, if continued, cut the Yellow Jacket vein at a depth of 300 feet. The surface improvements consist of a cook and bunk house, 22 x 45 feet; an ore bin, 24 x 40 feet, with an ore house and shop same size over it. The property is so situated on Miners Creek that an excellent water power can be had when needed at little expense to drive drills, air compressors, etc. The company is now patenting its property, which has been surveyed and approved by the surveyor general of the state. When this has been done, systematic development will be pushed with vigor, and the undoubtedly great possibilities of the property realized. There is little room to doubt, judging from the character of the ore taken out already, and from its location between the Yellow Jacket and Alpha on one side (both shipping mines), and the Maid of Sunnyside and Wisconsin Boy (properties which both show up remarkably well) on the other, the Kreutzer Sonata will at no distant day be reckoned one among the many great producers of the new mining camp.

Dr. Loui Weiss, the president and general manager of the above company, can make a success of it if anyone can, and his well-known business talents and executive skills have of late been directed toward putting the affairs of the Kreutzer Sonata in good shape. Dr. Weiss was born in Milwaukee, Wisconsin, July 20, 1854. He has been engaged in business and in the practice of his profession in Colorado for some years, but never embarked upon the fascinating pursuit of mining until 1891. He did, indeed, at one time, own a number of prospects at Summitville, Colorado but never gave them any of his personal attention. In 1891, in connection with John Cleghorn, Jr., S.A. Thomas, and John Ewing, Jr., he re-located the nine claims, which today constitute the property of the Kreutzer Sonata Consolidated Mining Company, to which he has since devoted a large portion of his time. In addition to the above properties, Dr. Weiss is at present interested in the Crown Point and

Highline, both at Creede, and the Black Diamond and Diamond Bar, at Camero. Dr. Weiss is a physician of high standing in his profession, and in addition to his large private practice, also fills the important post of resident surgeon of the Denver & Rio Grande Railroad. But not only is he a successful physician and mine manager; Dr. Weiss is the head and front of one of the most extensive drug concerns in the state, the Weiss-Chapman Drug Company, which has establishments located at Del Norte, Monte Vista, and Creede, and does a large business in painters' and assayers' supplies as well as in drugs and stationery."

Dr. Weiss also owned the Good Hope Mine at Vulcan near Gunnison, Colorado.[104] The Good Hope is the locality where several extremely rare copper telluride minerals were first found — among them weissite, named for Dr. Weiss.

The Denver Republican, July 17, 1892, reported that: "The Kreutzer Sonata folks are getting ready to do a great deal of work." The mine had made great progress by the end of 1892.[105] *The Engineering and Mining Journal* made the following reports:

October 28, 1893:
"In the Sunnyside district the work on the Kreutzer Sonata group is encouraging. Great blocks of ore carrying masses of wire silver are being taken out, and it is claimed that the pay grade is of sufficient volume to commence outputting; this will be done."

March 3, 1894:
"Sunnyside — At this camp considerable prospecting is going on. The Kruetzer Sonata group is being worked through two tunnels."

The shaft was drained into the new lower tunnel, thus permitting sinking on the ore body to resume and an attempt was made to intersect a rich sulfide vein carrying native wire silver that had been encountered in the top tunnel. Work was discontinued at the Kreutzer Sonata Mine by August 1894. The mine had some high-grade ore but not in shipping quantities.[106]

THE CREEDE FORMATION

As described in the Prologue, mineralized waters were discharged from the Amethyst fault zone into the Creede Formation through an ancient stream channel filled with sedimentary rock. These mineralized waters deposited economic minerals in the sediments of the Creede Formation.

The 400 Acre Consolidated Diamond Drill Mining Company's 1892 prospectus[107] describes the formation that they proposed to prospect by diamond drilling: "The ore bodies occur between strata of lime, porphyry, and trachyte and consist of quartz carrying sulphide of silver, iron, manganese, and native silver." In other words, the company was convinced, like many others at the time, that the veins were "flat" and on the "contact" between the lime and the porphyry, like those at Leadville. Many of the company's claims were west of the Amethyst Vein extending to Sunnyside and Shallow Creek over the Creede Formation. *The Denver Republican*, July 17, 1892, reported that the 400 Acre Company would be prepared to put three diamond drills to work about the first of August on the company's forty or fifty claims. The company made the claim that they could drill twenty-five feet in a twenty-four-hour day. Evidently their diamond drill prospecting did not find any commercial ore bodies in the Creede Formation. Their claims along the apex of the Amethyst Vein were included in the United Mines consolidation.

MONON HILL MINES

The Monon claim is located on the west slope of Monon Hill, a short distance east of Sunnyside. The silver ore was disseminated throughout the lower part of the Creede Formation, where it contacted a buried hill of volcanic rock.[108]

The Engineering and Mining Journal reported on March 3, 1894, that the Monon was being worked under a contract and on June 2, 1894, carried the following news item:.

> "*Creede Quintette Mining Company — At a meeting of this company the following officers were elected for the ensuing year: J.F. Benedict, President; F.M. Varney, Vice-President; Curtis J. Smith, Secretary; Thorton H. Thomas, Treasurer. These, with C.D. Hayt, of Denver, constitute the Board of Directors. The company owns the Monon group at Sunnyside, and will do considerable work on the property this summer.*"

The Quintette Mining Company leased their property on Monon Hill, the Monon and the adjacent Wicklow claims, to John

Knodel in 1895. The Wicklow claim had a twenty-foot vein of ore worth $5 a ton at the dump.[109] There is no evidence of any further mining at Monon Hill until 1901.

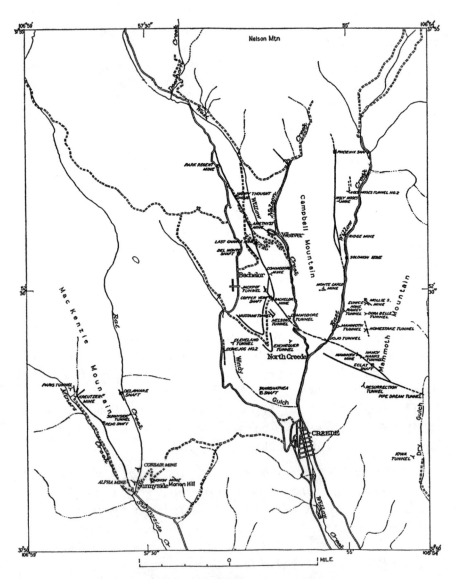

Map Showing Early Mines and Veins — Creede Mining District, Colorado

Based on Plate 26, U.S.G.S. Bulletin 811-B, 1929.

CHAPTER 9

THE NELSON-WOOSTER-HUMPHREYS TUNNEL TO THE RESCUE 1892 - 1918

THE NELSON-WOOSTER-HUMPHREYS TUNNEL, one of the greatest of Colorado's tunnel undertakings and Creede Camp's salvation, was the result of Charles F. Nelson's foresight to provide the means to overcome the economically prohibitive costs of pumping water and hoisting ore to the surface through shafts that faced the mines along the Amethyst Vein. The Nelson Tunnel was driven 2,100 feet northwest from the portal. The Wooster Tunnel branched from the Nelson Tunnel at 1,400 feet from the portal and was driven northerly a distance of about 6,900 feet on or along the Amethyst Vein, to the north end line of the Amethyst Mine. The Humphreys Tunnel was a 3,900-foot extension of the Nelson-Wooster Tunnel through the Happy Thought Mine to the White Star and Park Regent Mines. The tunnel intersected the Last Chance, Amethyst, Happy Thought, and Park Regent Shafts at a depth of 1,500 below the apex of the Amethyst vein.

As the bonanza ores near the surface were exhausted and the mines were deepened below the water table, pumping to drain the mines as well as hoisting ore through shafts to the surface became serious economic problems. The ruggedness of the topography at Creede Camp made the use of tunnels to solve drainage, ore haulage, and ventilation problems and provide access to the ore bodies the best solution. Two long tunnels were driven. The Commodore No. 5 Tunnel served only one mine — the Commodore — and was described in Chapter Eight. The Nelson-Wooster-Humphreys Tunnel furnished a down-grade outlet for ore from the rest of the mines along the Amethyst Vein to the railroad and eliminated the need for hoisting machinery, pumps, and wagon conveyance for fuel and ore transportation. It also allowed the merger of the scattered towns in Creede Camp into the City of Creede, where most of the miners and families lived.

Charles F. Nelson located the Nelson Tunnel and several adjacent claims during the summer of 1891.[1] The Nelson Tunnel and Mining Company was incorporated in 1892. The incorporators were C.F. Nelson, A.W. Brownell, J.P. Wallace, B.F. Kelly, W.J. Swift, E.N. Maynard, and C.A. Miller. The company was capitalized for $1 million.[2] Nelson retained stock in the Nelson Tunnel and Mining Company until his death on November 3, 1919, in Stockholm, Sweden.[3] He certainly had faith in his idea!

The objective of the company was to run a tunnel at an elevation of 9,175 feet above sea level northwest from West Willow Creek, below the Bachelor Mine at Bachelor — a distance of 3,000 feet and at a depth of 1,000 to 1,100 feet — to drain the mines lying higher than this level, and also to strike the veins of these mines at greater depth.[4] Another purpose of the tunnel was to intersect at depth additional veins that outcropped high on Bachelor Mountain.[5]

Stock Certificate — The Nelson Tunnel and Mining Company
Courtesy of Dave Bunk

Officers of the company were A.W. Brownell, president; C.F. Nelson, vice-president; B.F. Kelly, secretary; J.P. Wallace, treasurer; W.J. Swift, manager; E.N. Magner, superintendent; C.A. Miller, engineer; and M. S. Beal, attorney.[6]

The biographies of Magner and Beal were included in *Mines and Mining Men of Colorado*. Magner's biography includes a description of the objectives of the Nelson Tunnel project.[7]

> "*Edward N. Magner,* general manager of the Nelson Tunnel Company of Creede, is a native of Illinois, born in the town of Paris, in June 1859. The quietude of his native place gave splendid opportunities for him to cultivate an innate studious nature, and between his school hours he spent many moments in perusing with profit scientific works, principally those treating on steam and electricity, besides giving some attention to mineralogy and geology, so that in 1877, when in his nineteenth year and when he reached Colorado, he was intelligently equipped to follow the occupation of prospecting and mining.
>
> "He first visited Rosita and Silver Cliff, and when in 1878 the news of rich finds in California Gulch were heralded across the state, he went with the throng of treasure seekers to that locality. There he located the Sunnyside lode claim and made his first mining deal, banking $7,000 from the sale of this prospect lode. From Leadville, he went to Aspen, but more from a disposition to roam rather than for a discredit to the mineral resources of that part of Colorado. He left there and went down into New and old Mexico, and spent seven years between the two. For several years he was employed as manager by the Black Knight Silver Company, whose properties were located in southwestern New Mexico near Chloride, and he also acquired some good properties himself, among them the Cashier and Small Hopes, both of which are still shipping mines, and Mr. Magner still increases his bank account by dividends from them.
>
> "Four or five years of travel over the entire west brought him to Creede in February 1892. Turning his attention first to prospecting, in a short time he became interested with the promoters of the proposition to tunnel through Bachelor Mountain. All connected with the enterprise were comparative strangers at the time, Mr. Magner

*especially not knowing any of them. But, as all were intel-
ligent mining men, thoroughly conversant with its various
branches, it did not take them long to decide that Mr.
Magner would be the right man in the right place as general
manager of the mechanical end of a corporation, should
such be formed.*

*"The condition of affairs at that time as to the mineral
resources of Bachelor Mountain, strongly indicative by
the small amount of development work that the rich ore
body was obtainable only at great depth, suggested to this
coterie of mining men that a tunnel run into the mountain
3,000 feet in a [northwesterly] direction, gaining at its
greatest dept 1,400 feet, would, by the company acting as
a common carrier, bring in royalties from hauling from
the various drifts and stopes and from drainage, that
would allot handsome dividends to the investors. Besides
acting as common carriers for the producers, the company
would be entitled to all minerals 250 feet each side of their
center line and other location which may be made by then
so as to aggregate 1,500 feet each side of the center line
where there would be no interferences by prior location.*

*"A careful study of the work going on on the surface,
as well as an equally careful study of the formation of the
mountain, finally decided the projectors to locate a tunnel
site, starting at the base of a cliff on West Willow Creek,
a half mile west of the town of Creede, and under the
Manhattan, Bachelor, Senora, Mustang, and German
National lode claims, all which were at that time making
showing of good, strong veins dipping in a direction so as
to bring them through and across the lines of the tunnel.
A company was formed, styled the Nelson Tunnel
Company, and Mr. Magner was selected as manager.*

*"In February last the annual meeting of the stock-
holders endorsed the stewardship of Mr. Magner by re-
electing him to his old position. The promoters of the
Amethyst Electric Power and Light Company, having
learned of Mr. Magner's ability as an electrician, employed
him to look after their interests, and in consequence there
is not a word of complaint from patrons — on the contrary, naught but commendation for the excellent service
rendered by the company."*

"Marius Samuel Beal, lawyer, was born in Vevey, Switzerland County, Indiana, March 7, 1848. The father of the subject of this sketch was a lawyer, and lost no time in interesting this son (one of four) in the study of the musty volumes of his library, and thus while Marius was yet a boy. After spending three years at the Northwestern Christian University, at Indianapolis, of which the now famous institution of learning our recent president, Benjamin Harrison, was a patron, Mr. Beal was fully equipped for Life's battle. In 1866 he went to Kansas, settling in Pottawattamie County in 1868, where he practiced his chosen profession, giving special attention to commercial law, and became the agent and attorney for the Kansas Mortgage Company, the National Mortgage, and Debenture Company of Boston, and other financial institutions of like character, handling millions of dollars successfully for his clients, for twenty years making his headquarters at West Moreland. In 1888 Mr. Beal moved to Denver, there to represent the Boston concern and also the Denver Note and Brokerage Company. For some time after this move the money market was devoid of any activity, and Mr. Beal turned his attention to the regular practice of law. In February 1892, having previously made a business arrangement with Messrs. T.J. O'Donnell and W.S. Decker, of the Denver bar, he came to Creede, and soon accumulated an extensive corporation and mining clientage, among them the Nelson Tunnel Company (of which he was secretary), the Ramsey Mammoth Mountain Mining Company, and the Wabash Mining and Milling Company. His careful and judicious management of all business placed in his hands, his quiet yet warm nature, and his wide experience make him a valuable counselor, a fact which is gradually dawning upon many in the community, to the mutual satisfaction of both client and lawyer."

Office poetry existed even in Creede in the 1890s, as shown by this doggerel on a Nelson Tunnel and Mining Company letterhead:[8]

We propose to write a history of a little stock,
And we hope the meter written will never cause a shock
The jingle of the story may be trifle old,
But the truth cannot be twisted, and the story must be told.
And this is how it happened in April '92
That the Nelson Tunnel people before they were
quite through,

Dividing up the stock among the citizens of brains
Amongst the seven wise men, from the east
(by various trains),
Ran across this knotty problem, and they
swear it is complex,
How on earth can seven people get an equal share from six.
Here are Nelson, Kelly, Wallace, Magner, Swift
and Miller too,
Not to forget our president — Brownell, well known to you.
And Little Bertha's chosen, the six to represent,
For now the seven wise men are now waiting, all patient
If she cannot solve the problem of seven into six,
The shares will remain, as the boys say "in a fix."
We do not want them back, and not to spoil the rhyme,
She shall remain our mascot until the end of time.

The Colorado Sun of June 19, 1892, carried the following article on the initial work at the Nelson Tunnel:

"Today completes two month's work on the Nelson
Tunnel enterprise. One half mile of good wagon road has
been graded and built, three substantial bridges put over the
creek, the foundations laid for a 125 horse power air com-
pressor, the mountain cut in 120 feet, the same length of
double track in place, over which three cars are carrying
out the debris, and this distance is also timbered up. So far
all work in the tunnel has been done by hand, which has
necessarily been done, but eighteen inches a day now made
at the cost of $10.25 per foot. With the air compressor,
which has the capacity for working six drills, two drills will
be used and eight feet a day will be made, costing no more
than the total for the present amount of work per day. The
breast of the tunnel now reveals a large body of mineral
stained matter indicative of a strong lead.

"The surveying on this enterprise has been under the
supervision of Secretary Kelly, and experts coincide with his
theory that he is on a line with the best paying veins on
Bachelor Mountain. Calculations also show that the tunnel
will run under the Amethyst Mine 1,300 feet below its pres-
ent workings.

"As the business of the company will be mainly that
of a common carrier, threading the hill with a network of

track, running in all directions to carry ore from the drifts on the various veins they will strike, their cars propelled by electric motors, the entire workings lit up by electricity, the drills operated by compressed air which is derived by capturing the waters of Willow Creek falling over a Pelton wheel — all this combined will not only make it a novel sight, but the consummation of a most brilliant idea for the development of the riches of a section of Creede Camp, and a good paying investment as well.

"All of the ore will be carried out in the small cars of the company to a point 500 feet east, where it is dumped into the cars of the Denver & Rio Grande railway [sic], standing on a spur of their road which they will construct as soon as pay ore is reached in the tunnel. The company takes pleasure in showing visitors to Creede Camp the progress of their work, and a free hack is always at the disposal of those who desire to avail themselves of it."

An article about the Nelson Tunnel appeared in the March 3, 1894, issue of *The Engineering and Mining Journal*:

"The annual stockholders' meeting of this company was held recently and directors for the ensuing year elected as follows: J.O. Notestein, of Wooster, Ohio; J.T. Wallace, C.P. Cummings, F.L. Wallace, and R.B. Wallace of Monte Vista; Dr. J.P. Wallace, of Creede; Dr. J.H. Wallace, of Monmouth, Ill. The directors met and organized by electing Dr. J.P. Wallace, President, General Manager, and Treasurer, and C.P. Cummings, Secretary. Last year the big tunnel of this company, which is expected to prove up the southern extension of the great Bachelor Hill lead, ran 936 ft. of tunnel at a cost of $12.32 a foot. The working is now in the close neighborhood of where the vein is supposed to cross, and a few months' time is expected to make important disclosures in its locality."

The tunnel had reached a length of 1,450 feet by the May 26, 1894, and was being driven at a good rate.[9] The Nelson Tunnel and Mining Company's 1894 annual report[10] indicated that the tunnel had been driven 1,874 feet by the end of 1894. A distance of 874 feet had been driven during the year and the company anticipated intersecting the Amethyst Vein between 1,900 and 2,100 feet. By the end or February 1895, the tunnel had been driven into Bachelor

Mountain a little over 1,900 feet. The Nelson Tunnel was driven about 2,100 feet but did not encounter any ore, a distance considerably short of the proposed 3,000 feet.[11]

Negotiations between the Nelson Tunnel and Mining Company and the mines along the Amethyst Vein, with the exception of the Commodore Mine, were being held in 1895 to determine the royalties the mining companies would pay the tunnel company for transporting their ore.[12] President Wallace was asking for a royalty of $2.50 per ton of ore passing through the tunnel. At the time it cost $1.25 per ton to have the ore shipped over the roads by wagons. Wallace felt his asking price was fair, given that his tunnel would eliminate the costs borne by the mining companies of hoisting ore to the surface and pumping water. The mine owners felt that the tunnel company would make a large profit on its investment at a royalty of $0.50 to $0.75 per tons of ore passing through the tunnel and suggested that they would drive a tunnel themselves, unless the Nelson Company came to terms shortly. The records do not indicate the final result of the negotiations, but the mine owners did not carry out their threat to drive a tunnel themselves.

When A.E. Humphreys invested in the United Mines properties early in 1897, the Nelson Tunnel and Mining Company was bankrupt and unable to proceed with the tunnel. Through Humphreys' efforts, the

The Nelson Tunnel Portal — Date Unknown

Courtesy of Dave Bunk

Wooster Tunnel Company was organized and took over the Nelson Tunnel under a ninety-nine-year lease.[13] The Wooster Tunnel was most likely named after Wooster, Ohio, the original home of the Wallaces.

An August 1897 *Engineering and Mining Journal* carried a story about the tunnel:

> *"Another tunnel enterprise [Wooster Tunnel Company] has been inaugurated by the deal just concluded between the Nelson Tunnel Company and the Humphreys Tunnel Company, of Creede. The Nelson Tunnel Company has been driving into Bachelor Mountain for the past four or five years, and had attained a length of nearly 2,500 ft. in a direction a little north of west when it was decided to take a new departure in the effort to strike the great Bachelor [Amethyst] Vein. A crosscut was commenced at a point 1,400 ft. from the mouth of the tunnel. At about 400 ft. from the point of departure of the crosscut the vein was encountered and the tunnel from that point followed the foot wall of the vein to the present breast of the tunnel, 90 ft. from the main tunnel. The Nelson [Wooster] Tunnel Company has contracts with all the mining companies on the apex of the Bachelor [Amethyst] Vein except the Commodore, for the transportation of their ores through the tunnel up to the south line of the United Mines Company, upon which the Big Kanawha Leasing Company, organized by A.E. Humphreys, has a lease.*
>
> *"Recently, Mr. Humphreys organized the Humphreys Tunnel Company, which proposed to take up the tunnel where the Nelson [Wooster] Company will leave it, at the south end of the United Mines ground, and extend it north through the United Mines and Park Regent Ground. The Humphreys Tunnel Company has also made arrangements with the Nelson [Wooster] Company to take all of the contracts made with the latter by the mines on its line and manage the entire tunnel, paying therefore a very handsome bonus to the Nelson [Wooster] Company.*
>
> *"The Nelson [Wooster] Tunnel Company has made a contract with Mason, Hoge [Hoage] & King, of Frankfort, Ky., to complete its tunnel from the present heading to the south end of the United Mines property. The tunnel is to be a*

*single track, with numerous switches, and will be operated
and lighted by electricity, the motors having a capacity of 20
cars holding 1fi tons each, or a train capacity of 30 tons. The
distance from the present breast of the Nelson Tunnel to the
line of the United Mines Company is 5,600 ft., and the cost
of construction will be in the neighborhood of $150,000. It
is expected that it will be completed in a little more than a
year. The Humphreys Tunnel Company will then add 4,500
ft. to the length of the tunnel, developing the vein on the
United Mines, the White Star, and the Park Regent Mines.*

*"The total length of this great tunnel, from the mouth
to the north end of the Park Regent, will be 15,000 ft., with
900 ft. more running into the mountain in a westerly direction. The tunnel is expected to develop a rich silver-bearing
vein, on which are the Bachelor, New York, Last Chance,
Amethyst, United Mines, White Star, and Park Regent, all
of which will use the tunnel for transportation purposes.
The Commodore, also on the same vein, will have its own
tunnel. The Commodore alone is now producing 300 tons
of ore per day from the great ore chute in that property, and
the tonnage that will pass through the tunnel from the
seven other great properties on the vein when the tunnel is
completed will probably be very heavy."*

The tunnel contracting firm of Mason, Hoage, and King had just
completed the Chicago drainage tunnel and, on the basis of its experience, was given a contract to extend the Nelson Tunnel a distance
of 6,900 feet at $25 per foot. The contractor executed a bond for
$20,000 as a guarantee to complete the contract. In spite of consid-
erable experience in tunnel construction, it did not complete the
contract and forfeited the bond.[14.]

The handsome profits alluded to by *The Engineering and
Mining Journal* did not occur. R.B. Wallace of the Bank of Monte
Vista, Colorado, made this comment to a Nelson Tunnel and
Mining Company stockholder in a letter dated January 15, 1909:[15]

*"In reply [I] would say that over ten years ago the
Nelson Tunnel Company became badly in debt, and it was
leased for a long period of years to a new company, called
the Wooster Tunnel Company for which I am the
Manager. The Wooster Tunnel Company assuming the
debts of the old Nelson Tunnel Company, and paying the*

Nelson Tunnel Company a certain per cent on all the net earnings of the Wooster Tunnel Company. Until these net earnings that go to the Nelson Tunnel Company fully pay off the indebtedness of the Nelson Tunnel Company, assumed by the Wooster Tunnel Company, there will be no dividends."

By November 1898 the tunnel was under the New York and Chance Mines, and drainage was perceptible in several of the mines. Two shifts using machine drills were being used.[16] Salvation for Creede Camp occurred in 1899 when the mines along the Amethyst vein were drained of water as chronicled by *The Engineering and Mining Journal*:

June 10, 1899:
   "Last Chance — The Nelson Tunnel, at Creede, which is now half completed, has tapped the water in the Last Chance workings and the mine will soon be dry and men getting out ore from stopes idle for three years."

October 21, 1899:
   "Amethyst — The Sullivan Drill Company of Chicago has a contract to drain this mine at Creede. Three holes will be bored by diamond drills — one from the Nelson Tunnel to tap the bottom of the Last Chance shaft, another from the 9th level of the Last Chance to the 10th level of the Amethyst, and a third from the 10 fi level of the Last Chance to the 9th level of the Amethyst. The bottom of the Amethyst is 800 ft. above the Nelson Tunnel, and only 40 ft. above the bottom of the Last Chance."

December 9, 1899:
   "Nelson Tunnel — The water in the Amethyst is being lowered at the rate of 15 in. daily. The water in the Last Chance is now below the 11th level and pumping has stopped."

December 23, 1899:
   "Nelson Tunnel — This tunnel at Creede has over 800 ft. to go to strike the ground of the United Mines Company."

The Denver News carried the following stories about the de-watering of the Creede mines:

October 8, 1899:

"The second tapping operation of the unwatering of the Last Chance and Amethyst Mines was carried through without a hitch, and the drills reached the Amethyst ground late last evening. About 610 feet of drilling was necessary to reach the Amethyst and the drills have been going constantly for the last 12 days, water being reached yesterday."

November 24, 1899:

"Last Monday a body of water was encountered in the breast of the Nelson Tunnel that drove the men from their work, says The Creede Candle. *The water was struck by one of the air drills and the pressure was so great that the drill was forced out of the hole, despite all resistance, and the water is now squirting out of every seam in the breast; a stream shooting out from the drill hole a distance of 10 feet with such force that a hole is being washed in the wall of the tunnel. Work had to be suspended as it was impossible for men to stay in the breast, and it has been estimated that 3,000 gallons per minute is coming out of the tunnel, which is lowering the water in the Amethyst at the rate of 15 inches a day and the United Mines about 10 inches. It is now only a question of a few days when these mines will be drained and work resumed in the tunnel."*

By June 1900, the Nelson-Wooster Tunnel was 7,000 feet from the portal and drained the Amethyst, Last Chance, and United Mines. Ore from the Bachelor and Last Chance Mines was being transported through the tunnel.[17] *The Denver Times* reported on May 30, 1901, that the Humphreys extension of the tunnel was about 100 feet from the United Mines' Happy Thought Shaft and work was not progressing very fast. The tunnel face was 1.75 miles from the portal and, in the event of a breakdown, much time was lost in repairing the damage. Considerable difficulty was encountered connecting to the shaft, primarily from water flow.

By March 1902, the Wooster Tunnel Company had contracts, with the Bachelor, Amethyst, Last Chance, New York, and Chance Mines, and United Mines to transport all their ore below the 400-foot levels through the tunnel. It was charging an average of about $1 per ton. Ore was being delivered to the new Humphreys Mill[18] over a track extended about 2,400 feet beyond the portal as a surface tramway to the mill, equipped with mule haulage. The Humphreys Tunnel extension was being driven at the rate of 100 feet per month into the United Mines Company's ground.[19]

Professor Arthur Lakes of the Colorado School of Mines described the Nelson-Wooster-Humphreys Tunnel in an article published in *Mines and Minerals*:[20]

> *"The crosscut and adit tunnel are among the necessities in such a precipitous region; hence, to develop the above properties on a large scale a tunnel at the foot of the precipice was a necessity. Therefore, the Humphreys Tunnel was inaugurated as an extension of the great Nelson Tunnel, which was already on the ground, but terminated with the Amethyst claim. The tunnel from its mouth to the south end of the United Mines, which is 8,850 feet, is known as the Nelson, and from there on north through the United Mines and Park Regent is the Humphreys Tunnel, which, when completed, will be 3,000 feet. At 650 feet it reached the point where connection with the working shaft of the United Mines was made. This tunnel met with many different kinds of ground and had many difficult conditions to contend with. In one place the water gushed from a thousand seams in the breast with such force that it was impossible for the men to remain there, and going back 20 feet, it was bulkheaded and the work was resumed farther in the foot wall. Again, when the vein was cut, the water rushed out with such force from it that hundreds of tons of ore were washed out into the tunnel, and again it had to be bulkheaded to allow the work to progress. At frequent intervals, crosscuts were driven into the vein and the ore sampled. The vein was found of a uniform width of 5 1/2 feet with 4 1/2 feet of ore, averaging $30 per ton. The tunnel reached a point where connections with the shaft were to be made and, after cutting a station, a raise was started to meet the shaft, which was accomplished in about 50 feet, and when the two came together with great exactness. The size of the tunnel is 8 feet wide by 8 feet high, containing a double track, and will be lighted by electricity, and an electric motor will be installed. The work was projected years ago, but only now sees it nearing completion.*

"The Nelson Tunnel, one of the greatest of Colorado's tunnel undertakings, is the great artery tunnel of the district, and lies in the heart of it at the base of the stupendous cliff of Bachelor Mountain. This tunnel is the source of all the great enterprises that are under construction. It is controlled under a 99-year lease by the Wooster Tunnel Co. It was completed to the end line of the Amethyst Mine, 8,850 feet, and from there it has been continued by the Humphreys Tunnel Co. 650 feet further. Three shifts work in the breast, with power drills, and will extend the tunnel on for 3,000 feet. The Wooster Tunnel Co. expended $250,000 in completing the tunnel. The tunnel has been driven on the course of the vein most of its length, the exceptions being where the ore was too loose and caved; then it was driven alongside the vein in the foot wall. This has developed a great distance on the vein, whose uniformity of dip and strike give assurance of its continuance with depth. The Nelson Tunnel derives its revenue from royalties in the transportation of ore through the tunnel and for drainage."

The Creede United Mines achieved the consolidation of the more important companies at Creede with properties north of the Amethyst Mine, including the Humphreys Tunnel and Mining Company. The Humphreys Mill processed ore from the Happy Thought Mine delivered to the mill through the Nelson-Wooster-Humphreys Tunnel during the first half of 1905 and the company had planned an extension of the tunnel.[21] *The Creede Candle* issue of November 2, 1907, had the following:

"We were informed the first of the week that the Humphreys Tunnel would be into the Park Regent ground sometime this month. This means that it is only a question of a short time until there will be a great number of men put to work on that property and the big mine will be able to run steady one shift and probably two. The tests in the mill show that they are able to make a better saving than heretofore and the product in both lead and zinc is of a better grade."

By December 1909, the Humphreys Tunnel was below the Park Regent Shaft and an 800-foot raise from the tunnel to the bottom of the shaft was to be started in the immediate future to provide access for ore delivery to the tunnel and for ventilation.[22] *Mining Science's* issue of November 17, 1910, carried the following article about the tunnel and its value to Creede Camp:

> *"The Humphreys Tunnel, which is the extension of the Nelson-Wooster Tunnel, has been pushed along 1,500 ft. during the past year, and will be carried to the end lines of the Park Regent, Grab Root, and Apex claims. This has been brought about as the result of a compromise after years of litigation. Early in the year a raise of 700 ft. was started to connect with the Park Regent Shaft. In the extension of this tunnel over 1,000 ft. of stoping ground has been blocked out, which carries a first-class grade of milling ore, rich in cube lead*

Nelson Tunnel Surface Tramway to the Humphreys Mill — 1918 (Note the aerial tram buckets overhead)

J. Roy Packard Collection, Courtesy of the Creede Historical Society

> *[galena or lead sulfide], silver, and zinc. Not less than $150,000 has been expended in this stupendous work by the North Creede Mining Co. This bore is now about 2 1/2 miles in length and has cut thousands of tons of high and medium grade ores, not including the upraises."*

Creede Camp could see a rosy future ahead of it in 1912. *The Engineering and Mining Journal* of July 20, 1912, described future plans for the Creede United Mines Company:

> *"The Creede United Mines Co., a strong corporation, is carrying out plans which mean a larger production in about six months' time. The company owns the North*

Creede, Park Regent, Reno, White Star Leasing Co., a 15-year lease on the Wooster tunnel, three miles long, and controls the 300-ton Humphreys Mill at its portal. The tunnel is being equipped with a 60-hp. motor and 32- lb. rails, and will be driven 1000 ft. further, after which sinking, raising, and drifting will be done. It is said that the work planned will take 18 months to accomplish, and will create 10 years of ore reserves. Since September three miles of air line have been added for the mine. Seventy-five men are employed. A.E. Humphreys is at the head and ex-governor C.S. Thomas and W.H. Bryant, of Denver, are prominent members of the company. It is the same story with this company, that is heard from many others; ore left standing by the old workings as unprofitable, is now being mined and milled at a profit; last month $20,000 worth of concentrates were shipped."

The Humphreys Tunnel was ultimately driven 1,100 feet north of the Park Regent Shaft.[23] Emmons and Larsen stated that: "When the Humphreys Tunnel was extended northward from the bottom of the Park Regent Shaft, subterranean gases were encountered in considerable quantity, and it was necessary to employ a large exhaust pump to afford suitable working conditions for the miners." Frank E. Wheeler, who was superintendent for the United Mines in 1900, was quoted by V.V. Clark[24] as saying that the bad air in the Humphreys Tunnel appeared to come out of the hanging wall fissures and was impoverished in the oxygen content to a point where it would not support combustion and created a suffocating sensation to the individual. But such impoverished gases have never yet proved fatal to employees. Mr. Wheeler's opinion was that the cause of this deficiency in oxygen may be due to the air encountering a body of sulphide ore in its passage from surface to the tunnel, the ore readily consuming a part of the oxygen content. Judson Slater Hubbard distinctly remembered Wheeler making the comment that work was stopped in the Humphreys Tunnel because of "bad air" and the lack of ventilation at the end of the tunnel beyond the Park Regent Shaft, and that the ore values were still satisfactory.[25] "Bad air" was destined to be a problem for Creede miners from that time on.

The Nelson-Wooster-Humphreys Tunnel was essentially shut down in 1918 when the Humphreys Mill discontinued operations.[26] V.V. Clark[27] stated that:

"The abandonment of the tunnel by Col. Humphreys, together with the Happy Thought and Park Regent Shafts, and the Humphreys Mill was on account of his failure to obtain equitable freight and treatment rates from the railroads and smelters at that time. According to Mr. Wheeler he was unable to realize a profit under the conditions presented and closing down the various works appeared the only logical thing to do. In the meantime [in 1934], the tunnel has caved at various parts, likewise the shafts above mentioned, the mill machinery has been taken away and stolen, the power plant is antiquated and useless, and the whole enterprise has languished."

The year of 1918 was the start of hard times for Creede Camp and many other mining camps in Colorado and throughout the West. *The Engineering and Mining Journal* of January 18, 1919, stated that 1918 was probably the most disastrous year ever experienced by mining in Colorado. Restrictions on prices, wages, and other economic conditions from World War I seriously impacted the mining industry, and particularly small mines such as those at Creede.

CHAPTER 10

A TIME FOR
CONCENTRATION
1893-1918

AS THE MINES WERE DEEPENED, the rich oxidized silver ore was replaced by lower grade sulfide ore. This transition created a new era of mining at Creede Camp. The concentration of the valuable minerals in the ore prior to shipment to the smelters became necessary in order to materially reduce the cost of transportation and smelting. According to the records, well over half of the ore produced between 1904 and the abandonment of the Humphreys Mill in 1918 was processed and the concentrates shipped to smelters.[1] The ratio of concentration for the Creede mills was between 7 and 10 to 1, meaning that as few as 7 to as many as 10 tons of ore were reduced to 1 ton of concentrate.[2] Mills operated as early as 1893, but public records indicating tonnages and concentration ratios were not kept until 1904.

The silver value of the sulfide ore was considerably less than that of the enriched oxidized ore that made early-day Creede famous. In fact, its content in the lower grade sulfide ores made it a co-product with lead, zinc, and copper — not the all-important metal that it had been. No commercial quantities of zinc or copper were found in the early-day oxidized ores, but they became important co-products of the sulfide ore. Gold was produced in greater quantities from the sulfide ore than from the oxidized ore, primarily from the ore mined from the lower levels of the Happy Thought and Park Regent Mines. The Creede miners had hoped the gold values would dramatically increase with depth to take the place of the early-day silver bonanzas but, unfortunately, this did not happen.

The era of concentration was ushered in during 1893 by the mines on the Solomon-Holy Moses Vein, where sulfide ores were encountered at a shallow depth. The mining and concentration of sulfide ores from the Amethyst Vein began about the turn of the century. By 1900 the Happy Thought Mine on the north end of the Amethyst, operated by the Creede United Mines Company, was producing sulfide ores in quantity. The Amethyst Mine produced large quantities of both oxidized silver-rich ore and sulfide milling ore. The Last Chance-New York-Del Monte Mine had the greatest production of oxidized ores, followed in turn by the Commodore and Bachelor Mines. The Alpha and Corsair Mines near Sunnyside were still producing oxidized ores with a high content of silver.

Concentration or beneficiation — "ore dressing," as it was called at the time — is the process by which the valuable minerals are separated from the "gangue" or non-economic mineral component of the ore. The first attempt to treat ore was at Sunnyside in the 1880s, when an "arrastre" was unsuccessfully used to concentrate ores from the Alpha and Bachelor Mines. A ten-stamp mill capable of treating twenty tons of ore per day was constructed at the Park Regent Mine in 1896 to concentrate ore by amalgamation.[3] Amalgamation is the process where the native silver and/or gold is separated from the gangue minerals when the crushed ore is flowed in a water slurry across a sloping copper plate covered with mercury. The silver and gold adheres to the plate while the gangue minerals flow on. This concentration method proved unsuccessful at Creede.

Four mills were built near the turn of the century at Creede and were designed to concentrate the valuable minerals by wet mechanical methods. They were the Solomon and Ridge Mills on East Willow Creek and the Amethyst and Humphreys Mills on West Willow Creek. The latter two mills were of the side-hill type, so the ore passed through the process by gravity instead of being pumped or otherwise lifted. Power to the Humphreys Mill was provided by water or steam, depending on the available water volume. The Amethyst was powered by electricity generated at a steam plant, the Solomon by steam, and the Ridge by water. One of the needs of the Creede district was cheap and reliable electric power, such as was supplied to other districts in Colorado. Coal was expensive and the cost of hauling it to the mills from the rail heading added fifty to 100 per cent of the original cost of the coal.[4] Creede Camp had to wait for many decades before being served by an electric utility!

All four mills had the same basic design: first, crush and grind the ore to a fineness where the valuable mineral particles were separated from the gangue; and second, gravity separation of the valuable minerals in a water slurry by the use of mechanical equipment such as shaking tables, jigs, and canvas tables. Arthur F. Taggart, one of the "fathers" of modern metallurgy, described these three mechanical devices in his textbook on metallurgy.[5] His descriptions are given below in a somewhat simplified fashion.

The shaking table is a roughly rectangular table, eight to ten feet long, mounted at a slight slope in both directions on slides or rollers that permit the table to be moved back and forth along its long dimension. Riffles, parallel to the table's long dimension, are attached to the table's surface. Ore is introduced onto the table at its high corner in a water slurry. The valuable minerals are heavier than the gangue minerals and are therefore trapped behind the riffles and moved by the reciprocal action of the table to its end, where they are collected. The lighter gangue particles wash across the riffles and are eliminated from the process. Particles containing both valuable and gangue minerals are collected along the lower section of the bottom edge of the table as "middlings" and are generally recycled through the process.

The principle of jigging is best explained by quoting Taggart: "Man learned 2,000 years ago or more that if broken sulphide ore was shaken in water in one of the loosely woven baskets he was wont to use for screening, the sulphide particles concentrated at the bottom of the basket." Jigs used at Creede were a bit more sophisticated but used the same principle.

The canvas table, termed a "planilla" in metallurgical terms, is a sloping table covered with canvas. As the ore slurry passes over the canvas surface, the heavier particles adhere to the canvas and the gangue particles are washed off the table.

Flotation, today's most commonly used method to concentrate sulfide minerals, was discovered during the early part of the twentieth century and two of the Creede mills were modified to include flotation: the Amethyst in 1911 and the Humphreys no later than 1914. Flotation is the process where a slurry of valuable and gangue mineral particles is introduced into a tank, so named the "Callow" tank at the time, and agitated with low pressure air entering at the bottom. The valuable mineral particles adhere to air bubbles and are floated to the surface where they are removed from the tank. The gangue minerals settle to the bottom and are removed. Various chemicals are used to selectively cause the adherence of particular minerals to the air bubbles. Thus, for instance, lead sulfide can be separated by "selective flotation" from zinc sulfide. *Mining Science*'s February 1914 issue carried an article describing one story about the discovery of the flotation process:

"*J. Park Channing stated that: 'The father of flotation, or rather, I should say, the mother, is an American woman, Miss Carrie J. Everson, of Colorado. Miss Everson's brother, an assayer in Denver, received a shipment of concentrates in canvas sacks. These sacks, after emptying, were rather dirty, as they had been lying around for some time, and they were covered by oil. He therefore handed them to his sister to be cleaned. A woman's idea of cleaning is to use soap and water; she turned them inside out, put them in a tub, and proceeded to do the washing. In so doing she discovered that the sulphides floated to the top and that the siliceous gangue sank to the bottom. In 1885 she was granted Patent No. 348,157, covering flotation of metallic sulphides by the use of oil and water.'*"

Mining Science of August 1915 had the following comment about the acceptance of the flotation process in the San Juan mining districts:

"*There is consider activity in San Juan County this year resulting from experimental work on the ores of this section by the new oil flotation process. ... From the work done to date, the results have been good, and there is no question but that the oil process will enable an increase of from 15 to 20 percent in the average savings of values from the lead, copper, and zinc ores in the mines in this section.*"

Mineral Resources of the United States for 1911 listed the concentration mills operating in the Creede district in 1911 along with their major equipment and capacities. The Solomon Mill had been shut down prior to 1911:

Name	District	Process	Equipment	Capacity
Amethyst	Creede	Concentration	Rolls, jigs (Hartz type), Card tables, Chilean mills, trough classifier, Callow tanks, canvas tables.	100 TPD
Humphreys	Creede	Concentration	Crusher, coarse and fine rolls, trommels, 12 four compartment Hartz jigs, 3 Chilean mills, trough hydraulic classifier, and 12 Wilfley tables.	250-300 TPD
Ridge	Creede	Concentration	No crusher, disintegrating screen, trommels, 3 four compartment Hartz jigs, 3 Wilfley tables.	50-60 TPD

The Solomon Mill's equipment consisted of crushers, rolls, jigs, and shaking tables and had a capacity of seventy-five tons per day.

Since seven to ten tons of ore were treated to produce a single ton of concentrates sent to the smelter, what happened to the remaining six to nine tons of gangue or non-economic minerals? Most mills of the time dumped their waste product — called "tailings," which consisted of finely ground gangue minerals and unrecovered valuable minerals — in a water slurry into a nearby stream. This, of course, created pollution of the water. One of the first, if not *the* first, successful lawsuits to stop this practice in Colorado happened at Creede,[6] as will be discussed later in the chapter.

Emmons and Larsen[7] described the treatment of ores mined in the Creede district:

"*[The sulfide ore from the Amethyst Vein] was dressed in the Humphreys Mill, at North Creede, and in the Amethyst Mill, near the Amethyst Mine. The Humphreys and Amethyst mills are of the same general type, the equipment including crushers, rolls, classifiers, jigs, tables, and canvas plants. The zinc blende and galena are readily separated, giving clean concentrates, and the pyrite is not so abundant as to reduce the grade of zinc concentrates greatly. Gold and silver are recovered mainly with the lead concentrates or in the slimes. Two smaller mills, the Solomon and the Ridge, have been erected on East Willow Creek about 1 1/2 miles above North Creede. The ore of the Solomon vein is very soft, and some of it is crushed by rolls without preliminary breaking in a jaw crusher.*"

Next to Leadville, Creede was the most important producer of zinc in Colorado.[8] The Creede ore was unusual for the region in being free from iron. A high-grade concentrate, rivaling that of Joplin, Missouri, was obtained by simple wet concentration. Steven and Ratté[9] provided statistics on the value of production of minerals from the Creede district in the first part of the twentieth century:

"*Production from the Amethyst Vein from the beginning of detailed records in 1904 through 1910 ranged from about $1 million to $1.6 million per year, except in 1908 when production dropped to nearly $600,000. From 1911 through 1914, production ranged from $400,000 to $87,000 per year, and from 1915 through 1921, production ranged from $70,000 to $440,000 per*" *year. This irregular diminishing of production reflected the progressive exhaustion of the better grade ores in the main Amethyst Vein.*

"The Solomon and Ridge Mines were the most active mines on the Solomon-Holy Moses Vein zone during the early part of the century. Their last big production was in 1907 when more than $150,000 worth of metal was produced. The total value of production from the Solomon-Holy Moses Vein zone from 1904 until 1923, when mining activity was halted for more than a decade, is estimated at slightly less than $1 million."

The mines in Colorado were exempt from taxes prior to 1902 to assist an infant industry develop into a mature one. The Colorado legislature of that year framed a new revenue law to meet the needs of the state and determined that it was time to tax the mining industry its share to support the state.[10] This, no doubt, had an effect on mining at Creede. Ore production at Creede was 124,278 tons in 1904, the first year records of tonnages were kept. In 1906, thirteen mines produced 126,124 tons of ore. In 1908, seven mines produced 61,131 tons. Production stayed level, more or less, until 1914 when the annual production dropped to 27,952 tons. *The Engineering and Mining Journal* issue of January 5, 1915, reported on metal mining in Colorado in 1914 and stated, "There is little activity in the Creede and Aspen districts, both of which are hard hit by the low prices of lead and silver." The annual production rate stayed about the same until 1919 when it dropped to 16,718 tons. Creede Camp began hard times after several years of reduced mining activity.

Mining at Creede Camp continued from 1900 through 1918 on the three vein systems exploited during the early days — the Amethyst, Solomon-Holy Moses, and Alpha-Corsair — and at the Monon Hill ore deposit in the Creede Formation. The Wagon Wheel Gap fluorspar deposit was located during this period. Initial exploration on the fourth vein system — the Bulldog Mountain Vein — started during this period of time, even though the vein was not developed and exploited until the 1960s, Creede's second "boom."

AMETHYST VEIN SYSTEM

In addition to the early mines along the Amethyst Vein, new mines were developed and exploited, including the White Star, Captive Inca, and Equity Mines. Several new mining companies were organized during this period to mine the Amethyst Vein. These include the Triune Company, Volunteer Mining Company, Big Kanawha Leasing Company, Creede Mining and Milling Company, Humphreys Tunnel and Mining Company, Creede Exploration Company, a subsidiary of the American Smelting and Refining Company, Equity Mining and Investment Company, and others.

BACHELOR MINE

Most, if not all, of the ore production from the Bachelor from 1900 through 1918 was mined by lessees. Professor Lakes[11] had this to say in 1903:

> *"The Bachelor Mine is a good example of what a system of leasing or leasers can do. The mine is operated by leasers in different sets who have been able to maintain the property, pay the handsome dividend of $100,000 from the fact that they are personally interested and doing the work themselves and keeping down unnecessary expenses and taking care of the ore. The output of the mine has been taken through the Nelson Tunnel, at the mouth of which are their ore bins, grizzlies, and sorting tables."*

The Bachelor, under lease in May 1900, was producing fifty tons of direct shipping ore weekly. By November of the same year it was shipping fifty to sixty tons per day.[12] *Mining Reporter* of June 1901 reported that a three-foot wide body of ore had been encountered in the Bachelor Mine at a depth of 1,500 feet that assayed more than fifty ounces of silver to the ton. Very good news for Creede Camp. The Creede Home Mining Company, modeled after the Home Mining Company of Leadville, had a lease on the Bachelor in 1903. They reported the ore in the north drift was improving in quantity.[13] The Bachelor was worked by lessees in 1903 and a number of shipments of silver ore were made during the spring and summer.[14] Arthur Lakes reported in 1903 that ore valued at $250 to $300 per ton had been found 250 feet below the Nelson Tunnel level in the Bachelor Mine.[15] No corroboration of his statement was found in the literature; however, the Bachelor Shaft was sunk below the Nelson Tunnel level, and two companies explored the Amethyst Vein below the tunnel in 1912 and 1917, as will be described later in the chapter.

The U.S. Geological Survey's *Mineral Resources of the United States* listed the Bachelor Mine as producing direct shipping or crude

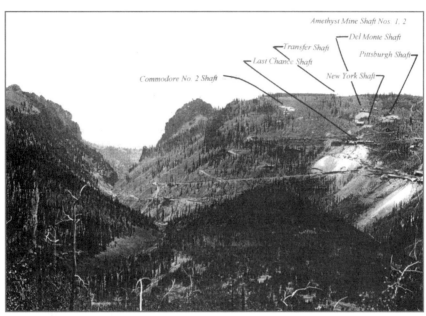

Mines on the Southern Amethyst Vein and W. Willow Terrace Road
Photo by E.S. Larsen — 1911, Courtesy of the U.S. Geological Survey

Mines on the Northern Amethyst Vein
Photo by E.S. Larsen — 1911, Courtesy of the U.S. Geological Survey

silver ore in 1906 through 1908, 1910 through 1912, and 1915 through 1918. *Mining Science* reported production from the Bachelor in 1909.

An experimental chlorination mill was tried on silver ores from the Bachelor in 1916 for a short period of time.[16] The process consisted of a salt roast, leaching with an acid solution, and precipitation on scrap iron. The process was not successful.

Emmons and Larsen in their 1923 report described the Bachelor Mine:[17]

> "The total production is estimated at $2 million, practically all in silver. The mine is exploited from four adits that have a vertical range of about 1,175 feet. The lowest of these is the Nelson or Wooster adit, which encounters the vein on the Bachelor claim about 1,931 feet from the portal. Tunnel 4, which is one of the principal adits of the Commodore Mine, is about 445 feet above the Nelson Adit, and Tunnel 3 (Commodore) is 401 feet above Tunnel 4. Tunnel 1, the highest tunnel is 329.6 feet above Tunnel 3. The Bachelor Shaft is sunk 125 feet below the adit, and thus the total development below Tunnel 1 is 1,500 feet."

COMMODORE MINE

At the turn of the century, the Commodore Mine was the only mine along the southern Amethyst vein not under lease, but it was being mined by its owner, the Commodore Mining Company. It was considered to be the greatest silver mine in Colorado with large reserves and was producing about 300 tons of ore per day worth about $40 per ton. The peak year of profitability for the Commodore was 1899 with the following years to be considerably different. Total dividends paid per share from 1900 through 1915 inclusive, a period of sixteen years, was only $0.60 as compared to $0.625 for 1899![18] Increased costs and lower grade ore as the mine deepened no doubt played a major role in the drastically reduced profitability of the operation. However, another factor most likely had a serious impact on the Commodore. *The Denver News* reported on October 4, 1900, that a bad cave-in had occurred in the Commodore Mine:

> "A large piece of ground in the Commodore Mine caved in a few days ago. The cave commenced at an old stope between Nos. 2 and 3 levels. Just before the night shift went off Thursday morning, the men heard an

ominous cracking and at once sounded the alarm. The
men all got out and the superintendent laid the day shift
off. The timbering in No. 3 Tunnel is very heavy and it is
not thought that the cave will break into the tunnel. The
broken ground, as near as can be ascertained at present, is
about 800 feet long and 150 feet high. The ground con-
tinued to break, more or less, until Saturday night and
work has been suspended in No. 3 Tunnel until the extent
of the damage can be ascertained and precautions taken to
prevent further injury."

By the end of 1900, the Commodore had increased its output, installed new electrically driven machinery, and had started sinking a shaft below the level of the Commodore No. 5 Tunnel.[19] In the spring of 1901, the Commodore shaft was being sunk (encountering very little water) and the recently installed electric machinery was working perfectly.[20] *Mining Reporter,* in its July 26, 1901, issue, stated the Commodore was installing ten-inch water column piping from the Amethyst Mine in the Commodore shaft. The Amethyst Mine had been drained by the Nelson Tunnel and had no further use for the pipe.

The Commodore was making average shipments of about 140 tons of ore per day in September 1901. This dropped to 100 to 125 tons per day by November 1902. By December 1902, the production rate had dropped to 2,500 tons of ore per month (about eighty-five tons per day). The ore contained primarily silver values with a small percentage of lead.[21]

Professor Arthur Lakes described the Commodore in the 1903 *Mines and Minerals:*[22]

"The Commodore is another old-time and important
silver mine. It is worked from a series of five tunnels pen-
etrating the mountain along the vein the full length of the
claims. These are all connected by raises at proper inter-
vals, and intermediate levels run to enable the quickest
and cheapest transportation of the ore to the surface,
where two tramways convey it to the railroad.
Development work is kept in advance of the stoping. The
use of electricity, both for lighting and power, is a marked
feature of these mines. Deep mining is now principally
aimed at. The depth at present attained in the big mines is
1,500 to 1,600 feet."

Commodore No. 3 Tunnel — Date
Unknown
Courtesy of the Creede Historical Society

On December 1, 1905, the Commodore Mining Company leased its property between the Commodore No. 5 Tunnel on the Commodore Vein to a crosscut a short distance below the outcrop, with the exception of a twenty- to thirty-foot strip of ore bearing ground immediately beneath the floor of Tunnel No. 5, to Dwigans & Company. The lessees were W.C. Dwigans, A.L. Wilson, Harry Van Horn, and Clarence Withrow under the name of Dwigans & Company. The lease also included the use of the company's aerial trams to transport ore to the railroad.[23]

A.E. Reynolds, president of the Commodore Mining Company, presented to the annual meeting of the company's stockholders on June 15, 1906, three proposals for the first real attempt at consolidating the several mining companies along the Amethyst Vein:[24]

> "The first being a proposition which has been in the possession of the Company for two years or more, showing the percentages various parties on the line of the Commodore Vein at Creede would be entitled to in a consolidation of the various interests named; to this was attached the criticism and opinion of the President of the Company for the consideration of the stockholders. The second communication was a proposition looking to the leasing of the various properties to the Commodore Mining Company, attached to comments of the President of the Company. The third was suggestions of the President of the Company for consolidation formulated by himself. These three communications were referred to Mr. C.F. Hughes, Attorney for the Company, Mr. Walter Cheesman, and Major L.E. Campbell as a committee with

the request that they give the three documents considera-
tion and formulate one or more suggestions in putting the
same in proper shape to be submitted to the other owners
on the vein for their consideration, with a view to now
effect a consolidation of the properties along the vein
belonging to the following companies:
> *The Bachelor Mining Company*
> *The Commodore Mining Company*
> *The New York and Chance Mining Company*
> *The Volunteer Mining Company*
> *The Last Chance Mining Company*
> *The Amethyst Mining Company"*

Consolidation did not occur for many years; however, two attempts were made prior to 1918, one by the Triune Company and the other by the Creede Exploration Company, a subsidiary of American Smelting & Refining Company. Both are described later in this chapter.

Dwigans & Company's lease was extended for four more years in 1907 and the lessee had a very profitable mining operation at the Commodore apex.[25] The Commodore lessees produced direct smelting ore from the upper workings above the Commodore No. 5 Tunnel from 1908 through 1918.[26] New lessees, S.B. Collins and Wallace I. Leary, were approved at a special meeting of the Board of Directors of the Commodore Mining Company on November 14, 1914.[27] The Commodore was not very profitable for the owners by the end of 1914, and dividends were only a quarter of a cent per share of stock in 1914 and 1915.[28] At a special meeting of the board of directors of the Commodore Mining Company held on December 2, 1914, the following resolution was made:[29]

> *"Resolved, that for the purpose of keeping the mine open*
> *and giving such men as are now employed therein an oppor-*
> *tunity to make their living for the succeeding winter, that the*
> *President of the Company at his discretion shall arrange with*
> *such of these men as desire to remain the opportunity to*
> *work such unmined portions of the ground as they may find*
> *to contain ore, under an arrangement to pay such a graded*
> *royalty as the ore produced will warrant."*

The stockholders of the Commodore Mining Company approved a contract between the company and the American Smelting & Refining Company (ASARCO) at the stockholders' meeting on March

28, 1917, in which ASARCO would lease the Commodore Mine as well as other mines in an attempt to consolidate the mines along the Amethyst Vein. An effort had been under way for a couple of years to effect a consolidation as described by A.E. Reynolds at the Commodore annual meeting on June 19, 1916:[30]

> *"For more than a year there have been some very active efforts made to consolidate the various properties from the Bachelor Company up through the properties owned by the Creede Mines & Milling Company, which is the old United Mines or Park Regent, into an operating and leasing company, taking leases uniform in character as far as possible for a 20-year period, with the intention of working these properties as a whole through the Commodore Shaft, which is down about 450 feet below the present tunnel level. The process has been slow because of the different ownerships and lack of interest in the property, and also some strong differences of opinion about the matter."*

The consolidation effort culminated in the formation of the Creede Exploration Company by the American Smelting & Refining Company. This company mined and shipped some ore in 1917 and 1918 from the consolidated mining properties.[31]

NEW YORK, LAST CHANCE, AND DEL MONTE MINES

After the turn of the century these three mines, for all practical purposes, operated as one mine even though they were not held by the same owners. A lawsuit filed in 1891 by the owners of the New York claim against the Last Chance Mine resulted in a compromise solution, the formation of the New York Chance Mining Company in 1892. Mary A. Coffin's suit against the New York/Chance Mining Company and its owners delayed production until June 1898. The Del Monte Mine was shut down in 1894 pending settlement of litigation with the Last Chance and did not reopen until 1902. The suit had a tremendous impact on Creede mining at the turn of the century, since no mining occurred in the disputed area for seven years. As previously discussed, the Del Monte people had appealed the case to the U.S. Supreme Court. The Volunteer Mining Company was organized as a holding company to settle the dispute between the owners of the Del Monte and the New York and Last Chance claims. The Volunteer Mining Company also owned stock in both the New York and Last Chance companies.[32]

A "Memorandum of Preliminary Agreement," dated February 7, 1902, between the New York Chance Mining Company, the Volunteer Mining Company, the Del Monte Mining and Milling Company, and the Del Monte Leasing Company was as follows:[33]

> *"Whereas there is and for many years has been pending in US Circuit Court for Colorado certain litigation between parties wherein there is involved the rights to certain ores, veins, and mineral deposits lying within the external boundaries and beneath the surface of the New York lode and the Del Monte and Aspen lodes, which said ores and mineral deposits are claimed by the parties of the first part as belonging to and being parts of a certain vein supposed to have its apex upon said New York mining claim, and the same are also claimed by the said parties of the second part by virtue of certain supposed extralateral rights, and further by virtue of certain veins and deposits claimed to have their apex and existing on and within the boundaries of the said Del Monte mining claim and whereas said Volunteer Mining Company is now the owner of title of the Del Monte and Aspen claims. Del Monte Leasing Company (A.E. Humphreys — President) has a lease on the Del Monte and Aspen lodes.*
>
> *"Del Monte Mining and Milling Company claims damages against the first party for ores extracted from the Del Monte lode."*

The Engineering and Mining Journal of April 5, 1902, carried the following story after the preliminary agreement was accepted by the parties:

> *"Last Chance — The troubles of this mine at Creede and of the New York & Chance Mine, which began in 1894 have been adjusted. In 1890 the Del Monte Company claimed the mine, alleging apex rights. The case was carried into the United States courts, where last winter a compromise was proposed, and this has been approved. The Last Chance is given the ownership of the mines, the Del Monte to have a lease for 20 years. There is a shaft 1,500 ft. deep, with levels at every 100 ft. The ore carries silver, mixed with lead and gold as depth is gained."*

On March 1, 1902, the stockholders of the Last Chance Mining and Milling Company ratified the action of the directors in giving a lease on their property to the Del Monte Leasing Company.[34] The directors were Henry R. Wolcott, Edward O. Wolcott, Ralph Granger, W.P. Ward, and Jacob F. Sanders. A similar dispute between the Del Monte and New York Chance Companies was settled in the same manner.

The settlement of the long-standing disputes meant a resumption of operations on the New York, Last Chance, and Del Monte properties. The Del Monte Leasing Company directed development of the New York, Last Chance, and Del Monte properties. A.E. Humphreys and Albert Collins were the lease operators.[35] Collins was the son of James H. Collins, who played an important role in the early days of Creede Camp. A.E. Humphreys, as previously discussed in Chapter Five, was the principle stockholder in the United Mines Company and an important mine developer at Creede.

The *Mining Reporter* stated in its May 1, 1902, issue: "It is very encouraging to the stockholders, and the district in general, to see the way the Del Monte is outputting, and the ore is of a high grade. It is something new to see this property shipping regularly since being tied up for eight years. The first dividend of ten per cent was paid yesterday to the stockholders." By December 1902, the Del Monte Leasing Company was shipping about 2,200 tons of silver ore per month to the smelters.[36] The Del Monte and New York Chance Mines shipped 1,000 to 1,200 tons of ore carrying forty to sixty ounces of silver and small values of lead and gold per ton to the smelters in 1903.[37] By July 1905, the Creede United Mines Company, headed by A.E. Humphreys, had consolidated several of the more important properties at Creede, including the Last Chance and New York Mines and the operations of the Del Monte Company and the New York and Chance Leasing Companies. The leasing companies were shipping up to 5,000 tons of ore to the smelters monthly, and it was anticipated that a larger force would be put to work under the direction of George Davis, manager, and H.E. Lees, superintendent.[38] The U.S. Geological Survey's *Mineral Resources of the United States for 1906* stated: "The Del Monte Leasing Company shipped silver-lead ores carrying some gold from the properties of the New York Chance Mining Company, the Volunteer Mining Company, and the Last Chance Mining and Milling Company. The New York and Chance Leasing Company also made a production from the New York and Last Chance Mines." The same publication reported that the Del Monte Leasing Company shipped silver-lead ore in 1907 and 1908.

Production from these properties continued in 1909. W.C. Sloan & Co. leased the Last Chance dump, concentrated the dump ore, and shipped it to the smelters at a profit; and in 1911 sulfide ore from the Last Chance and Del Monte lease was being shipped to the Humphreys Mill for concentration.[39] The Last Chance, New York, and Volunteer Mines also shipped ore to the smelters in 1911 and 1912.[40] Discoveries of sulfide lead and zinc ore were made in the Last Chance by the Creede Triune Mines Company, W.S. DeCamp, superintendent.[41] The New York, Last Chance, and Volunteer group of mines produced ore from 1915 through 1918.[42]

Emmons and Larsen described the Last Chance, New York, and Del Monte Mines:[43]

> *"The ownership of this group of mines is complexly involved, and records for the entire period of production are not available to the writers. Mr. Albert Collins estimates the production of the group at $19,000,000, the larger part of which he credits to the Last Chance. The portion of the vein included in this group was much richer than any other section of an equal number of linear feet on the Amethyst lode.*
>
> *"The New York and Del Monte Shafts are not accessible. The Last Chance, New York, and Del Monte claims are worked through the Last Chance Shaft and the Nelson Tunnel. The shaft is about 1,400 feet long and is sunk on or near the vein for the whole of its length. Twelve levels are turned from the shaft at intervals of about 100 to 200 feet on the incline. Above the collar of the shaft a short adit is driven southward on the vein. There are altogether over two miles of drifts and crosscuts."*

The Creede Exploration Company leased all of the mining properties on the Amethyst vein in 1917, including the Last Chance, New York, and Del Monte claims, and mined some ore from workings above the Nelson Tunnel level in 1917 and 1918. At the time, these claims were owned by the New York Chance Mining Company, J. Rodman, president, Denver; the Last Chance Mining Company, J. Rodman, president, Denver; and the Volunteer Mining Company, Judge H.G. Lunt, Colorado Springs.[44]

AMETHYST MINE

The Amethyst Mine had suffered a cave-in on December 5, 1893. N.C. Creede declined to pay his share of the expense of repairing the

mine and, as a result, transferred his stock in the Amethyst Mining
Company to his partners. Nearly two years after Creede's death, the
administrator of his estate filed suit in the U.S. Court against the
Amethyst Mining Company and David H. Moffat, Walter C.
Cheesman, Sylvester T. Smith, and L.E. Campbell, the only stockholders in the company, to recover a one-third interest in the mine,
alleged to be worth $5,000,000.[45] The suit was not settled until
1910. The Amethyst Mine was being worked by the Amethyst
Mining Company in 1900 under the direction of L.E. Campbell,
managing director, and Cyrus Miller, superintendent, and was the
heaviest shipper in Creede Camp.[46] In 1903, preparations to transport ore from the Amethyst through the Nelson Tunnel to the railroad had been made.[47]

The Creede Candle of March 5, 1904, carried the following
story about the lawsuit and litigation that was affecting the
Amethyst Mine and Creede Camp:

> *"The famous litigation of the administrator of the
> estate of the late Nicholas C. Creede against the Amethyst
> Mining Company and others was revived in the federal
> court before Judge Riner Monday afternoon, when J.W.
> Mills, appearing for the complainant, proposed the exam-
> ination of witnesses in Creede and Del Norte counties
> upon written interrogations. Attorney C.J. Hughes, for
> the respondents, objected to the proposed manner of pro-
> ceeding, and insisted upon the taking of oral testimony,
> and also criticized the form of the questions suggested.
> The court overruled all the objections except those rela-
> tive to the form of interrogation, which was amended on
> the spot. The time for filing of cross interrogatories was
> extended until March 7th.*
>
> *"This is an action where the attorneys for the admin-
> istrators for the N.C. Creede estate are trying to gobble a
> bunch of money from the Amethyst Mining company,
> they claiming fraud in the sale by Creede to the present
> owners of the mine. The unexplainable point in this case
> is the fact that N.C. Creede resided for a number of years
> in the vicinity of this mine after selling it and then resided
> in California several more years — in all over five years —
> and never intimated that there was any fraud in the trans-
> fer of the property on the part of the purchasers. But a lot*

of hungry attorneys, gazing upon a million dollar estate, discovered 'fraud' long after Mr. Creede's death. The injury this litigation has done to Creede can't possibly be estimated, for it has occasioned the Amethyst Mine to lay almost idle for the past five years when from 100 to 250 men would otherwise have been employed, thus depriving the district of the benefits of a payroll to that many men and curtailing the camp's output, and has more probably held the company from erecting a large concentrating mill to treat their ore, as the mine contains thousand of tons of low grade ore that could not be shipped unless concentrated. Creede Camp has long been eager to see this suit terminated, but the general opinion is that so long as the estates's millions hold out the matter will be hung up in the courts."

Fortunately, the lawsuit did not stop the Amethyst Mining Company from constructing a mill to concentrate the lower-grade sulfide ore found in the mine. *Mining Reporter* in its July 27, 1905, issue reported on the Amethyst Mill:

"Amethyst — A 100-ton milling plant is being erected at this property, which is located up West Willow Creek above Creede. The plant was designed by Messrs. L.H. Norton and J.J. Fitzgerald, respectively manager and superintendent of the milling department of the Creede United Mines Company. The machinery was furnished by Hendrie & Bolthoff, who have the construction work in charge under the personal direction of E.G. Mayhew of Denver. The equipment comprises a 9x15 Blake crusher, Bolthoff automatic feeder, two sets of 14x27 rolls, four trommels, four 4-compartment jigs, eight or more Card and Wilfley tables and two 5-foot Chilean mills. A novel mechanism is the shaking launder for dewatering the jig middlings before delivery to the Chileans (this mechanism was designed by J.J. Fitzgerald and has been in operation for some time at the Humphreys Mill of the Creede United Mines Company). The motive power is furnished by two 80 H.P. high pressure Kewanee boilers and a Corliss-Murray engine. The plant is expected to be in operation in about 100 days. Cyrus Miller of Denver is the general manager of the Amethyst company and Frank Ullman is superintendent."

The law suit filed by the Creede estate administrator continued in Federal Court until 1910, when Judge Phillips of Kansas City dismissed it.[48] *Mining Science* of July 14, 1910, carried the story:

> *"In the case of John T. Jones, executor of the estate of Nicholas C. Creede, versus David H. Moffat, Walter Cheesman, Sylvester T. Smith, Lafayette T. Campbell, and the Amethyst Mining Co., to recover a one-third interest in the Amethyst Mining Co., which was alleged to have been obtained from the late N.C. Creede by fraud, Judge Phillips directed that the bill be dismissed. As the suit was not started until nearly two years after the death of Creede in 1897, the judge in his opinion commented that clearly until the time he died Creede was in possession of all his faculties and was also possessed of ample means to have prosecuted the suit had he wished to have started one.*

The Amethyst Mining Company leased the Commodore electric plant in 1905 to light its mine and mill with electricity,[49] and in 1908 it was treating its sulphide ores in its 100-ton mill.[50] In 1909 the Amethyst employed sixty men and produced a lead and zinc concentrate.[51] Dismissal of the Creede estate lawsuit in 1910 cleared the way for full development of the Amethyst Mine that was by that time under lease to the Cyrus Miller Leasing Company.[52] H.C. Parmelee described the Amethyst Mill in 1910:[53]

> *"Of the three mills now in operation near Creede, the Amethyst is probably the most interesting. The crude ore treated there averages about 5 percent zinc and 10 percent lead, with some silver and free gold. The silver minerals are closely associated with the siliceous gangue, and there is a consequent heavy loss of silver in the tailing. The gold occurs free and may be seen on some of the tables treating the finer sizes of pulp. The lead and zinc minerals occur free enough to warrant coarse concentration with jigs, followed by intermediate treatment on tables, finishing with slime. Quite an extensive plant is installed to save the latter. The average saving of the total value is nearly 85 percent, the highest recovery being made on lead, next on zinc, gold ,and silver, the last suffering the greatest loss.*
>
> *"Ore is delivered at the head of the mill by an aerial gravity tramway, 1700 feet long, connecting mine and mill. The line has 18 buckets carrying about 500 lb. of ore*

Amethyst Mill and Dam — Date Unknown (Last Chance and Happy Thought Mines in the background)
Courtesy of Ken Wyley, Creede, Colorado

each, moving at about 200 ft. per minute, so that a bucket is dumped a little oftener than once a minute. This gives a capacity of about 125 tons in eight hours which is the capacity of the mill for 24 hours. The tramming and crushing department is, therefore, operated only one shift.

"At the tram loading station at the mine the ore is roughly sized by being passed over a grizzly with 1 1/2 inch openings. These two classes are separately trammed and dumped into separate bins at the head of the mill, the coarse passing over a second grizzly before going to the crusher, and the fine going directly to the crushed ore bins. The bin capacity for crushed ore is 75-80 tons, or sufficient to run the mill two shifts."

Emmons and Larsen described the Amethyst Mine in their study of the geology and ore deposits at Creede:[54]

"The mine was one of the first in the district to produce ore, and with the exception of a few relatively short intervals when it was shut down, it has been producing steadily since. The total production of ore and

concentrates is estimated to be about $4,000,000. In 1911 the mine was closed, but in 1912 it was under lease to the Creede Triune Mining Co. This company installed an electric power plant at Creede to effect a saving in freighting coal by wagon road. A three-compartment blind shaft on the Nelson adit level was sunk on the vein near the north end of the mine. Some new stopes were opened, and the mill was put into operation.

"The mine was worked through the Nelson Tunnel and the Amethyst Shaft. The shaft is about 1,283 feet long, as measured on the incline and is sunk on the vein, which dips about 55 degrees west.

"In earlier years, when the rich oxidized ores of the upper levels were mined, the ore was loaded into a tramcar at the shaft house and sent over an aerial tramway to North Creede, where it was loaded into railway cars and sent to the smelter. This tramway is now in ruins, and a shorter one connects with a mill on West Willow Creek about 800 feet from the Amethyst shaft."

The dam shown in the preceding photograph of the Amethyst Mill and Dam was constructed by A.E. Reynolds to store water from West Willow Creek. The water was taken by a pipeline to the Commodore Mine where power was generated.[55]

The Amethyst Shaft described by Emmons and Larsen was actually the No. 3 Shaft, and it extended from the surface at the apex of the vein to the Nelson Tunnel level. The Amethyst Mine workings consists of twelve levels extending on the vein north and south of the shaft. Amethyst Nos. 1 and 2 Tunnels were driven into the outcrop of the Amethyst ore body. The Amethyst No. 5 Tunnel was driven from West Willow Creek at the Amethyst Mill level to intersect the No. 3 Shaft, in order to eliminate the short aerial tram that had been constructed to transport ore from the collar of the No. 3 Shaft to the mill.[56] Ore was either hoisted or dropped to the No. 5 Tunnel level and then trammed directly to the mill.

The Creede Triune Mining Company was organized by John H. Berkshire of Kansas City, who was the president and controlling owner of the Cyrus Miller Leasing Company. The Cyrus Miller Leasing Company had previously secured leases on all of the Amethyst vein properties below the level of the Nelson-Wooster-Humphreys Tunnel south of the White Star Mine, with the exception of the Commodore, the first successful attempt to consolidate the mines.[57] *Mining Science*'s February 22, 1912, issue ran the following story about the new company at Creede:

> *"An organization looking to the rejuvenation of the camp of Creede, has just been perfected by a number of Kansas City and Denver capitalists. The properties involved are those belonging to the Amethyst, the Creede United, and Last Chance Co.'s, upon each of which company's properties long term leases have been executed in favor of John H. Berkshire of Kansas City, who has transferred the leases to the Creede Triune Mines Co. For some years past leasers have been working these properties, but from this time on all work will be under the direction of the new company. The principal work in the past has been done above the Nelson Tunnel level, but the intention now is to go below and develop the ore bodies that are known to exist at lower depths. It has been proven that, as depth is gained, the ore bodies widen and show better values in gold, as well as in lead, zinc, and silver. The intention of the Creede Triune Mines Co. is to expend about $200,000 in further development and equipment of the properties. A steam power plant is to be erected along the Rio Grande [sic] tracks in the spring, as soon as weather conditions permit, and the electric power connected at this plant will be transmitted to the mines and to the mill. The mill in question, a 150-ton plant, known as the Cyrus Miller or Amethyst Mill, has been operated by the Kansas City people interested for the past year or more."*

David H. Moffat, the principle owner of the Amethyst Mine, died on March 18, 1911, while on a trip to the East. The executors of his estate entered into a contract in 1912 with Philip Argall & Sons, mining engineers, to take over the management of the Moffat holdings in fifty-one mining companies in Colorado and adjoining states.[58] Perhaps this was a factor in the decision by the mine owners to consider a consolidation of the properties.

The Triune Mining Company was sinking the three-compartment Berkshire Shaft below the Nelson Tunnel level in the Amethyst Mine in July 1912; they planned to sink a second on the United Mines property and a third on the New York and Chance ground. They also were constructing a 300-horsepower electric plant in Creede to electrify their mining operation and the Amethyst Mill.[59] In September of the same year, the company, under the direction of W.S. DeCamp, was treating about 100 tons of ore per day in the Amethyst Mill and reported a strike of rich silver ore in the Happy Thought.[60] The Triune Mining Company reportedly made important discoveries of lead and zinc ore in the Last Chance Mine in 1912. The board of directors of the Commodore Mining Company approved a February 7, 1913, letter from A.E. Reynolds to the Bachelor and Triune Mining Companies stating that the Commodore Mining Company would work with them through the access below the Nelson Tunnel level provided by the Commodore Shaft.[61] Unfortunately, the Triune developments did not come to fruition. Regardless of the glowing reports in the media, the Berkshire Shaft was sunk only 100 feet below the Nelson Tunnel level, where exploration drifts were driven north and south from the shaft into Happy Thought and Amethyst ground without finding economic mineralization. The Triune Mining Company abandoned their exploration effort. According to the U.S. Geological Survey's *Mineral Resources of the United States*, the Amethyst Mill did not operate in 1915 or 1916. A second unsuccessful attempt to find ore below the Nelson Tunnel level in the Amethyst Mine was made by the Creede Exploration Company in 1917, as will be described later in the chapter.

UNITED MINES, CREEDE UNITED MINES, AND CREEDE MINES COMPANIES

The Happy Thought Shaft, under the direction of F.E. Wheeler, had been sunk about 1,250 feet by mid-1900 with about 550 feet left to the Nelson Tunnel level. The United Mines properties were being worked by the Big Kanawha Leasing Company, H.C. Rowley, superintendent.[62] The Big Kanawha Leasing Company had been organized by Colonel A.E. Humphreys in 1897. The Humphreys Mining and Milling Company was organized in 1898 to construct and operate a mill at the portal of the Nelson Tunnel.

The Denver Times carried an article in its May 30, 1901, issue about the start of work on the new mill for the United Mines and activity at the Humphreys Tunnel:

> "*Preparing to build United Mines Mill — George Davis of the Big Kanawha and United Mines Companies of Creede was at that camp a few days ago making arrangements for the commencement of work on the new*

mill of the United Mines Company. The plans of the mill have been completed and as soon as they are received at the mine a force of forty or fifty men will be set at work making preparations for the foundation. Contractors have been let for the machinery of the mill and the contractors say they can have it in place in ninety days.

"Men are now at work preparing the ground for the construction of ore bins at the end of the car tramway that runs from the Nelson Tunnel and the mill will be erected on the side of the mountain below the bins.

"The Humphreys extension of the Nelson Tunnel has about 100 feet to go before reaching the point where a connection will be made with the United Mines [Happy Thought] Shaft. Work is not progressing very fast as the breast of the tunnel is one mile and three-quarters from daylight and in the event of a break-down much time is lost in repairing damage. Considerable trouble has been encountered in seeking the shaft which has yet 200 feet to go, mainly from the water flow. It is regarded as certain however that the connection will be made by the time the mill is finished, when the company will at once enter upon an era of heavy production."

By the fall of 1901, the Humphreys Mill was ready to receive its machinery and the mill would have six floors. The lower four floors were ready for machinery and the upper two floors were almost ready. It was anticipated the mill would be in operation by the end of 1901.[63] *The Denver Times* covered the starting of the Humphreys Mill and the extension of the Humphreys Tunnel in its March 9, 1902, issue:

"The starting of the new 200-ton concentrating mill at Creede, constructed by the Humphrey Tunnel Company, marks an epoch in the mining industry in the state which is also going to bring Creede into the prominence it deserves. In the hands of a small coterie of determined mining men, who after satisfying themselves of the possible values, a most daring piece of work has been accomplished. Headed by A.E. Humphreys and George Davis, both southern gentlemen, yet of years of experience in mining, for three years past they, with the Nelson Tunnel Company, have been putting up thousands of dollars a

month to carry on the driving of a tunnel over 5,000 feet northward on Bachelor Mountain alongside the great Amethyst vein, to the south end line of the Happy Thought claim of the United Mines Company. From this point the Humphreys Tunnel took complete control of the tunnel and ran it to the Happy Thought shaft, where the tunnel level is 1,430 feet on the slope from the surface. It will be continued for about two miles further north, operating possibly a total of four miles on the known continuous vein of the mountain. It will furnish a cheaper method of operation for the Bachelor, New York, Last Chance, and Amethyst Mines before the Happy Thought ground is reached.

"The big mill is first to work on ores from the Happy Thought. It is running very satisfactorily already far beyond all expectations and turning out a first class quality of concentrates of lead and zinc. Where the company is now operating is in the thirteenth level of the mine and where the vein is five to seven feet wide, producing gold, silver, lead, and zinc values, of an average clear across the vein of $17.50, with $12 in gold and the balance principally lead. The mill is fully equipped with crushers, screens, Bartley and Wilfley tables, and slimes tables will be added.

"Manager Davis was present when the mill was started and was extremely gratified with the way it worked, as it is sometimes the case when a property gets its mill up there is something that goes wrong or else the ore body proper for milling gives out. But in this latter regard the builders of the Humphreys Mill are fortunate for there is blocked out in the Happy Thought property today probably 250,000 tons of sulphide ore of one character that nine month's previous experimenting in a mill constructed on the same plans as the present one treated very successfully."

The mill was also processing ore from the Bachelor and Last Chance Mines as well as ore from the Happy Thought Mine by March of 1902.[64] The ore was delivered to the mill through the Nelson-Wooster-Humphreys Tunnel. The June 26, 1902, issue of *Mining Reporter* stated the mill was shut down because the Happy Thought Shaft being clogged made it impossible to get sufficient ore to the mill to run it at full capacity. By July the mill was running at full capacity and the work in the main (Happy Thought) shaft and the connections with the levels containing the milling ore had been completed. Ore above the twelfth level in the United Mines property was concentrated at the Humphreys Mill. Ore below the twelfth level carried high gold values and lead and was shipped direct to the smelters.[65] By the end of 1902, the Big Kanawha Leasing Company was producing about 3,000 tons of gold-lead ore per month, from which the Humphreys Mill produced about 580 tons of concentrate. In addition to the milling ore, the company shipped about 700 tons of ore direct to the smelters.[66] The Humphreys Mining and Milling Company, operators of the Humphreys Mill and Tunnel, was extending the tunnel at a rate of about 100 feet per month in 1902. The Humphreys Mining and Milling Company, Big Kanawha Leasing Company, and Del Monte Mining Company were, for all practical purposes, one concern controlled by A.E. Humphreys. George Davis was general manager of all three companies and J.D. Hawkins was the general superintendent of the Humphreys Mill, with Mr. Winnerah in direct charge.[67]

The Engineering and Mining Journal, March 7, 1903, reported that the Humphreys Mill had been shut down because of the lack of water but would resume operations as soon as snow melt provided an adequate supply. By July 1903, the Humphreys Mill was back in production processing 200 tons of ore daily, making forty tons of lead concentrate and ten tons of zinc concentrate daily. The lead concentrate contained about seventy per cent lead with one and one-half ounces gold and nine ounces silver per ton. The zinc was sold to the Empire Zinc Company, whose works were at Iola, Kansas.[68] Professor Arthur Lakes described the United Mines property and the Humphreys Mill in 1903:[69]

> *"The United Mines Co. is a prominent group of mines on Bachelor Mountain, north of the Amethyst Mine, and is typical of that area. They have a continuous strong vein dipping west 52 degrees, and the various shafts have explored the great vein to a depth of 1,000 to 1,500 feet. In the incline of the vein the ore is silver lead. In the Chance and Amethyst the ore carries some gold values, especially with depth. They have a shaft of three compartments, 1,500 feet deep, and 6,000 feet of drifts divided among 13 levels in the mine. The plant is up to date in the way of compressors and other machinery.*

"The milling operations of the camp are best shown in the Humphreys Mill, for a description of which, as well as of many details of the mines, I am indebted to the editor of The Creede Candle, and to Mr. Tabor, long a resident of Creede.

"The Humphreys concentrating mill is one of the most important pieces of work that has been constructed in Colorado during the past year. This mill when completed will have a cost upwards of $100,000.

"The ore is trammed from the mines through the Nelson Tunnel and over a surface tram to the mill, where it is dumped into stock bins with a capacity of 600 tons. From there it is run onto scales, and then over a grizzly, the oversize put through a 10" x 20" Blake crusher. The undersize and the product of the crusher is fed automatically through roughing screens 3 feet x 3 feet in size, then through an automatic sampler to two pairs of 14" x 36" Jackson rolls. The material is then elevated and passed through two lines of revolving sizing screens, each consisting of four screens 3 feet in diameter by 6 feet in length. The screenings are then handled by 12 4-compartment Harz jigs, the tailings and middlings passing through three sets of 14" x 30" rolls, then to nine Wilfley tables for fine separation. Two Bartlett tables are used above the Wilfley tables to reduce the amount of lead in the slimes and handle that part of the ore passing through 16-mesh in the line of sizing screens. The Wilfley tables separate the zinc from the gangue. Here they are using eight large settling tanks to get rid of excess water before going to the tables. The oversize from the revolving screens is elevated by Frenier sand pumps to the rolls for regrinding. The concentrates from the jigs drop into hoppers underneath the jig floor and are delivered automatically from those hoppers into chutes or spouts leading to the ore or concentrate bins at the railroad track, which consist of six steel-lined bins, and which are directly under the launders driven by Bolthoff's patent launder gear motion. All the bins, spouts, launders, chutes, and hoppers are lined with 1/4-inch flange steel. The screen jackets are false lined and all other parts of the mill subject to wear are similarly protected. About 20,000 pounds of 1/4-inch steel lining is

used in the mill. The mill in all parts is completely lighted by electricity from a 165-light dynamo.

"The power from the mill is furnished by two Pelton water wheels, 4 feet and 6 feet in diameter, respectively. The 4-foot wheel has a Replogle governor and drives the tables and dynamo, and the 6-foot wheel runs the rolls and crusher. The tables are driven with American expansion pulleys. The power is distributed to the line shafts with continuous rope drives. The mill is heated throughout by the Sturtevant system, consisting of steam heaters, radiators, and one central galvanized air duct with a fan for the distribution of heated air through the building. The steam for the heater is supplied by a large boiler and the mill is thoroughly piped to supply water for fire protection as well as concentration, having the fire lines all connected direct to the power pressure line with 12 fire plugs distributed on all floors.

"The mill is as substantially built as possibly could be, the foundations being excavated out of the side hill, and the retaining walls are of masonry from 3 feet to 5 feet in thickness, there being over 5,000 cubic yards of masonry and rock and cement foundations are under all grinding machines.

"The water for the power and concentration is taken from the Nelson Tunnel which makes 3,000 gallons per minute. The water is first taken into 3-foot steel pipe about 600 feet in the tunnel in which it is conveyed out past the mouth of the tunnel and into a flume which is carried 2,000 feet alongside the track way to the penstock, when it descends into the power pipe, which is 24 inches and 22 inches in diameter and 400 feet long with a 200-foot head. The mill building extends 400 feet along the slope of the hill, having a base of 300 feet, its height being 200 feet from the wheel pit to the top of the crusher floor.

"The mill is designed and equipped with the intention of carrying out the most advanced ideas of ore concentration, reducing 6 tons of ore to 1 of concentrates, and is one of the most complete, as well as largest, mills of its kind in the state. The present capacity of the mill is 200 tons daily, but has ample power and sufficient strength in all transmitting machinery to provide for doubling the capacity at a later date.

"The Hendrie & Bolthoff Co., of Denver, furnished
the machinery and the construction of the mill has been
entirely under the direction of Raymond Whinnerah, and
this mill speaks for his skill and ability in this line."

Humphreys Mill and Commodore
Mine in the Background — Date
Unknown

Kate Owsley Collection, Courtesy of
the Creede Historical Society

As was the case in the spring of 1903, the Humphreys Mill was again shut down in the spring of 1904 because of insufficient water to run the steam power plant and the mill at full capacity; however the mill was running at full capacity in June.[70]

The original mill design called for the use of water from the Nelson Tunnel to process the ore and to provide power to run the machinery through the use of Pelton water wheels. Lester Pelton developed his water wheel in California and it proved to be much more efficient than water wheels used at the turn of the century. It was widely used throughout the country where water was available, and it could easily be put under pressure. This made it a better power source for use in Creede, with its abundant streams and rugged topography. It had one serious weakness in that a constant supply of water was necessary. Pelton's contribution was recognized in 1973 by the American Society of Civil Engineers.[71]

A steam plant to provide power to the mill and a pipeline tapping West Willow Creek were constructed in 1903-04, because it was found that the supply of water from the Nelson Tunnel was not adequate for both processing the ore and providing power for the mill. The combined supply of water from the Nelson Tunnel and West Willow Creek was insufficient to operate the mill during late winter and early spring, when natural runoff was at its lowest. The

October 4, 1906, *Mining Reporter* carried an article entitled, "Mills and Milling Practices at Creede, Colorado," that described the Humphreys Mill:

> "The Humphreys Mill has both water and steam power plants, the former being in service during high water periods of the year. The Humphreys Mill, in addition to having the largest capacity, is treating ore of average lower grade and making a higher percentage of extraction at less cost, than any of the other three plants. It is furthermore doubtful if any milling plant in the state, and particularly where wet crushing and concentration alone are practiced, is operating with equal economy and profit on ore of so uniformly low grade. The labor and power costs have been reduced to a minimum figure at this plant by the absence of elevators and by the installation of interesting automatic mechanisms for the handling of material in its progress through the mill. With the plant running at full capacity of 275 tons daily, a force of nine men (seven mill hands, with one foreman and one man on repairs) is sufficient except when steam power is used, which necessitates adding one engineer.
>
> "When running at full capacity, the monthly shipments of concentrate products amount to about 1,000 tons, 650 to 700 of which are lead. The concentrates are simply drained of their water before shipment in railroad cars. At the smelters the lead concentrates carry from 4% to 5% moisture, and the zinc from 7% to 9%.
>
> "The water supply for powering and milling purposes is taken from West Willow Creek, about one-half mile above the mill (the mine water flows from the Wooster Tunnel, uniting with the creek supply at the tunnel portal) by a 36-inch wooden flume, from which it is diverted at a point back of the mill into a 212-ft. column pipe of 16-in. diameter, delivering to the wheel pit. A 10-in. take-off pipe entering the main flume delivers the necessary milling water to a tank in the scale room, from which it is gravity piped to the various machines.
>
> "The wheel pit is separately housed and walled alongside the main mill building on a level with the railroad trackage. There are two Pelton wheels, one of 6-ft. and

Humphreys Mill with Rope Drive in Foreground — Date
Unknown
Donovan Cullings Collection, Courtesy of the Creede Historical Society

*another of 4-ft. diameter, attached to the same 75-ft. rope
drive (1 1/4 steel ropes) powering the mill shafting; the
two water wheels are arranged to run on the same shaft,
or may run disconnected, the smaller wheel having a separately attached shafting for powering the tables and
dynamos; the larger wheel powers the crushers, rolls, jigs,
and Chileans. From the power plant across the creek,
there is a 200-ft. angle (angle of about 15 degrees from a
right angle) rope drive of 1 1/2-in. wire ropes making connections with the main water wheel shafting above the
wheel pit.*

*"In the power house, there is a 200 h.p. 12x22x36
Corliss compound-condensing engine, steamed by two
coal-fired 150 h.p. Hendrie & Bolthoff boilers. It is but
rarely, however, that more than 150 h.p. is generated at
the power plant, and the engine is in commission only
about eight months of the year. Steam and water power
are jointly used for about 4 months of the year, and water
power alone for about 4 months.*

"Important economical features of the Humphreys Mill are: coarse crushing, gravity flow of material, labor-saving devices for dewatering and delivering pulp, and the splendid powering."

In 1904, the United Mines Company acquired the properties of the Winchester Mining Company and the Sewell Mining Company who owned claims lying west of the United Mines property. Negotiations to purchase the properties had been pending for some time and the purchase settled apex questions and extralateral rights.[72] The two companies deeded their claims to the Floradora Mining Company that was owned by A.E. Humphreys.[73]

The year 1905 presented a serious problem to the Humphreys milling operations. A lawsuit was filed against the Humphreys Tunnel and Mining Company by Anton F. Frank for dumping tailings into Willow Creek. The Frank lawsuit was one of the first, if not *the* first, in Colorado to stop the practice of dumping mill tailings into an adjacent stream.[74] Frank owned a quarter section of land purchased from the original homesteader, Julius H. Weiss, on the lower end of Willow Creek where it joins the Rio Grande River.[75] The lawsuit was filed by the plaintiff in Colorado's Twelfth Judicial District Court in Alamosa, Costilla County, Colorado, on February

North Creede and Humpreys Mill Power Plant and Rope Drive
Emma Swinehart Collection, Courtesy of Ken Wyley

28, 1905. Anton Frank stated in his complaint that the defendant had polluted Willow Creek and the Rio Grande River and the pollution had affected his ranch, livestock, and hay.[76] It is interesting to note that the clerk of the District Court at the time of the filing was one Silas Frank, who had been the postmaster at the Amethyst Post Office in 1892. Frank named several material witnesses, including Albert Pfeiffer of Rio Grande County, to testify to the pollution of the Rio Grande.

Albert Pfeiffer homesteaded on the Rio Grande River near South Fork, Colorado, and was a long-time friend of Kit Carson. He served in Carson's regiment for several years and in 1865 was appointed Indian Agent at Abiquiu, New Mexico. In 1866 he was breveted to Lieutenant Colonel for "meritorious service against the Indians in Arizona."[77]

After a change in venue to San Luis, Colorado, the case came to a jury trial on April 3, 1905. The jury rendered a decision in favor of the plaintiff and assessed damages at $1,072. Judge Charles C. Holbrook issued his judgement in the case on May 18, 1905:[78]

> "It appears from the evidence in this case that the defendant company is operating a large ore reduction mill on West Willow Creek near its junction with East Willow Creek, in which large quantities of ores are concentrated; that the tailings, slimes and poisons from the treatment of said ores are dumped and run into West Willow Creek at said point by which the waters of Willow Creek below, from which the plaintiff's ditch takes its supply of water for the irrigation of plaintiff's lands, are polluted and poisoned.
>
> "Plaintiff's lands for which he has no other means of irrigation, and which are not productive without irrigation, are hereby greatly impaired and his crops seriously damaged every year, and the tendency is to destroy the productiveness of his lands altogether.
>
> "While plaintiff's possessions are of small value as compared with the great expense incident to the erection of the extensive reduction works of defendant, and while the damages to plaintiff is small (if we are here precluded from considering like damage to other farmers and ranchmen) as compared with the vast mining interests which are dependent in large part upon this mill, the plaintiff is nevertheless

entitled to protection in the enjoyment of his property; and the evidence shows that the defendant can within a few weeks' time, and with comparatively small expenditures prepare to take care of its tailings on its own ground.

"Wherefore it is hereby ordered, adjudged, and decreed by the Court that on and after July 10, 1905, the defendant, its officers, agents, employees, and representatives be and they hereby are enjoined and restrained from dumping, running, or throwing the tailings from said mill or ore reduction plant into Willow Creek, West Willow Creek, or East Willow Creek.

"To which ruling of the Court the defendant duly excepts.

Charles C. Holbrook, Judge"

The Humphreys Tunnel and Mining Company asked that the verdict in the case be vacated and a new trial be granted, which Judge Holbrook denied, but he did enter an order allowing the company to appeal to the Colorado Supreme Court. Nevertheless, *The Engineering and Mining Journal* of September 7, 1905, stated that a settling dam for the tailings and slimes from the Humphreys Mill had been completed and would eliminate any future need to run tailings in the creek waters.

John Jackson described the Humphreys tailings disposal system.[79] A U-shaped wooden flume, two feet wide and one foot high, was constructed from the mill to a tailings pond at the southerly edge of Creede, east of the Emperius Mill site and west of the railroad. It was then extended to a 200-acre parcel of agricultural land owned by the company[80] south of the town of Creede near the present airport where the tailings were spread on the ground without any containment structures. The flume leaked along its entire length and its route could be followed by both smell and deposits of sand consisting of quartz and a green mineral, chlorite. The first tailings pond carried fair gold values, and a man by the name of James set up a trommel screen and jigs to try to recover both gold and lead, but his efforts failed. This was prior to construction of the Emperius Mill in 1934.

In 1905, the United Mines Company was consolidated with the Big Kanawha Leasing Company, the Humphreys Tunnel, and the Floradora Mining Companies to form the Creede United Mines Company, in which A.E. Humphreys was the controlling stockholder.[81] The officials of the Creede United Mines included:

L.S. Thomas, president; R.F. Kavanaugh, vice-president; B.B. Brown, secretary; George Davis, treasurer and general manager; J.D. Hawkins, general superintendent and engineer; H. E. Lees, mine superintendent; L.H. Norton, mill superintendent; and J.J. Fitzgerald, assistant mill superintendent.[82]

The Creede United Mines properties were reported to be in excellent condition in September 1905 and were increasing their production. The Humphreys Mill was running at full capacity.[83] In 1906, the Creede United Mines had a somewhat smaller production than in 1905, and again less production in 1907, but the company was doing a large amount of development work.[84] The Humphreys Mill was shut down on August 16, 1907, for an indefinite period and until the Park Regent was mined, the mill would run only about a week per month.[85] In fact, the Creede United Mines properties were idle in 1908.[86] A disastrous fire occurred at the Happy Thought Mine in December 1907 and was at least partially responsible for the 1908 shut down. The fire actually destroyed the shaft house, burned timbers in the upper part of the mine, and wrecked the shaft.[87] A description of the fire and its consequences were in the December 26, 1907, issue of *Mining Science*:

Scenic View of Creede Looking South from Inspiration Point — Date Unknown (The first Humphreys tailings pond is visible in the background.)
Photo by O.T. Davis — Courtesy of the Monte Vista Historical Society

> *"The Creede United Mines Company's power plant [shaft house] at the Happy Thought Mine was destroyed by fire on the 22nd inst., resulting in a loss of $100,000. The origin of the fire is unknown, as the plant had been closed down for several days. It is a disastrous blow to the Creede Camp, and will further curtail its production. Owing to the slump in the price of lead and silver, the majority of the mines in the camp are closed down, over 200 men being affected."*

Mining Science's issue of September 16, 1909, carried the following story about the revival of the Creede United Mines operations:

> *"The renewal of work in the United Mines properties and the continuation of the Wooster Tunnel and the re-opening of the Humphreys Mill means much for Creede. Litigation which has for years handicapped development is now out of the way and the contending interests have been consolidated. The resumption of work on the United, Park Regent, and Grab Root, other properties on the great contact, will be started in the very near future. A new company, under the name North Creede M. Co., has taken over a 15-year lease on all the Consolidated ground, has a lease on the Humphrey Mill, and is getting everything in order to work through the winter."*

By December 1909, the Happy Thought Mine was shipping about sixty tons of ore per day to the Humphreys Mill. The Humphreys Tunnel has finally reached a point below the shaft of the Park Regent Shaft and the mining of an 800-foot raise from the tunnel to connect to the bottom of the shaft was scheduled to start immediately. The raise would provide ventilation to the tunnel and an outlet to the mill for the North Creede Mining Company's ore.[88] Unfortunately, the Humphreys Mill did not operate continuously or at capacity. It processed only about fifty to sixty tons of ore per day in 1910 and 1911.[89]

The Creede United Mines had ambitious plans for its Creede operations. Extensive changes to the equipment and flow sheet of the Humphreys Mill, requiring a large force of millwrights and mechanics, were made in 1911 under the direction of Francis W. Boscoe, a consulting metallurgical engineer from Denver. The mill and the Happy Thought Mine were under lease to the Creede Local Mining Company, with Shrive Collins in charge as manager.[90] This was probably the time when the Humphreys Mill was modified to

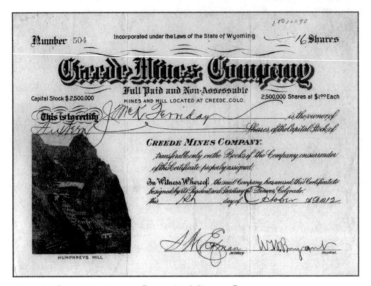

Stock Certificate — Creede Mines Company
Courtesy of Dave Bunk

include the flotation process, which would greatly improve the recovery of sulfide minerals in the ore. The mill's capacity was also increased to 250 or 300 tons per day.

A.E. Humphreys acquired the White Star and Park Regent properties, and combined them with other claims into the Creede Mines and Milling Company in 1912. That corporation was owned by Creede Mines, a holding company dominated by A.E. Humphreys and his close business associates.[91] The White Star Mining Company was one of the earliest companies organized at Creede, incorporated on July 1, 1892. According to Emmons and Larsen, the White Star Mine extended along the Amethyst Vein for about 750 feet, north of the Happy Thought and south of the Park Regent.[92]

The Engineering and Mining Journal reported on July 20, 1912, about Creede United Mines activities:

> "The Creede United Mines Co., a strong corporation, is carrying out plans which mean a larger production in about six months' time. is being equipped with a 60-hp. motor and 32-lb. rails, and will be driven 1000 ft. further, after which sinking, raising, and drifting will be done. It is said that the work planned will take 18 months to accomplish, and will create 10 years of ore reserves. Seventy-five men are employed. A.E. Humphreys is at the head and ex-governor C.S. Thomas and W.H. Bryant, of

> *Denver, are prominent members of the company. It is the*
> *same story with this company, that is heard from many*
> *others; ore left standing by the old workings as unprof-*
> *itable, is now being mined and milled at a profit; last*
> *month $20,000 worth of concentrates were shipped."*

By September 1912, the Humphreys Mill was processing 4,000 tons of ore per month under Shrive B. Collins, primarily from the new ore shoot found in the White Star Mine.[93]

Creede Camp received a tremendous Christmas present in 1912: Forty Creede miners, trapped by an underground fire, were rescued to celebrate Christmas Day alive and well with their families! The January 2, 1913, edition of *Mining Science* carried the story:

> *"A Mine Fire at Creede — Rescuers saved 40 miners,*
> *who were imprisoned in the Happy Thought Mine at*
> *Creede, Colo., which caught fire during the morning of*
> *Dec. 23. The fire raged for nearly 24 hours.*
> *"Before the 40 men could be saved it was necessary*
> *for the rescue parties to remove 50 tons of ore from an*
> *abandoned shaft in order to enable them to lower ropes to*
> *the men imprisoned, who were almost exhausted from*
> *heat and smoke. The fire is thought to have been started*
> *by the carelessness of one of the miners, who is reported*
> *to have left a stub of a cigarette on some timber in the*
> *mine.*
> *"The escapes were effected through a connection*
> *which recently had been made with the Park Regent Mine,*
> *an adjoining property."*

The Humphreys Mill had been shut down for more than a year, until February 1915, when it started processing ore from the Park Regent Mine.[94] It operated continuously in 1916 and 1917, processing ore from the Park Regent and Last Chance-Volunteer Mines, and was listed as a concentration-flotation mill in 1917.[95] It is probable that a flotation section was added to the mill in 1911.

The Humphreys Mill operated for a part of 1918 on Park Regent ore, producing lead concentrates, but discontinued operations in 1918.[96] Colonel Humphreys abandoned the Humphreys Mill, Humphreys Tunnel, and the Happy Thought and Park Regent Shafts at this time. According to Frank Wheeler, as quoted by V.V. Clark,[97] the abandonment was on account of Humphreys' failure to obtain equitable freight and treatment rates from the railroads and smelters at that time. According to Mr. Wheeler, Humphreys was unable to realize a profit under the conditions presented and closing down the various works appeared the only logical thing to do.

The Humphreys Mill added much to the general prosperity of Creede Camp. During the four years following its construction, over 400,000 tons of ore were taken from the Creede Mines property. The total output of the mine to date is estimated as not less than one million tons of crude ore, 300,000 tons of which were shipped direct to the smelter.[98] Albert Collins estimated the total production from the Happy Thought Mine at $3 million and that of the Park Regent at not more than $25,000.[99]

By 1934 much of the machinery in the Humphreys Mill had been taken away or stolen, the buildings were in a bad state of repair, and a general state of desolation was apparent.[100]

The Humphreys Reduction Mill Smolders in Ruin After a Late Night Fire Ignited by a Scrap Dealer Salvaging Metal for the War Effort in 1943

Photo by John Jackson

THE CREEDE EXPLORATION COMPANY

George H. Garrey, consulting mining geologist and engineer from New York City, examined the mines along the Amethyst vein system for the American Smelting & Refining Company (ASARCO) and submitted a report on his investigation on January 27, 1916. In his conclusion he stated in part that:

"In case your Company decides to try to consolidate the various properties along the Amethyst Lode under a working agreement where in return for financing the project your Company is given a majority control of the operating company. I would suggest to avoid annoyances in operation and also to, if possible, to obtain additional small tonnages of sulphide ores, that your Company endeavor to get leases upon, or control of, the entire properties instead of simply the portions of the properties located below the level of the Commodore or Wooster Tunnel levels.

"I am of the opinion that while development in depth will show long stretches of practically barren ground yet some shorter stretches will be found which will show good values in lead and zinc and probably commercially important amounts of gold and silver."

On the basis of Garrey's report, ASARCO decided to form the Creede Exploration Company to consolidate the properties along the Amethyst from the Bachelor through the Happy Thought Mines by long term leases in order to develop and mine the ore reserves they felt still existed.

A.E. Reynolds made the following statement at the annual meeting of the stockholders of the Commodore Mining Company on June 19, 1916:[101]

"For more than a year there have been some very active efforts made to consolidate the various properties from the Bachelor Company up through the properties owned by the Creede Mines & Milling Company, which is the old United Mines or Park Regent, into an operating and leasing company, taking leases uniform in character as far as possible for a 20-year period, with the intention of working these properties as a whole through the Commodore shaft, which is down about 450 feet below the present tunnel level. The process has been slow because of the different ownerships and lack of interest in the property, and also some strong differences of opinion about the matter."

The Engineering and Mining Journal of April 14, 1917, carried the following news item that had appeared in a Denver newspaper on April 4th:

*"Creede district expects revival if pending negotia-
tions culminate. Gerald Hughes, A.E. Reynolds, I.B.
Humphreys, Jr., L.E. Campbell, and Henry Hanington are
reported back of a merger that will include the Amethyst,
Commodore, Bachelor, New York Chance, Volunteer,
Creede, and Last Chance Companies. It is understood
that the plan calls for development at new depths —
below the Nelson Tunnel — in ground presumed to be
rich but which could not be reached because of heavy
inflows of water. It is proposed to invest a large sum in
plants for mining and milling. Finances have been fully
provided and no stock will be publically offered."*

ASARCO, Commodore Mining Company, and Mr. Gerald
Hughes owned all of the Creede Exploration Company stock.
The stockholders of the Commodore Mining Company approved
a contract between ASARCO, as party of the first part; Gerald
Hughes as party of the second part; and the Commodore Mining
Company as party of the third part on March 28, 1917.[102] Gerald
Hughes, son of Colorado Senator Charles Hughes, was a well-
known and influential Denver attorney who had become the
president of the First National Bank of Denver after David
Moffat's death.

The combining of all the properties along the Amethyst vein
under a twenty-year lease to the Creede Exploration Company, a
subsidiary of ASARCO, was effected in 1917. The Creede
Exploration Company, in addition to extensive development
work below the Nelson Tunnel level, shipped some ore from
mine workings above the tunnel level as well as from mine
dumps.[103] Several sets of lessees shipped considerable ore from
the upper workings of the Bachelor, Commodore, and New York
Chance Mines.[104]

By December 1917, the Amethyst (Berkshire) Shaft was being
unwatered; the Commodore Shaft would be unwatered when
machinery was installed; and a power plant was built at the
Humphreys Mill.[105] *The Engineering and Mining Journal* reported
on January 19, 1918, that the Commodore, Amethyst, and Creede
United properties were being developed by ASARCO.

H.A. Guess, president of the Creede Exploration Company, sent
a letter on June 15, 1918, to the property owners along the
Amethyst Vein that read, in part:[106]

"Gentlemen:

In reference to our twenty year lease agreement of March, 1917 covering the various Creede properties — after delays — got the Commodore shaft unwatered to the 450-foot level — making more water than anticipated — for all concerned lease agreement altered to read '350 foot level' instead of '450 foot level', —.

"The letter was sent to:

The Commodore Mining Company, A.E. Reynolds, President, Denver

The Creede Mines & Milling Company, A.E. Humphreys, Denver

Amethyst Mining Company, Col. L.E. Campbell, President, Denver

Volunteer Mining Company, Judge H.G. Lunt, Colorado Springs

Bachelor Mining Company, F.F. Struby, President, Denver

New York and Chance Mining Company, J. Rodman, President, Denver

Last Chance Mining Company, J. Rodman, President, Denver"

This alteration of the terms of the agreement was an omen of the future. This second attempt to consolidate the properties and develop ore below the tunnel level failed. The Creede Exploration Company sent a letter dated June 20, 1919, to the owners along the Amethyst vein notifying them of their intention to surrender the leases held by the Creede Exploration Company on their properties.[107] A.E. Reynolds visited the Creede Exploration Company's workings and reported to the stockholders of the Commodore Mining Company in a letter of July 1, 1919:[108]

"— before they (Creede Exploration Company) closed down and removed the pumps, allowing the mine to fill with water, I visited Creede and made an examination of the work, and I regret to say that it is my firm opinion that this vein is not mineralized below the No. 5 level at any point to a sufficient degree to warrant the expenditures of any more money —.

"The Creede Exploration Company was in operation over two years and expended over $500,000.

*"We have a certain amount of ore scattered through
the upper workings which under ordinary conditions, if it
could be mined continuously and shipped to the smelters,
might be exhausted in about two years."*

The shutdown of the Humphreys Mill and the Nelson-Wooster-
Humphreys Tunnel signaled the coming of hard times for Creede
Camp, and the abandonment of the Amethyst vein below the Nelson
Tunnel level confirmed it. It is interesting to note the Nelson and
Commodore No. 5 Tunnels were driven at the elevation where the
supergene or rich sulfide ore changed into the lower grade primary
hypogene ore zone in depth. There is no reason to believe the early
miners were aware of this transition in ore grade but set the tunnel
elevations on other considerations. The fact that the tunnels set the
lower limit of economic ore was probably no more than "luck."

CAPTIVE INCA MINE
Development of the Captive Inca claim, located on Deer Horn
Creek, about 6,000 feet north-northwest of the Park Regent Mine,
began in 1903 under the management of W.G. Boyle. John R.
Hanna of Monmouth, Illinois, was president of the company. The
company let a contract to sink a 5 by 15-foot shaft to a depth of 500
feet.[109] Little or no ore was found and the shaft was inaccessible in
1912.[110]

EQUITY MINE
The U.S. Geological Survey's *Mineral Resources of the United States
for 1912*, reported the Equity Mining and Investment Co. shipped
in 1912 for the first time a considerable quantity of silver-gold ore
from its mine, ten miles northwest of Creede. The Equity Mine was
idle in 1915 but operated in 1917 and 1918.[111] Charles Hollister
managed the Equity Mine from 1917 through 1919.

The Creede Candle's "Mining Edition" of January 1, 1927, had
the following information on the Equity:

*"The Equity Mine is an East-West fault fissure on the
south side of a fault block of a very great displacement.
The fault block is thrust up and its west edge, according
to Larsen and Emmons, is in the Amethyst Fault. In other
words, the Equity Fault is part of the Amethyst Fault
System. Unlike the other mines of the district the Equity
produces ruby silver and the ratio of gold to silver is*

considerably higher than that of the mines further south on the Amethyst lode."

MAMMOTH MOUNTAIN

Even though no commercial ore was found on Mammoth Mountain prior to 1900, prospecting and exploration work continued into the new century. *The Engineering and Mining Journal* of March 10, 1900, reported the Mammoth Mountain Consolidated Mining Company had leased the Nancy Hanks, Mammoth, and Mary Anderson claims and had opened an eighteen-inch streak on the Nancy Hanks, giving from forty to 100 ounces of silver per ton. The Mammoth was owned by D.H. Moffat, L.E. Campbell, and Walter Cheesman; the

Equity Mine — 1918

J. Roy Packard Collection, Courtesy of the Creede Historical Society

Mary Anderson by Philip Feldhauser, T.E. Schwartz, N. Thatcher, W.H. Combs, and the estate of Job A. Cooper; and the Nancy Hanks by Dr. Buchtell, Oney Carstarphen, D.J. Hutchinson, and Daniel Skinner.[112] *The Denver Times*, March 5, 1901, commented that the Mammoth Mountain Consolidated Company had driven its tunnel 2,000 feet and was drifting on the vein. The values obtained were not regular, but the operators expected to reach the main ore shoot soon, when they would have a mine that would amply repay them for their heavy expenditure. *The Denver Times* carried the following story in its February 21, 1902, edition:

> *"The latest news of new mineral comes from Mammoth Mountain. Lessee Montgomery, who is working the Nancy Hanks, has opened a four-foot vein of pay ore and he is getting ready for a shipment. This is one of*

the oldest locations in the camp. It had good surface indi-
cations, but many operators have failed to open a defined
lead until Mr. Montgomery took hold. Pay ore in Creede
must be worth about $25 at the mine. We pay a freight
rate to Pueblo of $4 and a treatment charge of from $7 to
$8. With silver at $0.55 and lead at $3.50 we can make
some money."

Serious exploration work continued on Mammoth Mountain until about 1905, when it was essentially abandoned. It was reported in 1902 that "all through the vein are small streaks of high grade ore and they have strong hopes of finding these streaks united in a short distance ahead, when the ore can be saved and shipped, and the chances are favorable for opening up a big body of shipping ore any day."[113] The chance of finding commercial ore never materialized and the continuing exploration on Mammoth Mountain proves that "hope springs eternal" in the prospector's heart and mind. There is no record of further exploration work after 1905 until 1918, when development work was done at the Silver King claim.[114]

SOLOMON-HOLY MOSES VEIN SYSTEM

The Solomon-Holy Moses Vein System was the second most productive zone in the Creede Mining District during the 1890s and early 1900s, even though it produced only a small portion of the district's metal production. Most of the vein system's ore came from its southern part, where the Solomon and Ridge Mines were most active. Sulfide ore was encountered at a relatively shallow depth in the Solomon-Holy Moses Vein System and the concentration of the ore became a necessity for profitable mining. The Ridge Mill was built in 1893 followed by the Solomon Mill two years later. Steven and Ratté[115] described the history of mining on the Solomon-Holy Moses Vein:

"The main mining activity during the 1890s, exclusive
of that on the Amethyst Vein zone, was on the Solomon-
Holy Moses Vein and the Alpha-Corsair Vein. Early min-
ing on the Solomon-Holy Moses Vein exploited high
grade oxidized ore from near the surface on the southern
part of the vein zone, but by the late 1890s, lower grade
sulfide ore below the strongly oxidized zone was being
developed in both the Solomon and Ridge Mines. We

estimate that approximately $800,000 worth of ore was produced from the Solomon-Holy Moses Vein prior to 1904, the earliest date for which we have found individual records for the different operating mines. Some of the high-level oxidized ores are reported to have contained as much as 80 ounces or more of silver per ton, but the primary sulfide ores generally contained only a few ounces of silver per ton.

HOLY MOSES MINE

The Denver Times of February 20, 1901, had an interesting story about the Holy Moses Mine and its owner, Charles Abbott:

> *"Holy Moses at Creede Comes Into Good Ore in an Upraise From Tunnel — If energy always receives reward the miners of Creede deserve well at the hands of the people. The camp has been struggling hard for years and the greater the difficulties encountered the greater the energy developed.*
>
> *"The Holy Moses was the first mine in which ore was discovered at Creede, and has been duly celebrated in the screeds of Cy Warman and the other men who glorified Creede in the days when it was 'day all day in the daytime and there was no night at Creede.' The mine was a heavy producer in the early days, owing to its elevated position the work was expensive and tedious and after a depth of 225 feet was reached the mine was closed to await development in the lower levels. There was a long time to wait, but the Second Chance Leasing Company undertook to drive a tunnel from the base of the mountain and after many vicissitudes in driving a tunnel 1,300 feet the vein was cut and an upraise on the ore body commenced. The upraise has now been completed and made a connection with the old workings 555 feet above the tunnel level — one of the longest upraises in Colorado. In the course of the raise a large body of milling ore was encountered, and Mr. Abbott, who has driven the raise at his own expense, says that he is going on with further development, as he expects to open a good body of paying ore. The vein was cut in a barren place and the tunnel company laid down on its contract, as Mr. Abbott was compelled to go ahead*

*on his own account. The man who has driven an upraise
555 feet single-handed deserves success, and the whole
state will rejoice to learn that he has struck it rich."*

In 1910, the Holy Moses was one of a group of mines owned by
Mrs. Esther R. Abbott, wife of the late Senator Charles H. Abbott
of Salida.[116] The Holy Moses Mine was active from 1915 to 1918.[117]

RIDGE MINE

The Ridge Mill was the first concentrator at Creede Camp and successfully produced lead and zinc concentrates into the next century.
The Engineering and Mining Journal reported on October 28, 1893,
that the Ridge Mill had proved so successful that its capacity and
power would be increased and the mine was producing ore steadily.
The capacity of the mill was nearly doubled in 1895.[118] Mining at
the Ridge was producing fifty tons of lead concentrate daily in early
1900 and was suspended in July of 1901 in order to install a new
hoist.[119] The mine materially decreased its production in the spring
of 1901 because of a heavy inflow of water, and in 1902 a new set
of lessees had taken over the mine.[120] *Mining Reporter* had the following news about the Ridge property in its June 2, 1904, issue:

> *"Creedmore Mining Company — Ezra T. Elliot, of Del
> Norte, has secured an option on the property of this com-
> pany, consisting of six patented claims and a concentrating
> mill; also upon the Mexico, Hiram, and St. Peters claims,
> owned by A.E. Reynolds, the consideration named in the
> option being $80,000. A payment of $40,000 is to be made
> in ninety days, and the balance in six months. Under the
> terms of the option the Creedmore Company is to receive
> $40,000 and Mr. Reynolds $40,000. The properties were at
> one time the largest producers of lead and zinc ores in the
> Creede district, and are said to have produced upwards of
> $500,000. The concentrating mill, which has a capacity of
> 60 tons, cost $25,000."*

The Ridge Mine and Mill were inactive in 1904 and most of
1905, but both began active operations in late November of 1905
under the direction of E.R. Mosher.[121] The Ridge Mine operation
was active from 1906 through 1912 with the exception of 1908,
when it was idle.[122] The November 17, 1910, issue of *Mining Science*
carried the following story:

REVIVING OPERATIONS AT CREEDE,
Special Correspondence

"Among the more noted zinc properties in the Creede district may be mentioned the Ridge-Mexico Mining Co.'s six patented claims and several not patented. They include the Solomon, Holy Moses, Ethel, Cliff, and others. These properties have produced several thousand tons of zinc, most of which has been marketed in Joplin, Mo. The group is now owned by Mrs. Esther R. Abbott, wife of the late Senator Charles H. Abbott of Salida. They are high grade in zinc and lead, and carry fair values in silver. Many of the Mineral County mines run high in zinc as well as lead and silver. With development more gold appears to be coming in, including zinc and lead.

"The Ridge Mine and Mill are under lease to S.A. Gardanier & Co., and it is claimed they are cleaning up a bunch of money out of the proposition."

H.C. Parmelee described the Ridge Mill in 1910:[123]

"From the point of view of the nature of ore treated, and the high quality of the zinc concentrate produced, this mill is one of the most interesting in the district. The same minerals occur in the Ridge ore as mentioned before, viz., galena, cerussite, and rosin and black jack zinc. The ore is easily mined, and as practically all of the values are in a stiff clay. The hard rock is sorted as waste and thrown over the dump. Large boulders of galena covered with zinc are frequently found in the clay.

"The nature of the ore eliminates crushing, and the first step in the milling process consists in disintegrating the stiff clay in a revolving disintegrating screen of the American Concentrator Company type. The machine consists practically of a revolving grizzly, jacketed with a screen and revolving in a trough of water. Heavy cast-iron hoods reduced the openings at each end, through one of which the ore is fed and from the other the barren rock discharged. One-inch bars extend from end to end of the trommel and into the face of the hoods. The screen jacket surrounds these bars and has 1 1/2 inch round openings. On the outside of the screen jacket are bolted at intervals elevator cups. The number of cups determines the

quantity of feed and may be increased or decreased as needed. At the discharge end of the screen is a plow-shaped casting which, in its revolutions, picks up and discharges any pieces of rock which may have been fed with the clay. The rock is taken to the dump.

"The ore, disintegrated by the revolution of the screen, falls through the openings into the trough, where it is picked up by the buckets and discharged onto an apron. It is then sized for jig and table work in the usual trommel screens to which it is elevated in the usual manner. The first trommel has 4-mesh screen cloth, the oversize of which is sent to rolls and again elevated. The undersize passes to a second trommel, which delivers two undersizes, one from each half of the trommel, and an oversize. The upper half of the trommel has 8-mesh screen, and the lower half, 6 mesh. The 8-mesh undersize is hydraulically classified, the underflow going to the fine jig and the overflow to the tables. The 6-mesh undersize goes to the medium jig and the oversize to a coarse jig.

"There are three four-compartment Harz jigs having 5-mesh, 6-mesh, and 8-mesh screens on the coarse, medium, and fine jigs respectively. Hutch products only

The Ridge Mill — Photo by O.T. Davis, 1896
(Note the Holy Moses Aerial Tramway tower and ore bucket.)

Courtesy of the Monte Vista Historical Society

*are made; lead concentrate in the first compartment, mid-
dling in the second, zinc concentrate in the third, and middling in the fourth. Zinc concentrate is occasionally
skimmed from the last compartment. The middling is
returned to the elevator and rescreened without regrinding. The coarse, medium, and fine jigs are run at 230
r.p.m., 240 r.p.m., and 260 r.p.m. respectively.*

*"Three Wilfley tables of an early date are used and do
good work. The first two make lead concentrate and middling, which [the] latter is retreated on the third table
where zinc and lead are separated. Most of the concentrating at this mill is done in the jigs, and the tables are not
relied upon as much as in the other mills where no jig zinc
concentrate is made.*

*"Crude Ridge ore assays about 1.5 oz. silver, 0.01 oz.
gold, four percent lead, and eight percent zinc. The pro-
portion of the two base metals to each other is the reverse
of that in the ore treated in the other mills.*

*"The zinc concentrate is of excellent quality, carrying
from fifty percent to fifty-six percent zinc, three percent
lead, 0.05 oz. gold, and 2.0 oz. silver.*

*"The Ridge Mill is provided with low-pressure water-
power. The 20-in. pipeline has a drop of about 100 ft.,
and water is delivered through a 3-in. nozzle to a 4-ft.
Pelton wheel at a pressure of 35 lb. Per square inch. The
mill has a capacity of 50 tons per 24 hours, but is run only
one 10-hour shift and treats about 20 tons per day."*

The Ridge Mill was shut down sometime between 1912 and
1916, probably nearer to 1912. The U.S. Geological Survey's
Mineral Resources of the United States for 1916, states, "None of
the other mills in the district (except the Humphreys Mill) were
operated, the remainder of the production being from lead and dry
silver ore shipped to smelters."

V.V. Clark visited the Ridge Mine with F.E. Wheeler, H.C.
Rowley, and B.C. Hosselkus, all Creede Camp old-timers, in 1934.
He mentioned the Ridge in his 1934 report:[124]

*"The mine has a production record of about
$1,000,000. It put out a large tonnage of sphalerite [zinc
sulfide] in earlier years. One car, which was shipped by
H.C. Rowley, ran as high as 64 percent zinc."*

SOLOMON MINE

The Creede Leasing and Milling Company erected a mill on the Solomon mining claim in 1895 having a capacity of 75 tons of ore per day. In 1998, the Solomon Mine was leased to Charles H. Abbott of Salida and H.C. Rowley of Creede. The mill was treating about forty tons of ore per day, and 500 tons of zinc ore were shipped to England in 1900.[125] The December 4, 1901, issue of *The Denver Times* had the following story:

> *"C.S. [C.H] Abbott is making a good thing out of the Solomon Mine on Nelson Mountain, a lead and zinc ore, which he is treating in his own mill. Mr. Abbott at one time worked the old Holy Moses, the first location of N.C. Creede, but finally gave it up. His profits from the Solomon were large enough in two years to pay for the mine and the mill. He is shipping concentrates regularly."*

The East Willow Mining Company, managed by Mr. Lockbridge, was operating the Solomon Mine property in 1902 and was processing about forty tons of ore per day, making lead and zinc concentrates.[126] By the end of 1903, the 3,000-foot Ethel Tunnel had been completed and plans to sink a winze below tunnel level were made in order to develop additional ore.[127] The September 7, 1905, issue of *Mining Reporter* stated that more ore was in sight, that the East Willow Mining Company was making larger shipments than in previous years, and that the lead grade was improving in depth. The October 4, 1906, issue of *Mining Reporter* contained an article on "Mills and Milling Practices at Creede, Colorado" that described the Solomon Mill:

> *"The Solomon Mill of the East Willow Mining & Milling Company has an equipment of crusher, rolls, jigs, and tables to afford a daily capacity of 75 tons. Remarkably high grade products, one a lead concentrate carrying from 75% to 80% lead with gold and silver values, and the other a 65% to 75% zinc concentrate, are shipped. The ore is higher grade than any milled in the camp. On account of its soft granulated state it is cheaply mined, requiring little, if any, powder for its breaking, and in its milling, little crushing is necessary."*

Mining Reporter, in an article on the "Zinc Industry of Colorado" in its March 7, 1907, issue, had this to say about the Solomon mining and milling operations:

The Solomon Mill — Date Unknown
Al Birdsey Collection, Courtesy of the Creede Historical Society

> *"The Creede blende usually carries appreciable quan-*
> *tities of silver and gold in proportions of $3 to $2. The*
> *Solomon Mine produces ore of 15% to 30% zinc tenor.*
> *Zinc concentrates of over 50% are turned out at the for-*
> *mer mill to the amount of 300 tons monthly. The concen-*
> *trates from the Solomon Mill run as high as 65% zinc.*
> *Lead concentrates of high percentage are also products in*
> *Mineral County."*

The Solomon Mine shipped crude silver-lead ore in 1907 but was idle in 1908; the Solomon Mill did not operate in 1910[128] and was most likely abandoned about the spring of 1911. The Solomon Mine reopened in 1916 and produced ore, probably ore shipped direct to the smelters, through 1918.[129]

V.V. Clark also mentioned the Solomon Mine in his 1934 report:[130]

> *"The Ethel Mine, south of the Ridge, has a gold vein*
> *from which about $25,000 was shipped, and another*
> *vein, in connection with the Solomon Mine, produced*
> *around $1,250,000 in gold, silver, lead, and zinc concen-*
> *trates, of which the gold assayed from $3 to $4 per ton,*
> *and the silver from three to four ounces per ton. The*

Ridge and Solomon veins join at about the top of the ridge
on Campbell Mountain."

MOLLIE S. AND EUNICE MINES

The Mollie S. and Eunice Mines operated throughout 1901. A.V.
Tabor made regular shipments of high-grade bromide ore (containing silver bromide).[131] The two mines produced silver ore in 1906
but only development work was reported in 1907 by the Mollie S.
Mining Company.[132] The Mollie S. Mine operated in 1912, 1915,
1917, and 1918.[133] Emmons and Larsen[134] described the mines as
they were in 1912:

> *"The Mollie S. Mine is high on the west slope of*
> *Mammoth Mountain, about one mile northeast of North*
> *Creede. The workings consist of four tunnels that have a*
> *difference in elevation of about 500 feet and aggregate*
> *about 1,300 in length. A tramway is built to deliver ore to*
> *a station on the wagon road on East Willow Creek from*
> *the dispatching station, 1,100 feet higher. According to*
> *Mr. Rufus Light, the owner, the mine has produced nearly*
> *$50,000.*
>
> *"The Eunice Mine is directly south of the Mollie S.*
> *Mine, and its principal tunnel is about 125 feet south of*
> *the portal of Tunnel 2 of the Mollie S."*

CHAMPION MINE

The Denver Times reported on May 23, 1900, that Zeb Wilson had
driven a crosscut tunnel 100 feet into the Kentucky Belle Extension
property and expected to cut the vein within forty feet. By July
1901, the tunnel had connected to the discovery shaft and some
good ore was being mined.[135] In September 1904, the Monte Carlo
Gold and Silver Mining Company was incorporated under the laws
of Colorado and capitalized at $1,250,000 for the purpose of min-
ing the Champion, Monte Carlo, and adjacent claims. Officers of
the company were F.J. Hale, president; G.W. Logan, vice-president
and treasurer; and Thomas Tribe, secretary.[136] The prospectus made
the following statements:

> *"The company owns the Champion, Equator, Harry*
> *T., and Monte Carlo claims, containing about 35 acres,*
> *located on Campbell Mountain. This mountain has*

shipped some of the richest ore ever shipped from Creede. The front or south side of this mountain rises to a height of 1,500 feet above the streams. At the rear of this extreme point is located the Champion Mine, belonging to the Monte Carlo Company.

"Development work consists of a tunnel over 600 feet long, and a drift run on the vein for a distance of 150 feet, the vein being from one to five feet wide. A second level, 50 feet below, has been started. The Company has already shipped from the top workings of the mine 32 car lots of ore, averaging $50 per ton. Instead of the ore being hoisted by hand to the top of the mountain, as formerly, a tunnel of 265 feet in length has been driven from the north slope to intersect Level No. 1, so that the ore can be taken out in cars, thus saving considerable expense in handling the ore in top workings.

"The ore from the top workings is sacked and packed by burros to the cars, a distance of four miles, but this can be obviated by building a tramway to the road below, and the ore can then be loaded on cars for $1.00 per ton. During the past year the Company has shipped a number of cars of good ore.

"The Company having now demonstrated that they have a valuable mine, wish to construct a tramway and install machine drills, so the ore can be mined rapidly and transported cheaply to the cars, and for this purpose offers a block of Treasury Stock at 15 cents per share, and we feel sure those seeking investments can find no better proposition, nor one that will net the investor a handsomer profit."

The Monte Carlo Gold and Silver Mining Company erected an aerial tram in 1906 and mined ore in 1907 and 1908.[137] *The Creede Candle's* "Mining Issue" of January 1, 1927, described the later history of the Champion Mine:

"The new owners improved the method of operation by installing an aerial tram by which the ore could be conveyed from an opening in the cliff to an ore bin or loading shed some 1400 feet below, where it could be reached by wagons and thus save the expense of packing it down the mountainside. At the time of its installation this was

Champion Mine Cliff-Side Ore Bin — June 2001
Photo by the Author

*the longest free swinging tram in the world, it being 1700
feet in length from where it was anchored in the rocks
above the opening of the mine to where it delivered the
ore at the loading shed.*

*"In addition to the installation of the tram, a tunnel
was cut into the mountainside a distance of 260 feet to
furnish a means of getting to and from the mine other
than by the shaft from the top of the cliff.*

*"With these improved methods the mine was devel-
oped rapidly and over $50,000 worth of high grade ore
marketed, but the panic of 1907 which sent the price of
silver to a level that made it unprofitable to mine under
the most favorable circumstances, forced the company to
close down and they have never resumed operations since
only on one occasion when the former manager took out
a few cars, but found that the high cost of labor added to
the increased freight rates and smelting charges made it
almost prohibitive to operate at a profit."*

The author, as a young boy in Monte Vista, Colorado, had a
neighbor, Alan Howard, an old-timer who had worked in the mines
at Summitville and Creede. Howard worked on the construction of
the Champion Mine cliff-side ore bin and told how he and others

CHAPTER 10: A TIME FOR CONCENTRATION

were let over the cliff on ropes to drill holes in the cliff face. Steel rods were then driven into the holes and wood boards were attached to the rods to form a platform to start the construction of the cliff-side ore bin. What a way to make a living!

William T. Jackson, Jr., John Jackson's father, worked at the Champion/Monte Carlo Mine in 1910. He helped Charlie Gratton hand cobb ore, i.e., breaking the valuable minerals away from the waste rock by using a hammer in order to reduce the amount of material transported off the mountain. John has the "cobbing plate" that his dad used.[138]

ALPHA-CORSAIR VEIN SYSTEM

Steven and Ratté[139] commented that: "Production from the Alpha-Corsair vein zone from 1904 until 1922, when mining ceased until the middle 1930s, was slightly more than $100,000, most of which was accounted for by silver. The most productive single year was 1904, when about $18,500 worth of silver was produced. In most other years only a few thousands of dollars worth of silver was produced."

ALPHA AND CORSAIR MINES

Motz & Peterson shipped several cars of ore monthly to the smelters in 1900.[140] The Corsair Mine reported ore with values of more than 200 ounces of silver per ton in 1901.[141] *Mining Reporter* had this comment in their July 4, 1901, issue:

> *"Creede — The Corsair Mine, which started in a very small way and with but very little capital, seems to be in a very prosperous condition. The company has now in the treasury over $10,000, has paid $5,000 in dividends, and a concentration mill is now under consideration."*

The mill was never built. *The Denver Times* carried the following on December 4, 1901:

> *"In the Sunnyside district F.E. Wheeler and Chris Stump are leasing in the old workings of the Alpha Mine and making pay shipments. Mosier & Rals are shipping ore from the upper workings, Dell Wilson and associates have a lease on the Delaware lode on which they have opened six feet of ore which assays well enough in silver to ship. The Sunnyside Development Company, a syndicate of Fort Collins and Loveland people, are following a promising lead which they believe to be the Corsair. In piercing the*

wall rock into the vein they broke in a big cave, the bottom of which is filled with water up to within a foot or two of the level of the tunnel. On the hanging wall side through which they drove lays a thin streak of ore two inches wide that assays eighty ounces, but what the rest of the vein is composed of they were unable to ascertain, as foul air prevented them from making a further investigation up to yesterday, nor has the size of the cave been ascertained.

"From the latter, Denver & Rio Grande employees, who constitute the company, are making regular shipments of ore that is adding to all their bank accounts."

The Corsair Mine shipped about 200 tons of silver ore per month in 1902 and twenty-five tons per week in 1903.[142] The president of the Corsair Mining Company reported to the stockholders on May 18, 1903, that two of the ore shoots extended below the tunnel level.[143] In 1904 the mine was leased for five years in two separate blocks, the main tunnel level being the dividing line. Zendler & Higgins leased the mine below the main tunnel level and Peterson & Co. leased the upper levels, and occasional shipments were made from the mine in 1905.[144] The Corsair shipped ore to the smelters in 1906, 1907, and 1916 through 1918; and the Alpha shipped in 1907, 1908, 1910, 1912, and 1915 through 1918.[145]

KREUTZER SONATA MINE

The Denver Times, December 4, 1901, stated that John Zang had a lease on the Kreutzer Sonata Mine and was following a promising seam of ore. He built the Zang Hotel in Creede that is now known as the Creede Hotel. Zang was murdered in 1911. *The Creede Candle*, June 17, 1911, told about Zang's death:

"One of the most horrifying murders in the history of the Creede district occurred last Sunday afternoon in the Stringtown portion of North Creede.

"John Zang, the well-known proprietor of the Zang Hotel, who has been here practically since Creede became Creede, was shot and almost instantly killed by Mrs. Michael Lefevre, who used a .45 caliber Colt's revolver, in her house on the North Creede Road during the absence of her husband."

Emmons and Larsen[146] reported in 1912 that the Kreutzer Sonata Mine was opened in 1892 and was said to have produced about $10,000, but it had not been worked for several years. The U.S. Geological Survey's *Mineral Resources of the United States* listed the Kreutzer Sonata as an operating mine in 1916.

CREEDE FORMATION

Geologists at the beginning of the twentieth century felt the possibility of economic ore deposits in the Creede Formation existed. Emmons and Larsen[147] stated that even though the principal ore deposits had been found in the volcanic rocks, it was possible deposits would be found in the Creede Formation and suggested any faults in that formation would be worthy of investigation as possible sources of ore. No deposits, other than those on Monon Hill, were located prior to 1918. The Monon Hill Mine produced ore from disseminated deposits at the contact between the Creede Formation and the lower volcanic rocks.

MONON HILL MINES

Coleman & Wheeler secured a three-year lease on the Creede Quintette property on Monon Hill in 1901 and commenced work.[148] Evidently the lease did not work out, because Charles Stone and his two sons had taken hold of the Monon lode on Monon Hill and had timbered the shaft preparatory to prospecting the property thoroughly in December 1901.[149] There was no further activity until 1910 when the Creede Quintette property shipped ore.[150] Emmons and Larsen stated that in 1912, according to one of the owners, Mr. Charles P. Eades, about five carloads of ore running from twenty-five to seventy-one ounces of silver to the ton had been shipped from the mine.[151] The ore was said to carry no lead, zinc, or gold. Larsen[152] had the following comments in his 1929 report:

> *"About 1914 or 1915 Samuel Magnusson, working the Monon Mine on a lease, found the large ore body that yielded nearly all of the metal of the Monon and Manitoba Mines. He produced some silver and then turned his lease over to A.B. [A.E.] Collins and H.R. Wheeler, and under their lease most of the production of the Monon was made. Some silver was produced later from the Monon and some from the Manitoba. The total yield of this deposit is estimated from reliable information at about $800,000, about ninety-five per cent in silver and the rest in lead with a very little gold and copper."*

Magnusson Tunnel to Collins and Wheeler Strike —
1918 (Eades Tunnel above the Magnusson Tunnel)
Courtesy of the Creede Historical Society

Monon Hill produced ore in 1916, 1917, and in 1918 when a large quantity of silver ore was shipped to the smelters.[153] *Mining America* told about Monon Hill in its March 16, 1918, issue:

> *"The Quintet Mining Company is an example of patience. After nearly 30 years of paying taxes on idle property, reincorporating after its original charter from the state had expired, the company for the last 4 months has been paying a dividend of 5 cents a share a month on its present capitalization of $50,000, and apparently the distribution will go on.*
>
> *"A.E. Collins, one of the successful lessees of the Creede district, took a lease on the Quintet claims at Sunnyside several months ago and soon opened on one of the great bodies of silver-bearing ore for which the district is famous. The company, which in its present form is a holding corporation for the original company whose charter expired, is now considering raising the capital stock to its old basis of $500,000. A meeting of the stockholders held in Denver on Monday was adjourned for 30 days to await the recommendation of the directors on the advisability of making the change."*

A.E. Collins opened up a silver bonanza in the Quintette property on Monon Hill in 1917 that was one of the few bright spots in Creede

Camp at the end of World War I. Never before had an ore body of such magnitude and richness been discovered in the district.[154]

The Monon Hill Mine was accessed by five tunnels (adits). They are from the lowest in elevation to the highest: Silver Horde, Moon, Manitoba, Magnusson, Eades, and Discovery Tunnels. The Moon Tunnel was driven by the Wabash Mines and Power Company, who operated the Monon property in 1918.

Moon Tunnel and Wabash Power Plant — 1918
Courtesy of the Creede Historical Society

BULLDOG MOUNTAIN VEIN SYSTEM

Ore deposits in the Bulldog Mountain Vein System were not found by the early prospectors. However, some came very close. A shaft was sunk in 1894 on the apex of the Bulldog Mountain vein on the Kansas City Star claim patented by J.A. Biles on April 5, 1894. The shaft was sunk to a depth of seventy feet but was inaccessible in 1912.[155] Dr. J.A. Biles, a physician of very high standing, was the resident surgeon for the Denver & Rio Grande Railroad in Del Norte, Colorado. He also had a medical practice at Creede. He was involved in exploring and developing his claim and was quoted as saying: "In 1894 the Kansas City Star ran assays from four to as high as eighty-two ounces silver per ton. In 1893 I got gold assays $12 per ton. Since that time [I] have had many more running small amounts."[156] The prospectus of the Bulldog Leasing, Mining & Milling Company told of Dr. Biles and his mining activities and why the Bulldog Company was incorporated:

"The Tale of the Bulldog — Creede made money, but it also made men. One of these was a physician with a big practice and a big heart. No story of this company would

be complete without the name of our beloved stockholder, Dr. J.A. Biles, known to all as the soul of uprightness, of old fashioned courtesy and sturdy American manhood. In his travel of mercy and skill to the miners of Creede, he himself became inoculated with the fever of mining. He finally became the owner of valuable claims, which he attempted to develop himself, but found he needed help. A small mutual company was formed of local people, who contributed $5.00 each per month to drive a tunnel to cross-cut the Bulldog lode.

"For three years the little company has doggedly dug its way into the bowels of Bulldog Mountain, 861 feet toward the goal; but prices have soared, labor is scarce, powder is high. Some of the members early lost their enthusiasm and dropped out from various causes. Some died, others suffered reverses, but the Bulldog continued to hang on. The little band dwindled to a number whose $5.00 monthly assessment represented too small a sum to complete the prospect within a reasonable time. Some of the members were widows; a number through ill health were unable to continue longer. It was then decided to reorganize the company on a non-assessable basis, so that none should lose his or her share. Recently the Bulldog Leasing, Mining & Milling Company has been incorporated under the laws of Colorado, with a capital stock of $100,000, at a par value of $1.00 per share. Eight thousand six hundred and forty shares were issued dollar for dollar for the money paid into the old partnership. A sale of $10,000 worth of the treasury stock has now been authorized by the board of directors. This money when received will be used solely for development work."

The officers of the Bulldog Leasing, Mining & Milling Company were C.H. Zink, president and director; J.W. Powell, vice-president and director; Thomas F. Howell, M.D., secretary-treasurer and director; J. Jackson, director; and Wade H. Howell, director.

J.W. "Jack" Powell was a well-known rancher in the Creede area. He came to Creede around the turn of the century and worked at the Humphreys and Ridge Mills. He homesteaded a tract of land at the mouth of Trout Creek Canyon up river from Creede.[157]

Dr. Thomas F. Howell was born July 4, 1871, in Kansas City, Missouri, and lived his young life on Howell's Island — an island in the Missouri River that was washed away by flood waters about 1928. He was a Kansas City fireman from 1895 to 1900 and attended the University of Kansas Medical School in Manhattan, Kansas, from 1900 to 1906. After graduation, he worked as a doctor for the Union Pacific Railroad until 1912 when he moved to Creede. He set up a medical practice at the request of Dr. John Biles of Del Norte. He moved from Creede to Alamosa about 1922 and practiced there until his death in September 1940. He was the designated physician for the D&RG Railroad. Wade H. Howell was a Creede miner and Dr. Howell's older brother.[158]

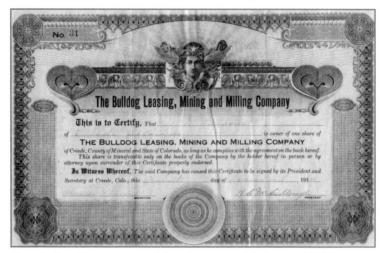

Stock Certificate — Bulldog Leasing, Mining & Milling Company

Courtesy of Les Turnipseed

This stock certificate, dated December 1, 1914, certifies that A.D. Parsons of Creede was the owner of one share of stock. The certificate was signed by H.C. McCullough, president, and Thomas F. Howell, secretary.

Marge Hosselkus, a long-time Creede resident, remembers Dr. Howell. He kept a glass jar full of candy for the kids at his office in his home on the mesa. Marge remembers stopping by for candy when she was a girl just starting to school about 1918. Her mother and/or grandmother did housework for the doctor.[159]

Dr. Howell's son, Tom, remembers his father telling stories about being a doctor at Creede — staying at homes during the winter for as long as it took to help the patient, attending births, accidents, broken limbs, frozen feet, and diseases. The flu epidemic in 1918 hit Creede with a vengeance and no doubt created a crisis for

Dr. Howell. Tom met an old man in 1953 who had known his father. The old man told Tom he had encountered Dr. Howell mid-winter in the early 1920s when he had frozen feet. He said the doctor stayed with him for nearly a week tending his feet, and he was very grateful for the kind treatment he had received.

According to its prospectus, the Bulldog Company's holdings included 861 feet of finished tunnel heading toward the Bulldog Mountain fault zone, which was designed to intersect it 550 feet below the Kansas City Star Shaft and 1,000 to 1,200 feet from the portal; the Nickel Plate Tunnel site; the Kansas City Star Shaft full of water; six non-patented mining claims; and bonds and leases on the Kansas City Star, Puzzle, and Conejos patented lode claims. The Conejos claim was patented on January 28, 1893 by C.C. Cotton, Hiram P. Griswold, Walter deG. Maud, and E.L. DeGolyer. The Puzzle was patented on October 14, 1895, by W.W. Dunlap.

The Bulldog Company's prospectus included a prophetic statement that: "A competent U.S. geologist pronounced our chances in his opinion the best in Creede. Our own Bulldog lode may yet prove to be the great undiscovered mother lode of Creede." The prophecy, however, did not come true for another half century, until the Homestake Mining Company developed and exploited the Bulldog Mountain Vein System. During the 1970s and early 1980s, Homestake's Bulldog Mountain Mine was the largest producer of silver in Colorado and the fourth largest silver producer in the United States. From the beginning of production in 1969 through the end of production in 1985, the mine produced 25.3-million ounces of silver and 48.6-million pounds of lead.[160]

WAGON WHEEL GAP FLUORSPAR MINE

The Wagon Wheel Gap fluorspar deposit was located on the eastern margin of the Creede caldera and about ten miles southeast of Creede, but it was not a part of the Creede district per se. However, the deposit was developed and exploited by Creede miners and is, therefore, included in the history of Creede Camp. The history of the development of the deposit is included in the 1920 Colorado Geological Survey Bulletin 18, *Fluorspar Deposits of Colorado*, by Harry A. Aurand:

> "An extremely large deposit of fluorspar has been
> developed by the American Fluorspar Mining Company
> one and a quarter miles south of the Wagon Wheel Gap

station on the Denver and Rio Grande R. R. This deposit is located on the east side of Goose Creek at a point directly opposite the Mineral Hot Springs, a resort well-known for its mineral waters.

"The vein was located in the belief that it was an extension of the Amethyst Vein at Creede. Both veins strike northwest and southeast and cut through country rock of the same type. On account of the resemblance of the amethyst and purple fluorspar to the radiating amethyst-quartz crystals found in the Amethyst Vein at Creede, no one appears to have known that is was fluorspar. As the fluorspar vein carries but little gold and silver, little attention was given to it. In 1911 the mineral was recognized by S.B. Collins, the president and general manager of the American Fluorspar Mining Company, and by 1913 development had progressed to the extent that 5,000 tons were shipped to Pueblo. During 1914 the mine was idle but reopened in 1915, and has been worked intermittently to the present time."

The deposit was discovered and claimed by prospectors named Tewkesberry.[161] Paul Davis, who worked at Creede as a mining engineer in the early 1940s, knew S.B. "Shrive" Collins. Shrive, who graduated from the Colorado School of Mines in 1901 as a mining engineer, was the son of Creede pioneer James Collins. Paul tells the story about Collins' acquisition of the claims on the fluorspar deposit as told to him by Shrive:

"When Emmons and Larsen, geologists for the U.S. Geologic Survey who were doing field work for their report on the geology and ore deposits at Creede, came to town, they could not find office space. Shrive Collins had more than enough space for his activities as well as theirs, so he offered to share his office with them, for which they were grateful. One day they came in from the field and met Shrive and one of them told him the next time he was in the Wagon Wheel Gap area, he ought to look at a prospect that two prospectors were working. No doubt much information was exchanged at the time. With a twinkle in his eye and a smile Shrive said, 'I just happened to be in the area the next day.' He was dressed, as was the custom of young mining engineers of the day, with boots,

Stetson hat, and a Brunton compass and rock hammer hanging from his belt. When he asked what they had, the prospectors said it was good amethyst quartz, thinking they had a real dude on the line. They knew it was fluorite with no silver values as did Shrive, but they did not know that Shrive was well aware of what they had. As a result of that meeting, Shrive bought the prospectors out. Both parties thought they had a good deal."

The Wagon Wheel Gap Fluorspar Mine was developed by two tunnels and several small shafts and open cuts. An aerial tram connected the mine with ore bins located at the foot of the hill near Goose Creek. Ore was hauled in wagons to Wagon Wheel Gap where it was loaded onto railroad cars. A surface tram track was constructed in 1917, crossing the Rio Grande River on an old wagon bridge to the railroad where the ore could be dumped directly into the rail cars. The grade was such that a mule could pull a number of cars and thus a large tonnage could be loaded on the railroad cars. Ore was shipped to both coasts. While some was shipped to the Colorado Fuel & Iron Company at Pueblo, a large quantity went to eastern markets.[162] A large force of men was employed at the Wagon Wheel Gap Fluorspar Mine in 1917 and 1918 and a large tonnage of fluorspar was mined and shipped.[163]

A concentrating mill, built at the mine about 1917, separated, by gravity, the fluorspar from the waste rock in a series of jigs. This worked well as fluorspar has a higher specific gravity than the rock. The mill was powered by steam engines driving one main shaft from which all the reduction machinery was motivated by belts or rope. A "hothead" diesel of early design powered a Sullivan air compressor that provided compressed air to drills and hoists in the mine.[164]

Wagon Wheel Gap is the type locality for creedite, an extremely rare fluoride mineral. It was first found and described prior to 1916 at the Wagon Wheel Gap fluorspar deposit and is found in very few localities worldwide.[165]

CHAPTER 11
EARLY MINE TRANSPORTATION

THE FIRST ORE MINED in the Creede Mining District came from Sunnyside in the late 1880s and was transported to Del Norte by ox team.[1] The Sunnyside mines were close to the existing wagon road that ran along the Rio Grande River. The terrain between the mines and the road is relatively flat river bottom land and connecting roads to the mines were easily constructed.

Conditions changed drastically when discoveries of rich silver ore were made high on the precipitous mountains rising from East and West Willow Creeks. The canyon floors were covered with dense willow thickets and forest. The earliest prospectors had only game trails to travel with their pack animals. Charles F. Nelson, in an interview reported in *The Denver News* (see Chapter One), stated during the winter of 1889-90 he and N.C. Creede were seven miles from the nearest post office in four feet of snow with snowshoes as the only

Primeval Willow Creek Canyon — circa 1889
Courtesy of the Colorado Historical Society

means of travel. They spent the summer of 1890 building trails to their discoveries so that development could start.

The trails built by the early discoverers were used by pack burros and mules to deliver supplies to the developing mines and to haul ore to the valley floor. Eventually they were widened and improved to allow the passage of supply wagons to and ore wagons from the mines. Frank W. Smith, a "mule skinner" at Creede during the early days of the camp, wrote:

> *"In the early days of Creede, a good many pack mules and burros were used to get the ore down from the mines. The Burro Punchers and the Mule Skinners were a rough, hardy set, always out for fun, and never let anyone down they liked. When it came to dances, which were held once or twice a week, they generally ran things to suit themselves. Among the outfits I hauled ore for were D.W. Hoover and Bill Morrow, Higgins and Chapman, and Bert Collins. Expert packers could pack anything from a 30-gallon barrel of whisky to a thousand foot cable, or a bedroom suite, and could throw the famous [or infamous] Diamond Hitch."* [2]

Part of a Pack Train — Creede, 1894
Courtesy of the Colorado Historical Society

Burro Train Hauling Lumber to the Mines — Creede, circa 1892
Courtesy of the Colorado Historical Society

Burro Bridge at West Willow Creek Falls — 1892
Courtesy of the Creede Historical Society

WAGON ROADS

It soon became obvious that an efficient means of transportation was required if the mines that were being developed were to become economic successes. Pack animal trails were definitely not the answer! The first answer was, of course, wagon roads. The roads under the best of conditions were steep, dangerous to travel, and difficult to maintain, particularly in the winter, given the heavy snows in the San Juans. Sleds were used in the winter months when the roads were covered with snow and ice. Wagons replaced the sleds when the roads were clear. Teams of horses were used to pull both conveyances. At the peak of the boom, nearly 200 horses were used on the ore hauls.[3] D.W. Hoover, an ore-hauling contractor for the mines, had horse barns in Creede that covered four acres at the time of the fire in June 1892.

West Willow Terrace Road to the Amethyst and
Last Chance Mines
Photo by E.S. Larsen, 1911, Courtesy of the U.S. Geological Survey

Frank W. Smith wrote about his life as a Creede "mule skinner" for his family before he passed away in 1951. This is part of his story:

> "*Before spring [1892], the railroad had finished the spur up to Creede; the Amethyst Mine was building a tramway; and two wagon roads were nearing completion to the mines. New machinery began to arrive. [D.W.] Hoover gave me the job of unloading and hauling the machinery up to where it belonged. I helped to place machinery in some 15 mines, and believe me, it was some job as some pieces weighed as much as 7 tons and not much road to haul over. We used as many as 18 head of horses on some loads and drove with a jerkline. I had two helpers, one to block the wagon and the other one to help me put the teams across the chains at the short turns.*"[4]

The Creede Transportation Company, 1893

Eugenia Wetherill Collection, Courtesy of Ken Wyley

The Creede Candle of September 14, 1894, carried this article that described the amount of material hauled by wagons to the Amethyst Mine:

> *"The Mineral Transfer Company has the contract for hauling the Amethyst machinery up the hill. Forty-five loads of sand, forty of brick, four of fire brick, the two big boilers, the compressor, the engine, hoister, pumps, and all make 120 loads. One of the big wheels for the engine weighed three tons and was taken up Tuesday. The plate on the air compressor, a 12-drill machine, weighs seven tons. Many of the pieces will tax the ingenuity of the haulers. But so far everything has been successful that has been attempted."*

A reporter who visited Creede in the winter months of 1892 (see Chapter Six) wrote: "Now and then a big ten-ton load of ore in a ponderous sled comes thundering down the steep road with the driver pounding his horses lustily and shouting at the top of his lungs. He is more afraid of sticking somewhere than of smashing all creation by colliding with it. Behind him come two or three more in the same style." In reality, the loads were most likely two to three tons of ore.

Frank W. Smith wrote about his experiences as a mule skinner hauling ore from the various mines during the summer months in wagons and in the winter on sleds:[5]

"I hauled ore from this mine [Nelson Tunnel] for a year. It was a short haul. You had to make 3 trips a day and unload it yourself; or make 5 or 6 trips and it was unloaded for you and you changed wagons. That was a snap and I would get through from two to three o'clock.

"When I hauled from the Last Chance Mine, there were from ten to twenty teams hauling. When the roads were bad we would be till dark getting in. It was hard work and dangerous, too, because the road was steep and got very icy in the winter.

"There were many funny things that happened on the trails and roads in those days. I remember one day, when the road was bad and icy, we were hauling on bobsleds with six or eight tons to a load. A fellow from Arizona we called Nancy Johnson, who wasn't used to bad, icy roads, was coming down and was pretty well in the lead. His team and sled got out of control and were hitting a pretty fast pace and he failed to make a short turn, landing in the creek. The water was not so cold as it came out of the mines but the weather was down about zero. So, before we could get him out, his clothes were frozen stiff, and we had to take him on down to the cabin where we unloaded ore. Believe me, it was some job, and besides, we had the wreck to clear up before we could get our loads down.

"Another time, it was me who had the bad luck, as I could not get stopped to put on more roughlocks. I was plunging down one of the steepest parts of the road and there was a high bridge at the bottom of it, located on a turn. So I began to throw my horse blankets, overcoat, shovel, etc., under the sled runners to help slow it down. Just before I hit the bridge the gravel had washed down in the ruts and served as an effective brake for the sled. Outside of one wheel horse losing a lot of hide and a few broken straps we were all right — only a little scared.

"Another time one of the fellows was following me down when we were hauling in wagons. He did not stop to put on an extra roughlock but just kept going. When he *got to the high bridge where it was very icy, his wagon slid around and the heavy load of ore pulled the horses off the bridge backwards. It killed three of the four horses but the man escaped. His name was Ed Payne. He was put on the gravel wagon after that, fixing up the road. A great many accidents occurred on the road, killing horses, and break-ing up wagons. Hauling ore was a dangerous job, but the teams had to be kept going regardless of the weather or bad roads as the ore had to be got to the smelters because the mines had to keep up their production."*

Ore Wagons — circa 1892

*John Gary Brown Collection,
Courtesy of the Creede Historical Society*

E.L. Bennett commented that: "The roads were steep, and not infrequently, a brake would fail, or in winter, a 'roughlock' would break with the result that the load got away and many horses were killed. The Black Pitch was a particularly steep section [about thirty per cent] where so many horses were killed. The less steep spot at the foot of the Pitch was called Dead Horse Flat."[6]

V.V. Clark had this to say about the early roads at Creede Camp in 1934:

"Good ore roads have been built throughout the dis-trict, some of them costing many thousands of dollars. The gradients of these roads are necessarily quite steep for short

stretches which preclude the use of auto trucks. For ore haulage heavy wagons and teams of horses are employed between the mines and railroad terminals near Creede. These ore outfits take one back to pioneering days in the West when auto transport was unknown, and wagon haulage was developed to a high state of efficiency."[7]

The Last Ore Wagon Down Black Pitch — 2001
(Displayed at the Home of Sheriff Phil Leggitt in Creede)
Photo by the Author

Teams of horses and wagons were used until 1937 to haul ore from the mines, at which time trucks replaced them.[8] John Jackson remembers the teams and wagons as a boy:

"Art Fairchild was the last teamster to haul ore from the upper Amethyst and Last Chance Mines with a wagon and four-horse team. My brother, Scooter, and I rode up with him in 1933 or 1934 on the wagon. He made us follow on foot on the down trip because of the danger of a runaway. There was an elevated ramp, 10 feet wide and 100 feet long, at the rail head by the Humphreys Mill for ease in shoveling ore from the wagons to the gondola cars. The ramp placed the wagon side slightly above the lip of the gondolas. Think of the effort required to shovel ore from the wagons after a harrowing trip down. It probably relieved much of the stress felt by the teamsters."[9]

AERIAL TRAMWAYS
Even though the roads to the mines at Creede Camp were good, considering the rugged terrain, only one major mine on the Amethyst

Vein relied on road haulage of its ore, the Last Chance Mine. The first choice of most of the mines for haulage of ore was the aerial tramway. These devices could span deep canyons and traverse slopes too steep for roads and were, in most cases, the more efficient method of ore haulage at Creede Camp. Nine aerial tramways were constructed on East and West Willow Creeks and the tenth was built at the Wagon Wheel Gap Fluorspar Mine.

The aerial tramways used at Creede Camp were of two types: double-cable (four rope) and single-cable (two rope) systems. A double-cable system was rarely used for distances of less than 1,000

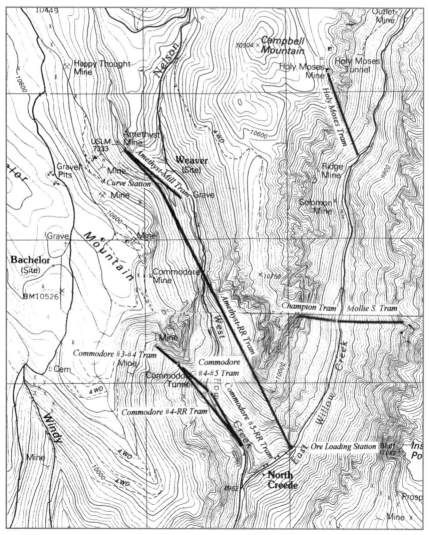

Aerial Tramways in the Creede Mining District

feet and consisted of: 1) two fixed tensioned track cables on which the carriers and attached ore buckets traveled; 2) a continuous traction rope for moving the carriers; 3) numerous carriers, consisting of a carriage and trolley to run on the fixed cables attached to the ore buckets, and clamps to grip the traction rope; 4) a station at each end to operate the traction rope and provide for loading and unloading the ore buckets; and 5) intermediate towers to support the cables. The single-cable or "jigback" tramways utilized at Creede consisted of: 1) a single endless rope running around large sheaves at each terminal and over small supporting sheaves at intermediate towers; 2) carriers and ore buckets supported at intervals from the rope; and 3) terminals for driving the rope and loading and unloading the ore buckets.[10]

Power to drive the rope for the Creede tramways was provided by the loaded ore buckets traveling down steep slopes lifting the empty ore buckets up slope. Good braking systems were needed to keep the systems under control!

The Trenton Ironworks supplied three double-cable aerial tramways of the Bleichert design — the Holy Moses, Amethyst, and Commodore Level Four Tramways. This design was developed in Europe by Adolf Bleichert & Company and proved very successful. The Bleichert system was patented in the United States in 1888 and was considered a great improvement over the single-cable systems in use at the time. The Trenton Ironworks was the sole agent for the Bleichert design and successfully built aerial tramways throughout the West.[11] Manufacturers of the single-cable or "jigback" units at Creede are not known. John Jackson was told, or read in an old publication, that an eastern company (likely the Trenton Ironworks) built the aerial tramways at Creede Camp for a base fee plus a royalty on tonnage, and that the only one that did not show a profit was the Champion Tramway.[12]

The Holy Moses Tramway was the first aerial tramway at Creede Camp. It was built to replace burros originally used to transport ore from the Holy Moses Mine high on the side of Campbell Mountain, first to the Denver and Rio Grande Railroad at Wagon Wheel Gap and then to the newly constructed branch that had been extended into East Willow Creek Canyon. Unfortunately, the railroad extension up East Willow Creek to the tramway terminus proved to be too steep (4.5 per cent) for rail service and was ultimately abandoned. Evidence indicates the tramway was used to transport high-grade oxidized silver ore from the Holy Moses Mine until it was exhausted and then was used to transport lead/zinc ore to the Ridge Mill starting about 1893. O.T. Davis' picture of the Ridge Mill taken in 1896 shows a tramway tower and ore bucket that most likely were used to transport ore to the mill. *Mining And Scientific Review* carried the following article about the Holy Moses Tramway that had originally appeared in the *Del Norte Prospector*:

> *"Among the great enterprises which have been carried forward at Creede during the past few months, the Holy Moses Tramway deserves special notice. This machine was put in operation December 17th [1891], and since then has been handling all the ore supplied as well as carrying up all the lumber and supplies used at the mines. Capt. Campbell, accompanied by the Trenton Iron Company's engineer, arrived in Creede October 3rd [1891], and the next day work commenced on the tramway, which work was carried forward with all possible haste till the completion of the line. This tramway is known as the Bluchert [Bleichert] or German system, and differs materially from all other systems of trams used in this country. The Holy Moses Tramway is 2,092 feet long and has a vertical rise of 1,080 feet. It is by far the roughest route and steepest grade of any tram of this system yet constructed in this country. The first 450 feet of this line is straight, and the line dips at an angle of 31 degrees. This straight line forms the tangent of a parabolic curve, which forms the remainder of the line. The three upper supports are rested on niches cut in projecting ledges of rock, with deep canyons between them. The remaining five supports are situated on slide rock. The highest support is 45 feet and the longest span is 210 feet. The tram is capable of carrying 110 tons of ore in ten hours. It has eleven buckets on the line at one time, which run at a rate of 250 feet per minute."*[13]

The Amethyst Tramway, a Bleichert system, connected the Amethyst Mine to an ore loading station on East Willow Creek just above its junction with West Willow. It was the longest aerial tramway at Creede Camp, traversing 7,000 feet. It traveled along Bachelor Mountain to a curve station where it made a slight bend. It descended Bachelor Mountain and then crossed West Willow Canyon, then ascended to the saddle at the southerly end of

Amethyst Tramway Towers

Above "Black Pitch" Looking
North

*Courtesy of the Creede
Historical Society*

Looking South Across West
Willow Creek

*Courtesy of the Colorado
Historical Society*

Photo by the Author — 2001

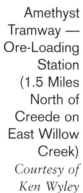

Amethyst
Tramway —
Ore-Loading
Station
(1.5 Miles
North of
Creede on
East Willow
Creek)
*Courtesy of
Ken Wyley*

Campbell Mountain and dropped down to the ore-loading station. The *Creede Chronicle* carried a story about the Amethyst Tramway in its March 22, 1892, issue:

> *"Contract Let and Work Started for its Construction. Yesterday morning the owners of the Amethyst let a contract to the Trenton Iron Company for the construction of a tramway from the mine to Upper Creede. Seventeen men were put to work at once and the tram will be completed in a short time.*
>
> *"The surveys were made in February. The length of the line will be 7,000 feet, or nearly 1 1/2 miles. When the tram is completed the output of the mine will be doubled."*

The tramway was put into operation in June 1892.[14] John G. Canfield, in *Mines and Mining Men of Colorado*, described the tramway:

Amethyst Tramway Curve Station
Courtesy of the Creede Historical Society

"All the appurtenances for successful mining are in use, the best of buildings enclosing the best of machinery, the track between the two shaft houses under cover, an ore house with a capacity of 200 tons lying along the track, and from this ore house starts an automatic tramway which conveys the ore 8,200 [7,000] feet down the hill to the Upper Creede depot, where it is loaded on the Denver & Rio Grande freight cars. This tram was set in full operation the latter part of June, one year from the location of the property, costing $38,000, is running fifty-nine buckets, and is capable of running down 250 tons of ore a day."[15]

The tramway was probably dismantled between 1910 and 1920. Only a few towers were standing and only the crib timber foundation of the curve station remained in the 1930s.[16] A few of the towers still stand today.

The Amethyst Mill Tramway was built to convey sulfide ore to the Amethyst Mill from the collar of the Amethyst No. 3 Shaft and was in operation in 1908; however, it was replaced by the Amethyst No. 5 Tunnel not many years afterward. Ore was then dropped down or hoisted up the No. 3 Shaft and then trammed directly to the mill. As described in Chapter Ten, the tramway was a 1,700-foot long gravity or "jigback" tram having a capacity of about 125 tons in eight hours from 18 ore buckets carrying about 500 pounds of ore each, moving at about 200 feet per minute.[17] Concentrates from the Amethyst Mill were hauled by horse and wagon to the railroad.[18]

The Commodore Level No. Four Tramway transported both Commodore and Bachelor ore from the Commodore No. Four (Manhattan) Tunnel ore bins to an ore bin at the railroad in the West Willow Creek Canyon. A contract was signed on November 11, 1895, between the Commodore and Bachelor Mining Companies that provided for joint use and occupancy by the Commodore Mining Company of certain levels, workings, and other property of the Bachelor Mining Company. The contract also stated that a Bleichert tramway, ore bins, and other necessary appurtenances be provided for convenient and economical handling and transportation of ore and waste from, and materials and supplies to, the mines of the parties hereto with equal rights of use.[19]

Commodore Level No. Four Tramway
Courtesy of the Creede Historical Society

The tramway, erected under the terms of the contract, consisted of upper and lower terminals and two intermediate support towers. From the ore bins at the Manhattan Tunnel to the ore bin at the railroad, the tramway was 2,600 feet long, covering a horizontal distance of 2,525 feet and dropping 614.6 feet vertically.[20] A.G. Hill sent a letter to the Commodore Mining Company on September 18, 1933, regarding repairs to the Commodore Tramway, stating "extensive repairs and cable replacements required."[21]

Evidently the repairs were made since the tramway was still in operation in the 1930s. John Jackson wrote that it was in operation when he was a youngster and that "it was one of the most thrilling sights I can remember. A surprising tonnage could be moved in a day's time from swinging buckets on the cables. Gus Swanson handled the unloading and Norman Alspaugh was the tram operator. The tramway was dismantled in the late 1940s."[22]

Woodrow Wintz and Paul Davis used the Commodore No. Three and No. Four Level Tramways to transport ore from above the Commodore No. Three Level to the ore loading station on East Willow Creek in 1940 or 1941.[23]

The Commodore Level No. Three Tramway transported Commodore and Bachelor ore from the Commodore Level No. Three to the Commodore No. Four (Manhattan) Tunnel, where it was dumped into an ore bin and then transferred onto the Commodore Level No. Four Tramway for delivery to the railroad. The November 11, 1895, contract between the Commodore and Bachelor Mining Companies also provided for this jigback tramway and stated that the cost of it would be shared by the Commodore and Bachelor Mining Companies.[24] The tramway was 777 feet long, dropping 405.4 feet vertically to the transfer at Level No. Four.[25] The tramway was repaired and used by Alvie Wintz, Woodrow's brother, and his son Harry in 1945 to move dump ores running twenty to forty ounces of silver per ton. The tram was dismantled in the late 1940s. The ore bin at the upper terminus of the tramway was rebuilt in 1939-40 by Charles Johnson after a disastrous fire in 1938.[26]

Ore Bin — Commodore Level No. Five Tramway — 2001
Photo by the Author

The Commodore Level No. Four Tramway ran from Level No. Four to Level No. Five, but it had little use. This jigback tramway was also repaired and used by Alvie Wintz to move dump ore. It was also dismantled in the late 1940s.[27]

The Commodore Level No. Five Tramway was erected shortly after the Commodore No. Five Tunnel was driven in the late 1890s. The upper terminal of the jigback tramway was a twenty-five-ton ore bin near the Commodore No. Five Tunnel portal, constructed to handle high-grade silver ore. The ore was hand trammed from the tunnel to the ore bin and then lowered by the tramway to the rail car loading bin on West Willow Creek. The tram had a four-foot diameter brake drum lined with wood to check the tram's speed and was still in operation in the 1930s.[28]

The Champion Tramway was, no doubt, the most spectacular of the Creede installations. It is sometimes called the Kentucky Belle Tramway, named after the Kentucky Belle Mining Company that was organized in 1894 to operate the Champion Mine. The Monte Carlo Gold and Silver Mining Company erected the tram in 1906.[29] It connected the cliff-side ore bin of the Champion Mine described in Chapter Ten to an ore bin at the bottom of the East Willow Canyon 1,400 feet below with a single span. The tramway was one of the steepest towerless tramways in the West, and its inclination was about forty-five degrees.[30]

The East Willow Creek Road washed out in a flood in the early 1980s. Unfortunately, the Champion and Mollie S. lower terminal and ore bin structure was damaged by the flood and, in order to get federal funding to rebuild the road, Mineral County had to tear the structure down and drop the tramway cables. Both tramways used the one structure for their lower terminals with side-by-side ore bins.

The Mollie S. Tramway provided ore haulage from the Mollie S. and Eunice Mines high on Mammoth Mountain and was constructed about 1906. The jigback tramway consisted of an upper terminal and ore bin, where ore was loaded into buckets, and three intermediate towers and the lower terminal and ore bin on the East Willow Creek Road, all in a common structure with the Champion Tramway. The elevation difference between the upper and lower terminals is about 1,100 feet. One tower, the center tower of the three, was still standing in 2001, but the others had fallen down. The cable that carried the ore buckets was 1.25 inches in diameter, and its sheaves were still in place, along with the wooden brake bands and lever, at the upper terminal. The towers and top terminal were constructed of locally cut timbers, as evidenced by adze marks on them.[31]

John Jackson remembers: "Time changes everything. Heavy snows and old age combined to bring ruin to the famous Mollie S. ore bin and upper tram house on East Willow Creek one mile north-

Champion and Mollie S. Tramways — Lower Terminal and Ore Bins — circa 1955

Courtesy of Ken Wyley

Mollie S. Upper Terminal and Ore Bin — 1976

Photo by John Jackson

east of Creede. A smaller jigback tramway ran from the Mollie S., south and a hundred feet higher in elevation, to the Eunice Lode, which also produced high-grade silver ore until 1936. The photograph [Mollie S. Upper Terminal and Ore Bin] was taken just forty years after my brother, Scooter, Les Turnipseed, Bob Oates, Ted Bucher, and I tried to operate the tram on a weekend visit to the mine, causing much damage to the lower building, which severely agitated the leasers of the mine."[32]

Mollie S. Tramway Center Tower — 2001

Photo by the Author

The Wagon Wheel Gap Fluorspar Mine Tramway, a jigback, with two supporting towers, operated by gravity, connected the upper workings with ore bins of 300 tons capacity, located at the foot of the hill near

Mill, Mine, and Connecting Aerial Tramway of Wagon Wheel Gap Fluorspar Mine

Photo by E.F. Burchard — 1926, Courtesy of the U.S. Geological Survey

Goose Creek. At the upper end of the tram, the terminal was equipped with a sloped screen or "grizzly," sorting platforms, and bins having a capacity of seventy-five tons. The ore was dumped over the grizzly; the larger pieces that did not drop through were sorted at the platforms and the waste rock removed. The remaining large pieces of valuable ore were thrown in with the fines, and the sorted ore was transported by the tramway from the upper to the lower terminal for storage until hauled to the railroad.[33]

RAILS

Transportation of ore out of and supplies into the mines served by tunnels (adits) was provided by horse or mule-drawn cars traveling on rails laid in the tunnels. In 1906, ore was hauled by horses from the mining areas through the Nelson-Wooster-Humphreys Tunnel in trains consisting of seven two-ton cars to the Humphreys Mill.[34]

The tracks extended on a surface tramway of about 1/2 mile from the portal to the mill. High-grade silver ore that was shipped to the smelters without being processed in the mill was diverted through chutes to a rail heading along West Willow Creek. Wood rail ties can still be found along the surface tramway that are almost worn in two by the hooves of countless horses and mules walking between the rails while hauling their loads in and out of the tunnel.

Surface Tramway to Humphreys Mill and Ore Chute to the Railroad

Courtesy of the Creede Historical Society

Andy Dooley, Ed Johnson's and Gene Dooley's grandfather, was a mule skinner at the Nelson Tunnel. Horses were used in the Amethyst No. 5 Tunnel as late as 1948-49. "Teddy" and "Brownie" were the names of two of the horses. The last horse, "Teddy," was taken to the John Dabney ranch to live out his remaining years after retirement from the mine. Vic Miller was probably the last mule skinner at Creede Camp.[35]

Surface Tramway to the Humphreys Mill — 2001
Photo by the Author

Livery at the Amethyst No. 5 Tunnel Portal — 2001
Photo by the Author

CHAPTER 12

HARD TIMES
1918-1933

CREEDE CAMP SUFFERED HARD TIMES from mid-1918 through the Great Depression until 1934, when the prices for metals increased to the point where mining was resumed. There was no mining to speak of from June 1, 1930, until 1934. Mine production from 1919 to 1930 averaged 7,167 tons of ore per year, only twenty-five per cent of the 1918 production of 28,372 tons. The value of the metals produced at Creede Camp fell from $726,027 in 1918 to a low of $124,767 in 1928, only seventeen per cent of the 1918 value.

This precipitous drop in production and the value of metals was the result of two major factors — first, the drop in metals prices and second, the exhaustion of ore in the main Amethyst Vein by 1920 that had yielded about ninety-five per cent of the district's production.

The following chart lists the prices of silver, copper, lead, and zinc from 1917 to 1931:

Year	Silver Fine Ounce	Copper Pound	Lead Pound	Zinc Pound
1917	$0.824	$0.273	$0.086	$0.102
1918	1.00	.247	.071	.091
1919	1.12	.186	.053	.073
1920	1.09	.184	.080	.081
1921	1.00	.129	.045	.050
1922	1.00	.135	.055	.057
1923	.82	.147	.070	.068
1924	.67	.131	.080	.065
1925	.694	.142	.087	.076
1926	.624	.140	.080	.075
1927	.567	.131	.063	.064
1928	.585	.144	.058	.061
1929	.533	.176	.063	.066
1930	.385	.130	.050	.048
1931	.290	.091	.037	.038

The Pittman Silver Act was passed by the U.S. Senate on April 18, 1918, the House of Representatives on April 22, 1918, and was signed by President Woodrow Wilson the next day. The Act set the price of silver at $1.00 per ounce. The Secretary of the Treasury, W.G. McAdoo, stated the main reason for the passage of the Act was that more silver was required to settle foreign balances instead of attempting to stabilize exchange by methods that required gold. Gold was greatly needed at the time as the base of the huge structure of credit created by government loans. Therefore, 350,000 of the silver dollars stored in the treasury were converted into bullion. The passage of the Silver Act essentially guaranteed the government would absorb the entire output of silver from mines in the United States until the Act expired in June 1923. This guaranteed price for silver was a boon to Creede Camp, and the mining of silver ores was again profitable for a few years. The guaranteed price was also the impetus for exploration of the Amethyst hanging wall veins and for the production of high-grade silver ore from them. Unfortunately, the general trend of mining in Colorado, including Creede Camp, declined until the depths of the Great Depression, when there was almost no mining done at Creede Camp. The following comments in *The Engineering and Mining Journal* describe the decline:

January 18, 1919:

"Mining in Colorado in 1918 — The last year of the war was probably the most disastrous which the mining industry of Colorado, as a whole, ever experienced. It seems certain that the artificial restrictions on prices, the increased wage scale, and other economic conditions resulting from the war, bore more hardly on the small producers than on the larger ones, and Colorado is typically a district of small mines. During the last three months of 1918 the influenza epidemic proved a most serious hindrance."

January 17, 1920:

"Mining in Colorado in 1919 — It might be questioned today whether 1919 was not even worse than 1918. A larger number of mines suspended operations in 1919 than in 1918.

"The principal changes in smelting conditions were a general increase in treatment charges and metal deductions. This contributed to decreased production, which, in turn, necessitated the closing of the Globe and Salida smelting plants."

January 22, 1921, Colorado:
"*After four disastrous years, the close of 1920 finds the mining industry in a more depressed condition than at any time in its history, though during the last month some signs of improvement have become apparent. For the first time since 1916, there is a surplus of skilled labor. There is reason to hope that in 1921 the average cost of mining may be reduced.*"

June 24, 1922:
"*Mining in Colorado — The dry eloquence of statistics is more than enough to depress any friend of Colorado. In 1900 the total output of the principal metals was worth over $50 million, whereas in 1921 the aggregate output was worth less than $14 million. In 1900 a dozen smelters were active; at that time American Smelting and Refining Company had seven smelters with 32 furnaces in blast; today only one furnace is at work in the Durango plant and three in the Arkansas Valley plant at Leadville.*"

January 20, 1923, Colorado:
"*Mining in Colorado looks much better than it has for a long time. This is due partly to the fact that it has looked pretty bad in recent years, and partly to some real constructive work done in the last year. The Metals Exploration Co., American Smelting and Refining Co. and, we understand, some of the railroad companies, have put their heads together in an effort to restore the industry.*"

The U.S. Geological Survey's *Mineral Resources of the United States* described the condition of mining in 1923:

"*The expiration of the Pittman Act (finally decided by the Treasury as June 2, 1923) was anticipated by the smelters in April, May, and June. The return to the market price of silver (average 64.87 cents for the year) on the cessation of the fixed price of $1 an ounce guaranteed to domestic silver producers during 1920, 1921, and 1922 and continued in 1923 until the 208,000,000 ounces melted in 1919 under the Pittman Act approached replacement in the United States Treasury, seriously cut down the net returns of those Colorado mines having ores* *whose principal constituent was silver. Several large silver mines closed between July and November, particularly at Leadville, Aspen, and Telluride.*

"The zinc mines in Colorado were nearly all idle from November 1920 to November 1922. The resumption of operations late in 1922 and early in 1923 resulted in a production of zinc somewhat comparable with the average yearly production of zinc in Colorado. The future of Colorado mining is greatly dependent on the price of lead and zinc."

When the Pittman Silver Act came to its end in 1923, another bill was introduced into the Senate and unanimously passed early in June of 1924, but the new Pittman Bill did not pass the House of Representatives. This, of course, created more decline in the silver mining industry. There was only one smelter operating in the state of Colorado in 1925 as compared to eight in 1903.[1] In 1928, only one furnace was in blast at Leadville's Arkansas Valley smelter.[2] All of the Creede metal mines were shut down on June 1, 1930, and did not reopen until 1934. The Clay Mine was the only operating mine at Creede Camp in 1932 and 1933, employing about ten men.[3] Hard times indeed!

AMETHYST VEIN SYSTEM

Larsen, in his 1929 report, stated: "Since 1920 the main Amethyst Vein, which had been the chief producer of the district, has furnished little ore, and most of the production has come from the west branch of the Amethyst vein in the Bachelor Mine, from veins in the hanging wall in the Commodore and other mines."[4] What ore was left in the main Amethyst Vein was primarily sulfide mineralization that required concentration to be economic and, unfortunately, the concentrating mills at Creede Camp had been abandoned. Intensive exploration and development in the hanging wall of the Amethyst Fault in the 1920s and 1930s disclosed several veins containing rich oxidized silver ore that could be shipped direct to the smelters at a profit, even at the low prices of the time. The efforts of these individuals — Albert C. Dean, Clarence O. Withrow, William C. "Billie" Sloan, Ben Miller, Erick Nelson, and Royal I. "Roy" Fisher — provided the impetus for the discovery of the hanging wall veins. The idea of hanging wall veins was not new; in fact it had been discussed as early as 1898 as attested by a conversation reported by V.V. Clark:

*"During a conversation between Frank E. Wheeler
and W.C. Sloan at Creede on July 15, 1934 the following
historical data were brought out relating to the hanging
wall veins of the Amethyst Fault, particularly with regard
to such veins in the Del Monte Mine. It was in June of
1898 that Mr. Wheeler tried to interest Col. Humphreys
in the theory that the hanging wall veins were of economic
importance, but the Colonel did not seem to warm up to
the idea, particularly since other engineers of Creede were
opposed to the theory."*[5]

George H. Garrey stated in his 1916 report to American
Smelting & Refining Company (ASARCO) that the Amethyst Fault
showed considerable displacement and that there were mineralized
hanging wall veins.[6] However, he did not recommend that ASARCO
explore the hanging wall, and they did not.

Perhaps now is the time to describe the genesis of the "hanging wall veins, " define the term "hanging wall," and again define
"crosscut" for those not familiar with geologic and mining terminology.

A fault, in geologic terms, is a fracture in the earth's crust created by the release of stresses within the crust. Movement may occur
along the fault and this movement is defined as "displacement." The
slope of a fault at right angles to its direction in a horizontal plane,
or "strike," is termed its "dip" — the number of degrees from a horizontal plane to the plane of the fault at 90 degrees to the "strike."
The Amethyst Fault has a dip of about 50 degrees to the west and,
as was described in the Prologue, is on the east side of the Creede
graben. Total displacement along the Amethyst Fault was in the
range of 1,200 feet.[7] This displacement caused stress in the rock on
the west side of the Amethyst Fault, or "hanging wall," that in turn
created tension fractures. Mineralization occurred in these faults as
it did in the Amethyst Fault itself.

"Hanging wall" and "foot wall" are mining terms that most
likely originated in the tin mines of Cornwall and were brought to
this country by immigrant Cornish miners. Simply stated, if one is
standing in a tunnel on a sloping fault or a vein deposited in such a
fault, the wall of the fault under foot is the "foot wall" and the wall
hanging over one's head is the "hanging wall."

"Crosscut" is a mining term for a tunnel driven at an angle to
the strike of a vein or fault.

BACHELOR MINE

The Bachelor Mine was operated by lessees in 1919, 1920, 1924, 1925, 1926, and 1927, producing oxidized silver ore that was shipped direct to the smelters.[8] John F. Vail, Albert C. Dean, and Charles S. Glascoe acquired the property in 1922 and incorporated it under the Bachelor Mining and Milling Company. The Bachelor Mine was leased to Albert C. Dean and William O. Gish by the owners in September 1924 and about $50,000 of smelting ore had been shipped by the end of 1926.[9]

As the Bachelor Mine was developed over the years, it became evident that the structural geology of the mine was somewhat complicated and a greater part of the production in the past, unlike the rest of the mines on the Amethyst lode, had been taken from the east branch of the Amethyst Fault, known as the Bachelor Vein. Albert C. Dean had driven a crosscut in 1922, westerly from the east branch, that intersected the west branch of the Amethyst Fault and opened a body of good ore. He drove a second crosscut from a point about 280 feet south of the north Bachelor property line on the Commodore No. Three Level that intersected the west branch of the Amethyst Fault, named the Dean Fault in his honor.[10] The vein in the Dean Fault was one of the first large hanging wall ore veins that was discovered along the Amethyst Fault zone.[11] *The Creede Candle*'s "Mining Edition," January 1, 1927, described Dean's plans for the Bachelor Mine:

> *"A considerable and valuable body of ore has been developed on the Number 3 level, and contemplated further development should add very materially to the ore now in reserve. According to Mr. Dean the Spar Vein will be developed from the Number 4 Tunnel, where a crosscut taps the vein. A drift will be run to the north end line of the property [Bachelor], a distance of approximately 860 feet on the Spar Vein. The developed ore on the Number 3 level will be dropped down a raise to be driven from the Number 4 level and the ore from both levels will be taken out the Nelson Tunnel.*
>
> *"Sometime in the future a cross cut will be run into the hanging wall to cut the so called Copper Vein. It will be driven from a point somewhere between the Number 4 and Number 3 levels.*
>
> *"Like the mines to the north on the Amethyst lode, the true hanging wall is essentially unexplored and development in this area will be watched with great interest."*

Mining on the Bachelor encroached onto the adjoining Commodore property. The Commodore Mining Company filed a suit against the Bachelor Mining Company, the Bachelor Mining and Milling Company, John F. Vail, Charles S. Glascoe, and Albert C. Dean in the district court at Creede on June 24, 1924, for trespass. The complaint alleged that the Bachelor Mining and Milling Company had illegally taken 5,000 tons of ore valued at $200,000 between January 1, 1922, and December 1, 1923, from the Archimedes claim owned by the Commodore Mining Company.[12]

On September 23, 1929, after a long delay, the district court at Creede rendered a judgement in favor of the Commodore Mining Company for the sum of $60,327.99, plus interest and court costs. On March 10, 1930, the Bachelor property was sold by the sheriff and bid for by the Commodore Mining Company to satisfy the judgement. The Bachelor Mining and Milling Company failed to redeem their property and the Commodore Mining Company received a sheriff's deed to all of the Bachelor property in Mineral County.[13]

COMMODORE MINE

A.E. Reynolds wrote a letter to the stockholders of the Commodore Mining Company on July 1, 1919, stating: "We have a certain amount of ore scattered through the upper workings which under ordinary conditions, if it could be mined continuously and shipped to the smelters, might be exhausted in about two years." The Commodore Mining Company entered into an agreement with Frank E. Wheeler on February 19, 1921, for the sale of all of its property and to close the affairs of the company. The agreement was extended to March 22, 1922, when it expired without anyone purchasing the property. As a result, the company gave Gerald Hughes an option on the Commodore. Hughes was not successful in finding commercial quantities of ore and he gave up his lease in 1923. Hughes' mine foreman, Clarence O. Withrow, took over the lease and he was successful in finding high-grade ore. On October 15, 1927, it was recommended to the board of directors of the Commodore Mining Company that the Commodore Mine be re-leased to Clarence Withrow. At a special meeting on April 27, 1927, the board of directors were informed that the lease had been confirmed, and Withrow had agreed to furnish and supply all needed and necessary money to complete development and prospecting in the hanging wall of the Commodore Vein to the north in the company's property and country adjacent thereto, as well as such other development work as said Withrow considered advisable.[14]

The Creede Candle's "Mining Edition," January 1, 1927, carried the following story about Clarence Withrow and his success at the Commodore Mine:

> "*Celebrates End of Third Successful Year under Withrow Lease — Under the Withrow lease and thru [sic] the efforts of Mr. Clarence Withrow the Commodore Mine in the last three years has shipped 17,849.41 tons of silver-lead ore having a gross value of $861,571.36 or nearly $49.00 per ton. We happen to know the ore reserves now under development are large and the possibilities of developing further reserves in heretofore un-prospected territory are excellent. The Withrow lease has a rosy future.*
>
> "*Not many years ago all of these mines were thought to be worked out. The Creede Exploration Company after spending a large sum of money in deep exploration gave them up in disgust. Up to that time it was the Amethyst fault proper that was mined. The fact that the hanging wall might be of value apparently was not seriously considered. Mr. Withrow, realizing this, drove a cross cut from the old Commodore Number 3 level into the hanging wall, cut several veins, one of which, the so-called Intermediate Vein has proved to be of bonanza value. In places this vein is so close to the old workings that it is a mystery how it was overlooked. The fact remains that the hanging wall of the Commodore and the rest of the mines on the Amethyst lode is virtually unexplored. This fact is being more forcibly recognized every day.*
>
> "*Mr. Withrow by no means enjoyed the comforts of a bed of roses while pursuing the development program that has proven up the present mine. Had he not had years of experience in the mines of the Amethyst lode he might very well have passed up a number of good bets. The veins in the hanging wall are irregular, in fact, somewhat similar to the stockworks of some of the famous tin mines. Apparently the key to successful prospecting of the hanging wall is intelligent development and a 'nose for ore.'*
>
> "*In the last three years Mr. Withrow has driven over 1800 feet of drifts and crosscuts. He has averaged over 500 tons of shipping ore per month and is now sending over 700 tons per month to the smelters.*

*"He has repaired and rebuilt run down equipment
and is in a condition to handle a much larger tonnage if
necessary.*

*"The lease is now incorporated under the name
'Withrow-Commodore Lease Incorporated.' Mr. Withrow
is President and tho [sic] he won't admit it, we figure he is
the guiding spirit.*

*"Before we close and before Mr. Withrow gets the
opportunity of deleting the personal references that we
have made, we want to say that his development in the
hanging wall of the Commodore is a big thing. We congratulate him on his success and feel that he is in a fair
way of making a still bigger one.*

*"Withrow on the Commodore, and Dean and Gish
on the Bachelor have proven that the hanging wall of
these properties is a mine in itself. In the last three years
these properties have produced over $1,000,000 of
smelting ore."*

The Withrow-Commodore lease was the principal operator and
shipper at Creede Camp in 1927 and produced ore in 1928 and
1929.[15] Esper S. Larsen reported the following production data:

*"Production from the Commodore mine by the
Withrow Leasing Co. from January 1, 1924 to July 14,
1927 were kindly furnished by Mr. Withrow:*

Ore	*Dry tons*	18,656
Silver	*Ounces*	1,440,995
Lead	*Pounds*	850,308
Gross Value		$935,718
Average Value per Ton		$50.154
Average Silver per Ton	*Ounces*	77.23

*"All or nearly all of this output came from the small
veins in the hanging wall of the main Amethyst Fault."*[16]

At a board of directors meeting of the Commodore Mining
Company on June 16, 1930, the president of the company was
instructed to confer with Clarence Withrow on the advisability of
stopping production at the Commodore and holding the reserves
until such a time that the price of silver improved. The directors and
the Withrow-Commodore Lease, Inc., agreed that it would be advisable to discontinue shipments while the price of silver remained at

such a low price as to not allow a reasonable profit on the mining operations. Accordingly, the mine was closed down. The Commodore Mine remained closed from June 1, 1930, until it reopened in January 1934.[17]

LAST CHANCE, NEW YORK, AND DEL MONTE MINES

The Del Monte and Chance Mining Company of Creede shipped ore from the upper levels of the New York and Chance Mines in 1919.[18] Lessees continued to operate the New York, Last Chance, Del Monte, and Volunteer group of mines from 1920 until June 1, 1930.[19] *The Creede Candle* described the activities in the Last Chance, New York, and Volunteer Mines in its January 1, 1927, edition:

> *"Sloan and Morgan, who have been operating in the New York, Last Chance, and Del Monte for the last five years have opened an ore shoot in the hanging wall and are very well pleased with the outlook. In a few words, the hanging wall of the developed properties is essentially unexplored and the comparatively small amount of development work that has been done has been richly rewarded.*
>
> *"Last Chance, New York and Volunteer Mines — They lie between the Commodore Mine on the south, and the Amethyst Mine on the north and have been under lease for the last five years to John G. Morgan of San Diego, Calif., and W.C. Sloan of Creede. Although they are owned by three separate companies, they are worked as one mine, from a single shaft on the Last Chance claim and from the Wooster Tunnel which was driven along the strike of the fault the entire length of the claims at a depth of approximately fifteen hundred feet from the surface on the dip of the vein. This section is credited with a production of more wealth than any equal number of linear feet on the Amethyst lode; the total amount now having passed the twenty million dollar mark.*
>
> *"The present lessees heretofore have directed their efforts along the main fault, but recent developments in the hanging wall have been so encouraging that an active campaign of prospecting the hanging wall side of the fault is now being worked out by Mr. Sloan who is directing operations, having just been granted a five year extension of their lease by the owners of the property. Besides the*

work contemplated by the lessees, they have sublet a large block of ground above the Wooster Tunnel on the south end of the New York claim to Carpenter and O'Laughlin, who is now actively engaged in re-timbering the Del Monte raise, from which a considerable tonnage of silver lead ore was shipped some years ago, and which with the present price of lead, it is thought a good profit can now be made."

The Morgan and Sloan Lease on the New York, Last Chance, and Volunteer Mines shipped several cars of relatively high-grade silver ore to both the Golden Cycle Mill and the Leadville smelter in 1927.[20] Larsen reported in 1929 that Morgan and Sloan drove a crosscut into the foot wall in the Last Chance Mine and found a small vein about fifty feet from the main tunnel and shipped a few carloads of ore mined from the vein.[21]

Last Chance
No. 2 Tunnel
Ore Bin —
1974

*Photo by
John Jackson*

John Jackson described the picture: "The ore bin stood lonely and neglected in 1974 when Minerals Engineering Company began removing 'waste dumps' below the Last Chance Shaft. The waste dumps contained low-grade silver ore, which was processed through the company's reduction mill located at the south end of Creede. The No. 2 Tunnel, 200 feet west of the ore bin, connected to the Number 2 Level of the Last Chance Shaft and served to transport ores from the caved area near the shaft and hanging wall veins explored by Manager Ben Miller."

Ben Miller was a German mining engineer and the manager and superintendent of the Last Chance Mining and Milling Company. Miller worked for Ralph Granger and was the overseer of leases on the company's property. He also made sure the company received its fair share of ore from the Volunteer Mine. Miller was a gifted engineer and geologist and guided the Last Chance through hard times. He, his wife, and daughter, Sophie, first lived in the superintendent's residence near the Last Chance Shaft for several years before moving to Creede. Miller moved to California where he later died.[22]

Last Chance
Superintendent's
Residence — 2001
Photo by the Author

William C. "Billie" Sloan was one of the pioneers of the exploration of the Amethyst hanging wall and deserves much of the credit for the success of finding economic ore in the Last Chance, Del Monte, and Amethyst Mines. Sloan had the good fortune of hiring two mine foremen who were common-sense geologists and excellent miners with noses for ore — Roy Fisher and Erick Nelson. Both of these gentlemen were, to a large degree, responsible for Sloan's success in finding hanging wall ore deposits. Roy Fisher was a small man who eventually lost an arm to cancer. Even though he was the mayor of Creede for several years, he never used the town's water system but relied on a well in his backyard. He had the habit of dumping ashes from his stoves on Main Street, but no one objected. Erick Nelson was born in 1895 in Bachelor and spent most of his life in Creede Camp as a miner and leaser. William T. Jackson, Jr., John Jackson's father, and Erick were lifelong friends. Nelson was a good scholar and excelled in what few sports early-day Creede provided. He was a man with high morals and ethical values.[23]

AMETHYST MINE

The Amethyst Mine produced ore in all the years between 1920 and June 1, 1931, when all the Creede mines shut down, except for 1921, 1926, and 1927.[24]

The Amethyst Leasing Co., under the direction of William C. Sloan, had a lease on the entire Amethyst property and on that part of the Pittsburgh, which is north of the south end line of the Amethyst. *The Creede Candle* of May 5, 1928, had this headline: "Strike at Amethyst Runs 840 Ounces." The story below the headline was enthusiastic:

> *"Another four-foot vein was opened this week in the Amethyst Mine, carrying values in silver which assayed here at 840 ounces per ton. Specimens were not picked and the samples sent to Denver yielded an assay of 809.60 ounces. The Amethyst Leasing Company, composed mostly of local parties, are driving a crosscut tunnel thru [sic] the hanging-wall, running in a westerly direction by which they expect to cut the Pittsburg vein. Last week, when 160 feet from the portal, a four-foot vein was cut which gave good assays. Only twenty-one feet beyond this was found the high grade ore of this week. These veins being so much richer than was expected and the fact that each streak grows higher in silver as they get deeper into the mountain would indicate that when the Pittsburg is reached, it will prove a bonanza beyond the dreams of avarice.*
>
> *"Not only will shipments be made from the Amethyst in a very short time but other claims along this fault are now assured of the values in the hanging-wall on their properties."*

Like so many miners' dreams, the "bonanza beyond the dreams of avarice" did not happen. In reality, by 1929 the Amethyst Leasing Company had driven a crosscut 230 feet into the hanging wall of the Amethyst vein that had intersected several veins. Some ore, having a grade of 200 ounces of silver per ton, was mined and shipped. This success led to considerable activity in prospecting the hanging wall.[25]

The Pittsburg claim was leased to William C. Sloan of Creede for five years from June 1, 1927, to June 1, 1932. On September 20, 1928, a sub-lease agreement was made between W.C. Sloan of Creede and B.T. Poxson and Herman Emperius of Alamosa for all that portion of the Pittsburg claim lying north of a vertical plane parallel to the south end line of the Amethyst and passing through a point designated as the north side of the Amethyst No. 3 Shaft.[26] The Pittsburgh was listed as a producing mine in 1929 and 1930.[27] Emperius and associates sub-leased that part of the Amethyst Mine north of the No. Three Shaft with the intention of driving a cross-cut into the hanging wall.[28]

The story about how the Pittsburgh sub-lease came to be is told by Lee Scamehorn in his book, *Albert Eugene Reynolds — Colorado's Mining King*. In 1926 Emperius and Poxson secured a lease on the Ocean Wave Mine near Lake City. Two years later, the partners decided that the venture was not successful, so they packed up their equipment and headed for Alamosa. They spent the night in Creede where they met Sloan, who offered them a sub-lease on the Pittsburgh claim. They accepted.[29]

Upper Amethyst Ore Bin and "Steeple" — 1974

Photo by John Jackson

Poxson and Emperius' sub-lease was on a block of ground 200 feet wide by 400 feet long. The total capital investment for the lease was $2,900. The operating crew consisted of a foreman and two miners. After drifting approximately sixty feet, the miners encountered a high-grade ore body. This ore, as well as from others discovered later in the oxidized zone, were shipped crude to the smelter and averaged from eighty to 200 ounces in silver per ton.[30]

This Poxson and Emperius mining operation, known as P&E, was the beginning of the Emperius Mining Company, which played an important part in Creede Camp's history for about forty years. The story will be told in Chapter Fourteen.

Ore was passed from the Sloan Tunnel, named for William C. Sloan, to sorting tables at the Upper Amethyst ore bin, where waste rock was discarded and the valuable ore was stored in the bin. The Sloan Tunnel serviced the Amethyst, New York, and Del Monte Mines. The bin was later used by the P&E mining operation.[31]

CREEDE MINES

Very little mining was done on the Creede Mines properties after the abandonment of the Humphreys Mill and Tunnel in 1918. The ore was primarily sulfide and without a mill, it could not be mined at a profit. However, some ore was produced from the Happy Thought Mine in 1929 and the first half of 1930. *The Creede Candle's* "Mining Edition," January 1, 1927, had these comments on the Creede Mines Company:

> *"The company controls about two miles along the Bachelor Vein and half of it has been developed and has produced a million tons of ore. The work has been limited to the main vein. No prospecting has ever been done to determine possibilities in the hanging wall, which proved so valuable in all other mines to the south. There is every reason to believe that bodies of commercial ore will be found in the hanging wall formation and the possibility of this property north of the Park Regent Shaft is actually as favorable for large bodies of gold, silver, lead, and zinc ores as that part of the vein that produced a million tons of ore, and in view of the fact that when this ore was produced the average price of lead was below $4.00 and the zinc contents were more or less a penalty, there is no reason under present milling and market conditions that ore of half the value heretofore mines could not be made to pay a handsome profit."*

The *Candle's* comments about finding commercial ore bodies in the hanging wall and to the north of the Park Regent Mines was prophetic.

EQUITY MINE

The Equity-Creede Mining Company operated the Equity Mine in 1919.[32] The mine was idle from 1920 until 1926 when several carloads of silver ore were shipped to the smelters.[33] *The Creede Candle's* "Mining Edition," January 1, 1927, had these comments:

> *"Knowing that Mr. Charles Hollister managed the Equity Mine in 1917-19 we backed him up against the desk in the post office and pried some information out of him on the status quo, etc. of the property. Here is what he said:*
> *"'The Equity Mine is now under bond and lease to the newly-organized North Amethyst Mining Company.*

*Besides developing the present ore shoot, the company pro-
poses to explore the foot wall of the Equity fault to find the
downward extension of the ore shoot from the old surface
workings, of which $17,000 was extracted. Also a shaft is
to be sunk at the junction of the Equity and Amethyst
lodes.' According to Mr. Hollister that is the big bet."*

The North Amethyst Mining Company, a Colorado Corporation having 700,000 shares of capital stock at $1.00 per share,
owned claims covering the apex of the Amethyst Vein north of the
Creede Mines property and had a five-year lease on the Equity Mine
— a group of nine claims — and an option to purchase the Equity
Mine and its equipment. The officers of the company were: Charles
Hollister, president and Creede mine operator; George D. Meston,
vice-president and Pueblo, Colorado, real estate investor; Edward
Futterer, secretary and Creede mining engineer; and Bruce E.
Watkins, treasurer and Pueblo, Colorado, businessman.[34]

Development work at the Equity in 1927 by the North Amethyst
Mining Company produced several cars of highly siliceous silver
ore. No development work was done in 1928, but a twenty-ton
flotation mill and an electric power plant were built.[35] Larsen
described the Equity Mine in 1929:

*"The Equity Mine is just east of West Willow Creek
about 6 miles north of Creede. An old wagon road to the
mine by way of Bachelor has been abandoned, and a new
road has been constructed that keeps near the bed of West
Willow Creek as far as Nelson Creek, follows up Nelson
Creek for about three-quarters of a mile, crosses the ridge
into the valley of West Willow Creek, and runs near that
creek to the mine. The road is narrow and rough and has
some very steep grades and some soft parts but is passable
to a powerful automobile. In 1927 the property was being
prospected, under bond and lease, by the North Amethyst
Mining Co., under the direction of Messrs. Charles
Hollister and Edward Futterer.*

*"In August, 1928 the company was erecting a mill to treat
the ore. The total production of the mine to August, 1927 is
reported as $91,000 gross with silver at $0.56 an ounce."[36]*

The Equity Mine shipped a four-ton lot of ore to a smelter in
1929. Other than the one shipment, no work was done and the
twenty-ton flotation mill, built in 1928, was idle.[37]

MAMMOTH MOUNTAIN

The Silver King claim was listed as a mine in 1919 and was operated by the Silver King Leasing Company of Creede.[38] The following article appeared in *The Creede Candle*'s "Mining Edition" of January 1, 1927. The article certainly reinforces the idea that "hope springs eternal" for the prospector:

"Resurrection Tunnel — This is one of the most promising prospects in Creede district situated on the south slope of Mammoth Mountain, it is driven in northeasterly direction.

"About 900 feet in from the portal a strong fault crosses the tunnel. This was thought to be the vein, a drift being run on it 600 feet north 20 degrees west; however no values were found and the work was resumed in the main tunnel, which is now in 1900 feet from the portal. The breast is in foliated Willow Creek Rhyolite much stained and crushed, fractures cemented with quartz, chloride stain, and other signs indicating the nearness of an ore body.

"The property consists of a group of nine claims owned by Mr. Wm. T. Barnett and is now operated by a small leasing company after the Midwest Company of Detroit gave up their lease two years ago, Al Turnipseed and Fred Monkemeyer doing the work.

"On the west slope of Mammoth much float is found, fragments of quartz of great size, larger than any heretofore mined in Creede. A great amount of work has been done in this locality to find the sources of this float, without any success whatever.

"A close study of conditions on the surface and underground revealed the fact that these masses of float are from the upper section of a great vein much higher up the mountain to the east, and have been carried down by an immense landslide or surface fault. The tunnel is now driven into this new territory and the recent good showing of enrichment in the wall rock points toward the correctness of this theory. The lessees are much elated over the outlook and expect to tap the vein at any time.

"The discovery, right above the town, of a bonanza like the famous Amethyst would indeed be a boon for

Creede Camp and insure prosperity for many years. The existence of such a vein is conceded by all miners and prospectors familiar with the ground and developments are watched with much interest."

Larsen wrote in 1929: "Since the preparation of the earlier report [1923] considerable prospecting has been done on the faults on the southwest slopes of Mammoth Mountain. The main faults in the area have been considerably prospected, and the Mammoth Tunnel has been extended, but no ore bodies have been found." [39] No further recorded mining activity occurred on Mammoth Mountain until 1975, when exploration was done at the Silver King claim during the second boom at Creede.

SOLOMON-HOLY MOSES VEIN SYSTEM

HOLY MOSES MINE

There was very little activity at the Holy Moses Mine during Creede's hard times. The mine was listed as an operating mine in 1922 and 1923. [40] V.V. Clark reported in 1934: "A great state of desolation appeared all over the property as if it had been abandoned for many years. We were told that bear had hibernated in one of the important working shafts, which tells a story of abandonment for a considerable period." [41]

SOLOMON MINE

The Colorado Bureau of Mines *Annual Report for 1919* lists the Solomon Mine as producing silver and being operated by the C.M.S. Mines Company and the Creede Contact Mining Company. The records indicate that the Solomon was idle from 1920 to 1934.

MOLLIE S. AND EUNICE MINES

According to the U.S. Geological Survey's *Mineral Resources of the United States*, the Mollie S. Mine was operated only in 1922 and 1923. No activity at the Eunice was recorded.

ALPHA-CORSAIR VEIN SYSTEM

Larsen reported in 1929 that about $600,000 had been produced from the Alpha-Corsair Vein. Nearly all of the silver produced came from the upper workings, chiefly above water level, and in most of the mines the ore was of low grade in the lower workings and became too poor to work in depth. [42]

ALPHA AND CORSAIR MINES

According to the U.S. Geological Survey's *Mineral Resources of the United States*, the Corsair Mine was operating only in 1922, 1923, and 1925.

KREUTZER SONATA MINE

The Creede Candle's "Mining Edition" of January 1, 1927, stated that: "The Kreutzer Sonata group is being developed by the Miami M and M Co. This company has been working steadily for two years." There is no other record of activity at this mine during hard times.

CREEDE FORMATION

There was considerable activity at the Creede Formation during the 1920s and 1930s. Silver was mined at Monon Hill in the early 1920s, and the total yield of the Monon Hill deposit up to 1929 was estimated from reliable information at about $700,000, about ninety-five per cent in silver and the rest in lead with very little gold and copper.[43] The discovery of silver in the tuff beds of the Creede Formation southwest of the Bachelor Mine created much excitement but no mine development to speak of. In addition, some of the tuff beds were found to be partly altered to bentonite, and this material was mined at the Clay Mine for use as an oil filter.

MONON HILL MINES

The Colorado Bureau of Mines *Annual Report for 1919* listed two operating mines on Monon Hill that produced silver. The Manitoba Mine was operated by the Manitoba Leasing Company and the Monon Mine was operated by the Wabash Mines and Power Company. These mines continued to produce silver in 1920, 1921, and 1922.[44] *The Creede Candle*'s "Mining Edition" of January 1, 1927, had an interesting story about the Monon Mine:

> "*Charlie Stone to Tap Monon — Twenty-five years ago, Mr. Stone had a lease on the Monon Mine at Sunnyside. The Monon is credited with a production of a quarter of a million dollars. Five years later Mr. Stone acquired three claims which he believes to be on the Monon Apex. The claims are called Pandora 1, 2, and 3. For twenty years he has been financing the development himself and now has a cross cut tunnel 1200 feet long and believes that he is approaching the Monon Vein. He will continue work in the spring. If faith and perseverance deserves a reward, Mr. Stone has earned it.*"

Stock Certificate — The Wabash Mines and Power
Company

Courtesy of Dave Bunk

Evidently, Charlie Stone did commence work in the spring of 1927. The records indicate that 200 feet of development work was done in 1927 and 1928.[45] Unfortunately for Charlie, there was no mining until 1936.

BEDDED DEPOSITS

The Colorado Bureau of Mines *Annual Report for 1919* stated: "Some excitement was caused by the discovery of silver in a bed of tuff near the top of Bachelor Mountain. Several cars of ore have been shipped from various openings in this deposit but the ore is not as extensive as was at first supposed." The excitement of a new discovery did not result in a new silver mine, but it was an interesting non-economic silver occurrence that was described in a letter to the editor of *Mining and Scientific Press,* printed in the May 14, 1921, issue:

> *"Sir — In the spring of 1919 mild excitement was caused in Creede, Colorado, by the finding of silver ore in a 'flat vein' near the top of Bachelor Mountain, about a mile and a half from town. The original discovery was made by Fred Monkemeyer on the River View claim, on the east slope of the mountain. The bed was traced for a thousand feet to the north and for a greater distance to the*

south and west. There was a rush to secure leases on that
part of the deposit already covered by claims and to locate
the unappropriated outcrop. Considerable work was
done, mostly with disappointing results, as in only a few
places was ore found in workable quantities."

Prospectors had investigated the Creede Formation as early as
1892 for economic mineral deposits and found none, except for
those at Monon Hill. Fred Monkemeyer's discovery that parts of the
Creede Formation tuff beds gave good assays for silver no doubt created much excitement. Larsen described the activities at the bedded
deposits southwest of the Commodore Mine in his 1929 report:

"A number of tunnels were run in the tuff beds, and
about ten carloads of carefully selected ore was shipped to
the smelter. This ore is said to have run from twelve to
thirty ounces of silver to the ton, averaging about seven-
teen ounces, and one car carried 2 fi per cent of lead.
    "These so-called 'flat veins' are really beds of tuff that
have been mineralized. The chief mineralized bed is about
160 feet above Commodore No. 3 Tunnel and extends
around the hill, about on the level, nearly to Windy
Gulch. The beds contain some black carbonized frag-
ments of wood, and these are especially rich in silver, run-
ning as high as 3,000 ounces to the ton."[46]

V.V. Clark told of a conversation that he had with Fred
Monkemeyer in 1934: "He [Monkemeyer] reports having found a
petrified tree in this formation in the Uncle Sam Mine. It was about
twelve inches in diameter and eight feet long. The heart of the tree
was a black, soft material and assayed 870 ounces in silver. The outside assayed 180 ounces in silver. The formation all around the tree
for some two feet was conglomerate, and it assayed 60 ounces of silver per ton."[47]

The man who made the discovery of silver in the tuff beds in the
Creede Formation was a very active prospector at Creede Camp.
Besides the tuff beds, Fred Monkemeyer was engaged in prospecting
at Mammoth Mountain and was a member of the group exploring at
the Bulldog Mine. The *Mineral County Miner* carried a story about
Fred Monkemeyer by John LaFont in its April 29, 1982, issue:

"Fred Monkemeyer was a dynamic man, and he did a
lot of hard work. He owned a cute little comfortable

cabin in North Creede, owned today by Lynn Headlee of Del Norte. He never married until he was in his 70s and his wife did not live very long. He lived into his 80s. Jim French was county judge when Monkemeyer got married. He asked him if he takes this lady to be his lawful wedded wife. Monkemeyer's reply was 'sure ting.'

"He was a good blacksmith and made drift pins for us ranchers. He was a top-notch single jacker and entered the hand drilling contest on the Fourth of July several times and even won it the year he was 82 years old. He always sharpened his own hand steel for the drilling. At one time about the turn of the century, he held a lease on the 'Blanket Vein' or 'Flat Vein' as it was called, near the Commodore Mine. He gave it up and shortly afterward it turned out to be a very rich deposit [not really]. He said, 'I should have stayed on the Flat Vein. I chust missed it.'

"He prospected on East Willow Creek off and on for a few years. A firm headed by Ralph Peacock from Detroit was driving the Resurrection Tunnel on Mammoth Mountain in the early 1920s. Billy Barnett was kind of a supervisor for them. They gave up on it after a couple of years and Monkemeyer got interested in it. He built a good trail from just above his cabin on East Willow Creek to the Resurrection Tunnel and hiked up there and drove the tunnel by hand several hundred feet."

Clay Mine — Circa 1930
Courtesy of the Creede Historical Society

CLAY MINE

It was reported in 1929 that Ben A. Birdsey had recently discovered bentonite near Creede.

Bentonite, a non-metallic mineral found in the lower member of the Creede Formation, was found to make a superior filter for clarifying various oils.[48] The Clay Mine was developed by the Metalloid Corporation and bentonite was shipped in 1933 and 1934. Ten men were probably employed in 1933.[49]

Clay Mine — Circa 1929
From L to R: John Nelson, Ben Birdsey, Sam
Birdsey, Norman Alspaugh, unknown, unknown
Genevieve Hargraves Collection,
Courtesy of the Creede Historical Society

BULLDOG MOUNTAIN VEIN SYSTEM

George Bancroft, a well-known mining engineer of the time, was hired in 1926 to make an investigation of the Bulldog Mine.[50] His report suggested that the Bulldog Fault had been cut at a horizon where ore bodies might be expected. The fault at that point was split into six or eight barren fissures occupying a shear zone thirty feet wide. He suggested the fissures would likely unite in either direction, and where they unite an ore body was very apt to be found. The fact that the fault fissures made considerable water was a good sign. He further suggested the company drive drifts north and south along the fault. Bancroft's report stated the Bulldog Tunnel had been driven 1,113 feet by July 26, 1926, where it had penetrated the Bulldog Fault. The company had advanced the tunnel 252 feet since 1914.

The Creede Candle's "Mining Issue" of January 1, 1927, had the following article on the Bulldog:

"Bulldog Leasing, Mining & Milling Company — During the summer and fall a number of men have been employed in development work on the properties of this company located on the Bull Dog fault system. Mr. E. J. Lieske was in charge and says that operations will be resumed immediately after the first of the year when the present tunnel will be extended toward the Kansas City Star Shaft from which values of 87 ounces of silver and $13 in gold are reported to have been taken. The opening up of workable ore on the Bull Dog Fault would be of very great value to the Creede district, and we wish them all the luck in the world.

"Commencing about July 1st, the Bulldog Leasing, Mining & Milling Co. had Mr. Geo. Bancroft, a mining engineer of the best reputation, looking over all of their holdings, and after a very careful examination and survey he reported very favorably, and immediately the company began doing extensive development work thru [sic] the Bulldog Tunnel.

"During the course of prospecting while driving a drift about 758 feet from the portal of the tunnel a vein of approximately four feet wide was opened up. This vein carried little or no values, but according to Mr. Bancroft's theory this vein is apt to open up into an ore bearing chute momentarily, the company expects to finish driving this drift, also resume work on the main tunnel shortly after the first of the New Year, or as soon thereafter as the weather will permit.

"The company has started another drift, which at present is in about 80 feet, this drift is aimed to cut directly under the Kansas City Star Shaft out of which the figure so familiar to all of us, Dr. J.A. Biles, has gotten some good assays, but being handicapped by water, was forced to abandon this shaft. This drift should according to survey reach its destination in the next 60 feet.

"This company in the past few months have spent approximately $5000, considering that it is one of the oldest companies in this district prospecting year after year,

sending its money to develop our camp, we can't help but congratulate them on their unfailing efforts and wish them success in the New Year, which we are confident is bound to come. He who tries is bound to win."

Herman Emperius, who was vice-president of the Alamosa National Bank, made this statement to Fred Monkemeyer of Creede in a letter concerning the Bulldog Company, dated April 10, 1928:

"Now, Fred, the boys are losing their faith and believe that another sixty days ought to develop something worthwhile and if not they believe they have given it a fair trial and that ought to be enough. Hoping that you will be able to prove to us that you have uncovered a mine within that period."[51]

Larsen's report on mining in the Creede Mining District in 1929 did not mention any activity at the Bulldog property. Presumably exploration work had been discontinued, which was unfortunate. Records of the Colorado Department of State show that the Bulldog Leasing, Mining & Milling Company became defunct and inoperative on October 12, 1931 — no doubt a victim of the Great Depression.

Robert A. Boppe, who was chief engineer for Homestake's Bulldog Mountain Mine, said that the Nickel Plate Tunnel came very close to intercepting the Puzzle vein of the Homestake Bulldog Mine. The tunnel was about 200 feet from the vein; however its elevation was too high to intercept good ore. He also stated that some of Homestake's best ore came from Dr. Biles' Kansas City Star claim, including a stope where massive, highly compacted native silver wire nests were found. When the vein material containing the wire silver nests was cut with a diamond saw, the resulting surfaces looked like pure silver. These specimens were made into jewelry by a local artisan. If the Bulldog Leasing, Mining & Milling Company had extended the Bulldog Tunnel about 200 feet further along the Bulldog Vein, they would have found rich silver ore and made the big discovery instead of Homestake a half century later![52]

WAGON WHEEL GAP FLUORSPAR MINE

The Colorado Bureau of Mines *Annual Report for 1919* stated that a steady production of fluorspar has been made from the property of the American Fluorspar Company at Wagon Wheel Gap. The deposit was worked intermittently until 1925 when the Colorado

Fuel and Iron Corporation purchased the deposit from S.B. Collins. *The Engineering and Mining Journal* reported on January 14, 1928, that the Wagon Wheel Gap Mine had produced an average of 500 tons per month of fluorspar that was shipped to the Colorado Fuel and Iron Corporation for use at its steel mills at Pueblo, Colorado. The mine was shut down during the depths of the Great Depression but reopened in 1934.

As described in Chapter Ten, cars loaded with fluorspar were hauled to the railroad by teams of horses. A very tragic accident happened in July 1927 as one of the "horse trains" approached the railroad depot. A young girl had caught her foot in a rail switch and could not remove it. Her mother came to her aid and, unable to free the child's foot, held her daughter as the cars sped toward them. Both the child and her mother lost their lives in the accident[53] and were buried in the Creede Cemetery.

CHAPTER 13

THE TOWNS OF CREEDE CAMP: FROM BOOM TO BUST 1900-1934

THE TOWNS OF EARLY Creede Camp, Creede, Sunnyside, Bachelor, Weaver, and Stump Town had essentially been consolidated into two towns, Creede and Bachelor, by the turn of the century. A few people continued to live in Sunnyside, Weaver, and Stump Town past 1900, but very few. Sunnyside was a ghost town by 1900. Weaver was largely abandoned when the Amethyst Mill closed, but a Mrs. McDermott was the last Weaver inhabitant. She moved out in the 1930s.[1] Stump Town was not incorporated and no records exist to determine when it was abandoned. Most likely the miners and their families left Stump Town when the Nelson-Wooster-Humphreys Tunnel eliminated the need to access the mines through the shafts along the apex of the Amethyst Vein.

BACHELOR
The *Colorado State Business Directories* contain the following information on Bachelor's population and business establishments from 1900 to 1910:

	1900	1905	1910
Population	200	100	150
Clothing/Gen. Merchandise	3	0	0
Grocers	1	2	0
Hardware	1	1	0
Restaurants	1	2	0
Saloons	3	2	1
Hotels	1	0	0
Physicians	1	0	0
Attorneys	0	0	0

By 1910, the only business establishment left in Bachelor was one saloon. It was obvious that Bachelor was becoming a ghost town. Only a few cabins were left, together with a boardwalk along Main Street in 1934 to mark the site of Bachelor.[2] Harold Wheeler drew a map in 1917 of Bachelor as it existed in 1908 with numbered localities. He also provided a list of descriptions for the localities shown on his map:[3]

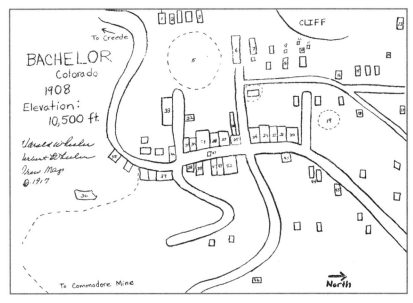

1. Catholic Church
2. Jail
3. Jenneve Lee, Grandpa's first girl-friend
4. Protestant Church w/ Belfry
5. Baseball Field
6. School
7. Barn
8. McCoygue
9. Backhouse
10. Grandpa's House
11. Woodshed
12. Backhouse
13. Allen's House
14. Andy Uran
15. Jordan
16. Adams

17. Pump
18. Berry
19. Where Grandpa first saw Grandma, "the little red-headed girl" picking flowers on the hill
20. Burnt Boarding House with Stove
21. Boarding House
22. Scotch
23. Cap Eades Store
24. Barn
25. Saloon
26. Bowling Alley
27. Saloon
28. Grocery Store
29. Dry Goods
30. Barber Shop

31. Saloon
32. Barber Shop
33. Town Hall
34. Liquor Store
35. Doc
36. Cemetery
37. Fleming
38. Saloon
39. Boarding House
40. Drug Store
41. Meat Market
42. Boarding House
43. Boarding House
44. Storage
45. Dunleavy
46. Lamp
47. Town Dump

Bachelor lasted as a town until about 1916; however, in the 1920s, many homes were still standing and three were occupied. One older resident built a fifty-foot snowshed from his cabin to the outside privy. He didn't appreciate shoveling snow. The remaining Bachelor residents moved to Creede in the 1930s. The last to move were Garrett (Red) Marshall and his mother. Red had the Shell gasoline station at the lower end of Creede.[4]

Main Street — Bachelor, 1910
Courtesy of the Denver Public Library Western History Collection

CREEDE

At the turn of the century, the town of Creede extended from North Creede, located within the East Willow Creek Gulch, to South Creede outside the constricting walls of Willow Creek Canyon below the confluence of East and West Willow Creeks. The connecting section of the town, called Stringtown, was "strung out" along the banks of Willow Creek. Creede's population in 1893 was 6,000[5] and had dropped to 1,173 in 1900, as recorded in the U.S. Census. The population continued to decrease dramatically from 1900 to 1930, reflecting the reduced production of metals at Creede, as was the case at most other mining areas of the West. Creede's 1930 population was twenty-eight per cent of that in 1900. The *Federal Census* lists the Creede populations from "boom" to "bust":

Year	Population	Year	Population
1890	0	1920	500
1900	1173	1930	334
1910	741		

The *Colorado State Business Directory for 1900* listed the following kinds of business establishments in Creede that year: hotels (3), saloons (4), grocers (7), physicians (4), bicycles (1), attorneys, restaurants, mines and mining, livery, feed store, laundry, lumber, dentist, blacksmith, jeweler, cigars and confectionery, painters, assayers, school, orchestra, opera house, and dry goods/mercantile.

As the population decreased, so did the business community. The *Colorado State Business Directories* listed the business establishments at Creede for the following years:

	1905	1910	1915	1920	1925	1930	1935
Clothing/ Gen. Merchandise	7	2	5	3	3	2	2
Grocers	5	3	0	1	0	1	3
Hardware	4	2	1	1	1	1	1
Restaurants	2	1	1	1	1	0	2
Saloons	4	3	2	0	0	0	0
Hotels	4	1	3	3	1	2	2
Physicians	2	1	1	1	0	1	1

Creede's transformation from a wide-open, "rip-roaring" mining camp town to one where families could raise their children in a more law-abiding environment occurred in 1906 when wide-open gambling became illegal throughout Mineral County. *The Creede Candle* of May 12, 1906, had the following story:

> *"Creede Reforms — Gambling was closed tight in Creede last Saturday night and in all probabilities will remain closed hereafter as the people behind the move are determined that the law pertaining to such matters shall be enforced from now on.*
>
> *"Saturday evening, Deputy Sheriff T.A. Wheeler visited all of the saloons and issued the orders that closed the games of chance and on Monday night when the city council was in session a delegation of citizens, consisting mostly of ladies, waited upon the aldermen and demanded of them to have all gambling devices removed from the saloons and that all saloons be closed at 12 o'clock at night on weekdays and to be kept closed all day Sundays. The same orders were enforcing the movement throughout the entire county. The orders have been complied with by the proprietors of the various saloons without any resistance or trouble and since then everything has been*

conducted as per the request of the citizens who waited upon the council."

The Alamosa Journal of May 3, 1907, carried the following story about Creede's transformation:

"The town of Creede is now booze proof, jaglessly harmless, absinthelessly pure and nothing but denatured tarantula 'licker' can be procured only on a written permit from the entire city council, marshal, and dog catcher. Green cloth individuals have been told to skiddo and the paraphernalia of the gambling parlors has been confiscated by the man who wears the big star and chews Battleax plug. Oh, Creede's goin' some."

The reformation of Creede also meant the "ladies of the evening" were not accepted in the community as they were in the past. Several of these ladies married influential citizens of Creede and became respectable. They loved to play bridge and cribbage in their later years and, because they did not have children, they doted on the youngsters of Creede and were most charitable. A couple of them were good musicians, one with an exceptionally good voice for popular or operatic songs, and they were all good cooks.[6]

Canyon Above Creede — Photo by M.R. Campbell, 1905
Courtesy of the U.S. Geological Survey

Town of Creede — Photo by E.S. Larsen, 1911
Courtesy of the U.S. Geological Survey

The Creede Candle's issue of February 12, 1916, reported the city of Creede would be changed to an incorporated town. This action was necessary since the population of Creede had fallen below the minimum for city status and the article stated that the change would place the town on a more economical basis.

Mineral County and the citizens of Creede promulgated the policy of "pay as you go" early in the history of Creede Camp. That policy was continued through hard times with the result that Mineral County was not in debt and had some $45,000 in the treasury in 1934. Moreover, it was the only county in the United States not employing federal relief monies in 1934.[7]

DISASTERS

Creede suffered more disasters — both natural and man-made — than most mining towns in the West. Floods, fires, and pestilence had serious impacts on the town and its citizens before, during, and after hard times.

The town of Creede was built in the narrow canyon formed by Willow Creek and, as a result, suffered from flooding nearly every spring. In 1905, a major flood destroyed over a mile of Denver and Rio Grande Railroad tracks in the canyon and much of the grade and two bridges were washed away. Rail service to the mines was disrupted for nearly a month.[8] Creede was cut off from train service on

October 5, 1911, for six days and lost communications with the rest of the world because flood waters washed out the rails and the telegraph and telephone lines.[9] Floods continued to damage the community and finally Willow Creek was contained in a wooden flume that ran through town. Even so, flood waters were a constant threat throughout the years. *The Creede Candle* described a devastating spring flood in its June 23, 1917, issue:

> *"It is almost an impossibility to estimate the amount of damage that has resulted from the high water of the past week. The Creede Exploration Co. has sustained the heaviest damage, but is only awaiting normal conditions to rebuild the damaged property. The D&RG Railroad property has been damaged to a great extent. The tracks between the water tank at the mouth of Windy Gulch, and North Creede is practically totally destroyed, including the removal of two railroad bridges. The trestle in South Creede is damaged to an extent that the passenger train failed to reach town Wednesday. The bridge crew and extra section men are busy, but until the water recedes to a flow nearly normal, the repair work will not be much gained.*
>
> *"North Creede is a deplorable sight since East Willow Creek has been coming through the town. Other buildings than the Cliff Hotel and Holy Moses Saloon, have fallen into the creek, among those were the Ostrum building and the Lempke Assay office. The street and bridges have been destroyed.*

North Creede after the Flood — 1917
J. Roy Packard Collection, Courtesy of the Creede Historical Society

Stringtown after the Flood — 1917
J. Roy Packard Collection, Courtesy of the Creede Historical Society

"The mine dumps up both East and West Willow Canyons have been washed away, and have to a great extent been responsible for much of the destruction lower down. When the water was at the highest it was estimated that fifty tons of rock were moving each minute. These rocks filled the channel and the water rapidly spread.

"The section known as Stringtown is a heap of rocks and driftwood. The residents abandoned their homes and moved to Creede. The wagon road is completely obliterated. Great logs have been washed into it, saying nothing of rocks and soil. North Creede is only accessible by following the trail up along Bachelor Mountain.

"The damage to the town of Creede is very insignificant to that up the canyon. The flume carrying Willow Creek did wonderful work, but must undergo much repair after the flood season. The street which has been washed out near the section house will necessitate expending a large amount.

"In addition to the losses of the mining companies, the railroad, the town, and individuals, work in the camp will be delayed indefinitely. The freight train has been unable to reach North Creede and mines for more than a week and some time must elapse before tracks will be ready for traffic. Mine operations are practically at a standstill. The chutes and the ore bins are filled and no cars to load. The Creede Exploration Company has much

material lying in cars on the sidings awaiting the opera-
tion of the freight train.

"Old time residents report that in past years they have
seen as much water in the canyon but never the amount of
damage."

Fire as well as flooding plagued Creede. The fire in the morning
of June 5, 1892, essentially destroyed Creede. Three years later on
October 17, 1895, fire swept through the town again and caused
$150,000 in damages.[10] In 1902 two hotels and twenty houses in
upper Creede burned. *Mining Science*, May 12, 1910, discussed fires
in mining camps and stated that camps built in narrow canyons such
as Creede were particularly at risk since the draft in a narrow
canyon acted as a fire flue. Fortunately, no more major fires
occurred during Creede's hard times to make life for its residents
more difficult. A fire that occurred on December 28, 1920, was
described in the *Creede Firemen Ledger*:

> *"All members in town assembled at the Wolfe Hotel*
> *fire but the fire was beyond control as the pump refused*
> *to pump and the chemical soon was empty and a second*
> *story fire soon ended the bucket [line] idea. But saved*
> *adjoining buildings. All furniture downstairs saved except*
> *large range left at request of city alderman. Cause over-*
> *heated stove. Total loss $7,000; Insurance $3,000;*
> *Telephone line damaged $300."[11]*

The Engineering and Mining Journal, January 18, 1919,
reported that during the last three months of 1918, the influenza
epidemic at Silverton and Creede was appalling. According to a partial list from newspaper files and death records, at least thirty-six
deaths from the flu occurred in Creede in 1918.[12]

THE RAILROAD

The Denver and Rio Grande Railroad reduced service to Creede
after the silver panic of 1893. Even so, standard gauge trackage was
completed to Creede in 1902 and passenger service continued until
1932.[13] A bold experiment in providing passenger service from
Alamosa to Creede commenced on August 1, 1929, when the
Denver and Rio Grande Railroad began the operation of a gasoline
motor car in place of the regular passenger train. The motor car was
known as the "Toonerville Trolley" in Creede. The experiment was
a failure and the motor car was withdrawn from service after six

months and two days and the standard passenger train was put back into service for two more years.[14]

NEWSPAPERS

Early day Creede Camp had many newspapers — fourteen, as a matter of fact, in Creede, Bachelor, Sunnyside, and Wason. Only two survived past 1900 — *The Creede Candle* and the *Bachelor Tribune*. The *Bachelor Tribune* went out of business in 1903. Cy Warman, known as the "Poet of the Cochetopas," established the *Creede Chronicle*, a weekly paper that published from 1892 until 1895.[15]

Lute H. Johnson came to Creede Camp with a hand press and established *The Creede Candle* as a weekly on January 7, 1892. The last issue was published Saturday, December 30, 1930. The paper was discontinued by L.G. Schwalenberg because of ill health and its assets were sold to Harvey E. Jones, owner and publisher of the *Del Norte Prospector*, who promised the citizens of Creede that he would publish news about the people of Creede and happenings in and around the town and Mineral County. *The Creede Candle* had been the voice of Creede and Mineral County for almost forty years.

THE TELEPHONE COMES TO CREEDE

The Creede Candle told about the telephone's arrival in its January 13, 1906, issue:

> *"The telephone is in. Thursday afternoon the linemen got in with the wire and at 4:30 o'clock Denver was called up by Foreman C.B. Bliss with the test phone attached to the end of the wire. A temporary wire was run into Mr. Bliss' room in the Zang Hotel and communication held with the head office in Denver.*
> *"In celebration of the event, today the company threw the line open to the public free of charge to communicate with any point in the state.*
> *"The toll line phone has been temporarily placed in Hord-Todd & Co.'s store until the new central office can be equipped, where it will be found to accommodate those wishing to communicate with the outside world within the next ten days. The rate for toll service is 25 cents added to the Del Norte.*
> *"The company's full crew is now in the city, consisting of thirty-five or forty men, and they are all busy hanging the cable and completing the main line and set-*

ting poles throughout the city preparatory to putting in the exchanges."

ELECTRIC POWER

Creede's first source of electric power, the steam electric power plant built in 1892 by the Creede Electric Light and Power Company, burned down November 8, 1925.[16] The community faced the problem of deciding whether to build another steam-powered generating plant or to construct a hydroelectric plant to meet its electric power needs. *The Creede Candle*, January 1, 1927, described how the question was resolved and its results:

> *"Finally after much discussion the two plans [steam vs. hydro-electric] were submitted to the people at the general city election, and the hydro-electric won out.*
>
> *"After nearly a year of careful consideration, East Willow Creek was selected as the site for water power by the Wineland Engineering Co., of Pueblo, Colo., and the lucky bidder for constructing the hydro-electric project was Hassellman and Keller, also of Pueblo, Colo. The work was begun September 15, 1926 and completed December 1, 1926.*
>
> *"The hydro-electric plant and water system at Creede consists of a concrete diversion dam located on East Willow Creek approximately 600 feet upstream from the portal of the old Revenue Tunnel, the stream flow at that point at normal times is approximately 6.5 cubic feet.*
>
> *"The dam as above mentioned is not a storage dam, but acts as a head gate to divert the water to one side into a penstock which is triple-screened, each screen being of smaller mesh to keep debris from the pipe line. The penstock is self-cleaning by a valve system in front of each screen and it is not necessary to shut down the plant to clean the penstock of debris.*
>
> *"The pipeline is a 14-inch sectional wooden, creosote treated, and steel wrapped conduit, the steel bands being wound closer as the line nears the power plant 2,550 feet down the stream as the pressure at the plant under full head is 50 pounds per square inch by the fall of 124 feet.*
>
> *"The line is safe from frost under three feet of dirt, and is reduced from 14 inches to one 1 1/4-inch nozzle*

and one 2 1/2-inch nozzle of the 50 H.P. Pelton Wheel which is the prime mover for the generator. The two noz- zles of the wheel are controlled by deflectors connected to a hydraulic governor of the Pelton patent, the bearings of the wheel are self-oiled by oil rings which rotate with the shaft, the generator is belted to the wheel by leather belt- ing, of a length of twenty foot shaft centers. The genera- tor is a product of the General Electric Co., a 2300 V. alternating alternator with a capacity of 37 fi K.W. and has a direct connected exciter. The switch board is on compact design and has all the necessary instrument and circuit features for safety of the distribution system nearly one mile away, and is distributed by five distribution transformers on a 220 V. three wire secondary main, and balanced for residence service of 110 V., two wire drops picked from each side of the 220 V. mains.

"After nearly a month of service, it has ground out approximately 1500 K.W. and a daily consumption of 50 K.W. at the Board. At this writing the water in East Willow Creek and in fact all creeks of Mineral County are the lowest they have been in years and to overcome two obstacles, one, ice on the penstock screens, the other low water, the work of piping the 60 degree water of the Revenue Tunnel to the penstock of the dam has begun, and we feel sure that the Revenue water will not only give us nearly one cubic second foot of 60 degree water to increase our water supply, but it will keep our screens in the penstock clear of ice during the slush period."

The hydroelectric plant served Creede for many years. It was finally replaced about 1940 with a diesel-driven generator.

WATER AND SEWAGE

The Creede municipal water system was first constructed in 1892 and consisted of wood pipe taking water directly from East Willow Creek. Over the years, the wood pipe was replaced by cast iron pipe. East Willow Creek was the system's source of water for about a century. A new water system was installed in the 1990s that utilizes water from wells adjacent to the Rio Grande River.

Creede did not have a municipal sewage system for many years and was dependent on individual septic systems until the 1980s.

Willow Creek served as the sewage system in earlier years. Florence McCarty remembered Willow Creek about 1910 as a child in Creede:

> "It [Willow Creek] was the ugliest and most horrible example of water pollution imaginable. All the way through town garbage was dumped into it, privies were built over it. If one trapped a mouse or picked a chicken, or a cat died, all were thrown into the creek. It was deadly. Our parents warned us about getting wet, wading or even getting a drop of it on our hands or clothing."[17]

THE BURRO QUESTION

The January 22, 1916, issue of *The Creede Candle* described the problem with burros that were turned loose during the winter months to fend for themselves:

> "The deep snowfall brings the burro question before the Creede people. During the summer months every one of these little animals is claimed by some one and put to hard work. In the winter, when feed is high, they are turned out to rustle or starve. After the deep snow they are compelled to live on the few scraps that are thrown out of kitchen doors. The hungry burros are pests, as they will eat clothes off the line, brooms or anything they can get. During the day they are rocked and dogged from one place to another. At night they prowl around in search of something to eat, and disturb people's slumbers.
>
> "The humane officer informed this paper that he was powerless to protect them, unless the city council would enforce the loose stock ordinance. Be it as it may, something should be done. It looks to a blind man, that a humane officer has power to arrest anyone who neglects to feed their livestock. Why not compel the summer owners to care for them the year around? Never mind the boys who claim or have burros in their possession, their parents can be held responsible."

SCHOOL TIME

Creede had schools as early as 1892. The Mineral County High School was built about 1916 and served the community and county until a new high school was constructed in 1949. Florence McCarty described attending school in Creede about 1910:

"Attending school in Creede was a hazardous under-taking, and a real challenge. The schoolhouse was about midtown, a yellow frame structure up against the mountain to the east. There were two grades to each room, except the chart class had a room of its own. The principal taught the seventh and eighth grades. Children who lived near the school went home at noon time. Others brought their lunches and would sit along the side of the building or wherever they pleased. Many climbed on the mountain in warm weather. Few days passed when a child did not climb some way up the mountain."[18]

CHURCHES

Early Creede was served by three churches — The Mission Church of the Immaculate Conception, St. Augustine's Episcopal Church, and the Congregational Church.[19]

The first Mission Church of the Immaculate Conception building was constructed in 1897. The church was moved from its original location in town to a spot on the mesa to the west in 1973.

Episcopal services in Creede were started in 1897 by the Reverend Charles Y. Grimes. He held services, helped during the summer by theological students, in a rough building shell with seventy kitchen chairs. The St. Augustine parish was organized in 1905. St. Augustine's, at the southeast corner of Creede and Fifth Street, was built 1905 to 1908.

The original Congregational Church was located between the Beaumont Saloon and Willow Creek and was destroyed by the June 5, 1892, fire that devastated Creede. The church was rebuilt in 1905 at the northeast corner of Creede and Fourth Street of red brick and of a design called the "Akron Design" that originated in Akron, Ohio, in the 1800s. The church bell came from the Congregational Church in Bachelor. The stained glass windows were given to the church by the Creede lodges.

LODGES

Creede Camp had many lodges and fraternal groups in its early days. *The Creede Candle* listed the following organizations represented in Creede in 1907:

1. *Amethyst Lodge No. 94, Ancient Free and Accepted Masons;*
2. *Rio Grande Chapter No. 35, Eastern Star;*

3. *Creede Lodge No. 506, Benevolent and Protective order of Elks;*

4. *Columbian Lodge No. 87, Knights of Pythias;*

5. *Creede Camp No. 33, Woodmen of the World;*

6. *Creede Lodge No. 55, International Order of Odd Fellows;*

7. *Woodfern Lodge No. 62, Daughters of the Revolution;*

8. *Commodore Tent No. 32, Maccabees;*

9. *Amethyst Circle No. 21, Ladies of the Grand Army of the Republic;*

10. *Amethyst Aerie No. 1012, Eagles;*

11. *Bachelor Lodge No. 58, Ancient Order of United Workmen;*

12. *Happy Thought Hive No. 80, L.O.T.M.;*

13. *Uniform Rank, Creede Company, No. 31, Knights of Pythias;*

14. *Happy Thought Council No. 38, Fraternal Aid Association;*

15. *Miners Union No. 20 of Creede, Western Federation of Miners; and*

16. *Creede Fire Department.*

REMEMBRANCES OF CREEDE

John Jackson grew up in Creede in the late 1920s and 1930s. He knew Creede during the hard times and thereafter. His remembrances of life in Creede as a boy are most interesting. Some of them follow:

"I was born in the 1920s during a bleak period in Creede's history. The town had less than 400 residents and fully a third of the houses were vacant. Both our neighbors, Ed Snow and Charles Matson, were old-time miners and prospectors who did carpentry work, blacksmithed, or sharpened saws during the winter months then headed for the hills in the spring.

"Living conditions were not the best — drafty, uninsulated houses, outdoor biffies for the main part until 1936 when a water system was installed. Most homes would go unplumbed for bathrooms until the 1950s and freeze ups were always a problem. Roy Fisher, a venerable

former miner, councilman, mayor, and mentor, continued pulling his water from a backyard well with rope and bucket years after tap water was available. Lewis Oppy was among several who supplied the most needy with the state's deer and elk herd's roasts and steaks. Much of this hunting activity for meat occurred out of season and was, therefore, illegal. It has been rumored that some of the local law enforcement officials turned a blind eye to poaching for a good cause.

"John Mattern operated a theater until 1936 when the Mercantile Block burned, destroying Neef's Liquor Store, Webber's Mercantile Store, Parker Drugstore, Frank's Barbershop, and the theater. Senator Lawrence Phipps, owner of the Phipps Ranch at Wagon Wheel Gap, held his annual birthday party for Creede's residents with a spirited baseball game as the finale. A circus and carnival rides were a yearly event. The Elks staged 'smokers,' boxing matches among the locals, and the Civilian Conservation Corps invited us to films shown in the barracks and also had a boxing team to combat with local pugilists.

"The Fourth of July Celebrations were important events in Creede. Jim French, Al Hibbs, Slim Earle, Elmo Tucker, and others of the Elks Lodge staged very diverse celebrations to appeal to young and old, locals, and visitors. The hanging of the killer of Bob Ford (sometimes billed as The Hanging of Bob Ford) was a highlight of the events and often with disastrous results. In one hanging, a black cape with noose attached was placed over the victim who was mounted on a horse. The noose was designed to go under the arms for a safe hanging but all the participants were drunk and the noose ended up under one arm and over the neck of 'Bob Ford.' It was such a sterling performance that one of the least drunk of the crew decided to check and cut the poor fellow down before he really expired. As near as I can remember, that was the last hanging staged on the Fourth.

"In one extraordinary celebration, one hundred silver dollars were hidden on the hillside east of town for the youngsters, called Creede's 'Silver Rush.' I believe they were all found. A liquor race was staged on Main Street with a quart of good whiskey leading a bottle of gin,

bottle of rum, and several bottles of lesser desired spirits in a 'V' design. Frankie Davis outdistanced all competitors, lost his footing several feet before reaching the liquor and lost a generous amount of skin as he slid up to his I.W. Harper [bottle of bourbon whiskey]. The most interesting to the locals was the whiskey drinking contest held after noon with the bottle resting in the sunshine to be warmed beforehand. The contestant had to give his full name, bottoms up a full two-ounce glass, and then give an impromptu speech. A few retired to the shadows to vomit, some weren't able to speak let alone give a speech. One, who had been practicing a few hours, keeled over to sleep it off, and there were always several ties that taxed the most experienced drinkers to the hilt. Slim Earle, a long, lanky mechanic, was the longest reigning champion."

CHAPTER 14

REBIRTH – THE HANGING WALL VEINS 1934-1972

A STROKE OF A PEN ended Creede Camp's hard times. President Franklin D. Roosevelt signed a presidential proclamation stating that American silver producers would receive 64.64 cents per ounce from December 21, 1933, to April 10, 1935. The average price of silver in New York had been 28.2 cents in 1932 and 35 cents in 1933.[1] The "pegged" price was almost twice the average price in 1933!

The Creede mines quickly resumed operations and the citizens of Creede again had jobs and did not need to "live off the land" as they had for several years. The Commodore Mining Company reopened in January 1934.[2] Other mines in the camp followed suit, and by the end of 1934, the Amethyst, Commodore, Creede Mines group, Del Monte-Last Chance-New York-Pittsburgh group, Wagon Wheel Gap Fluorspar, Clay (Bentonite), and other mines were shipping ore. About 200 men were employed in the mines.[3] Additional mines commenced operations in 1935, including the Consolidated Moses Solomon Mines Company group, Corsair, and the Mollie S.[4]

The U.S. Census gives Creede's population in 1940 as 670 as compared to 334 in 1930 — certainly an indication that Creede Camp was having better times. Creede's population dropped to 503 in 1950 and 350 in 1960, but rebounded to 653 in 1970.

On May 22, 1934, President Roosevelt asked Congress for legislation stating that the policy of the United States was to maintain twenty-five per cent of the total value of the currency of the country in the form of silver. Senator Key Pittman introduced Senate Bill 3658 on the same day. This legislation was enacted by Congress on June 13th and signed by the president on June 19, 1934. The Silver Purchase Act of 1934 authorized the secretary of the treasury to purchase silver and issue silver certificates.[5]

For newly mined silver, American producers received 71.11 cents per fine ounce from April 11, 1935, to April 24, 1935; 77.57 cents from April 25, 1935, to December 31, 1937; 64.64 cents from January 1, 1938, to June 30, 1939; and thereafter, by the Act of July 6, 1939, 71.11 cents. The drop in the price of silver to 64.64 cents on January 1, 1938, was responsible for 10.5 million ounces less silver from American mines in 1938.[6] The Treasury of the United States continued to acquire all newly mined U.S. silver except during the war years of 1941 to 1945, when most of it went to supply the large war demand. The Act of July 31, 1946, raised the statutory price to 90.5 cents per fine ounce.[7] This price held until 1961 when a Presidential Order took the United States Treasury out of the silver business and placed silver on the open market. This move resulted in an increase in the price of silver to $1.04 by the end of 1961.[8] The move to place silver on the free market instead of being under government control created the climate for Creede's second boom, the subject of Chapter Fifteen.

The renewed mining activity at Creede Camp again brought forward the issue of concentrating the ores to reduce the cost of transportation and smelting and, thus, reducing the grade of ore that could be economically mined. As early as 1920 and later in 1934, movements were afoot to get the mine owners and lessees to agree to send their ore to a proposed custom mill.[9] Thomas Patterson Campbell was the financier and prime mover for the custom mill that was finally built. Leadville's *Carbonate Chronicle* carried the following story in its October 25, 1937, issue:

> *"New Ore Reduction Mill is Ready to Start at Creede — Thomas P. Campbell of Denver, the chief backer constructing the mill, became interested in the Creede Camp about 20 years ago. His grandfather, the late U.S. Senator Thomas Patterson, left three mining claims in the Creede Camp in his estate at the time of his death."*

The ore reduction or concentrating mill, designed to treat 100 to 150 tons per day, was constructed and owned by Creede Mills, Incorporated, who had contracts to treat the aggregate of 100 tons per day of ore produced by the leading mining operators in Creede Camp — the Commodore-Bachelor Mines, New York-Last Chance-Del Monte-Pittsburgh group, and Amethyst group.[10] The mill was located on a hillside at the southern end of the town of Creede where open flat land provided space for off-stream tailings disposal.

Ground was broken in July 1937, and the mill was completed and placed in operation the latter part of October 1937. It was running at capacity by the end of that year.

Jack Trompen of Del Norte managed the construction of the mill and Jake Jacobsen was the first mill superintendent. Raymond Lane excavated the basement of the superintendent's house with a team of horses and a Fresno scraper for a fee of $10 or $15 per day for the team and driver. A princely sum in 1937.[11]

The following explanation for the need of a mill was given in the Emperius Mining Company's Annual Report for 1937:[12]

> "After four years of steady production on high grade ores, this type of ore is becoming less in evidence that any time in the history of the camp.
>
> "Costs for hauling, transportation and smelter were computed for ore of a value of $15 per ton:

Hauling	$ 1.25 per ton
Freight	2.75 per ton
Smelter	8.00 per ton
Total	$12.00 per ton

> "Under new mill operation schedule during 1937, charges on the same class of ore were:

Tailing Loss	$ 3.00 per ton
Hauling	0.75 per ton
Mill Charge	3.50 per ton
Total	$ 7.25 per ton"

The following description of the mill and its power plant was taken from an article in the magazine, *Mining World*:[13]

> "The mill produced a gold-silver-lead concentrate by using bulk flotation. The ore's mineral content varied considerably, thus requiring exceptionally careful assaying, mixing of the mill feed, and reagent control.
>
> "Trucks were used to haul the ore from the mines under contract to four 100-ton coarse ore bins. Each bin was assigned to a single mine. A 30-inch conveyor delivered the ore from the bins to the crushing plant, consisting of a 9 x 21-inch jaw crusher, a pulsator screen with 3/4-inch openings, and a 20-inch cone crusher. The jaw crusher was set for a 2-inch product and the cone crusher for a minus 5/8-inch product. The minus 5/8-inch product was sampled and conveyed on a 16-inch belt over four

Creede Mills, Inc.'s Custom Mill Owned by the Emperius Mining
Company — 1940. Tailings Pond in the Foreground. White
Structure at Right is Mill Superintendent's Residence.

Photo by John Jackson

*100-ton fine ore bins where the ore was deposited in the
appropriate bin by a tripper.*

*"Automatic feeders on each bin fed the crushed ore
from each bin to a 6 x 6-foot open end ball mill via 16-
inch conveyor belts. The ball mill discharge went to a 12
x 16-inch mineral jig in a closed circuit with a 54-inch
classifier and the ball mill. The jig concentrate contained
about 100 ounces of silver and 10 percent lead per ton.*

*"The classifier overflow went to the flotation section
consisting of 13 cells. From the last of the float cells, the
concentrate was thickened in a 8 x 10-foot thickener and
filtered in a 4 x 6-foot drum filter. The concentrate ran
about 250-360 ounces of silver, 0.3 ounces of gold and 19
percent lead per ton. Tailings from the flotation cells
reported to a shaking table where values not removed by
the flotation circuit were collected. Then the tailings were
sampled and assayed before being transported to the adjacent off-stream tailing pond by an elevated launder. The
mill was equipped with a complete laboratory.*

"A diesel-electric power plant was installed to provide power for the mill instead of constructing a high voltage power line from Del Norte, 38 miles away. The town of Creede's municipal power plant was too small to carry the mill load. Mill electricity was produced by the plant for two cents per kilowatt-hour."

The U.S. Bureau of Mines' *Minerals Yearbook for 1939* reported on the new concentration mill's positive impact on Creede Camp:

"The local market for ore furnished throughout 1938 by the custom flotation mill of Creede Mills, Inc. stimulated production in the Creede district and resulted in an increase of 42 percent over 1937 in the district output of silver. In 1938 the company treated 35,179 tons of ore, of which about 70 percent was newly-mined and 30 percent came from dumps. The following properties supplied the ore treated in 1938; Alpha-Corsair, Amethyst, Commodore-Bachelor, and New York-Last Chance-Del Monte-Pittsburgh group and Manitoba and Monon mines."

The U.S. Bureau of Mines' *Mineral Yearbook Review of 1940* carried the following comments about mining at Creede Camp in 1940:

"Silver production in the Creede district increased 45 per cent in 1940 over 1939, following a 30 per cent increase in 1939 over 1938 and a 42 per cent increase in 1938 over 1937. The output of gold and lead recovered from the silver ore also increased in 1940. Much high-grade silver ore was shipped direct to the Leadville smelter, but the bulk of the ore from the district was concentrated in the custom flotation mill of Creede Mills, Inc., and the concentrates produced were shipped to the Leadville smelter. The mill was operated by Creede Mills, Inc., from January 1 to September 1, when it was leased to the Emperius Mining Co., which ran it the rest of the year. The Emperius Mining Co. also acquired the mining leases of Creede Mills, Inc. in the Sunnyside [Creede Mining District] area."

Leasing of Creede Mills, Inc.'s, custom mill by the Emperius Mining Company was one of the most important milestones in the history of Creede Camp. By controlling the only mill in the district, Emperius was able to consolidate the most productive mines at Creede into one mining entity, as will be described later in this chapter.

World War II had a huge impact on mining at Creede Camp. The U.S. Government's Order L-208, which placed restrictions on the mining of gold and silver, went into effect October 8, 1942, as part of the war effort. Mining of high-grade silver ore was stopped and sulfide ores containing lead, zinc, and copper that were needed for the war effort were developed and mined. This meant that most of the ore at Creede Camp had to be concentrated in the mill controlled by Emperius before shipment to the smelters. Order L-208 was rescinded by President Harry S. Truman on July 1, 1945.[14] Price controls for lead, zinc, and copper had been instituted by the U.S. Government during the war and were removed on June 30, 1946.

AMETHYST VEIN SYSTEM

Ore production from the Amethyst Vein System in the middle to late 1930s was primarily from the hanging wall veins in the Commodore, Last Chance, New York, Del Monte, and Amethyst Mines. Some production was noted from the northern part of the main Amethyst Vein in the Happy Thought, White Star, and Park Regent Mines. The Commodore Mine supplied most of the camp's ore in 1934 and continued to produce ore until the early 1940s. The Emperius Mining Company, the successor to the Poxson and Emperius sub-lease described in Chapter Twelve, was organized in June 1934. The company brought the hanging wall veins in the Last Chance-New York-Del Monte group into production. Extraction from these veins progressively dominated mining in the Creede district, and by 1942 Emperius had gradually consolidated adjacent mining properties until it controlled most of the mines on the Amethyst and related veins and conducted all mining as a single consolidated mining operation.[15]

The lack of consolidation of mining rights along the Amethyst Vein System that had seriously affected efficient mining during the early history of Creede Camp was finally resolved a half century after the ore deposits were first discovered! Unfortunately, the consolidation was not positive for all. Some of the owners faced the prospect of selling or leasing to Emperius and lessees; many individual miners lost out and suffered financial and job losses as a result of the consolidation. On the other hand, the Emperius Mining Company provided jobs for Creede miners and their families for

many, many years because the consolidation resulted in more efficient mining.

The histories of the mines along the Amethyst Vein System will
be described up to the time of their consolidation by lease or purchase into the Emperius Mining Company. The history of Emperius
will then follow.

BACHELOR AND COMMODORE MINES

A one cent per share dividend was declared at the annual stockholders meeting held on June 15, 1934, and the advance notice for
the meeting, dated May 15, 1934, made the following statement:

> *"As silver advanced to a more favorable price, opera-*
> *tions were resumed at the Commodore Mine in January of*
> *this year and shipments are now being regularly made.*
> *During February, March, and April the lessees shipped 14*
> *cars, about 700 tons, of silver ore of good grade and the*
> *future prospects for the mine are very encouraging."*[16]

V.V. Clark visited the Commodore Mine in 1934. At that time,
the mine manager was D.G. Withrow, son of Clarence O. Withrow
who held the lease on the Commodore Mine. D.G. Withrow graduated from Wyoming University in 1927. He had worked at Creede
prior to attending college and since graduation had been an assistant
to his father in charge of the Bachelor-Commodore Mines. Clark
described how the Commodore ore was processed: "The mine run
ore is passed over a grizzly [sloping bar screen], the oversize being
hand-sorted. The shipping ore assays around 100 oz. of silver per
ton, no gold, 1.5 per cent to 2 per cent lead and no zinc. From 5 to
6 railroad cars of ore is shipped monthly from the Commodore
hanging wall fissures."[17]

The lease agreement between the Withrow-Commodore Lease,
Inc., and the Commodore Mining Company expired in June or July
1935 and was not renewed. Clarence O. Withrow was the lessee and
Anna R. Morse was the president of the Commodore Mining
Company. The company then leased the Commodore and Bachelor
Mines to George H. Garrey and Ben T. Poxson from August 1,
1935, to August 1, 1938. Garrey and Poxson agreed that a company
would be formed to which the lease would be assigned without con-
sideration. The Wilson Leasing Company was organized about
August 3, 1935, to take the lease. The original stockholders were
Oscar Ball, Joseph Wilson, Anna R. Morse, B.T. Poxson, W.C.

Sloan, G.H. Garrey, and Edward Thoruler. Ball and Wilson were miners. The Withrow-Commodore Lease, Inc., sold their mining equipment to Commodore Mining Company on August 12, 1935.[18] These events ended a company that had been in the forefront of discovering the hanging wall veins and bringing Creede Camp out of hard times.

Anna Reynolds Morse, the daughter and sole heir of A.E. Reynolds, was born in Columbus, Wisconsin, on January 26, 1884. She married Bradish Morse in 1913. Morse was a partner in the Morse Brothers Machinery and Supply Company of Denver, Colorado. After A.E. Reynolds' death in 1921, Morse looked after his wife's properties that she had inherited from her father. Even though most of Reynolds' mining properties did not produce income for the estate, the estate and its successor, the Reynolds-Morse Corporation, earned royalties in excess of $94,000 from the Withrow Lease in 1925 and 1926. The royalties dropped dramatically afterwards. Bradish Morse died on December 27, 1931. After her husband's death, Anna Morse successfully managed the affairs of the Reynolds-Morse Corporation as president. She married George Garrey in 1938.[19] Garrey, a well-known geologist, was very familiar with Creede Camp. He had made a field examination of the mines along the Amethyst Fault and submitted his report on them to American Smelting & Refining in 1916.

George H. Garrey was born in Reedville, Wisconsin, in 1875. He went to the University of Chicago, graduating in 1898. While there, he was on the football team. He taught school for two years after graduation before returning to the University of Chicago for an advanced degree in geology. While studying for his advanced degree, he was an assistant to Alonzo Stagg, one of the great football coaches of all times. Garrey then attended the Michigan College of Mines for two years and was awarded the degree of Engineer of Mines in 1904. He first went to work for the U.S. Geological Survey before joining the American Smelting & Refining Company. He opened a consulting and engineering firm in 1911. Garrey prepared the technical evidence to support the Commodore Mining Company's successful trespass suit against the Bachelor Mining Company brought in 1924. He then became closely associated with Colorado mining properties, particulary those at Creede, Summitville, and Pitkin County, Colorado, and with Ben Poxson, co-founder of the Emperius Mining Company.[20]

The Colorado Bureau of Mines' *Annual Report for 1935* stated that: "The Wilson Lease, successors to the Withrow Lease, on the Commodore Mine, are sending out a fair tonnage of high grade silver ores, together with pushing forward a new campaign of development and prospect work with an increased force of men."

LAST CHANCE, NEW YORK, AND DEL MONTE MINES

Steven and Ratté described the Last Chance, New York, and Del Monte Mines in their 1965 report on the geology and mines of Creede Camp:

> *"Initial discovery and development of the hanging wall veins in the Last Chance-New York-Del Monte group were on the Last Chance 2 level, high on the vein, where a complex of intersecting silver-rich veins was discovered. These veins provided most of the production from this group of mines until the early 1940s. Mining was conducted through the Last Chance 2 Tunnel until 1937."*[21]

This group of mines were all under lease (Morgan and Sloan, and Munsell) and operating profitably in 1934. The Last Chance was mined under the direction of Ben Miller, and Glen Munsell was leasing the Del Monte.[22] Creede Mills, Inc., contracted in the summer of 1937 to purchase ore from Morgan and Sloan for their new custom mill. Morgan and Sloan continued to successfully lease the Last Chance, New York, and Del Monte Mines until 1939.[23] The Emperius Mining Company commenced their operation of the Del Monte-New York-Last Chance-Pittsburgh group of mines in 1939 under a sub-lease from Morgan and Sloan.[24] According to the company's annual report for 1937, the Emperius Mining Company previously had a lease or sub-lease on the Last Chance Mine, or a portion of it, in 1934:

> *"The Company enjoyed a profitable year even though the grade of our ore gradually decreased, as might be expected after a steady operation on high grade ores for the past four years.*
>
> *"Renewed the Last Chance lease for an additional five years beginning 1 January 1937. Secured additional acreage from Last Chance Company, over and above that formerly held by the Company.*

"Pittsburg lease for an additional five years beginning 10 January 1938 also granted."[25]

AMETHYST MINE

The Amethyst Leasing Company was operating the mine in 1934 under the local direction of William C. Sloan and Erick Nelson, mine foreman.[26] The Amethyst Mine was a consistent producer of high-grade silver ore in 1935 and greatly contributed to the number of men employed and the tonnage of ore produced from Creede Camp.[27] Production from the Amethyst continued into 1939 under the Amethyst Leasing Company. Creede Mills, Inc., took over the lease on the Amethyst in February 1939.[28]

Creede Mills, Inc., reopened the Amethyst No. 5 Tunnel that had been inactive for a great many years. The tunnel's purpose was to intersect the veins at depth and provide transportation for ore mined above tunnel level. It was to be equipped for heavy haulage when necessary. Creede Mills, Inc., also started a campaign of prospecting and development work.[29] The Emperius Mining Company secured a lease on the Amethyst Mine from the Amethyst Mining Company in 1940.[30]

CREEDE MINES

The Creede Mines, Inc., operated the Park Regent Mine in 1935 under the direction of F.E. Wheeler.[31] The U.S. Bureau of Mines' *Minerals Yearbook for 1936* stated that the Creede Mines group was a producing mine in 1936 but does not name the specific mine. Creede Mills, Inc., took over the Creede Mines group on a lease early in February 1939 and operated the Happy Thought Mine.[32] The Emperius Mining Company acquired the Creede Mills, Inc., lease on the Happy Thought Mine in 1940, which expired on January 1, 1950.[33]

F.W. Anderson, consulting geologist, investigated the Creede Mines property for Judson S. Hubbard, vice-president of the Humphreys Investment Company, and submitted his report in December 1950. In it, he recommended the Emperius lease be renewed since that company was in the position to develop property owned by Creede Mines. However, the lease was not renewed because Emperius had been lax in following the terms of the lease in previous years.[34]

THE EMPERIUS MINING COMPANY

The Emperius Mining Company was incorporated in June 1934 as a closely held corporation consisting primarily of the families of Herman Emperius and Benjamin T. Poxson. The company was named after Herman Emperius.[35]

Herman Emperius was the mayor of Alamosa, Colorado, for a number of years and was well known throughout Colorado in business and municipal government circles. He was the president of the American National Bank in Alamosa and was one of the largest land owners in Colorado's San Luis Valley. He grew up in Alamosa, lived there most of his life, and died in September 1932 at Pueblo, Colorado.[36] Emperius' father built and operated Alamosa's first meat market. The Emperius family arrived in Alamosa in 1877, when the Denver and Rio Grande Railroad was laying tracks into the town. Emperius remembered seeing Indians coming from far and near to look at the train — a great iron horse to them — and he recalled there were many saloons and dance halls on Sixth Street where shooting scrapes were common occurrences in the early days.[37]

Benjamin T. Poxson was a well-known business and political figure in Colorado when he died at the age of 97 on July 29, 1990. He held positions as a public servant, was a miner, banker, an aide to several Colorado governors, and a personal friend of many of Colorado's important people. Poxson was born on June 12, 1893, in Jackson, Michigan, and moved to Alamosa, Colorado, in 1914 to be a teacher. He was appointed principal of the high school in 1915. He began his career in public service when William "Billy" Adams, the "cowboy" governor of Colorado, appointed him to fill a short-term vacancy as Alamosa postmaster. After two years as Alamosa's postmaster, he moved to Denver to be Governor Adams' secretary, actually performing the work of governor, except for signing bills, while Adams was ill and incapacitated. Poxson served as the head of the Colorado Industrial School for Boys in Golden; was president of the Colorado Mining Association; chairman of the Colorado Home for Dependent Children; and chairman of the Colorado Racing Commission for many years.[38]

Poxson's mining ventures were in Colorado mining districts associated with George H. Garrey and/or Herman Emperius. Their ventures were the Fairview-Cleopatra Mines; lessee of claims in Chicago Park near Pitkin; the Ocean Wave Mine at Lake City; the Summitville Gold Mines; the Gold Links Mining Company at Summitville in Rio Grande County; and the Emperius Mining Company at Creede.[39]

Even though the Emperius Mining Company was a family owned corporation, other individuals received shares, including several of the first miners employed by the company, namely Erick Nelson and Al Turnipseed, and possibly others. They were awarded two shares of stock each in lieu of full wages. Other miners, including Frank Davis, were unable to take shares in place of pay because of the need to support their families. Les Turnipseed, son of Al, sold his father's two shares back to Emperius many years later.[40]

At its inception, the company's initial operations were quite modest. In 1937 the superintendent's residence at the Last Chance was used by Madeline Wintz as the cook house to feed Emperius miners. Her husband, Woodrow, was one of the miners.[41]

The hanging wall veins that had been discovered as early as 1929 provided the Emperius Mining Company's ore into the 1940s. The Colorado Bureau of Mines' *Annual Report for 1939* listed Emperius as the operator of the Volunteer, Del Monte, Pittsburgh, Last Chance, and New York Mines. The company's 1939 annual report stated:

> "The company enjoyed a profitable year in 1939. Produced both milling and smelting ore. New leases have been secured during the year on our main properties. ... Inasmuch as the silver price seems to be more permanently established, we have expanded the development program. At the end of last year one month of ore reserves in sight. ... During the past year we completed around 3000 feet of new development. ... Have six months of ore reserves in sight."[42]

Creede Mills, Inc., notified Ben T. Poxson on September 1, 1940, that they would be unable to continue purchasing milling grade ores from Emperius for processing through their custom mill. After extended negotiations, Emperius leased the mill on September 9, 1940, for ten years. Emperius operated the mill at full capacity afterwards by increasing production from its mines to offset tonnage lost from other producers.[43]

Emperius also acquired the mining leases of Creede Mills, Inc., when it leased the mill, including the Amethyst and Happy Thought Mines. Emperius also held a fifty per cent interest in the Creede Leasing Company, which during 1940 secured leases on the Commodore and Bachelor Mines.[44] Presumably the Creede Leasing Company replaced the Wilson Leasing Company that had been previously organized.

The consolidation of the mines along the Amethyst Vein System was essentially completed in 1940, when Emperius took over the operations of Creede Mills, Inc. Ben Poxson had these comments about Emperius' activities in 1940, where he described the company's development that disclosed that ore bodies in the hanging wall would secure the future of the company and assure the rebirth of Creede Camp:

> *"During the past year about 5000 feet of new development. Will do 7,500 feet of new development next year. As a result of 1940 development work, seven new veins were discovered of which five have been productive. Our past development has disclosed ore bodies throughout a network of veins in territory 500 feet or more away from the early-day workings."*[45]

The OH Vein was discovered in 1938 or 1939 when two crosscuts on two different levels were driven into the hanging wall on the Amethyst Mining Company properties.[46] Originally it was thought the vein was the Overholt Vein that had been explored in the Commodore Mine. When it was determined to be a different vein, its name was shortened to "OH" to avoid confusion. It extended northwest from the Amethyst Vein. The OH Vein was by far the most productive of the hanging wall veins. Most of Creede Camp's production from the 1940s until the second boom in the 1960s came from the OH Vein. In fact, it produced ore until the Emperius Mining Company closed its mining operations in 1972. Emperius began extracting ore from the south end of the OH Vein in 1939, and ore was hoisted from the 7 and 9 levels to the Amethyst 5 level.[47] The OH Vein follows an extensive, nearly vertical fault that was undetected for many years because the vein does not outcrop on the surface nor does it join the Amethyst Fault in a recognizable manner.[48]

Even though the OH Vein was not exposed on the surface, the "claim system," as defined in the Mining Act of 1872, clearly states that the owner of the claim over the highest reach of the vein, even though it is hidden, has the right to mine the vein within its extended side lines. A look at the map *Official Surveys of Creede Camp* shows that most of the ground anywhere near the Amethyst and the hanging wall veins was covered by a mass of mining claims early in the camp's history. However, several "open fractions," or land not covered by active mining claims, lay over the hidden apex of the OH Vein.

Noel L. "Bo" Roberts located open fractions on the apex of the OH Vein and staked two claims on them that he named Texas Girl and Sybil R. Texas Girl consisted of 128 feet between the Equinox and Robinson claims and Sybil R. covered 630 feet north of the Creede Mines property. Both claims produced considerable ore and were eventually sold to the Emperius Mining Company. Bo Roberts was a mining man of some note who had worked in many places, including South America, and was an excellent practical geologist who "knew his rocks."[49]

The December 1941 issue of *Mining World* carried a story about the Emperius Mining Company under the headline, "Emperius Revives Mining in Once Fabulous Creede":

> *"Although not completely deserted, Creede faintly strug-gled, with the aid of the never-say-die spirit of a few old prospectors and the presence of the Mineral County Courthouse to keep its listing in the Postal Guide. In 1927 [1928], B.T. Poxson, a former Alamosa County judge and Secretary to the Governor of Colorado, and Herman Emperius, banker, operating the Poxson-Emperius Lease, proved there were still values left in the cliffs which had been overlooked by the old-timers. Today the Emperius Mining Co., with B.T. Poxson as president, has brought Mineral County second place among Colorado silver producing counties.*
>
> *"Working on the theory that the ore bodies of the Amethyst Vein, which was second only to the Comstock Lode, were similar in geology to the Comstock, Poxson and Emperius took a lease on the Last Chance in 1927. After cleaning up the old workings, crosscuts were started in the east-dipping hanging wall, seeking parallel veins. The soundness of the theory has been well-proved and the success of the operation borne out by the steady increase in the scope of operations until today the Emperius Mining Co. has under lease and is operating the entire string of claims along the 2 1/2 mile Amethyst Vein.*
>
> *"The officers and directors of the company are: B.T. Poxson, president and general manager; and E.E. Wheeler and O.E. Bannister, directors. Geo. H. Garrey, former geologist for the Guggenheim interests, is consulting geol-ogist. E.W. Nelson, whose entire mining career has been spent in Creede, is general mine superintendent. Tyrus*

Poxson, son of the president, is assistant superintendent. W.L. Anderson is in charge of all milling operations. Paul Davis is in charge of fire assays and Willard Caton handles the wet assays in the assay office."

The consolidated operations of the Emperius Mining Company in 1942 included the properties of all the major mines on the Amethyst Vein System and the mining claims over the OH Vein apex. The property controlled by Emperius covered an area two miles long and over a half mile wide. Twelve mining levels had been opened up and all the mines had been connected in order to solve ventilation problems. A total of 41,600 tons of ore was mined by Emperius in 1942, of which 7,750 tons were shipped directly ASARCO's Leadville Smelter. The balance was processed in the mill before being sent to the Leadville smelter. Approximately 750 ounces of gold, over one million ounces of silver, and a quarter of a million pounds of lead were produced. An average of 160 men were employed under the direction of Erick W. Nelson, assistant general ,anager, and W.L. Anderson, mill superintendent.[50]

Erick William Nelson was a miner's "miner." His education came from the "school of hard knocks." He made careful geologic observations and had the astute ability to correlate his observations with his intimate knowledge of the mines to locate ore — known in the mining business as "having a nose for ore." Without Erick's capabilities, it is likely that the original P&E sub-lease would have failed and there would not have been an Emperius Mining Company. He was the very soul of Emperius and had the respect and admiration of geologists, engineers and, above all, his miners. Nelson was born in 1895 in North Creede, was a good scholar, and a standout athlete in the few sports available in Creede at the time. He started his career as a miner in the days when drilling holes in the rock was done by hand and then he leased and mined properties throughout Creede Camp. He became Emperius' mine superintendent in 1935 and rose to general manager in the late 1940s. Nelson never married but cared for his mother, Annie, and an old friend from the boom days, Gus Swanson. He spent many years serving as Mineral County commissioner before retiring to Phoenix, Arizona, in 1954 where he died in 1963.[51]

Early in 1943, shortly after the passage of Government Order L-208, the War Production Board ordered Emperius to discontinue the production of high-grade silver from the upper oxidized ore zone and to start mining and milling the lead-zinc ores in the underlying sulfide zone. This meant that the bulk flotation process used in the mill would have to be modified to selective flotation to be able to separate the lead and zinc. The War Production Board gave Emperius bonuses for complying with the order.[52]

The Commodore and Emperius Mining Companies entered into a contract on August 1, 1943, in effect until September 1, 1990, to rehabilitate and maintain the Commodore No. 5 Tunnel for the mutual benefit of both parties so that ore could be economically transported from the mines along the Amethyst Vein System. The agreement called for Commodore to furnish land near the tunnel's portal for facilities such as ore bins, dry rooms, blacksmith, and machine shops constructed by Emperius for use in their mining operation. Emperius also agreed to install a compressed air line in the tunnel.[53]

Immediately, Emperius Mining Company started rehabilitating the Commodore No. 5 Tunnel to provide access to and haulage from the mines and commenced constructing the necessary facilities at the tunnel's portal. The largest facility constructed at the tunnel portal was a thousand-ton, six-compartment ore storage bin designed for side-dump rail cars delivering ore from the mines and truck haulage from the bin to the mill at Creede. The six compartments allowed for separate storage of ore from different mines. Charles G. Johnson was the architect and supervisor of construction.

John Jackson worked on the construction of the ore bin in 1943 before reporting for Army duty. Most of the heavy support timbers were in place before he left. He wrote about his experience in constructing the bins in a story in the June 22, 1978, issue of the *Mineral County Miner:*

> *"When it was determined that the ore storage bins would be built and the site selected, Sam Birdsey began excavating the three benches of the foundation with a Hansen Brothers bulldozer. Gene and Harry McClure were the drillers. I was the nipper in blasting outcrops and large boulders Sam couldn't dislodge. Charlie [Johnson] ran a leveling transit throughout the excavation, prepping for the next phase which would be pouring concrete for the piers, an exacting job keeping forms level and in line. There would be little room for error when we began standing timbers.*

"The long 10" x 10" timbers were all sawed by hand near the old blacksmith shop where we also drilled the holes for draw bolts. Charlie and I.D. Crawford welded dollies from two sizes of pipe with zerc fittings to grease the inner pipe. The timbers were cradled in the dollies and we then pulled them with two-man tongs to the construction site. The first story of the superstructure was raised entirely by hand, from there Charlie set up gin poles to hoist and swing the heavy timbers in place.

"It was such a relief to have Gene and Harry McClure on construction at the same time. Both were muscular, hard workers, and a pleasure to work with. Not a day went by that Gene didn't play a prank on someone from nailing John Slater's pants cuff to a timber to distracting Bernie's mule that would cause no end of trouble for Bernie, usually ending with a tirade of adjectives aimed in Gene's direction and an offer to trade punches on the waste dump.

"Charlie Johnson was a harsh taskmaster for this crew that had a pay scale ranging from 50 to 62 cents per hour. There were no coffee breaks and each minute on Charlie's jobs were spent laboring, but he taught all of us much that was a help in later years and we felt there wasn't a more self-disciplined or dedicated worker on the Emperius Mining Company payroll."

The production of lead, zinc, and copper, strategic metals for the war effort, was increased after the start of World War II. New lead and copper recovery equipment was added to the mill in 1943. The company suffered from a shortage of manpower but maintained its normal production levels of about 40,000 tons of ore at the expense of the development of new mine ore reserves. Miners normally doing development work were being used for production and, as a result, the reserves of developed ore were rapidly disappearing.[54]

The U.S. Bureau of Mines' *Minerals Yearbook for 1944* described the Emperius Mining Company's operations:

"The Emperius Mining Co., which in 1944 controlled nearly all mining properties in the Creede district, operated its 100-ton flotation mill during the entire year on ore from the Amethyst, Bachelor, Commodore, Equinox, New York, Last Chance, Del Monte, Aspen, Happy Thought, and Robinson [on OH Vein] Mines. Lead-

silver-gold concentrates were shipped to the smelter at Leadville. The company also shipped lead-silver ore to the Leadville smelter from the Amethyst, Commodore, Last Chance, Del Monte, Aspen, and Robinson [on OH Vein] Mines. The company continued work on its transportation tunnel [Commodore No. 5 Tunnel] at the lower end of Willow Creek Canyon; over 1 mile of the proposed 2 1/2 miles of the tunnel has been completed. A complete surface plant, consisting of ore bins, machine and blacksmith shops, lighting plant, drying and sorting rooms, compressor plant, and locomotive shops, is near completion at the portal."

The Emperius Mining Company controlled nearly all the mining properties at Creede Camp in 1945. The company operated the flotation mill under lease until March 1945 when it was purchased from Creede Mills, Inc. All ores milled during the year were obtained from company-controlled properties, with the exception of some ore mined by lessees. No custom ores were purchased during the year.[55]

The Colorado Mining Association's *Mining Year Book for 1945* described Emperius' operations after the end of World War II:

"During the year the mines have operated at about one-half capacity due to labor shortage. As mining labor

Ore Bins at the Commodore No. 5 Portal — 2001
Photo by the Author

returns to the camp, new development work has been
undertaken, which eventually will connect all properties
of the Amethyst Vein System.

"The new 1200 Level Transportation Tunnel
[Commodore No. 5 Tunnel] has been advanced well over
one-half of its contemplated two mile length. An electric
locomotive and new two-ton rocker dump cars have been
installed in this transportation tunnel. In addition to the
former 1000 ton storage bins at Amethyst No. 5 Tunnel,
a new set of 1200 ton ore bins, dry rooms, and sorting
rooms has been erected during the past year at the 1200
Level Transportation Tunnel. Additional compressor
capacity is being installed at the portal of this tunnel.

"Considerable additional machinery has been
installed in the milling plant, consisting of new jigs, a new
filter plant and a complete drying plant and power house
for drying of concentrates.

"It is expected that before the close of the coming year
that the production will equal or exceed the pre-war pro-
duction of 40,000 tons per annum.

"Concentrates and high grade ores are shipped to the
American Smelting & Refining plant at Leadville, Colo."

Emperius' production did not return to pre-war levels for several years. The mining industry of Colorado operated at about half
capacity in 1946. Approximately two years of extensive development work would be required to bring the mines back to their
pre-war production levels. The lack of miners during the war years
and shortly thereafter created the problem.[56] During the war the
mining industry lost many miners who were drafted into the armed
forces, unlike agriculture where farmers, in many cases, were
exempted from the draft so they could grow crops necessary for the
war effort. Fewer miners meant that the mining industry had to
produce more strategic metals for the war effort with a reduced
work force. In order to meet their quotas of metal production, the
mining companies used their miners to mine developed ore but did
not have the manpower to do the development necessary for future
ore production. Development work consists primarily of driving
mine openings such as drifts, crosscuts, raises, winzes, etc., for
access to the ore and to provide the means of transporting the ore
out of the mine.

The lack of manpower in the mining industry seriously impacted the war effort. So serious was the problem that the War Department released 4,000 experienced miners from military service so they could return to work in the mines. One Colorado mine, the Climax Molybdenum Mine near Leadville, received the largest single allotment of 160 so-called "soldier-miners."[57] There is no record of soldier-miners at Creede Camp.

Emperius Mining Company's production for 1947 was less than 24,000 tons, far from their pre-war 40,000 ton annual production. Even so, Emperius was the largest producer of silver in Colorado in 1947.[58]

The 1200 Level Transportation Tunnel, located below the most productive areas in the mines, was completed for nearly two miles in length in 1946. The tunnel would allow the development of an additional 500 feet of the hanging wall veins below their deepest workings. Emperius Mining Company felt they had sufficient ore reserves to operate at full capacity for twenty years, assuming a reasonable level of metals prices.[59]

Prior to the completion of the 1200 Level Transportation Tunnel, all the ore extracted from the upper levels of the OH Vein was oxidized and had a high proportional silver value. In 1947, mining of primary sulfide ore at the lower levels of the vein began and by 1949 the ore was either all sulfide or partly oxidized sulfide ore. The silver value in the new ore type was significantly reduced from the previous eighty per cent of the total value of the ore down to thirty per cent. However, lead's relative value increased from fifteen to forty per cent and zinc again became a recoverable metal.[60]

The company's mill was modified in 1949 to improve its efficiency for the selective flotation of lead-silver and zinc concentrates.[61] In 1951, Emperius produced more than their pre-war annual production. The company mined 45,230 tons of ore and employed seventy-three men under the direction of Erick W. Nelson, general manager, and T.T. Biddle, assistant general manager and mill superintendent.[62] Emperius ranked fourth in Colorado in silver production in 1950 and 1951.[63] The company produced 40,085 tons of ore in 1952, of which 39,527 tons were concentrated in the flotation mill. The balance was shipped direct to the Leadville smelter.[64] An additional bank of flotation cells was added to the mill circuit and the 1200 Level Transportation was 9,000 feet long in 1953.[65]

The company ranked high in Colorado in the production of gold, silver, lead, and zinc in 1954, but production dropped

Emperius Mill with the Town of Creede in the
Background — circa 1965
From the U.S. Bureau of Mines Information Circular 8370

dramatically in 1955 because the concentrating mill and diesel
power plant were destroyed by fire on August 15, 1955. The fire
was started when explosive chemicals ignited in the muffler of a
diesel engine in the power plant after an engine overhaul. *The
Denver Post* reported that a diesel engine exploded at the Emperius
Mill at Creede, Colo., destroying it, and causing damage estimated
at $500,000. The blaze started Monday evening and was not extin-
guished until Tuesday. Kenneth Dabney, William Kolisch, Sr., and
Billy Kolisch were injured.[66]

Construction of a replacement mill with a capacity of 150 tons
per day and a new power plant commenced in October 1955 and
was operational in June 1956.[67] Emperius was Colorado's fourth
largest silver, lead, and zinc producer in 1957.[68]

The Valley Courier of April 17, 1956, interviewed Tyrus Poxson
who described the new mill:

> *"Tyrus B. Poxson, President and General Manager of
> the consolidated mine and mill operations, in a personal
> interview with a Courier reporter recently stated, 'We are
> shooting for May 1 to start operations.' The new mill,
> substantially confirmed to be the 'last word in design and
> mechanization' has been under construction for approxi-
> mately six months. It is being built to replace the original
> structure destroyed by fire last August.*

"*Stockholders of the mining company voted last November to spend $617,000 to rebuild the mill, power plant, and other facilities which were razed by the fire.*

"*B.T. Poxson, one of the original stockholders of the company and who formed the present corporation, said however an additional $50,000 was needed to rebuild the mill and facilities and make it the most modern in the country.*

"*Tyrus Poxson in describing operations of the ultra-modern processing plant stated one man will now be used in operations where it previously required two. He said one man will be able to watch the complete works from one central point and control them by merely pushing a button.*

"*He said a new flotation procedure has also been included in the modernized structure. Smaller but more flotation machines will be installed, also a larger Allis-Chalmers 'ball mill' grinds the ore to 100 mesh and the selective flotation method separates the metals from the slag.*

"*Poxson said 12 flotation machines will be used on lead and eight on zinc. Previously six were used for each one.*

"*Some years ago the principal mining product was silver, but during the last war it was changed to lead and zinc because of the demand by the government for the latter.*

"*Approximately 14,000 tons of ore are now stockpiled and ready for processing when the mill goes into operation. Following the disastrous fire, employees of the mine and mill started stockpiling the ore for the day when the mill should begin operations again.*

"*Tyrus Poxson said they are taking all precautions possible in the construction of the new mill to avoid another fire. He said, in the old mill, the power providing diesel units, believed to have started the fire, were in the mill itself. He said in the new mill three diesels will be installed as a unit separately from the mill.*

"*Poxson said they expect to process about 200 tons of ore daily. He said other similar operations usually process more because of the lower grade ore.*"

Residents of the town of Creede and the Upper Rio Grande River area started negotiations with the San Luis Valley Rural Electric Cooperative in 1953 for the construction of a power line to the Creede area so that reliable electric power would be available. The Emperius Mining Company was one of the parties involved but discontinued negotiations in November 1955, when they purchased their own 1500 KVA diesel generating unit. The power line to Creede was finally constructed in 1961.[69]

The Emperius Mining Company was the third largest producer of silver, lead, and zinc in Colorado in 1958. However, operations were suspended on June 1, 1958, the first shut down in 25 years, but commenced again in November 1958 and were near normal by January 1959. The reason for the suspension was falling metal prices. Lead and zinc concentrates from 26,500 tons of ore were shipped to the American Smelting & Refining Company's Leadville and Amarillo, Texas, smelters, respectively.[70]

Emperius was the third largest producer of silver, lead, and zinc in 1959 and 1960; however, the American Smelting & Refining Company's Arkansas Valley Smelter at Leadville would be shut down in 1964 because of a lack of ore.[71] This would, of course, create higher costs for transporting concentrates to a more distant smelter in the future.

As the distance from surface openings increased, natural ventilation was much less effective and mining operations in some areas had to be suspended when low barometric pressures during storms occurred. Oxygen-deficient gases emanating from the veins during periods of low barometric pressure had been a problem at Creede Camp since the time of the Nelson-Wooster-Humphreys Tunnel.

A crosscut was started from the 1200 Level Transportation Tunnel (Commodore No. 5 Tunnel level) to connect with the Park Regent Shaft in order to provide better ventilation to the north end of the OH Vein workings. The lack of good ventilation in the northern limits of the mine had become very critical to continued mining operations. The crosscut intersected another vein in February 1961 that was similar to the OH Vein and was named the P Vein.[72] P Vein provided additional ore, but the ventilation connection to the Park Regent Shaft was never made.

In place of the Park Regent Shaft ventilation connection, Emperius installed mechanical ventilation fans in the Amethyst and Commodore Tunnels in 1961 to provide positive pressure ventilation in the mine workings to improve working conditions for the miners.[73] State Mechanical and Electrical Company of Pueblo, Colorado, installed the equipment and electrical system under the direction of Joe Salyer, superintendent.[74]

The properties of the Commodore Mining Company were acquired by Emperius on November 1, 1961.[75] The Reynolds-Morse Corporation, owner of the Commodore Mining Company, and Ben T. Poxson had jointly purchased mining properties at Summitville, Colorado, in 1950. Poxson surrendered his one-fourth interest in Summitville for the Commodore Mining Company's properties at Creede.[76]

Considerable improvement in mine ventilation in 1962 enabled Emperius to operate on a steadier basis during the year and the company ranked third in Colorado in silver, lead, and zinc production.[77] The mine and mill were inactive during the first part of 1963 until May 15th, when operations were resumed and production returned to normal.[78]

The last large tract in which controlling interest was purchased by the Emperius Mining Company was the Amethyst Mining Company's property, which was acquired in 1964. By this time, Emperius had under their control, either by ownership or lease, an area four to five miles in length and from 2,000 to 4,000 feet in width.[79] Emperius, however, did not control the Creede Mines nor the Equity Mine properties on the north end of the Amethyst Vein System.

The Emperius Mining Company was a steady producer after better ventilation was provided to the mine workings. In 1967, the company had the second largest output of copper in Colorado and was the sixth largest producer of both lead and zinc.[80] Emperius' copper production fell in 1968 because of a 5,000-ton drop in ore production and a lower copper content of the ore; however, the company was a principal producer of lead and zinc in Colorado from 1968 to 1970 and was the second largest producer of silver in 1970.[81]

Emperius curtailed its mining and milling operations during the first quarter of 1971 because of low lead and zinc prices. About forty workers were terminated.[82] Emperius Mining Company was forced to shut down the majority of their operations in 1972 because there was no smelter to buy their zinc. Exploration work was being done on the Commodore.[83]

It is interesting to note that in 1970 there were 214 zinc mines in the United States, but the number had dropped to only sixty-eight in 1972. During the same period, eight U.S. zinc smelters were closed. American Smelting & Refining Company's Amarillo, Texas, zinc smelter was one of them. It was closed in 1972 because of pollution problems.[84] Emperius had sent their zinc concentrates to the Amarillo smelter.

The U.S. Bureau of Mines' *Minerals Yearbook for 1972* reported that "Minerals Engineering Company leased mining properties and facilities from Emperius Mining Company and Creede Mines, Inc. comprising nearly 2,000 acres of patented claims in the Creede mining district, the 150-ton per day Emperius Mill and Mine and plant equipment. The lessor agreed to conduct development and exploration over a 3-year period. Should the company discover sufficient ore reserves, the mine would be reopened."

EQUITY MINE

There was very little activity at the Equity Mine during Creede Camp's rebirth. In 1946, Paul Davis shipped 280 tons of silver ore from the Equity Mine dump to the Emperius Mill.[85] Davis recalled the project in 2001, stating that he and his brothers-in-laws [Wintz brothers] shipped the Equity sorting dump. The dump ran twenty ounces of silver per ton and, at 90.5 cents per ounce, it probably paid little more than the cost of sampling and transportation.[86]

The machinery in the mill built by the North Amethyst Mining Company in 1928 was salvaged as scrap during World War II. Harry Ellithorpe and Sons and Gavin W. Skinner bought the Equity Mine property at a tax sale in 1952. The Equity was reopened in 1953 by Skinner who sampled the property. The Ellithorpe-Skinner partnership was canceled and Les Turnipseed was given a quit-claim deed to Skinner's share of the property. Turnipseed used the remaining buildings for his elk hunting guide business until the Ellithorpes sold their share to Joe Cox of Monahan, Texas, and Bibs Wyley, a resort owner from Creede. Turnipseed then purchased the Cox and Wyley shares in the Equity Mine.[87]

The Equity Mines, Incorporated, operated the mine during the summer months of 1965 through 1967 under the direction of Les Turnipseed. Thirteen hundred tons of ore were shipped containing 0.06 ounces of gold and sixteen ounces of silver per ton.[88]

SOLOMON-HOLY MOSES VEIN SYSTEM

The Solomon-Holy Moses Vein System was the third most productive ore zone at Creede Camp, but it supplied only a few per cent of the metals produced in the district. Since the ore deposited in the Solomon-Holy Moses Vein System didn't contain large amounts of silver, the mines along the vein did not profit to a great degree from the "pegged" price of silver of December 1933.

HOLY MOSES MINE

Producing mines in 1935 at Creede Camp included the Consolidated Moses Solomon Mines Company group.[89] There is no record of any further production until 1952, when the T.O.C. (Texas-Oklahoma-Colorado) Development Company shipped a few tons of lead-silver-gold ore from the Holy Moses Mine.[90]

The Jackson Mining Company, organized by John Jackson, leased and operated the Holy Moses in 1954 after Jackson resigned from the Outlet Mining Company. Based on information from Peter Weiss, who had worked in the Holy Moses in 1920, Jackson and his brother, "Scooter," sank a winze on a narrow high-grade vein. Within twenty-five feet, the vein widened to five feet, and the Jacksons were able to ship five railroad cars of high-grade gold, silver, and lead ore. Unfortunately, the ore body was in the shape of a "chimney" and did not extend either laterally or in depth.[91] John Jackson, in a letter to the author dated December 17, 2000, wrote about an unusual attempt to concentrate ore from the Holy Moses:

> *"In 1954, I hired Paul Hosselkus to help tram two railroad cars of sulfide ore as the last gasp before closing the Holy Moses Mine. An old gentleman and his son from California who were acquainted with James Muir, Jr., drove to the mine and informed me they were setting up a jig [milling device that separates heavy minerals from waste rock with an up and down motion employing water with various-sized screens in a box-like container] and wanted to borrow some of my sulfide ore. I had enough left over to haul a ton to them and watch this new enterprise. The jig was the old man's own design and, apparently, he was well-versed in such milling. When in place and sufficient water at hand, the young fellow began hand operation of the cam as his father covered the upper screen with my ore. He stood back, tapping one foot in time to the rhythm of the cam, and, with tobacco juice running from the corners of his mouth, barked 'make 'er pop, boy, make 'er pop.' I enjoyed each minute of this comical end to the Jackson Mining Company."*

The Sublet Mining and Milling Company was formed on November 15, 1955, and operated the mine from 1956 through 1960 on an intermittent basis. Considerable exploration and development was done in 1957 and 327 tons of ore were shipped to a smelter. The company drove a tunnel that intersected the Solomon Vein. It proved to be barren for the most part. Sublet treated some lead ore from the Holy Moses in its mill at Creede in 1958 and, in 1960, the company shipped a small quantity of silver ore.[92] The Sublet Company was organized by Paul Snyder and a partner named Smith. Both were naval retirees associated with James Muir, Jr. C. Ernest King, a Navy flier and a friend of James Muir, Jr., was the secretary and manager of the company.[93]

A gravity mill was constructed in 1946-47 by Williams, Wright, and Weaver near the Creede Cemetery on the east side of Slaughterhouse Gulch to process ores from the Solomon and Ridge Mines. The operation was short-lived but was revived for the Holy Moses ore in 1958. Wallace Wright lost part of his left hand in an accident while he was working on the machinery and the mill was abandoned shortly thereafter.[94]

PHOENIX MINE

John Jackson's father, William T. Jackson, Jr., negotiated a lease on the Phoenix Mine from the Moffat Estate. David Moffat had purchased the Phoenix in the 1890s but no commercial mining had ever been done on the property. Young Jackson drove a tunnel in 1949 from the Palo Alto claim to intersect the Phoenix Vein, using a jackhammer, a small com-

Phoenix Shaft Head Frame Built by John Jackson — 2001
Photo by the Author

pressor, and a square point shovel for the unbelievably low cost of under $6 per foot. The tunnel was in a poor location and intersected a barren area of the fault. The original discovery shaft was then cleaned out, re-timbered and sunk another sixty feet. A drift south from the deepened shaft encountered a vein of lead carbonate assaying over fifty per cent lead and twenty plus ounces of silver to the ton. The Outlet Mining Company was organized to mine the newly discovered ore body. William T. Jackson, John Jackson, and Gavin Skinner were general partners, while James Muir and Associates were limited partners in the company. The name "Outlet Mining Company" was selected to honor Gavin Skinner's grandfather, who had driven the Outlet Tunnel in the early 1900s. In October 1951, under the direction of John Jackson as mine manager, two railroad cars of the ore were shipped from the Phoenix to the Arkansas Valley Smelter at Leadville.[95]

The Outlet Mining Company shipped 1,292 tons of ore from the Phoenix Mine in 1952 that averaged 7.66 ounces of silver per ton and was 18.46 per cent lead. In 1953 the company shipped 2,438 tons to the Arkansas Valley Smelter in Leadville. The Outlet Mining Company continued to produce lead-silver-gold ore from the Phoenix Mine until 1956, when it was given a DMEA (Defense Minerals Exploration Administration) grant for lead-zinc exploration. The Gormax Mining Company made one small shipment of ore from the Phoenix in 1956. The Phoenix Mine produced some ore in 1959 and 1961.[96] By 1956 an estimated $500,000 worth of metal, mostly lead and silver, had been produced from the Phoenix Mine.[97]

GORMAX MINE

The Gormax Mining Company was organized by Gordon and Maxine Smith of California. Gordon was a retired sailor from the U.S. Navy. The company drove a tunnel on the J.I.C. lode north of the Phoenix Mine after receiving a DMEA grant to explore for lead-zinc ore on their property. There is no record of ore production by Gormax except for the small shipment from the Phoenix Mine in 1956. Scooter Jackson was the mine operator.[98]

RIDGE AND MEXICO MINES

The Ridge Recovery Tunnel was designed to intersect first the Ridge, and then the Solomon Vein at depth. In September 1934, the tunnel was in 230 feet from its portal, and H.C. Rowley estimated that an additional thirty feet of tunnel would intersect the Ridge. Evidently ore was developed, since the Recovery Tunnel shipped some ore in 1934.[99]

No further mining activity is recorded for the Ridge group of mines until 1943, when the Ridge Leasing Company operated the Ridge the second half of the year and shipped lead-zinc ore to a Tooele, Utah, concentrating mill. The same company operated the Ridge during the first part of 1944 and shipped ore to a different Utah mill, the custom concentrator at Midvale. The Ridge Mining Company made small shipments of lead and zinc ore in 1945. The New Ridge Mining Company shipped ore in 1946 through 1948 to either the Arkansas Valley Smelter at Leadville or a custom concentrator. The Ridge Mine was worked by lessees from January to November 1949 and shipped several cars of lead-zinc ore. Stephen and Ratté estimated that the Ridge Mine had an annual production of between $1,000 and $20,000 from 1943 to 1949.[100]

The Outlet Mining Company did development at the Mexico Mine in 1962. The Mexico claim is adjacent to the Ridge Mine and is one of the so-called Ridge group of mines. Development work continued in 1963 by the King Solomon Mining and Milling Company and its predecessor, the Outlet Mining Company. Frank and Lee Davis leased the Mexico during the summer months of 1964 and produced some ore. King Solomon continued development work in 1965. However, there is no record of production from either the Ridge or Mexico after 1949.[101]

James Muir, Jr., was the head of the King Solomon Mining and Milling Company. The company was formed from the Outlet and Sublet Mining Companies on March 20, 1961. Muir had been a Chief Petty Officer in the U.S. Navy from Palo Alto, California. His wife was the niece of Noel "Snuffy" Oates, a member of a pioneer Creede mining family. Muir's visit to Creede sparked an interest in hard rock mining and milling. He and his associates, sailors at the San Diego naval base, provided funding for mining operations on the Solomon-Holy Moses Vein System. As previously mentioned, John Jackson resigned from the Outlet Mining Company in 1954. Shortly thereafter his father, William T. Jackson, Jr., sold his share of the Outlet Mining Company to James Muir, Jr. and Associates who, in turn, incorporated the company into the King Solomon Mining and Milling Company. This company consolidated the mines on East Willow Creek and built a gravity concentrating mill at Phoenix Park to process ores from the Solomon and Ridge Mines as well as ores from the Outlet Tunnel driven to the King Solomon Vein north of those mines.[102]

SOLOMON AND ETHEL MINES

There is no record of any ore production from 1919 until 1934, when the Ethel Mine near the south end of the Solomon-Holy Moses Vein System was opened briefly in the general flurry of mining activity that followed "pegging" of the price of silver. The New Ridge Mining Company operated the Solomon Mine in 1946 and 1947, and the mine was under lease the last three months of 1950.[103]

The T.O.C. Development Company was formed by James French, Eugene McClure, and Gene Gulik to explore and develop the Solomon Mine. T.O.C. began work in 1951 with Dick Lehman and Woodrow Wintz as miners. T.O.C. produced ninety-four tons in 1951. The T.O.C. Development Company shipped 308 tons of lead-silver-gold ore from the Holy Moses, Solomon, and Ethel Mines in 1952. The 1951-52 production was valued at about $20,000.[104]

The Outlet Mining Company operated the Solomon Mine in 1961. Its successor company, the King Solomon Mining and Milling Company, restarted operations in 1966 and built their gravity concentrating plant to wash the clay from the ore in 1968. Development continued through the summer months of 1971, when both the mine and mill were closed. One of the largest lead-zinc mining companies in the United States, Eagle-Picher Industries of Miami, Oklahoma, investigated the King Solomon property in 1971 prior to the closing. John Steuver and Paul Hosselkus dismantled the mill building after the machinery had been salvaged.[105] This was the end of mining on the Solomon-Holy Moses Vein System.

MOLLIE S. AND EUNICE MINES

The Mollie S. Mine was a producing mine in 1935, as was the Eunice Mine in 1936 and 1937. Al Turnipseed, Eugene Thom, and Lee Shillings leased the Mollie S. and Eunice Mines and used the aerial trams described in Chapter Eleven to transport the high-grade silver ore they mined.[106]

ALPHA-CORSAIR VEIN SYSTEM

The only mine that was active on the Alpha-Corsair Vein System after the Great Depression was the Corsair Mine. Value of ore produced ranged from a few thousand dollars to about $12,000 per year, and all but a small percentage of the value was accounted for by silver.[107]

CORSAIR MINE

The Corsair Tunnel was repaired and the water taken out of the shaft a distance of 200 feet below the tunnel level in 1934. The

Corsair was a producing mine from 1935 through 1940. B.F. Palfreymen of Provo, Utah, leased the mine in 1937 and Helmick and Wright of Creede leased it in 1939.[108]

No further activity at the Corsair is recorded until the H & B Construction Company of Monte Vista, Colorado, opened the mine in 1961. H & B was owned by Gordon Hosselkus of Creede and Fred Baker of Monte Vista. Baker had a tremendous impact on the history of Creede Camp, as will be told in Chapter Fifteen. He was well acquainted with Stella Dysart, the "Uranium Queen" of New Mexico, having formed a drilling company to explore for uranium for her. Baker convinced Dysart to put up the funds to explore the Corsair Mine and adjoining properties. After two years of disappointing results, Dysart stopped the work and took her firm out of the silver mining business.[109]

CREEDE FORMATION
MONON HILL MINES

Most of the ore mined in the Monon Hill Mines after 1934 came from margins or extensions of ore bodies developed and largely extracted during the main period of mining there between 1918 and 1922. Approximately $50,000 worth of ore was mined from 1934 to 1941. Most of this ore was concentrated in the Creede Mills, Inc., custom mill. Exploration was in progress at the Monon Hill from 1952 through 1958, but no production was reported.[110]

A.L. Moses and Associates started mining operations at the Manitoba-Ontario Mine on October 29, 1936. Weaver and Oates began operations at the Monon Mine in 1937. Both mines were open through 1940. The Monon Mine operated in 1941.[111]

Starting in 1953, the Monon Mining and Leasing Company prospected the foot wall in Monon Hill using the Big Six (Silver Horde) Tunnel for access. The company was financed by Shorty Williams of Alamosa and Wallace Wright of Creede. Ivan Weaver and Gordon and Harry Hosselkus did the mining work. Several minor veins were encountered but none proved to be of value. The prospecting effort continued until 1966.[112]

CLAY MINE

The Clay Mine was actively producing bentonite clay in 1934 but was inactive in 1939. Ben A. Birdsey, developer of the mine, died in 1937 and his death ended the Clay Mine operation.[113]

MIDWEST MINE

There are many minor fault zones at Creede Camp that may be mineralized to some degree. One of them lies between the Amethyst and Bulldog Vein Systems and strikes northwesterly across the ridge between Nelson and West Willow Creeks. The Midwest Mine was developed on this fault zone.

John Jackson is well acquainted with the history of the Midwest, and this is his story of the mine:

> "Steve McDermott owned several claims northwest of the Midwest Tunnel that generated much interest after a kidney of high-grade gold ore was discovered on the Edith lode. It was only 10 tons, but it sparked the driving of the Knauss Tunnel at a lower level and, eventually, entry of Midwest Mining Company under the direction of Elwood Neff in 1926. Midwest Mining Company drove a tunnel northwest from Nelson Creek a distance of nearly a thousand feet with 900 feet on a vein structure composed mainly of marcasite (iron sulfide) and clays enclosing crushed lead, zinc, and copper minerals in appreciable amounts but not of productive grade. The mine folded in 1929.
>
> "In 1945 John Van Buskirk and Emmett Dabney relocated the Midwest claims using the name "Gateway" and spent several winters cleaning up caves, stockpiling the better ore, and driving 50 feet [of tunnel] by hand on a stringer [narrow vein] from the fault. In the 1950s, Emmett deeded his half to John and John enlisted his son-in-law, Whitey Miller, a veteran miner, to help in trying to clean the former tunnel to its face. The soft, argillized structure had caved too badly and they were unsuccessful.
>
> "I bought the mine in 1958 and spent every available minute and dollar in another vain attempt to reach the face [end of the tunnel]. In 1968 Allan and Clara Phipps offered to help and at the same time Colorado Fuel and Iron Corporation (CF&I) formed a mining exploration company under the direction of Les Wahl. I contacted Mr. Wahl and, through his efforts, CF&I agreed to join us in a well-funded effort to drive a new tunnel 2,500 feet which would place the breast [end of the tunnel] approximately under the Edith shaft of Steve McDermott's early prospecting.

"This was the culmination of a prospector's dream. A mineralized structure to follow, new equipment, and enough funding to see it through to a productive mine. The tunnel size was six by eight feet with excellent ventilation, a diesel trammer [locomotive], and the latest mucking machine and drills. The crew consisted of Charles Steele, mechanic and outer maintenance; Mike McClure, Jim Morrow, and Sid Samuels, miners; John Jackson, manager; Clyde Mathews, geologist; and Davis Engineering, claim staking and mapping. Previous to our formation of Gateway Access Company — New Midwest Mining Company, I had started the tunnel and it was well into solid rock for a concerted effort in 1969. My brother, William C. 'Scooter' Jackson, was killed in a mining accident in Homestake's Bulldog Mountain operation in March 1969. He had joined me in all my ventures and his death greatly dampened my enthusiasm.

"With a spirited crew we drove the tunnel to the initial goal at a cost of less than $28 per foot, approximately one-third of the estimated cost, but the elevation proved to be above the most favorable ore horizon. We encountered good values in two areas and had planned to sink on one, but Crane Company had taken control of CF&I and elected not to fund any additional exploration. The mine closed in 1971 with no production. Allan and Clara Phipps took their loss most graciously and our friendship strengthened over the years. I still have faith in Nelson Mountain."[114]

WAGON WHEEL GAP FLUORSPAR MINE

The Wagon Wheel Gap Fluorspar Mine reopened in 1934, produced a large tonnage of fluorspar for Colorado Fuel & Iron Corporation's plant in Pueblo, Colorado, and employed a large number of men at the mine and mill.[115] Colorado Fuel & Iron operated the mine from 1934 until July 1950, when it was closed. The original access to the mine, the Collins Old Main Tunnel, was too inefficient for CF&I's mining operations and it was abandoned and three new mine levels were developed. CF&I conducted an exploration drilling program in 1974 that located additional fluorspar reserves. The company sold the surface rights to their six patented claims in 1984 but

Wagon Wheel Gap Fluorspar Mine and Mill Complex — 1969
Photo by John Jackson

retained the mineral rights. CF&I produced 118,023 tons of fluorspar concentrates from the mill.[116]

Charles E. "Ed" Johnson worked at the Wagon Wheel Gap Fluorspar Mine from December 1946 to May 1949. He describes the mine and mill operations:[117]

> "During the time I worked at the gap, we used mules pulling six one-ton cars from a raise about 1,000 yards to the upper level of the mill. Three hundred feet above us was another level where cars were pulled by a small battery operated motor called a Mancha electric trammer. There were from five to seven levels in the mine. The mine operated six days a week and about 200 tons of ore were mined per day. The pay was $98 for two weeks of work.
>
> "The mill used jigs to process the ore after it was crushed. The mill operated the jigs two shifts and the crusher three shifts a day. The fluorspar, being heavier than the rock, was separated by gravity in the jigs and the rock went into a waste bin and was used as road gravel. Trucks were used to haul the concentrated fluorspar to the railroad tipple at Wagon Wheel Gap.
>
> "The mill had three coal-fired boilers which ran a large steam engine connected to the mill machinery by a

series of flat belts. A three-cylinder diesel engine ran the air compressor and bit hammer. A small electric generator provided electricity for the workers' houses, boarding house, bunkhouse, and, of course, the mill. The coal for the boilers came from the Trinidad coal mines that was trucked into a storage yard by the Wagon Wheel Gap Railroad Depot. It was then shoveled off the ground and hauled the two miles to the mill."

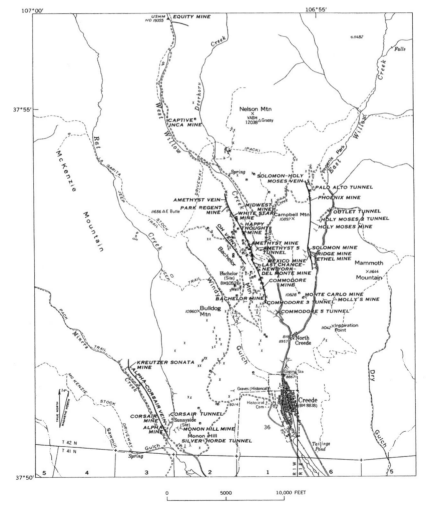

Productive Veins and Principal Mines at Creede Camp
Based on Figure 2, U.S.G.S. Professional Paper 487, 1965

CHAPTER 15

THE SECOND
BOOM
1960-1988

THE SECOND BOOM AT CREEDE CAMP was sparked by a preliminary report in 1960 by Stevens and Ratté suggesting that the Bulldog Mountain fault zone appeared to be a favorable structure to prospect.[1] It was fueled by the dramatic increases in the price of silver that followed the 1961 Presidential Order ending government controls over the price of silver.

Stevens and Ratté, in their 1965 report on geology and ore deposition at Creede Camp, made further suggestions for prospecting at Creede Camp and made the statement: "Additional ore bodies might well exist on other faults in the graben, and some areas appear particularly promising." These areas included the northern section of the Amethyst Vein, the Bulldog Mountain fault zone, and the Creede Formation.[2]

As the price of silver increased in the 1960s, the investor-speculator was added to the demand side of the silver market. Federal Reserve silver certificates, authorized by the Silver Purchase Act of 1934 that had ended hard times at Creede Camp, were redeemable for silver held by the U.S. Treasury. When the market price for silver exceeded $1.29 per troy ounce, a profit could be made by redeeming silver certificates for silver from the U.S. Treasury and then selling the silver on the open market. Silver coins could be melted at a profit when the silver price rose above $1.38 per ounce. Public Law 88-36 of 1963 repealed the Silver Purchase Act of 1934 and authorized printing Federal Reserve notes not redeemable in silver. The Coinage Act of 1965 eliminated the use of silver in dimes and quarters and reduced the silver content of half dollars. In 1967, all silver coins were withdrawn from circulation and holders of silver certificates were given one year to redeem the certificates for silver. Without the linkage between silver and the U.S. monetary system, investor-speculators and industrial users determined silver's price.[3]

The story about the price of silver during the second boom would not be complete without mentioning Nelson Bunker Hunt and his attempt to corner the silver market. His attempt had a tremendous impact on Creede Camp, and, again, an artificially high price for silver created the climate for the second boom as had happened in the early 1890s.

Bunker Hunt was the second oldest of H.L. Hunt's fourteen children. H.L. Hunt was the founder of a multi-billion dollar oil business who promoted his ultraconservative political views on his own radio program. Bunker Hunt was born on February 22, 1926, in El Dorado, Arkansas, where his father had just made his first oil strike. Hunt served on a U.S. Navy battleship during World War II and attended Southern Methodist University for six months after his discharge before going to work for his father. With the income generated from the trust fund set up for him by his father, Hunt was able to make large financial deals as a young man. He speculated in oil and gas exploration and commodities. He began buying silver as an inflation hedge in the early 1970s. He noted that the annual production of silver in 1973 was 300 million ounces, only sixty per cent of consumption. He decided that the rising demand for silver would make a steep increase in its price inevitable. By 1978 Bunker Hunt and his brother, W. Herbert Hunt, held an estimated twenty-million ounces of silver, then valued at $100 million. As the price of silver skyrocketed in the late 1970s, the Hunts were able to turn their profits into more silver and silver futures, which caused the price to go even higher. The Hunts and Saudi Arabian investors formed the Bermuda-based International Metals Investment Corporation, which purchased 40.5 million ounces of silver during the six months beginning in June 1979. During the same period, Bunker Hunt purchased 42 million ounces and his brother another 26.6 million ounces. By January 1980, the price of silver had reached $52.50 per troy ounce. However, the attempt by the Hunts and their Saudi counterparts to corner the world silver market failed. The system they used to acquire silver meant putting up only a fraction of the cash value, and it worked fine as long as the price rose or, at the very least, held steady. Owing to worldwide recession and a reaction to the higher silver prices, industrial demand for silver was in decline. In addition, the Chicago Board of Trade and the New York Commodity Exchange raised the margin requirements for buying silver and limited the number of futures contracts buyers could purchase. These factors caused a dramatic drop in the silver price to

$4.88 per troy ounce in June 1982, and the silver bubble burst. However, because of panic in the financial markets and a fear of inflation, investment demand for silver increased sharply shortly thereafter and the price rose to $14.74 in February 1983. Prices gradually dropped from the fourth quarter of 1983 through 1985. Low prices for silver forced many mines to close in 1985, including all but one at Creede.[4]

The U.S. high and low silver prices, in dollars per troy ounce from Handy & Harman's daily quotations, during the period from 1970 through 1989 are listed in the following table:

Year	Low	High	Year	Low	High
1970	1.57	1.93	1980	10.80	48.00
1971	1.29	1.75	1981	7.95	16.45
1972	1.39	2.05	1982	4.88	11.21
1973	1.97	3.28	1983	8.34	14.74
1974	3.27	6.70	1984	6.26	10.04
1975	3.91	5.23	1985	5.57	6.74
1976	3.82	5.10	1986	4.87	6.20
1977	4.32	4.96	1987	5.36	10.20
1978	4.83	6.30	1988	6.01	7.99
1979	5.96	28.00	1989	5.02	6.17

Further interest in Creede Camp's potential was stimulated by a report on the district in a 1965-66 U.S. Bureau of Mines study of the silver production potential of the United States. The report stated that of the major silver mining districts of the past, Creede was selected as one of the most promising and a detailed study was undertaken. The study of Creede projected an increase of silver production to as much as one million ounces yearly, possibly starting in 1969, and that the Creede district probably held undiscovered ore.[5]

Companies with mineral exploration geologists equipped with diamond drills and scientific methods came to Creede Camp during the second boom instead of the thousands of prospectors that descended on the district during the 1890s. The use of modern exploration techniques and equipment helped the latter-day scientific prospectors, or explorationists, discover hidden ore deposits that the early-day prospectors failed to locate. Many of these companies were small without great resources, but some were nationally known. There were conflicts between the companies and a few cases of "skullduggery," but not to the degree that occurred during the first boom. The scene at Creede Camp was described by *The Denver Post* in its September 4, 1980, issue:

"Creede, which became one of Colorado's most excit-
ing mining camps together with Cripple Creek in the 1800s,
remains today one of Colorado's best areas geologically.

"Two sizable exploration projects are under way
there, one by the Homestake Exploration Group in a joint
venture with Minerals Engineering Co. of Denver and the
other by Chevron Resources Co., a Chevron subsidiary,
on property held by Minerals Engineering.

"The Chevron project is being carried out by the
Harrison Western Corp. of Denver, which has a $3 mil-
lion contract to complete an exploration tunnel by the end
of the year. Harrison Western is using about fifty employ-
ees in the five-month program that involves diamond
drilling and crosscutting.

"At the same time Chevron Resources has thirteen
geologists mapping the mine and Joe Dewey, project man-
ager of Chevron's Creede office, predicted another two
years of exploration and evaluation work ahead.

"The work being done by Chevron is on 10 leasehold
interests including the old Emperius [Mine]. Minerals
Engineering ran the mine and mill intermittently from
1972 to 1976.

"The Homestake Group is busy exploring the possi-
bilities of a big open-pit operation on the Creede
Formation. There the ore grade would be relatively low
but the quantity of minable rock would be large.

"What put Creede on Colorado's modern mining map
is the 10 year-old Bulldog Mine-Mill operation of
Homestake Mining Co. It produced just under 100,000
tons of ore averaging 14.7 ounces of silver per ton last
year to keep Homestake Colorado's No. 1 silver mining
company. Lead by-product totaled 1,378 tons."

The most frenetic period of exploration activity during the second boom occurred in 1981, when land that had been withdrawn
from mineral entry for a dam on the Rio Grande River at Wagon
Wheel Gap was reopened to mineral exploration. The U.S. Bureau
of Reclamation had spent years on the design of a dam that was not
to be built. Homestake Mining Company, Todilto Exploration, Utah
International, Nye Metals, Earth Search, Minerals Engineering
Company, and Chevron were all staking and overstaking each

other's claims, and tempers grew short at times. The activities were quite like those during the first boom in the 1890s.[6] No economic mineral deposits were discovered by all this activity on the re-opened land. Such frenzied staking of mining claims did not happen in Creede Camp proper, since most of the mineral areas were already covered by claims and Fred Baker had blanketed Bulldog Mountain with claims at the onset of the second boom.

BULLDOG MOUNTAIN VEIN SYSTEM

By far, the most successful of the explorationists during the second boom were Manning W. "Bill" Cox and Fred Baker, Jr. Shortly after the 1960 preliminary report by Steven and Ratté was issued, Bill Cox contacted Fred Baker and suggested he stake claims over the probable surface projection of the Bulldog Vein System. Baker did so by blanketing Bulldog Mountain with claims. He abutted his claims, the Baker Claims, on all sides of the Kansas City Star that had been patented by Dr. Biles in 1894.[7]

Bulldog Mountain, Incorporated, was organized by Baker, Clarence Hocker, and John Getz, all of Monte Vista, Colorado, to hold and explore the company's block of sixty-one mining claims.[8] Bill Cox contacted Humphreys Exploration Company and inter-ested them in exploring the south end of the Bulldog Vein. Humphreys drilled five surface diamond drill holes between October 2, 1961, and March 24, 1962. They found no values. Cox then contacted Homestake Mining Company and Homestake leased Bulldog Mountain's property on September 4, 1963.[9]

McCulloch Oil Company of Los Angeles, California, purchased the Bulldog Mountain, Incorporated, holdings in February 1968 from the previous owners, Fred Baker, Jr., and William Cox of Aspen, Colorado; Dick Lehman and Paul Mitchell of Creede; and the John Getz (Monte Vista) heirs. The Homestake Mining Company's lease and mining operations on about fifty-five claims previously held by Bulldog Mountain was not affected by the change in ownership. No consideration was announced, but the assumption was that it was sizeable.[10] According to rumors at the time, Cox and Baker each received a million dollars.

Fred Baker, Jr., was an important figure in Creede Camp's sec-ond boom. He and Cox were the "movers and shakers" behind the latter day exploration of the Bulldog Mountain Vein System after it had lain forgotten and idle for many years. Baker grew up near Monte Vista, Colorado. His father was in charge of maintenance at

Fred Baker, Jr. (L) and Manning W. "Bill" Cox (R) —
circa 1965. Ready to examine "Pogo" claims owned by
John and Inez Jackson.

Photo by John Jackson

the Colorado State Soldiers and Sailors Home at Home Lake two
miles east of Monte Vista. As a young man, Fred, Jr., worked as a
trail rider for the U.S. Forest Service in the Creede area. He married
Mildred Hosselkus, a Creede native, in 1945. When exploration for
uranium began in earnest, he and Marion Kinman formed a drilling
company that did exploration drilling for Stella Dysart at Grants,
New Mexico. He returned to Creede in about 1960 after he had
promoted several mines to Dysart, who put up a great deal of money
for exploration — the Corsair Mine at Sunnyside, the Bird Creek
Mine at Spar City, and others. His wife's nephew, Gordon
Hosselkus, and Baker did exploration work at the Corsair under the
name H&B Construction as described in Chapter Fourteen. While
staking the Baker Claims on Bulldog Mountain, he and and his family lived in Monte Vista but moved to Aspen, Colorado, in 1965.
There, he and Bill Cox went to work for McCulloch Oil Company.
During their tenure, Baker and Cox sold Bulldog Mountain,
Incorporated, to McCulloch. Afterwards, Baker became involved in
the Statesman Mining Company. He and Edwin Smart, a promoter
from Blanding, Utah were the principals. A limited partner in the
company was famed cowboy actor John Wayne. Statesman worked
on mine exploration projects in Mexico, Arizona, and Colorado,

and finally at Creede Camp in 1973. The Bakers left Aspen in 1968 for Sequim, Washington, where Baker bought land with the idea of building a marina. He couldn't give up the idea that he could hit another bonanza somewhere, so he continued prospecting as well as building his marina. John Wayne had continued to loan him money that he couldn't pay back. In the end, he lost his land in Sequim. Fred Baker, Jr., died of a heart attack in 1994 at the age of 65.[11]

Bill Cox was a geologist working for Conoco at the beginning of his association with Fred Baker. In 1965 he was a consulting engineer with his own company, Manning W. Cox Associates, in San Francisco, California, and in 1980 he was the manager of the Sunshine Mining Company in Coeur d'Alene, Idaho.[12]

BULLDOG MOUNTAIN MINE

Bulldog Mountain, Incorporated, extended the Nickel Plate Tunnel and did the initial diamond drilling in 1961, leading to the discovery of rich silver ore in the Puzzle Vein. The tunnel, originally driven sometime between 1914 and 1920 at an elevation of 9,940 feet above sea level, was one of the properties owned by the Bulldog Leasing, Mining & Milling Company in the 1920s. The original Nickel Plate Tunnel intersected the upper portion of the Puzzle Vein, where only a two-inch wide barite seam was found. The tunnel was abandoned. The Emperius Mining Company sampled the vein cut by the Nickel Plate in the 1950s, but decided that the low metal value in the samples did not justify purchasing the property. No further work was done until 1961.[13]

Steven and Ratté followed up their preliminary report on Creede Camp with a final report in 1965, stating their reasons for considering the Bulldog Mountain Fault zone as a potential source of ore:

> *"In a preliminary report on the Creede district, we suggested that the Bulldog Mountain Fault zone appeared to be a favorable structure to prospect. These faults constitute an antithetic zone within the main subsided block of the Creede graben and probably intersect the Amethyst Fault zone at depth. As the Amethyst Fault zone was abundantly mineralized, it seems logical that mineralizing solutions also had access to the Bulldog Mountain Fault zone. Emmons and Larsen reported assays of from a few ounces to 87 ounces of silver per ton from scattered shafts and pits along the surface trace of the eastern branch fault.*

"The prospected near surface formations are under-lain by at least 100-200 feet of soft Windy Gulch tuff, which may have inhibited upward passage of mineralizing solutions. The underlying hard rhyolites of the Campbell Mountain and Willow Creek Members of the Bachelor Mountain Rhyolite would be much more favorable hosts, as they enclose the known ore bodies on the other main fault zones in the district."[14]

The Nickel Plate Tunnel had been driven into the soft Windy Gulch tuff. The first Homestake tunnel, the 9,700-foot level, was driven into the underlying hard rhyolites at an elevation 240 lower than the Nickel Plate. This tunnel exposed rich silver ore in the Puzzle Vein, thus proving Steven and Ratté's theory correct. Robert A. Boppe described this bonanza to the author:

"While driving tunnel on the 9,700 foot level, the miners intercepted some of the most beautiful native silver ever discovered in the Creede mines. There was wire silver that looked like steel wool, massive leaf silver over an inch wide, and large amounts of ruby silver [pyrargyrite]. When the miners went into the mine and saw what the previous shift had blasted into, they could not believe their eyes. It was likened to a pirate's treasure chest, only much larger! This high-grade ore pocket was mined upwards a distance of 240 feet from the 9,700 foot level."

Production from the Puzzle Vein began in 1969. Thus, the statement in the Bulldog Leasing, Mining & Milling Company's prospectus issued in the 1920s that "our own Bulldog lode may yet prove to be the great undiscovered mother lode of Creede" was finally proven true!

The history of the development of Bulldog Mountain Mine that took six years from the time the property was leased in 1963 is taken from Homestake Mining Company's in-house publication, *Sharp Bits, Summer 1969:*

"Homestake's entry into the Creede District came as a result of a U.S. Geol. Survey report indicating a possible ore occurrence in a vein structure located on Bulldog Mountain, northwest of Creede. The property was leased from Bulldog Mountain, Incorporated who had started mineral exploration of the vein structures. Early explo-

ration was carried out under the direction of Homestake's San Francisco exploration office.

"During Homestake's early exploration period, diamond drilling was attempted. While this method revealed some mineralization, it was largely unsuccessful as a tool for evaluation of the vein. The vein consisted of both hard and soft materials with cavities called 'vugs.' Core recover from diamond drilling was so poor that an accurate measure of the deposit could not be made using this technique.

"A decision was made to drive a tunnel into the mountain for further exploration and evaluation. In June 1964 a tunnel was started at an elevation of 9,700 feet above sea level. It was driven along the vein for about 7,000 feet and is known as the 9700 Level. Levels at Creede are named according to their elevation above sea level.

"Exploration on this 9700 Level showed encouraging mineralization consisting of silver sulfides, native silver, and lead sulfides. However, the commercial value of the deposit had not been determined at this point, because the vertical extent of the ore was unknown.

"In August 1966 a new tunnel was started 340 feet below the 9700 Level. This tunnel was driven oversize and relatively straight to accommodate future production haulage [five-ton side-dump mine cars pulled by 6- and 7-ton locomotives] and ventilation as well as to provide exploration access to the lower area.

"Work on this level [9360] showed that ore values extended at least to the 9360 Level. In February 1968 the decision was reached to build a mill. Operation of the Bulldog Mountain Mine seemed economically feasible at the existing silver prices.

"Bulk samples were tested in the metallurgical laboratories of the Colorado School of Mines Research Foundation at Golden, Colorado. About 25 tons of representative ore were trucked to the laboratory and run through the crushing and sampling plant. Samples were 'cut' for the more than 70 flotation and gravity concentration tests which developed the final flow sheet for silver and lead recovery. The test work covered a period from October 1967 to March 1968. The results of these tests thus provided the basis for the mill design.

"Homestake's metallurgical and construction engineering personnel worked closely with the Engineering Design Company and The Galligher Company, both of Salt Lake City, Utah in designing the 300 ton-per-day mill. The contract to erect the mill was awarded to State, Inc., of Pueblo, Colorado. At the peak of the construction project over 80 men were employed on the mill and other related facilities.

"Because of the short building season in the Creede area, all construction was so planned as to complete those jobs vulnerable to cold weather, and before the summer and fall season ended.

"As soon as the ground thawed in May 1966 excavation in the mill plant area began. Even as this was in progress, work began on the numerous concrete foundations required to support heavy mill machinery. As foundations were completed, much of the mill equipment was installed immediately. This required precise leveling and aligning to assure proper meshing with other equipment installed later.

"In September 1968 the erection of the mill building was completed. This was a laminated wood beam structure. While a metal building was considered, the wooden structure was chosen because of better insulating qualities and its resistance to fire. Wood will char quickly but still stand, whereas light metal buildings tend to collapse in a fire.

"Construction work inside the mill continued with additional equipment being installed, concrete floors poured, and steel decking welded in place. Plumbing, wiring, and painting all proceeded as scheduled. The mill was completed and ready for a trial run April 1, 1969 (eleven months after the construction project was started).

"During the mill construction, ancillary facilities were also being built. A new office, an assay laboratory, and a sandfill facility were erected by Homestake crews comprised of local people as well as some employees transferred temporarily from our Black Hills Operations in Lead, S.D.

"A tailings dam also had to be constructed to retain the slimes discharged from the mill. [The fine particles in the mill tailing, or 'slimes,' were separated from the

The Homestake Mill — 1969

Courtesy of Robert Boppe

coarser sand particles. The slimes were retained in the tailings pond and the sands were pumped back into the mine as fill through the sandfill facility.] This tailings pond is probably Colorado's finest. Approval of regulatory agencies of both the State and Federal Governments was required concerning the storm run-off, decant system, type of fill, and its compaction. The dam has storage capacity for approximately four years of operation. It was designed so that capacity could be increased as needed. All water, instead of overflowing the dam, is re-circulated back to the mill for re-use.

"After the usual start-up problems, the mill proved to be capable of its 300 ton-per-day design capacity. Two methods of recovery, flotation and gravity concentration are used in the mill. Flotation concentration consists of chemically conditioning the wanted minerals so they adhere to air bubbles rising in the flotation tank. Unwanted waste material is depressed to the bottom of the tank and a separation is thus made. Gravity concentration depends on the greater weight of the wanted minerals to create a separation. The lead and silver

Homestake Mine and Mill Complex
From Sharp Bits, Summer — 1969,
Courtesy of the Barrick Gold Corporation
This view shows the mill (left), mine buildings (center),
and the 9360 Level portal (lower). The top road leads to
the 9700 Level. The tailings dam is behind the hill to the
right of the water tank (top center).

*concentrates from the mill are shipped by railroad car to
a smelter at El Paso, Texas.*

*"The start-up of the new Bulldog Mountain Mine and
Mill complex marked the culmination of over six years of
coordinated efforts by many Homestake employees and
other people. Thus, a new mining enterprise has been created which now provides jobs for many people, tax revenues for government, and silver badly needed by
industry. Our employees at Creede look to the future with
pride and enthusiasm."*

The Homestake Mill was described by Daniel Jackson, Jr., in an
article in the May 1974 *Engineering and Mining Journal,* entitled
"Homestake's Hard Work Pays Off at the Bulldog Mountain Mine":

*"Ore at minus 12-inch is discharged from a coarse ore
bin by a variable-speed National Iron apron feeder onto a
belt conveyor which discharges into the crusher building.*

A vibrating grizzly removes primary undersize, and plus 2 1/2-inch material goes to a Denver-Rogers jaw crusher. Grizzly undersize and crusher discharge then goes to a rod-deck vibrating screen. Oversize from this screen is reduced to minus 7/8-inch by a Symons Standard cone crusher. Screen undersize and crusher discharge is conveyed to a 700-ton bin prior to being conveyed to the grinding section of the mill.

"Fine ore from the storage bin is fed to a Marcy rod mill which discharges at 74% solids to a Denver-Simplex jig and onto a Wemco spiral classifier. Feed rate to the rod mill ranges from 13 to 16 wet tons per hour.

"Classified sands discharge to a Denver ball mill equipped with a scoop feeder. This mill discharges at 70% solids to the spiral classifier. Classifier overflow is screened for chip removal and then pumped by a Denver SRL-C pump to a Krebs cyclone. Cyclone overflow is returned to the ball mill and the overflow, at 28% solids, goes by gravity to a conditioner ahead of the bulk flotation section.

"Bulk flotation is conducted in eight No. 36 Galigher rougher cells and the concentrate is cleaned in two additional No. 36 cells. Tailings from these circuits are reconditioned and fed to a scavenger bank of eight No. 36 cells. Scavenger concentrate is cleaned in two No. 36 cells and recleaned in two No. 24 cells. Bulk cleaner and scavenger recleaner concentrates are combined and pumped to an Eimco thickener. Thickener underflow is filtered on an Eimco disc filter. Filter cake, at approximately 12% moisture, drops into the concentrate storage area.

"Silver-lead concentrate is trucked to the DRGW railhead approximately 3 miles away and then loaded into flat-bottom gondolas for shipment to Asarco's El Paso smelter. Normal shipping lots consist of ten 60-ton cars."

The Bulldog Mountain Mine and the Idarado Mine at Ouray accounted for sixty-seven per cent of Colorado's silver output in 1969, and the Bulldog was the major source. The Bulldog Mountain Mine was the largest silver producer in Colorado in 1970. It produced more than 100,000 ounces of silver and was also a major producer of lead.[15]

In 1970 the Bulldog Mountain Mine staff included: Tom J. Connolly, general manager; "Bud" Ames, mine superintendent; Rudy Werber, mill superintendent; Watson Hanscom, geologist; and Robert Boppe, mine engineer. The property consisted of sixteen patented mining claims, about 173 unpatented claims, plus six mill site claims, water rights, and various surface holdings.[16]

The story of Homestake's purchase of the Kansas City Star claim is interesting. The committee that sponsored the annual raft race down the Rio Grande River had purchased the claim from the county for back taxes many years after the demise of the original Bulldog Leasing, Mining & Milling Company and intended to raffle it off piecemeal as part of its raft racing activities. The committee had raffled one-tenth of the claim that was won by a woman in Denver prior. The committee sold their nine-tenths to Homestake for a fair price; however, the Denver woman demanded $10,000 and a new car for her share. Homestake paid her price. The Kansas City Star proved to be one of Homestake's richest properties.[17]

Extensive exploration and development work, consisting primarily of a 450-foot winze below the 9360 Level, was conducted in 1971 at the Bulldog Mountain Mine. The Bulldog was the state's largest silver-producing mine in 1971, producing seventy-seven per cent of the state's silver. Mine development at the lower level encountered a large volume of water in 1972, which required the installation of larger-than-anticipated pumps and a redesign of the underground electrical power system. As a consequence, development proceeded at a slower rate than expected.[18] Homestake purchased the Bulldog Mountain property under conditions of their lease from McCulloch Oil on September 26, 1973, and completed royalty payments to Bulldog Mountain, Incorporated, in October 1974 to acquire full ownership of the Bulldog Mountain Mine.[19] Two mines, the Bulldog and Idarado, produced fifty-nine per cent of Colorado's silver in 1974.[20]

The Bulldog Mountain Vein System consists primarily of two main mineralized zones — the West Strand Vein and the Puzzle or East Strand Veins. The target of the initial exploration effort was the West Strand Vein; however, the Puzzle Vein and its rich ore was reached first and development of the West Strand was deferred until the latter part of 1973.[21]

Ventilation had been a serious problem in the mines at Creede Camp from the early days and the Bulldog Mountain Mine was no exception. Homestake installed a forced-air ventilation system that introduced air into the 9360 Level by a large fan, which maintained a positive pressure in the mine to keep the oxygen-deficient air in the vein fissures and out of the mine workings, thus eliminating a hazardous condition for the miners. The air was exhausted through the 9700 Level.[22]

The Bulldog was the major source of silver in 1975 and 1976. Homestake constructed the world's first carbon-in-pulp plant for recovery of silver that had been going to the tailings pond with the slimes fraction. State, Incorporated, of Pueblo, Colorado, started construction in April 1976 and the plant was completed by year-end at a cost of more than $2 million.[23] Homestake described the carbon-in-pulp process as follows:

> *"The process consists of agitation leaching of the slime tailings with lime and dilute cyanide solution in a thick pulp. Silver is dissolved and removed from the solution by agitating the pulp with granular carbon which adsorbs soluble silver. Processing makes use of a multiple-stage, counter-current system of screens and tanks to separate and advance carbon through the pulp stream. The carbon, which is rapidly loaded with silver, is separated and sent to a stripping cone where silver is eluted with a dilute hot caustic solution. Metallic silver is then recovered from the caustic solution by electroplating on cathodes of steel wool, which are melted down. Crude silver bullion is then poured into bars.*
>
> *"Since 1969, 500,000 tons of tailings, containing approximately 3 troy ounces of silver per ton, from the flotation circuit were deposited in the old tailings ponds. During the next five years these tailings will be processed through the carbon-in-pulp plant."*[24]

Homestake employed 136 people at their Creede operations in 1976 with a payroll of more than $19 million and produced 1.65 million ounces of silver and 2.2 million pounds of lead. A new tailings impoundment was completed in August at a cost of $900,000.[25]

The Bulldog and Leadville's Sherman Mine were the principal silver producers in Colorado in 1977. By the end of 1977, over 8.5 miles of tunnel had been driven on five separate levels at the Bulldog. Exploration drifting on the West Strand Vein System indicated significant ore-grade mineralization. A newly constructed water treatment plant was put into operation in 1977 to improve the quality of the mine water discharge.[26] The Bulldog was the largest producer of silver in Colorado in 1978 and in 1980 it yielded more silver than the next five producers combined.[27]

The U.S. Bureau of Mines described operations and major improvements at the Bulldog Mountain Mine in its *Minerals Yearbook for 1980*:

> *"Homestake Mining Co. spent $1.5 million on capital improvements at its Bulldog Mountain Mine, plus another $750,000 for underground equipment in 1980. Shops, offices, mill, and equipment were updated. Ore production was opened up on the 9,000-foot level. A steel liner was placed in the 830-foot ventilation shaft to control a cave-in problem, and ventilation capacity was doubled by rearranging the airflow to provide air intake through both portals and exhaust through the shaft. Mine power capacity was doubled, as was compressed air capacity for operating drills. A new telephone system was installed. The carbon plant, used for secondary recover of silver, was modernized. A new water treatment plant was opened October 1 at a cost of $1 million. The company claimed that treated mine water discharged into Willow Creek actually was more free of heavy metals than the creek itself. The 175-employee mine, which had an annual payroll of more than $4 million, was Creede's largest employer. The Bulldog Mine ranked seventh in silver mines in the United States in 1980."*

In 1981, the Bulldog produced nearly as much silver as all the other mines in Colorado combined. Ore was extracted from five working levels spaced at 200-foot intervals, connected to the surface by two tunnels. Rubber-tired diesel loaders were introduced into the mine in 1981 to improve productivity. However, depressed prices for silver resulted in a sharp reduction in revenues and operating earnings, about $13 million in 1981 compared to $26 million in 1980. The carbon-in-pulp plant, which treated the slime portion of the mill tailings and also tailings during the summer months, was shut down in October 1981 because silver prices made it uneconomical to operate.[28]

The Bulldog produced about two-thirds of Colorado's silver in 1982 and more than half in 1983. Homestake cut back production at the Bulldog and reduced the work force from 150 to about 100 in 1982 because of low silver prices. Nevertheless, by year-end, the silver market and profitability of the mine improved, and the mine ended the year with a profit. The company granted the employees a seven per cent wage increase. The carbon-in-pulp plant was reopened in December 1983 but closed in July 1984 because low silver prices made it, once again, uneconomical to operate.[29] The Bulldog was the largest silver producer in Colorado in 1984; however, more ore was mined during the year but the average silver content was lower.[30]

The U.S. Bureau of Mines' *Minerals Yearbook for 1985* had the following comments following the closure of Creede Camp's last major mine, the Bulldog Mountain Mine, in 1985:

> *"The State's major silver producer, Homestake's Bulldog Mountain Mine at Creede, closed at the end of January because low silver prices made it uneconomical to continue operations; the mine did not reopen during the year. About 97 of the 114 workers, one-sixth of the population of Creede, were laid off. It was the first total shut down of the mine since the beginning of the Bulldog project in 1963. The Bulldog Mine produced about 1.5 million troy ounces of silver in 1980; 1.4 million in 1981 and 1982; 1.3 million ounces in 1983; and slightly less than that in 1984. With production costs of $7.50 to $8.00 per ounce, it was uneconomic to operate with silver prices at about $6 per ounce."*

This closure essentially ended Creede Camp's century of mining, even though minor production of ore and exploration for metals, particularly silver, continued for several more years.

AMETHYST VEIN SYSTEM

The Amethyst Vein System was actively mined during the second boom and was explored for new ore bodies as never before.

THE EMPERIUS MINING COMPANY

The Emperius Mining Company mined sulfide ores from the OH and P Veins until 1972, as described in Chapter Fourteen. As the price of silver increased in the 1960s, the company made plans in 1964 and 1965 to prospect for oxidized silver ore above the sulfide zone. A raise was driven from the Commodore No. 5 Tunnel upwards a distance of 400 feet to the Commodore No. 4 Level. The newly opened Commodore No. 4 Level was equipped with air, water, power, and transportation, and crosscuts were driven and prospecting for new silver veins was started. Emperius spent over

$400,000 in preparation for the exploration program. Most of the expenditures were made between 1968 and 1972, and normal sulfide ore production was somewhat curtailed as miners were assigned to the exploration program.[31]

Emperius shut down their mining and milling operations in 1972. The reason given was the lack of a smelter to purchase their zinc concentrates. However, other factors likely played a part in the decision, including wage competition with the Homestake Mining Company's new Bulldog Mountain Mine, poor working conditions for the miners, and more stringent safety and environmental laws that had been enacted by the state and federal governments. The company's closure stopped its efforts to get back to its roots — the mining of high-grade oxidized silver ore that had been so successful in its early days.

CREEDE MINES

The Humphreys Exploration Company entered into a contract in 1961 with the Office of Minerals Exploration to explore for silver-lead-zinc ores on the Creede Mines, Inc., properties on the northern Amethyst Vein System. The contract was for the expenditure of $187,600, with a fifty per cent participation by the U.S. Government.[32] Some exploration drilling was done in 1962 by the Humphreys Engineering Company.[33] There is no record of any discoveries from this activity.

Buttes Gas and Oil Company, a diversified resource company located in Oakland, California, gained control and management of Creede Mines, Incorporated, in 1976. Buttes consolidated management of all its mineral activities in Humphries Mineral Industries, Incorporated, a wholly owned subsidiary located in Denver, in 1982.[34]

MINERALS ENGINEERING COMPANY

Blair Burwell, a 1919 graduate of the Colorado School of Mines, was the founder of Minerals Engineering Company. The company was started in Grand Junction, Colorado, to provide drilling services for companies involved in uranium exploration on the Colorado Plateau and was very successful. Later, Burwell acquired tungsten mines in Montana and was financed by the General Electric Company. General Electric was interested in sources of tungsten. Unfortunately, the metallurgical process to recover tungsten from the ore was not successful, and the project was terminated. Charles Melbye, a consulting geologist and a 1950 graduate of the Colorado

School of Mines, was hired as president of the nearly bankrupt Minerals Engineering Company in 1972. He reached a negotiated settlement with General Electric and they took over the tungsten project. Melbye had previously consulted for James Muir, Jr., at the Holy Moses Mine and, based on his work for Muir, felt that Creede Camp held large reserves of silver, lead, and zinc.[35]

Charles Melbye recognized the need to consolidate the various mines, held by several owners besides the Emperius Mining Company, in order to have an integrated operation. He was assisted by John Tippit, a mining attorney of Denver, Colorado, who was Minerals Engineering's attorney at the time and also Ben Poxson's friend and attorney. They brought Minerals Engineering and Emperius together in 1972. Frank McKinley, president of Creede Mines, Inc., owned by the Humphreys family, agreed to lease the Humphreys properties, including the New York, Happy Thought, and Park Regent Mines, to Minerals Engineering. Leases for the Emperius and Creede Mines properties and the Emperius Mill were signed on January 15, 1973. The Last Chance Mine was leased from Ralph Granger's granddaughter, Helen Granger Talmadge, who was living near San Jose, California.[36]

The U.S. Bureau of Mines' *Minerals Yearbook for 1973* had the following report:

> *"Minerals Engineering Company negotiated a limited partnership agreement with Statesman Mining Inc. to develop base metal prospects formerly owned by Emperius Mining Co. and Humphreys Mining Co. near Creede. A total of $1 million will be expended on exploration over a 3-year period. During the year, a mining crew, geologist, and an assayer were employed in testing copper, gold, lead, silver, and zinc mineralization in the sulfide and oxide zones. Roads were improved to the Chance and Commodore Mines to allow haulage of about 400,000 tons of stockpiled ore to the mill. Engineering and design studies were underway to determine the optimum operating rate at the mill. Production was scheduled for early 1974."*

As previously described, Fred Baker received a considerable sum of money from the sale of his Bulldog claims, and he became involved in Minerals Engineering's plan for the development of Creede Camp. He and Edwin Smart of the Statesman Mining

Company and John Wayne, the actor, as a limited partner, were brought in to help develop the mines and expand the Emperius Mill. The Minerals Engineering limited partnership raised one million dollars for the project. In addition to their mining venture, John Wayne, Manning W. Cox, and Fred Baker purchased about 240 acres of land on Miners Creek at Sunnyside and forty acres at Blue Park as an investment. Wayne visited Creede during the summer of 1975 and was Charles Melbye's house guest. A fish fry was held by the town of Creede in his honor and all of the townspeople were able to meet him. Wayne's son, Ethan, was with him. Unfortunately, after two days Wayne had to leave Creede's high altitude. He had flown to Creede's airport in his private jet where it was parked until his departure.[37] *The Pueblo Chieftain* carried the following story in its August 23, 1973, issue:

> *"John Wayne, famous Western star, caused a commotion in Creede Wednesday when he came to town to look into some mining and land interests. Tourists and townspeople alike were open-mouthed as they saw the tall man with the famous gait amble down the street. No cowboy was in evidence, however — Wayne was wearing a baseball cap. Mrs. Paul Hosselkus has a souvenir she will treasure, since it was her birthday. The 'Duke' signed a birthday card for her. Wayne said he had plans to attend the Creede Repertory Theater Wednesday night, putting the student actors in a nervous state anticipating the cowboy star as a member of their audience."*

In 1973, Minerals Engineering Company opened up the Emperius Mine for exploration and development work and acquired the assets of Statesman Mining Company. Statesman's main asset was its interest in the Emperius Mine.[38]

The Emperius Mill's capacity was expanded to 300 tons per day in 1973 at a cost of $750,000 by Mill Superintendent Miller, who came from Carlin, Nevada. Tony Mastrovich, formerly the resident manager of American Metal Climax's Uranium Company at Grand Junction, Colorado, was general manager for Minerals Engineering's Creede operations. The Emperius Mine and Mill went into production in October 1974.[39]

Minerals Engineering produced more than 20,000 ounces of silver and 500 tons of zinc in 1975 and produced silver, copper, lead, and zinc in 1976.[40] Due to lower prices for metals in 1976, Minerals

Engineering shut down mine operations on August 9, 1976. Milling operations continued until October 30, 1976, on ore trucked from existing mine dumps. The roof of the Emperius Mill caved in as the result of a heavy snow in late 1976. There was no further Minerals Engineering mining or milling operations at Creede Camp. Anton Faust, a banker, was made president of the company upon Charles Melbye's departure.[41] *The Pueblo Star Journal* reported on the closing of the mill in their October 31, 1976, issue:

> *"Current heavy losses and a lack of environmental research [all environmental regulations at the time were complied with] were blamed for the closing here Saturday of the Minerals Engineering flotation mill for an indefinite length of time.*
>
> *"Underground mining operations at the old Emperius Mine were curtailed here in August because of Minerals Engineering's inability to sustain an adequate grade and tonnage of ore, and because of a zinc smelter strike which excluded a market for zinc, roughly a third of the operating revenue. Gene [Wardell], manager of Minerals Engineering here, said most workers knew in advance of the closing and found employment elsewhere or are drawing unemployment compensation.*
>
> *"The company president, A.G. Faust of Denver, explained the mining firm's plight in a prepared statement. He said that operation losses at Creede had exceeded $25,000 per month since last July. The losses resulted from marginal economics involved in processing lower grade ores from surface dumps and burdensome mine and mill royalties which combined to exceed 25 per cent of the mill's monthly smelter income.*
>
> *"Faust said his company has been negotiating with several large companies to obtain funds for a major exploration and capital improvement program here. 'The industry feels, as we do, that our Creede properties have significant exploration potentials,' he said, adding that it will take considerable time and additional capital to develop sufficient reserves for an economic operation."*

The only activity at the Emperius Mine in 1977 was underground and surface diamond drilling by Houston Oil & Minerals Corporation. Minerals Engineering approved Houston's option to lease

the Emperius Mining Company and Creede Mines properties in June
1977, and their option was relinquished on December 2, 1977.[42]

There were conflicts between companies and individuals during
the second boom, as would be expected. One such case was reported
in *The Wall Street Journal*:

> *August 28, 1980 — John Wayne Partner Settles SEC
> Charge on Takeover Effort — Stan Crock, Staff Reporter
> of The Wall Street Journal.*
>
> "The Securities and Exchange Commission charged
> that Mr. Hickerson failed to disclose that he and the late
> actor had teamed up to seek control of Minerals
> Engineering Co., a Denver-based developer of mineral
> properties. Mr. Hickerson joined forces with Mr. Wayne
> after the company's management had enlisted him to help
> resolve a dispute between Mr. Wayne and the company,
> according the SEC.
>
> "Mr. Hickerson, who lives in Denver, settled the SEC
> staff charges by agreeing to comply with stock-ownership
> reporting requirements in the future.
>
> "Also named in the charges was Merit Energy Corp.,
> which the SEC says considered trying to take control of
> Minerals Engineering. Merit also agreed to comply with
> stock-ownership reporting requirements. Mr. Hickerson
> and the company didn't admit or deny any wrongdoing.
>
> "According to the SEC, the dispute Mr. Wayne had
> with Minerals was over a 'significant business transaction
> requiring shareholder approval.' The SEC said Mr.
> Wayne, who held an 11.6 per cent interest in Minerals
> Engineering, opposed the transaction, which the SEC
> didn't identify further.
>
> "In May 1977 Mineral's president, Anton Faust,
> brought Mr. Hickerson, who held a 5.5 per cent interest,
> to Mr. Wayne's Newport Beach, Calif. home to try to
> resolve the rift, the SEC said. But Mr. Hickerson ended up
> suggesting that he and Mr. Wayne join together to exert
> influence over Mr. Faust, according to the SEC. Mr.
> Wayne liked the idea and filed suit against the company a
> week later, the agency said.
>
> "That summer, Mr. Hickerson met with Mr. Wayne and
> his son, Michael, to discuss a proxy fight for control of the

company, the commission said. In the summer of 1978, Mr. Hickerson proposed changing Minerals' business from mineral exploration to oil and gas exploration, the SEC said. Finally, in January 1979, Mr. Hickerson decided to form a new company to take over Minerals and engage in oil and gas exploration, according to the commission.

"Merit Energy was the vehicle for doing that, the SEC said. The company eventually bought 19.5 per cent of Minerals' stock, including the big blocks held by Messrs. Wayne and Hickerson, the commission said.

"Merit Energy and Mr. Hickerson should have disclosed the formation of the group of Minerals stockholders, the plan to transfer the 19.5 per cent of Minerals' stock to a new company and Mr. Hickerson's plan to change Minerals' business, the agency said." [43]

Chevron Resources Company, a subsidiary of the oil giant, signed a letter of intent on June 28, 1978, to option the Minerals Engineering holdings at Creede. Chevron began their investigation on March 1978 at the suggestion of Paul Eimon, a well-known mining geologist who had faith in Creede's potential. Surface exploration commenced in July 1978 and underground exploration in April 1979. [44]

Chevron reopened a number of old workings to obtain bulk samples. Reports indicated that Chevron has found and sampled 400,000 tons of old stope fill, which assayed about ten ounces of silver per ton. There may also be several million ounces of silver in the old mine dumps. The hanging wall system, containing hundreds of veins and veinlets plus some mineralization of the rhyolitic country rock between them, was one of Chevron's key exploration targets. Chevron was seeking enough ore for an open pit operation which would produce on a scale of several thousand tons per day. [45]

Harrison-Western Corporation contracted with Chevron for the underground evaluation, including mine rehabilitation, drifting, crosscutting, diamond drilling, and the collection and preparation of bulk ore samples. [46]

The exploration work continued until December 1981, when Chevron formally announced that they were not going to exercise their option. Chevron spent six to seven million dollars on their Creede exploration effort. [47] Obviously, Chevron Resources was not able to justify a large open pit mine.

On September 9, 1982, Pioneer Nuclear Inc. leased Mineral Engineering's holdings along the Amethyst Vein System but relinquished their lease in 1983. Paul Eimon, who had started the joint exploration project between Chevron and Minerals Engineering, was Pioneer Nuclear's vice-president for exploration.[48]

Pioneer drilled over sixty underground and six surface drill holes. In 1983, Pioneer did extensive underground and surface studies, including geologic mapping, geochemistry, geophysics, and metallurgy. Most of the drill holes were located to confirm the existence and continuity of vein mineralization in the central part of the Amethyst No. 5 Level mine workings.[49]

Even though Pioneer Nuclear did not exercise its option to enter a development and operating agreement, it continued to work with Minerals Engineering in a long-term exploration program on the Amethyst Vein System. An exploratory drift was driven southwest from the Commodore Mine to further probe the Amethyst and Bulldog Veins near an area where Homestake reported new vein discoveries last year. Diamond drilling and a geophysical survey were also part of the exploration program. In 1985, ore bodies on the Amethyst Vein System northwest of Creede were defined, following two years of exploration at the Commodore Mine.[50]

The last shipment of silver ore from the Emperius Mine was made by Pioneer Nuclear in March 1985. Five hundred tons of ore averaging twenty-five ounces of silver per ton were shipped to the Hidalgo Smelter in New Mexico in a truck convoy. The ore came from stopes in the hanging wall veins on the Amethyst No. 5 Level.[51]

T. Boone Pickens' Mesa Limited Partnership, Amarillo, Texas, absorbed Pioneer Nuclear Inc. in July 1986. Mesa drilled north of Emperius Mine along the Amethyst Vein System.[52] This was the last known mining activity on the properties of the Emperius Mining Company and Creede Mines, Inc.

Minerals Engineering Company had become a dormant holding company by this time. John Wold, an oil, gas, and uranium developer as well as a U.S. Representative from Wyoming, purchased control of the company. Through the efforts of Charles Melbye, CoCa Mines, a Denver exploration company, was merged into Minerals Engineering Company. The resulting company retained the CoCa name and was in charge of the Creede properties. Hecla Mining Company, based in Idaho, then absorbed CoCa Mines.[53]

EQUITY MINE

The Homestake Mining Company commenced underground exploration at the Equity Mine during the summer months of 1971.[54] Homestake purchased the property of Equity Mines, Incorporated, owned by Les Turnipseed, in 1974.[55] The U.S. Bureau of Mines' *Minerals Yearbook for 1984* had the following report on Homestake's activities at the Equity Mine:

> *"The company continued a major underground exploration project at the Equity Mine, about 8 miles from the Bulldog Mine, which included driving a decline, drifting, diamond drilling, bulk sampling, metallurgical testing, and engineering studies. Homestake confirmed it had struck silver and was trying to confirm the size of the ore body. Crown Resources Corp. and joint venture partner Sutton Resources Inc. signed an agreement enabling Homestake to acquire a 55 per cent working interest in 331 claims totaling 6,000 acres adjacent to the Equity property."*

Homestake continued work on the Equity Mine in 1985 by completing the decline and production tunnel and beginning drifting along the Amethyst Vein System to sample and test the ore. Although the company had not commented about their discovery, rumors suggested a major silver strike. One participant stated that: "Creede is the most exciting gold and silver camp in the United States today."[56] The decline into the Equity and North Amethyst Veins was driven a distance of 8,136 feet on a fifteen per cent slope.

The Denver Post carried a story about Homestake's rumored rich silver strike at the Equity in its August 15, 1985, issue:

> *"A discovery twice the size of the 1859 Comstock Lode in Sierra Nevada — the richest lode in American history — is said to have been found by Homestake Mining Co. near Creede.*
>
> *"If the industry rumors prove true, the Homestake find would become the richest lode — with a market value of $4.6 billion.*
>
> *"But don't pack the burro just yet. Rumor, overstatement, and optimism have been the historical handmaidens of gold and silver rushes in the West. But modern-day forces have added a twist to this story. The company's quote on the New York Stock Exchange has risen more*

than $2.75 in the last two weeks to close at $27.75 last Wednesday.

"Homestake is 'creating a lot of excitement' in the Creede area, said Mike Sloan, a stockbroker in the Monte Vista offices of Dain Bosworth, Inc. 'They're being very, very secretive, although I'm told they do have a very good find in the Equity area.'

"Speculation about the rich find has been fueled in recent weeks by Homestake's refusal to discuss its Equity Mine in detail. Company officials would only read statements from its annual report to respond to questions.'

"'We have not announced anything, and we won't until we have something to announce about what the grade might be and what the size of the deposit might be,' said Richard J. Stumbo, Jr., Homestake vice president — finance. 'We don't know.'"

Property north of the Equity was owned by Crown Resources Corporation and Sutton Resources, Inc., both Canadian companies, joint venture. The Crown-Sutton joint venture management felt that the vein structure would pass into their property and the Apex Law would apply; that is, they would be able to mine the down dip extension of the vein. However, the Crown-Sutton property was leased and drilled by Homestake in 1986. Homestake continued underground exploration at its northern Amethyst silver-gold vein deposit in 1987. Ore grade mineralization in the vein was identified, but the continuity of the vein was not established.[57]

The vein was not continuous and did not contain commercial amounts of ore given the price of silver at the time. The U.S. Bureau of Mines' *Minerals Yearbook for 1988* stated: "Homestake Mining Co. ceased the exploration program in Mineral County that would have kept the mining claims valid, deeming exploration too expensive to pursue. Homestake reported that copper, gold, lead, and silver were extracted from inventory piles at the Equity project."

Ore mined from the North Amethyst (Equity) was trucked to the Bulldog Mill and stockpiled. When the exploration project was discontinued, Homestake restarted the Bulldog Mill and processed the better grade ore for a period of six weeks in the summer of 1988. The concentrate was shipped by truck to a smelter in Montana and Homestake received payments of nearly $500,000 for gold, silver, and lead.[58] This was the last shipment from the district, signaled the end of high hopes for another bonanza silver deposit, and was the end of mining at Creede Camp.

MAMMOTH MOUNTAIN

Creede Ventures, a joint venture of the Homestake Mining Company and Freeport Exploration Company, employed Boyles Brothers Drilling Company of Golden, Colorado, to explore for silver veins on the Silver King claim on Mammoth Mountain in 1975.[59]

Todilto Exploration and Development Corporation prospected the Amethyst Vein on Mammoth Mountain east of Creede. Todilto opened the old Resurrection Tunnel during their exploration work. Coronado Resources, Incorporated, Vancouver, British Columbia, purchased Todilto's Creede property for approximately $480,000 and performed drilling and geochemical testing in 1985.[60] Even though some mineralization was undoubtedly found, no mining resulted from these Mammoth Mountain exploration efforts.

SOLOMON-HOLY MOSES VEIN SYSTEM

Mining properties on the Solomon-Holy Moses Vein System had been consolidated by the King Solomon Mining and Milling Company in 1961. Homestake leased King Solomon Mining and Milling's properties on November 8, 1963, but relinquished them on October 29, 1974.[61] Evidently no economic mineralization was located, so the mines along East Willow Creek did not join Creede Camp's second boom.

ALPHA-CORSAIR VEIN SYSTEM

Minerals Engineering Company was listed as the operator of the Corsair (Cowboy Johnson) Mine at Sunnyside in 1980.[62] The Sunnyside Tunnel (Cowboy Johnson Mine), the Kreutzer Sonata second and third levels, and the Alpha Tunnel that connects to the Corsair main level were opened in 1983. Underground geologic mapping and geochemical sampling indicated the presence of silver and base metal mineralization.[63] Minerals Engineering and the Santa Fe Mining Company, a subsidiary of the Santa Fe Railroad Company, formed a joint venture to explore the Alpha-Corsair Vein System in 1985.[64] No mineable ore bodies were found as a result of this latter-day exploration.

CREEDE FORMATION

The first exploration of the bedded deposits of the Creede Formation occurred in 1892 by the 400 Acre Consolidated

Diamond Drill Company, as described in Chapter Eight. Silver was found in the Creede Formation in 1919 and several carloads of ore were shipped. At that time, Fred Monkemeyer found petrified wood rich in silver in a tuff bed, afterwards named the Monkemeyer Sandstone.

Minerals Engineering invited Freeport Exploration to visit their Creede properties in 1973; however, Freeport was not interested in the underground mines, but it was interested in the Creede Formation. Tom Steven, the U.S. Geological Survey geologist of the 1965 report on Creede, had taken twenty-six samples of the Creede Formation on Bachelor Mountain that had averaged six ounces of silver per ton. This information had never been published by the Survey and Freeport found the data most interesting. A Freeport geologist recommended that Freeport contract with Minerals Engineering to drill a series of holes in the Creede Formation to test for disseminated silver and, thereby, earn an interest in the deposit if it proved to be large enough to be amenable to mining as an open pit operation. In May 1974, Freeport signed a joint venture agreement with the Creede Associates, Limited, to explore and develop the Creede Formation. Creede Associates was formed by Minerals Engineering and Statesman Mining Company, including John Wayne. Freeport began geological mapping of the surface and collecting samples in June 1974 and drilled a series of nine holes starting the following September. These holes indicated the presence of silver and additional drilling followed.[65]

Minerals Engineering Company signed an option agreement with Homestake Mining Company for their fifty per cent interest in the Creede Formation Project — called the Creede Venture — in March 1976. Minerals Engineering had previously acquired the Creede assets of Statesman Mining Company. Freeport reluctantly accepted Homestake entry into the Creede Venture. After Homestake's entry into the venture, exploration activity increased. Homestake drove a 680-foot exploration adit, or tunnel, in Creede terminology, into the Creede Formation to obtain bulk samples for metallurgical testing and as access for underground drilling. This adit, named the Freeport Adit, was completed in January 1977. In late 1977, Freeport offered Homestake their share of the venture for $2.5 million, but Homestake declined. Chevron also declined in January 1979. Minerals Engineering purchased Freeport's interest in March 1979 for a reported $1 million payable over four years. The final payment was made in 1983.[66]

Minerals Engineering drilled eight surface and nine underground diamond drill holes in 1980 and 1981. An independent evaluation of the property estimated proven and probably mineral reserves of about 3.3 million tons of ore containing 6.39 ounces of silver per ton. CoCa Mines drilled two additional holes in 1988 to complete exploration of the Creede Formation. Metallurgical testing of the Creede Formation ore indicated that recovery of silver would be quite low, and this fact is probably the main reason that the deposit was not developed.[67]

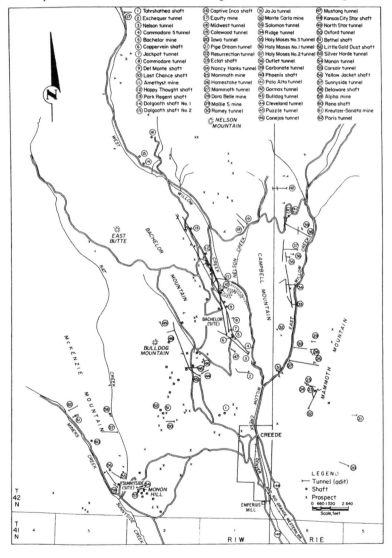

Principal Mines and Prospects, Creede District

Based on Figure 2, U.S. Bureau of Mines
Information Circular 8370, 1968

CHAPTER 16
THE MINERS

NO HISTORY OF CREEDE CAMP would be complete without the story of the individuals who worked in the mines and mills. Underground miners are a special breed of highly skilled workers that perform hard physical work. They work in places that have a total lack of natural light and face hazards from falling rock, cave-ins, fires, poor ventilation, and the dreaded silicosis or "miner's consumption," among others. The use of explosives and mining machinery add to the risks of the profession.

The early-day miners at Creede Camp came from all parts of the United States and probably from other parts of the world. Miners from Cornwall, England, were prevalent among miners of the West, as were the Irish. Immigrant miners from Italy, Sweden, Finland, Mexico, and the old Austrian Empire were also well represented in Colorado mines but not at early-day Creede Camp. Most, if not all, of the names in the Creede Cemetery originated in either the British Isles or the northern European countries. However, miners of Mexican extraction worked at the Fluorspar Mine at Wagon Wheel Gap. When it closed they migrated to the Gilman, Colorado, mine operated by the New Jersey Zinc Company.

Of all the groups represented in the western mines, those from Cornwall probably had the greatest impact. As previously discussed, much of mining terminology used in the western mines came from Cornwall. The Cornish tin and copper mines were shut down in the mid 1800s primarily because the mine workings had been deepened below the water level. Technology at the time was not sufficiently advanced to allow pumping of the water economically, thus leading to mine closures. Many skilled Cornish miners immigrated to the United States to find work in the coal mines of the Allegheny Mountains, the Michigan copper mines, and the lead mines in the Ozark Mountains. They migrated westward as mineral deposits were developed in the West.[1]

These Cornish miners were called "Cousin Jacks." The story behind the name is interesting. A mine operator, needing experienced miners, was told by a Cornish miner in his employ to "send my cousin Jack money for passage across the ocean to America and he will work for you." And, as a result, mine operators sent for many, many "Cousin Jacks." Cornish women were called "Cousin Jennies" in the mining camps.

The miner's name for a lunch bucket is "pie can" to this day. The term originated from the meal the "Cousin Jacks" took underground consisting of a meat pie baked in a crust, called a "pastie pie," and coffee. The lower portion of the pie can was filled with hot coffee and the upper container, similar to that in a double boiler, held the pastie pie and the coffee kept it warm.

The Irish came for a different reason — the potato famine in 1846. Many immigrated to the United States instead of facing starvation in Ireland. Of all the different groups who mined in the West, only the Irish had no experience in mining and, in general, they worked in the mines only until something better came along. Pity the poor Irishman on a shovel working for a "Cousin Jack" boss. There was no love lost between the Irish and Cornish at the time.[2]

SUPERSTITIONS

The early miners had many superstitions, among which was the belief that a woman's presence underground meant bad luck. In fact, if a woman went underground, the miners would immediately vacate the workings. In Colorado, this belief kept women out of the mining profession until the late 1960s, when the state legislature passed a bill that guaranteed a woman's right to work in a mine. One superstition that originated in Cornwall was the belief in "tommyknockers," or the spirits of miners killed in underground accidents. These ghosts played tricks on the miners as they worked underground. *The Denver Times* carried the following story about "ghosts" at Creede Camp in its January 3, 1903, issue:

> *Ghostly Figures Seen in the Big Kanawha Mine at Creede*
> *"Weird stories of ghostlike figures seen at the entrance of the mine shafts and tales of groans and moaning sounds being heard from the bottom of the shafts are related by mining men who have just returned from the property of the Big Kanahwa Mining Company at Creede. These tales, which rival those of 'Babette' of whom Frank Daniels sang, are said to have become so impressed on many of the men employed in the Big Kanawha*

Company's mines that they have quit work and sought places in other mines where the unnatural sights and sounds are unknown.

"The first man to relate a ghostlike tale of his experiences while working at the mine was Niel McQueg, an engineer. It was about five months ago that, while standing at the end of the tram, he saw a man not more than twenty feet away. Thinking it was one of the miners employed at the place he spoke to him. He received no reply and again he addressed him. Again he received no reply, and this time McQueg determined to find out who the man was. He approached to where the figure had been, and as he neared the spot the man disappeared. No trace of the man could be found. McQueg swears that he saw a man, but the moment that he approached to where the figure had been it vanished as if by magic. Not even the slightest trace of a man could be found and none of the men working around the mine at the time saw anything of a stranger, nor were any of them near the place where McQueg had seen the figure at about the time the engineer saw the vision.

"Shortly after this three distinct signals to hoist the men given from the station were heard in the bottom of a shaft where Henry S. Jones and some others were working. At the time the signals were given no one was nearer the place than fifteen feet and the search made to discover the person who gave the signal has been unavailing.

"Three days after this strange occurrence on June 26, 1902 Henry Jones was killed by falling out of the bottom of the skip, a distance of several hundred feet down the same shaft from which the mysterious signal to hoist the men had been given.

"These three occurrences made a great impression upon many of the men and particularly the more superstitious of them. But ten days ago another strange thing happened in the mine which caused the belief in the power of unseen things to become stronger fixed in the minds of many. While Lane Pearl, one of the shift bosses, was working with others in the mine he heard a distinct moaning sounded as though some one had met with a severe accident. He immediately stopped work and began an

investigation of the place from which he thought the sounds came. He made a most thorough investigation, but could find nothing. He then proceeded through the mine and questioned every employee at work as to whether anyone had been injured or if they had heard any moaning sounds. Finding that the men were all right, he concluded that it was James W. Westlake, the superintendent of the mine, who had been injured. Pearl then set about to find Westlake, whom he soon located uninjured.

"But this was not the last of the series of strange happening in the Big Kanawha Mine. A few days ago Oscar Montgomery, an employee who is engaged in tramming, approached one of the shafts when he distinctly saw the figure of a man standing near the entrance. He spoke to the figure, but received no reply. Suddenly the figure vanished as Montgomery approached. It was impossible for anyone to get away from that place, and Montgomery concluded that the man had made a sidestep and had fallen down the shaft. Accordingly Montgomery descended the shaft to investigate, but despite his search and questioning of his fellow employees he was unable to discover that any stranger had been down or that anyone had fallen down the shaft.

"When the news of this latest appearance of the strange figure around the mine became noised among the men, many who had only laughed at the stories before began to believe them. Others quit work and have sought places elsewhere.

"Investigations made at the mine have revealed one thing only which, it is said, will account in some way for the strange sights and sounds which have been heard by the men. It is claimed that escaping steam from some of the machinery in the bottom of the shafts is responsible for the strange occurrences. This steam in escaping is said to give forth the sounds which are not unlike those of moaning. Again the strange appearance of figures thought to be men in different parts of the mine is said to have been caused by the steam coming forth in volumes at times from the entrance of the mine and in the darkness or dim twilight this volume of steam looms up as though it were a man standing at the opening of the shaft. But

then this explanation has not satisfied the more superstitious of the miners, whose belief in things supernatural has grown so strong that they have sought work in mines where the 'steam' does not escape."

John Jackson tells stories about "tommyknockers" he met during his mining career:[3]

"I believe most long-term miners have a ghost story to tell; however most keep such happenings a secret. I operated a tugger hoist [a small hoist powered by a compressed air motor] at 580 winze in the Amethyst Mine for brief periods while leasing and contracting. It was the same hoist where a frayed cable snagged the jacket of Bruce Manning in 1942 and dragged him into the spool as he was hoisting ore from 700 level. The single wrap on his upper torso crushed his ribs and suffocated him. I wasn't at all comfortable around that particular hoist and when lifting loaded cans (sump buckets). I could plainly hear a voice begging, "please help me" over and over until I dumped the can and the weight was off the cable. It nearly drove me bonkers until I narrowed the sounds down to an overhead area where the sheave (pulley) was hung and I found the sounds were produced by protesting bearings. I installed a new sheave and silenced the voice.

"Another time Floyd Dooley and I were waiting in a crosscut from 3 shaft on Amethyst 5 level for the day shift crew to pass so we could blast farther back in the crosscut. We could hear the sounds of two miners walking by 3 shaft and talking. Floyd thought we should turn our lights off, sneak up behind them and scare the hell out of them. Where this happened is a straight shot from the shaft to the portal East with a curve to the South where the sounds came from. From our perch all we had to do was sneak past the lip of the chute and surprise them. Floyd was just ahead of me and when we should have been within a few feet of the exiting miners he exclaimed, 'Well, I'll be damned.' We could see light at the portal and there was nobody in the tunnel. I ran back to the South drift to see if they had turned back for some reason and could find no miners nor could I see any lights in the distance. When I returned to where Floyd was still

shaking his head, he said, 'Jackson, we'd better not tell anyone about this.'"

Dick Lehman told the following story about his meeting with a ghost in the 1989 *Creede Souvenir Book:*

"Some mines had ghosts that prowled the workings. One even had a horse that appeared in a stope. I talked to a miner who had seen it. Stories such as that I laughed at and went on about my work. Then came the time I wondered.

"It happened in the late 1930s. I was working on a small level in the Last Chance Mine. It was night shift and only two of us were working that shift; me, the miner, and Frank Miller, the outside man who cared for the air compressor.

"I timbered my working place, set up my machine, a stoper, and started drilling. I was alone in the mine, but thought nothing of it and had nothing on my mind but my work until....suddenly, I had the terrible feeling that somebody or something was standing on the drill plank behind me. I turned off my drill and then began a struggle, a terrible struggle, to turn around and look. All the stories I had heard about ghosts in the mines passed through my mind in perhaps a second. To turn was agony, but I did. I could see nothing, but the feeling of a presence persisted. It seemed as though my hair was raising my hat and light above my head.

"I dropped down out of the stope and fairly ran outside. Frank saw me and came to ask why I had come out. 'You can't have drilled out. Is something wrong?' he asked. 'I am going home,' was my answer. 'You are going home? Why?' 'Frank, I can't tell you why, but I am leaving.' The feeling was no longer with me, but I could not have gone back underground at that time.

"The next afternoon I showed up for my shift and although many curious glances were directed my way, nothing was said. I went to my working place and finished my round. The feeling of an unseen presence was gone or I could not have stayed. Never since have I had such an experience, nor do I ever want to feel again as I did that night. Now, I always listen to such stories and can

*relate to the fright, horror, and even the dismay of any
miner who was unfortunate enough to have been in such
a place at such a time. I can relate because I KNOW, BUT
I DON'T KNOW WHAT IT WAS!"*

BOARDING HOUSES

The early-day miners at Creede Camp settled near the mines to be
within walking distance of their places of employment. This, of
course, was the reason why Bachelor, Stump Town, North Creede,
and Weaver were settled. After the Nelson Tunnel connected the
mines along the Amethyst Vein, most miners left the outlying communities for the town of Creede and commuted to work through the
tunnel. Many of the miners, particularly those without families,
lived in boarding houses located near the various mines. Living close
to the mines was particularly important in the early days. The heavy
snows in the San Juans during the winter months made travel even
for short distances very difficult and meant that the outlying communities and boarding houses would be isolated for many days until
the roads were cleared by primitive means.

Mining camp boarding houses were primitive to say the least. As
many as thirty men lived in a single boarding house room with two-
tier bunk beds. The miners furnished their own bed rolls. The food
served to the miners was in most cases very good. It had to be to

Boarding House at the Amethyst Mine —
Winter of 1908

*Al Birdsey Collection, Courtesy of the Creede
Historical Society*

keep the miners satisfied so they would not leave for another boarding house with better food at a different mine. As one can imagine,
boarding house life was boring and the miners went to the always
present saloons, gambling halls, or the red light district for enter-
tainment.[4] The last boarding house at Creede Camp provided
lunches, but not lodging, in 1940 for miners using the Ruth Elder
Tunnel. The lunches were almost always chile made with venison, in
or out of season, by Madeline Wintz.[5]

LABOR RELATIONS

There is no evidence of serious labor strife at Creede Camp, even
though the notorious Western Federation of Miners Union had a
local, Miners Union No. 20, at Creede — the only union in Creede
Camp's history.

The mine owners and miners reached an agreement over wages
and working conditions in 1893 after the collapse of the price of silver. The terms of the agreement were not given.[6] Labor strife that
plagued the other San Juan mining camps in Cripple Creek and
Leadville did not happen at Creede, or at least was not reported.
The miners accepted a twenty-five-cent reduction in their daily
wages, to $2.75 a day in wet mines and $2.50 in the dry, in August
1897 to keep the mines open.[7]

The eight-hour law went into effect on June 19, 1899, with no
reduction in wages to improve working conditions in the smelters;

Early Day Creede Miners — Date Unknown (Andy
Dooley is the tall man on the left side of the picture.)
Courtesy of the Creede Historical Society

Early Day Creede Miners — Date Unknown (John
Jackson's grandfather, William T. Jackson, Sr., is third
from the right, bottom row.)
Courtesy of the Creede Historical Society

however, the workmen had to enter and leave their work place on
their own time. Prior to the passage of the law, workmen were
expected to put in ten- to twelve-hour days or more for their pay.
The smelter owners refused to pay the same wages for a reduced
work day, and the workmen struck. Over 700 men were idled at
Creede Camp during the strikes against the smelters that lasted from
June until late August 1899.[8]

The Western Federation of Miners was organized in 1893 and
quickly gained a stronghold in the San Juans. A local union from
Creede was one of the four from Colorado represented at the
Western Federation of Miners' organizational meeting in Butte,
Montana, May 1893. By the early 1900s, the Western Federation of
Miners had locals at Ophir, Henson (Lake City), Ouray, Rico,
Durango, Silverton, Ironton (Red Mountain), Telluride, Creede, and
Dunton, all in the San Juans.[9] Other Colorado locals were at Cripple
Creek and Leadville.

The first strike called by the Western Federation of Miners was
at Cripple Creek in 1894, and there the union established the reputation of being a violent organization. Dynamiting of mine property
and beatings of nonunion workers won the strike for the union. The
union's second strike in Leadville was not a success. The mine

owners were successful in reopening the mines with nonunion labor with the help of the Colorado state militia.

The union's reputation for being a violent organization was reaffirmed in Telluride during a 1901 strike. The mine owners hired nonunion miners to replace the striking miners. Both camps were armed and a battle between the two factions ended in three deaths and six serious injuries. The striking miners surrendered when promised fair treatment; however, many were forced to leave the region, some leaving on foot.[10]

After the strike, the owner of the Smuggler Mine was assassinated while he sat eating dinner with friends at his home — shot by an assassin through the dining room window. Charles A. Chase, manager of the Liberty Bell Mine at the time, felt he was a target for assassination and feared for his life. He changed his habit of walking to work to riding in a tram bucket for protection.[11]

The Western Federation of Miners adopted a resolution in 1903 empowering the executive board to call upon all unions of the organization to support a local union when necessary. Thus, the executive board was empowered to call out every union in its jurisdiction.[12]

Creede's Miners Union No. 20 went broke supporting a walkout at a Wyoming mine, likely as a result of the 1903 resolution. There was considerable ill will about the situation among the Creede miners, who vowed to run any union representative out of town in the future.[13]

In 1903 the Western Federation of Miners had established itself as the most militant labor union in American and had 180 locals located in most of the western states.[14] The union called a strike at Cripple Creek in 1903 that lasted a year and a half with a heavy toll in lives and property. Harry Orchard, a union organizer, blew up a train station in Independence, a mining town near Cripple Creek, killing thirteen nonunion miners and wounding others. This was the beginning of the end of the Western Federation of Miners. Miners Union No. 20 was active in Creede as late as 1907.

According to Al Birdsey, the building that was the Western Federation of Miners union hall in Creede was built in 1900. It is now called Pappy's Place and is located on the northern end of Creede Avenue. It was the residence of Byron "Pappy" Fairchild, Sr., for many years.

There are two sides to the Western Federation of Miners story. Many of the early-day mine owners and operators in the West were hard, ruthless, and well organized. The individual miners had little chance of upholding their rights. Striking miners were blacklisted and found it difficult, if not impossible, to find a job at another mine. Sometimes they were actually deported from the mining district. There were no safety laws, workmen's compensation, or state or federal laws to protect the miner.[15] It is no wonder that the mining industry faced serious labor strife!

The Colorado General Assembly passed a law in 1904 making it incumbent on employers to pay their employees at least every two weeks. The Commodore Mining Company posted notice that the regular payday would be on the fifth of each month, but those who desired their pay on the twentieth could call at the office and get it. On the morning of the twentieth, about twenty men called at the office and received their pay, accompanied by their time checks — the notice of their discharge. The discharged men asked their fellow miners to support a strike, but met with little encouragement.[16]

The Engineering and Mining Journal of July 3, 1926, had an article entitled "A Quarter Century of Mining Progress," describing improvements in mining during the past twenty-five years:

> *"The period shows marked improvement in labor, living, and general welfare conditions. The condition of the worker both in his home surroundings and in the mine and surface plants has been improved. Wages have increased. Safety and first-aid work, by enlisting the active co-operation of the workers, has made in numerous instances a reduction in the number of accidents. The Bureau of Mines has justified its existence by its leadership in this field. Industrial compensation laws has improved the status of the injured worker."*

MINERS COMPENSATION

Most of the mining at Creede Camp from 1900 until after the depression was done by leasing. Mining properties were leased by small companies or, in many cases, individual miners. The leases were set up to give the mine owners a percentage of the net smelter returns for the ore mined and smelted. The leasers bore all the costs of production, transportation, and smelting and had to accept the financial risks involved. Some of the companies and individuals leasing properties did very well, but most made the equivalent of wages or less. Leasing, like mining, was and is a very risky business.

A notice filed with the Colorado State Industrial Commission in 1922 set wages for Colorado metal miners at $4 per day effective

March 1, 1922. This applied to all the principal camps except Cripple Creek, where the scale was twenty-five cents less.[17]

The Emperius Mining Company used three methods for paying their miners — day's pay, contract mining, and leasing. Workmen providing services such as transporting ore out of and supplies into the mine and those working in the mill were paid by the day. In the early 1950s, the pay scale was $10 per day. The actual work of mining, such as driving drifts and excavating ore in the stopes, was done by contract — that is, payment for piece work such as driving a foot of drift of a certain size, mining a cubic foot of ore in a stope, etc. Skilled contract miners could increase their pay two- to three-fold by hard work and, in many cases, breaking or ignoring safety rules as described by the following story:

> *"Les Turnipseed and I [John Jackson] drove many thousands of feet of drifts and crosscuts in less than ideal conditions singlehanded. We both liked to work alone, and mucker drifts were prized by us because we could cycle a round in little over a half shift, giving us time for an evening fishing trip or hell raising if we could find someone to 'spit' (light the fuses) for us. Les was driving a crosscut during this period of 1951 and was unable to find anyone to spit for him, so he crawled up on a waste rock pile to sleep off a harrowing night. This happened to be the day that John 'Smiles' Doyle, state mine inspector, arrived to visit our workings. When he saw Les sprawled out he told the shift boss to let him sleep, but Les woke up and greeted them. This was an area of low oxygen, silica dust floating around, and generally poor ventilation. Smiles asked Les, 'Are you making lots of money?' Les replied, 'Yeah, I'm doing pretty good.' Smiles advised, 'Better save it, young fellow, because in 30 years or less you are going to be needing it.' Smiles was right."*[18]

Certain areas in the mine were leased out as previously described. Paul Davis described a lease he held with his brothers-in-law and the risks involved in leasing:[19]

> *"Woodrow Wintz, Alvie Wintz (my brothers-in-law), and I had a lease on the Archimedes claim in 1946 to 1948. We timbered the raise located on the end line of the Archimedes claim from Commodore No. 5 level to a point well above the Commodore No. 4 level, a distance of 450*

Creede Miners — circa 1936. From Left to Right: Clarence
Withrow, Noel Oates, Garry Marshall, Alvie Wintz
Courtesy of John Jackson

*feet. Not much of the Commodore No. 4 level was open, I
can't remember how much. I was drilling ore in the
Amethyst Vein, just above 4 level, one morning and Alvie
was working in the raise and had climbed down to the 4
level station for something. He heard some loose rock
falling in the raise below 4 level and got me out of the stope
I was working in. We went to the 4 level station and
decided to eat our lunch a little early and see what developed. There was no doubt there was enough movement in
the raise to alarm us. We scampered down the raise about
300 feet to E sublevel. We had about 100 tons of ore stored
between E sublevel and 4 level and thought if we pulled the
chute boards, transferring the ore between 5 level and E
level, the pressure on the timber might be relieved.
Whatever had been moving broke the timber and all 100
tons crashed past us and took all the timber out to 5 level.*

*"All three of us were broke. The company [Emperius
Mining Company] was good to us but would not let us re-
timber the raise again. We were allowed to start a new
raise on the Dean Fault about 100 feet in the hanging wall
from the Archimedes raise. The proposition was that we
would drive a three compartment raise, two ore passes,
one manway. The manway to be used by both the*

company and us, one ore pass for the company, one for us. The company paid us $7.00 per foot. We drove that raise 350 feet. One day when we were working in the new raise we heard a deep, powerful noise, a crack. There is no doubt that there had been movement along the Dean Fault. To my dying day I will wonder if the cause of the disaster in the Archimedes (Endline) raise was not the result of movement in the Amethyst fault."

The Homestake Mining Company's hourly rate for miners in 1985, when the mine closed, was $12.80 plus $4.20 in benefits. The average contract miner made $30 to $32 per hour and a few made much more.[20]

TRAMP MINERS

Tramp miners were common at Creede Camp into the 1950s. Tramp miners moved from mining camp to mining camp, many times following the weather — northern camps in the summer and southern camps in the winter. Miners who lived in Creede repeated this ditty about tramp miners:

Fred Gulzow — Mill Worker and Prospector
Courtesy of John Jackson

Creede Miners at Upper Amethyst — 1939. (L to R) Charles Slaght, Paul Davis, Woodrow Wintz, Pete Walker
Courtesy of John Jackson

Muckers come from Bisbee,
Timbermen come from Butte,
But it takes a miner from Creede
to keep muck in the chute.

The tramp miner worked at one mining camp until he had a stake large enough to get him to the next camp on his itinerary. He would then call the mine or "hole" he was working in "deep enough" or "deep enough and well timbered," then voluntarily quit to "tramp" to the next mine. These tramp miners helped disseminate new ideas and technology throughout the mining industry. Many times they solved problems at the mine where they were employed by applying knowledge they had gained at other mines. Unionization, technical changes, new laws, and efforts by mining companies to keep good miners, such as medical plans, vacations, and retirement plans, ended the day of the tramp miner.

MEMORIES OF MINERS AND MINES

John Jackson grew up and worked at Creede Camp. He shares the following memories of the miners and mines he knew so well:

"Born in the 1920s, I was with and around owner, leasers, and prospectors with mining interests during a bleak period in Creede's history, the town had less than 400 residents and fully a third of the houses were vacant. Both our neighbors, Ed Snow and Charles Matson, were old time miners and prospectors who did carpentry work, blacksmithed, or sharpened saws during the winter months then headed for the hills in the spring. It is inconceivable to adults of today that the gates of life were opened for youngsters, barely potty trained, to explore wherever their legs and abilities would carry them. I'm not sure our parents trusted us that fully or whether they just thought us expendable. I remember a time when brother Joel was overdue at the supper table and our parents showed some anxiety. Scooter and I had already decided which one of us would get his bed and his helping of tapioca pudding. We shared a bed and the thought of having a bed of one's own with an individual pillow overpowered any sentimental feelings. He returned, uninjured, and dashed our hopes.

"When morning chores were behind us we could hitch a ride with teamsters, Milton 'Tex' Allsworth or Witt

Thomas, who were hauling mine props to the Amethyst and Last Chance Mines, or we could ride up with Arthur Fairchild, who hauled ore with four horses drawing a wagon capable of holding two-and-one-half tons of ore. Art called my brother and I 'Scoot' and 'Scatter,' which pleased us, and he seated us on either side of him where he could put an arm around us and hold us on tight turns. Art and his son-in-law, Bill Kolisch, would later form the Creede Transportation Company and haul ore with Ford trucks moving four tons per load in grain beds. In 1939 they would convert to all-steel beds and trucks with two-speed rear ends that could carry upwards of five tons with ease, and Mineral County would be plowing roads with a Caterpillar RD-6 tractor dozer for winter operations.

"Our first dark hole ventures took us to prospects in the immediate Creede area. Windy Gulch, branching west from upper Creede, received much attention for its 'flat vein,' a horizontal stratum in the Creede Formation. Nearly all the holes on the north side of Windy Gulch were in the flat vein circling east and north to the Mustang lode near Commodore No. 3, where Fred Monkemeyer was tunneling in a promising stratum. Charles Matson's prospect was in Windy Gulch itself. These gentlemen preferred to be left alone at their labors, but, if needing a break, would share a story with us or let us pump the bellows that forced air to their forges lined with soft coal and glowing in the center to heat their hand steel and picks for sharpening and tempering.

"Arthur Leonard's prospect, in a gulch on the east side of Creede, was within our reach and on our route to Mr. Bessey's tunnel in the upper region of Dump Ground Gulch, where marcasite [iron sulfide] had replaced travertine. The Bessey prospect assayed only traces of precious metals. Explosive reports echoed in Dry Gulch, to the east, where loggers cutting mine props used up excess energy in a vain pursuit of riches.

"As our stature increased so did our kingdom, allowing us to visit Ben Birdsey's Clay Mine two miles south of Creede, where the first mechanical mucker [excavator] in the district was introduced and ran on rails. Ben had a crew of four men including his brother, Sam, who

improvised a Model A Ford engine with transmission on steel wheels to tram the bentonite from the mine. An air shaft had been driven to the surface to exhaust the fumes; however, all became ill with carbon monoxide poisoning and they returned to hand tramming. On one work day, Scooter and I happened by the air shaft, removed the lid where a pack rat had a nest on a timber, and began throwing rocks at the rat. This produced much activity in the mine where the rocks were narrowly missing the miners and swearing we rarely heard reached our ears. We replaced the lid and hurried on our way.

"*Norman Alspaugh was producing silver ore from the Wabash stope of the Moon Tunnel on Rat Creek under the Eads and Magnuson lodes of Monon Hill, with the help of a short crew and steam power to drills and pumps generated by a coal-fired steam engine. We weren't allowed underground, but there was excitement enough in the sounds and smells of the steam engine.*

"*The Silver Horde (Big Six) Tunnel, also of Monon Hill in Sunnyside proper, was in the development stage and off limits to us. Lew Bruns, James Oates, et al., were employed by a group of Denver financiers, including the Zangs, who formerly owned and operated a hotel in Creede and co-owned many Sunnyside properties.*

"*A half mile from the Moon Tunnel, up Rat Creek on the west side, Charles Lee was working his Sunnyside Tunnel to intersect a vein discovered by McKenzie [MacKenzie] in 1884. This tunnel would later be worked by Carl Stone and called the Cowboy Johnson Mine.*

"*A 16-inch diameter thin steel pipeline ran from a wooden dam near Weaver down the canyon and past the Nelson Tunnel to provide water for the great Humphreys reduction mill that was located on the west side of the junction of East and West Willow Creeks. If we couldn't catch a ride with the teamsters, we sometimes scaled the heights by walking up the pipe. This was a risky journey, as the pipe was suspended several feet from the ground in places and a slip would surely have injured one severely in a fall to the rocky bottom. It was a tremendous relief for me to reach solid ground where the canyon narrowed and I could step off.*

"At this time, 1934-35, Ben Miller had a crew working in the Last Chance No. 2 Level caved area, producing
high-grade silver as well as hoisting the ore Erick Nelson
was hand mining from a narrow vein he had leased on the
900-foot level. The ore was shipped to the American
Smelting and Refining Company at Leadville and hauled
with teams and wagons to a loading dock just above the
Humphreys Mill. To the northeast, Noel Roberts was
sinking an exploratory shaft above the Midwest Mine as
well as working his Sybil R. and Texas Girl claims that
would become steady producers in the 1940s and 1950s.

In East Willow Creek canyon Al Turnipseed, Eugene
Thom, and Lee Shillings were leasing the Mollie S. and
Eunice Mines, utilizing a short jigback tram line from the
Eunice workings to the Mollie S. ore bin and thence via a
multi-bucket tram line to a larger ore bin near creek level.
On a Sunday excursion, when the men weren't working,
we became tram operators. Les Turnipseed, son of Al, was
the brakeman, Bob Oates was in charge of dumping buckets, Ted Bucher, Scooter, and I were the muckers and loaders. Everything went smoothly until we overloaded a
bucket with waste pieces of steel and cast iron. Les wasn't
able to stop it at the unloading point where it left the cable
and tore out part of the superstructure. Bob jumped clear
just in time. Not only had we damaged the ore bin but we
had mixed waste rock and junk with the miners' high-
grade silver ore. We became persona non grata at the
Mollie S. Mine until it closed.

"A mile north of the Mollie S. lower bin on the west side
of the creek, Alec Duncan and John Nelson were tunneling
on the southerly extension of the Holy Moses Vein, supplied
with compressed air from the Ridge Mine/Mill complex to
run their rock drills. To the north of this tunnel a half mile,
Allen Hosselkus was working to get down to solid rock on
the Cliff claim, where he would later be joined by John
Nelson to sink a shaft on stringers of the Holy Moses Fault,
assaying well in silver and lead. Allen and John used a Model
T Ford truck to hoist sump buckets of rock broken by hand-
drilled holes and explosives. It was a lucky leaser who had
the advantage of compressed air and rock drills. In our visits
to the Last Chance and Amethyst Mines, steam engines were

still in use but the bulk of the mining was by hand, especially in caved areas where the most experienced miners worked fine ore from around large boulders. Noel Oates was an expert with a picky-poke, a pointed bar used to fashion holes for explosives, and could always find work where his expertise was needed.

"My first underground experience for pay was in the rehabilitation of the Commodore 5 level tunnel. Erick W. Nelson was mine manager at the time, my father, William T. Jackson, was the foreman of this phase, and the crew consisted of Charles Johnson, John Slater, Harry McClure, Gene McClure, Bernie Soward, Billy Weaver, and myself. Paul Davis was the company engineer and would survey and direct the linkup as well as add to the firm's holdings in a bitterly cold, snowy staking job with me as his chainman. The engineer's salary of that day was $150 per month and my helper's wage was $4 per eight-hour day.

"I would continue mining and leasing for another 24 years, during which a lease on the Holy Moses lode put me in proximity with a lease held by one of the finest miners and prospectors I have ever known. Alvin "Alvie" Wintz was working the Solomon-Ridge Mines to the south of me, and he was a living encyclopedia of East Willow Creek mines. He produced his ore with hand steel or drill, in good times or bad, with an optimism that infected all who shared that world of black holes. In 1945, a raging creek fed from deep snows swept part of the Ridge ore bin away and, with it, most of Alvie's high-grade ore. Lesser men would have thrown in the towel but Alvie, with the help of his wife, Edith, went back in the hole and recovered his loss."

Charles E. "Ed" Johnson worked in and around mines most of his life as did his father, Charlie Johnson, and his grandfather, Andy Dooley. Ed worked at Wagon Wheel Gap from December 1946 until May 1949. He was hired by the Emperius Mine on October 15, 1949. Ed left Creede and worked at other mines — the Climax Molybdenum Company's mine near Leadville, Colorado, and AMAX's Buick Mine in Missouri. These are Ed's memories of the miners he worked with at Wagon Wheel Gap and Creede:

"The Wagon Wheel Gap Fluorspar Mine operated three eight-hour shifts a day, six days a week. The miners

were Clarence (Kayo) Slaght, Hank Slaght, Joe Y. Vigil, Nick Martinez, Dave Fresquez, Joe Duran, Joe A. Vigil, Walter Duran, and Andy Pacheco. Miner's helpers were Jack Sword, Delmar Dale, and Milton Rogers. William C. "Scooter" Jackson, Donald Powell, and myself were the mule skinners that hauled ore from the mine to the mill.

"Firemen for the coal-fired boilers were Byron (Pappy) Fairchild, Arthur Swartzbeck, Shorty Hileman, Deacon Card, the interim minister of the Creede Congregational Church, and a man they called Hutch. Two of these were relief firemen.

"The mill operated the crusher three shifts per day and the jigs two shifts per day. Harry Larson, Johnny Wright, and Kenny Terrell ran the crusher. The jig men were O.B. (Ben) Helmick and Felix Lovato. There were three truck drivers, Byron Fairchild, Jr., Jess Walker, and Winfred (Windy) Keeling. They hauled ore and coal, graded roads, and framed timber sets for the mine.

"Billy Bond, Art Davis, and a boy called Bob (last name unknown) were ore sorters. Bill Kroll was the underground timberman. Clem Rhodes was day foreman and Frank (Slim) Anderson was night foreman in the mill. Ora Platz was the Diesel operator and blacksmith. Ernest Booth was the resident book keeper and paymaster. James Whitney was the resident manager.

"On October 15, 1949 I was hired by the Emperius Mining Company as a day's pay trammer at $1.10 per hour by I.D. Crawford, mine foreman. I was green and not knowledgeable at this job but knew that you must clean the track and put oil on track curves to make the job easier. I worked about a week assisting Lynn (Chappie or Key) LeZotte. Chappie was beastly afraid of dynamite, so I did all of the blasting of boulders in chutes that wouldn't come through (secondary blasting).

"After about a week of tramming to the Northwest Raise, an ore pass on the Amethyst property, Floyd (Zero) Ott asked if I would tram for him two days a week on contract, which was okayed by I.D. Crawford. Ott, Harry (Red) Marshall, and Leo Brenner were working a 250-foot long stope with a vein ranging from six to 10 foot wide south of No. 3 Raise from Commodore No. 5 level

to *Amethyst 1100 level, and it would top out on Amethyst 800 level on the south side of No. 3 Raise.*

"I drove 50 feet of drift with the old crank Leyner drifter with a four foot steel change on Amethyst 800 level, using an air slusher and a one-half ton car for mucking. I worked 57 shifts on that contract and made $95! Not much pay but a good lesson. Eugene Dooley was finishing up a small stope on the Robinson property. This was from 1100 level to 900 level with a small pillar separating Amethyst and Robinson properties.

"North of Dooley's stope was another one being driven from 1100 to 900 levels by Dick Walker and a man named Jimmy Mitchell. Jimmy had only one hand and on his right arm was a metal hook that served as his hand. A stoper was rigged so he could use it with one hand and the hook.

"Before tungsten carbide bits came into use, the miners used conventional steel bits, which were sent out when dull in a 50-pound carbide can. These cans were sent to the Emperius Mill where William Swinehart ground them and sent them back each morning. This stimulated the hiding of steel and bits at the end of the shift so no one would steal your steel and bits.

"I trammed for several months for Woodrow Weaver and Fred Lane, the last stope from 100 to 900 levels on the Robinson claim. At one time I was on three contracts each week — Ott's for $18 per shift, Mirchell's for $16 per shift and Weaver and Lane's at $14 per shift. This made it a lot better than tramming on company time at $1.10 per hour. All of these stopes were shrinkage stopes and only enough muck was pulled from the stope so that the drillers had room below the solid ore to drill the next round.

"Number 4 and 5 Raises separated the Robinson property from the Texas Girl claim, a claim leased from Noel Roberts by the Emperius Mining Company. John Jackson and his brother Billy [Scooter] Jackson did some stoping between Commodore 5 level and 1100 level on the Robinson claim. George Logue and Walt Randolph worked a similar stope on the same level but on the north side of the Northwest Raise on the Amethyst property. Bobby Oates and Woodrow Wintz drove one-half of 5 Raise between the Texas Girl and Robinson claims. The

Rowe brothers, three of them, drove 5 Raise for some 60 feet and I drove it on through to 900 level. I fell 50 feet when my platform broke, but I was unhurt. After the experience, I never went back there again.

"At this time Tommy Phillips and Herbert Lyn (Pee Wee) Hutchinson were driving a raise on the OH Vein from Commodore 5 level, and just north of them Leroy Brown and Leslie Turnipseed were driving an open stope from the same level and mucked it with a B-12 mucking machine.

"George Kershner and Donald Powell were the two motormen. George Kershner was the motorman each day while mucking the main heading. Ernest Egan and Charles Slaght started Number 4 and 5 Raises (three compartments), two man ways and an ore pass in the middle.

"Charles Slaght and young Byron (Barney) Fairchild drove the main heading for a half year, then Leslie Turnipseed drove the main heading for quite a long time. They used an Ingersol six-foot shell, automatic Leyner using two changes of steel from a post and saddle arm setup. One eight-foot round four days a week and the fifth day was for laying track and putting in air and water pipe.

"John Nelson, John Slater, Alex Johnson, Charles A. Johnson (brothers from Alamosa) worked in the outside shops. Charles G. Johnson [Ed Johnson's father] was outside timberman. Pappy Fairchild and John Van Buskirk were ore sorters in the Commodore No. 5 ore bin. Compressors were outside and gas driven while I was there, then later on they were moved inside and were electrically driven.

"To the best of my knowledge all the men named in this entry are deceased except John Jackson, Leslie Turnipseed, Lawrence Potts, Gene Dooley, and myself. All are in their late 70s or early 80s age wise.

"Leonard (Pug) Sutherland, Melvin (Red) Johnson, and Paul (Shorty) Dunkel also worked this area but are also deceased."

Charles Melbye, president of Minerals Engineering Company in the early 1970s, relates this story about the dangers of having long hair, very popular at the time, while using rotating machinery:

"When we were operating, some of the young miners were wearing their hair very long, which is dangerous around machinery. I mentioned this to Gene Wardell, and he was after them, but they had not yet responded. One day, one of the young miners was operating a stoper drill in a stope, and his hair caught in the rotating drill steel. It tore out over half the man's hair by the roots. That evening, without any further urging, they all went down to the barber and had a haircut."

MINERS AND WILDLIFE

The topic "Miners and Wildlife" does not refer to Saturday nights and saloons that were well represented in the town of Creede. It does refer to the relationship between Creede miners and creatures of the wild as related by John Jackson.

"Miners appeared to have a special knack for taming feathered and furred creatures. No prospect hole was completely settled until Canadian Jays (camp robbers) and squirrels were scurrying around begging for handouts. Miners, though dirt poor for the most part, were notorious for sharing their lunches with creatures of the wild.

"A nearly blind prospector on Miner's Creek, north of Sunnyside, had several camp robbers in his menagerie that he had tamed and named. They were on his shoulders, knees, and even perched on his hat at feeding time. Mr. LeFefvre greeted them from a chair by his cabin where he tucked bits of bread under his collar, up the sleeves of his shirt, and in the crease of his hat. The birds unerringly found it all and seemed to enjoy the game.

"Sam Birdsey and his sons, Norman and Rocky, rescued a calf elk from starvation one winter. Before it had recovered enough to return to the herd, Sam had taught it to gently pull nourishing pellets from his lips.

"Art Davis and Scooter Jackson had a unique rapport with animals, and the meaner or gruffer one sounded, the more the creatures vied for their attention. Art had a pet chipmunk at the Phoenix Mine that would ride his hand to his mouth as he was taking bites from a sandwich with the chipmunk filling his jaws at the same time. One day the chipmunk must have felt that Art was getting more

than his share and he bit him on his index finger as a warning. William C. "Scooter" Jackson was the only miner I know to have successfully coaxed a pika (rock rabbit) to lunch. While we were sinking a winze in the Holy Moses Mine, he spent nearly an entire year during noon break gaining the confidence of the young pika. While it would never clamber over him as the chipmunks did, it would eat from his hand and stand its ground as long as I remained still.

"Monte Jay Larson loaded his pie can with unshelled peanuts for his pet pack rat in the Commodore ore bin, and God help the person who mistreated any of the creatures.

"Pack rats were generally welcome underground and our Bondholder tunnel housed one of the cleanest and most amusing pack rats that I encountered in all my

mining experiences. Gene Wardell and I were driving an exploratory crosscut to intersect silver veins at a higher level from the tunnel. We had timbered loose ground just inside the portal and a pack rat immediately took up residency with a nest of spruce bough tips and cones. We called our new partner 'Zeke' and marveled at his intelligence. As soon as Zeke smelled fuse smoke, he jumped on the elevated air line and ran out to a hole in side cribbing until the smoke cleared from the

William C. "Scooter" Jackson at the Holy Moses Mine — 1954 (Note that Scooter has a chipmunk by his neck, on his knee, and in his pie can.)

Photo by John Jackson

explosions. At night he would work his way into the compressor building where he arranged short ends of fuses, nuts, bolts, and small cones in a neat, orderly row along a bench. Zeke loved to get on the valve cover of the Diesel engine and let the fan blow dust from his coat of fur. When we shut down, after mucking out, for lunch, he went from the engine to his place of importance by our bench where we fed him. He especially liked lettuce and onion greens. His perch on the valve cover proved to be his undoing. A bit of tail and a piece of fur on the shroud, noticed on shutting down the engine, told me Zeke had journeyed too close to the fan. We found our pack rat in the nest, mortally wounded, and on closer examination our Zeke was a lady.

"While driving the Midwest tunnel, we ate near the timber pile on warm days, where both chipmunks and ground squirrels found safety and handouts. Jim Morrow and Sid Samuels, miners, tied two hard-cased cookies with holes in their middle on the ends of a 10-foot length of heavy string and threw the works out to waiting squirrels. There was a tug of war for nearly 10 minutes around the area before a camp robber winged in, ran the squirrels off, and flew off with the prize.

"The following account doesn't qualify as a miner's pet story but it serves to illustrate that miners must be prepared for any eventuality on entering a dark hole. In 1948, Gavin Skinner and I were leasing a block of ground on Amethyst 500 level using the straight 1,000-foot long 500 level tunnel for access. It was in May and West Willow Creek was still roaring from its high level of the night as we walked the trestle above the creek. I was in the lead, we were equipped with carbide lamps which, if you kept the reflector polished, could spotlight 25 feet in advance. It was with this spot that I saw a lone eye barely above track level and it scared me. Gavin ran into me when I stopped and I pointed out the problem. Closer examination found a very large and battered beaver who had his home washed out by high water that ground and bumped him along the channel until he found refuge in the tunnel some 700 feet from the portal. Hide was missing, one eye was swollen shut, he was angry and not about to be displaced again. Gavin thought

Dick Lehman, I.D. Crawford, Shifters, and Erick Nelson, Assistant General Manager, Emperius Mining Company — 1942
Courtesy of the Colorado Mining Association

he could rope him and lead him out to the creek, where he could return to the meadows above and start life over. We retrieved a rope from the ore bin; Gavin made a passable loop and at the first throw it came back considerably shorter, another loop, another throw. The old boy still had sharp teeth. To shorten the story, I won't go into the many ideas that scared hell out of both of us. Finally, with Gavin shining his light in the beaver's one good eye, I was able to take a running leap over his head and with Gavin leading the way we managed to move him slowly from the tunnel and along the bank to calmer waters, where he could soak his wounds."

UNDERGROUND LIGHTING

Even on the darkest night there are light sources, however dim, where most people work and live. The lack of light underground is absolute — a complete darkness that can only be experienced by being underground without artificial light. Prior to 1900, miners had only candles or oil lamps to light their way underground and their work places. By 1890, oil lamps had been essentially replaced by candles in the western mines. The miner's candlestick, most likely an adaptation of the colonial candlestick, was made of wrought iron and consisted of a handle or loop leading to a spike designed to insert into a timber or crack in the rock, a candle thimble or clip to hold the candle, and a hook to hang it. The safety lamp that was designed to detect methane was not used in hard rock mines, such as those at Creede Camp where methane did not occur.

The carbide lamp was introduced about 1900 but did not become popular as a source of lighting in mines until 1910.[21] The first carbide lamps were carried by miners and later were designed to be attached to "hard boiled" safety hats worn by the miners. The carbide lamp burned acetylene gas produced by adding water to

W.L. Anderson, Mill Superintendent, Emperius Mining Company — 1942
Courtesy of the Colorado Mining Association

calcium carbide. The lamp consisted of two closed compartments, an orifice, a flint lighter, and a reflector. The bottom compartment contained calcium carbide and the top compartment water. An adjustable needle valve dripped water onto the carbide and acetylene gas was the result of the chemical reaction when the two combined. The gas was forced through the orifice in the center of the reflector, where it was lit by the miner who cupped his hand over the reflector to contain the gas as he struck the flint. Carbide lights had to be recharged several times during a shift. Miners kept a piece of fine window screen wire attached to their lamps to ream the orifice when it plugged up and doused the light, sometimes at the most inopportune moment. Carbide lamps were being used at Creede Camp into the 1950s, even after electric cap lamps were available.

Electric cap lamps are superior in most respects to the carbide lamp — no open flame, no potential for burning one's arms, much better light, no fumes or production of carbon dioxide. The electric cap lamp attaches to the miner's safety hat and is powered by an alkaline battery strapped to a lamp belt worn by the miner. There was one definite disadvantage to the electric cap lamp at Creede Camp. It did not burn with a reddened flame or go out in "bad" air like the carbide lamp!

Miners typically dumped the depleted residue, slaked lime, from their lamps at their work place. The residue sometimes reached the mill with the ore and created problems in the milling circuit. The mill superintendent gave lectures to the miners in the early 1950s to NOT dump spent carbide into the ore.

WORKING CONDITIONS

Emmons and Larsen described mining techniques used in the Creede Camp mineral deposits in 1923:

> "Conditions are favorable for cheap mining, as the veins are nearly everywhere of good width. They have been subjected to very extensive fracturing and crushing, so that much of the work has been done with pick and shovel. Much ore in one of the largest stopes was run out or 'milled' from the bottom without previous blasting or breaking. At present nearly all the stoping is done with hand drills. Owing to the fractured condition of the rock the miners find their labor lighter than in many neighboring districts." [22]

The fractured condition of the rock may have made the Creede Camp miner's work easier than in other mining districts, but Creede had a problem with "bad" or "gassy" air that many camps did not have. Bad or gassy air is oxygen-deficient air that issues from openings in the vein structures during periods of low barometric pressure and contains mainly nitrogen with little oxygen. A study of the oxygen-deficient air, or gas, was made in 1903 by Harry A. Lee. The gas is lighter than normal air and is found in the top parts of the workings. The gas is colorless, warm, and is said by some to have a sweetish taste. An analysis of the gas showed ninety-six per cent nitrogen and four per cent oxygen by volume. [23]

The northern section of the Amethyst Vein where ventilation was not good was particularly susceptible to the problem of oxygen-deficient air that at times prevented access to the mine workings. Paul Davis wrote about the problem in the 1940s:

> "Oxygen deficient air in some parts of the mine was a real problem. As I recall, the miners working in drifts off the Albion and Winchester cross cuts at one time were furnished with candles which could burn for eight hours. The candle was lit when the miner got to his face (working location) and if and when the candle went out the miner

was to do the same. In those days only carbide miners lamps were used. As the oxygen supply decreased the flame on the carbide lamp got shorter and redder until it finally went out. One paid attention as it was not a good situation to be a mile or so underground with no light and no life-sustaining air."[24]

In the 1950s, miners tramming ore through certain drifts during periods of low barometric pressure would place candles along the way and if they started going out, it was time to leave the area. One miner told of attaching an air hose to his clothing while lighting or "spitting" dynamite fuses so he would have air to breathe while doing the work. Surveying inactive workings took special precautions. The first surveyor advancing into the inactive area would wear a carbide lamp and the surveyor following had an electric camp lamp. If the carbide lamp indicated gassy conditions, both surveyors would then have an electric light to get out.[25]

The oxygen-deficient air not only affected the miners but also the horses and mules used to haul ore trains out of the mines. John Jackson relates :

"In 1944, Minnie Pearl, a female mule, was first employed in the Amethyst Tunnel but stood two hands taller than the horses and was transferred to the more spacious Commodore 5 Tunnel. Before her transfer she was being used by Dick Lehman on the outer haul. At 3 vein switch the loaded train was late and Dick went south to help in loading from the chutes. Minnie Pearl became lonesome and wandered along the Albion drift to the north trending 580 drift and followed it to its end where she patiently waited as Dick searched first outside and then frantically looked for tracks of her shoes. When he found her, the carbide lamp on her harness was burning very low and Minnie Pearl was even lower from the oxygen-depleted air in the dead end."[26]

The Homestake Mining Company resolved their oxygen-deficient air problem by installing a forced air system at the Bulldog Mountain Mine, as described in Chapter Fifteen.

The miner's life was not easy under the best of conditions, as related by Paul Davis, who came to Creede in February 1940. Paul remembers his first mining job at 50 1/2 cents an hour:[27]

"In the summer of 1938 I worked as a mucker in the Idaho Maryland Mine in Grass Valley, California. [Simply put, a 'miner' drills and blasts ore and a 'mucker' shovels it into a mine car.] This was a period during the Great Depression and jobs were hard to find and hold. In this active mining area there were many Cornish miners who definitely had an advantage in getting jobs. My work was on the 900 foot level mucking 15 tons of broken ore each day plus laying plats, extending rail, tramming [pushing mine cars by hand] to an ore pass [a near vertical opening leading to an ore chute on a lower level in the mine], and helping my miner set up and tear down the drill, load dynamite into the holes, and blast. The next day we would switch headings, he would drill the heading I had mucked the day before and I would muck the heading he had drilled and blasted the day before.

"The shift boss took me to my work place the first day and showed me what was to be done, then pointed to a shovel and stated that it was my partner. His statement as he left was, 'When I come around I expect to see only ass and elbows and they had better be moving.' In those days there was no requirement that two men had to work together underground and it was necessary to learn to do many things alone.

"I worked at the Smuggler Union Mine at Telluride when the company was paying miners $4 and muckers $3.50 a day. From there I went to Creede, where underground miners were getting $4 a day and those on contract were doing much better."

Mary Midkiff Johnson came to Creede in the 1940s for a vacation and never left. She married a Creede miner and has lived in Creede since. Her first husband passed away and she remarried, another miner named Ed Johnson. This is a story about her first husband:[28]

"Every time I see a lot of snow or below zero weather here in our little town of Creede, it brings back memories of the early 1940s and all the men who worked in the mines and the conditions they worked under.

"Most all of the miners rode the 'crummy' to work from town and paid $7 a month for the privilege. A

'crummy' was a pickup with a canvas top over the bed in which the miners rode. The ride during the summer was not bad, but during the winter months, the ride was miserably cold. As the 'crummies' would come to town after work, the men would jump off at the bars in town for a 'couple of warmers,' as they called their drinks. Most of the wives would have the wood stoves going hot and a big pot of coffee on the back of the stove. As the men entered the house, their clothes would be frozen from the waist down.

"I would put newspapers on the floor in front of the stove for my husband's clothes to thaw out while he was drinking coffee and telling of his day's work (mostly cussing). I always had a washtub sitting in the kitchen full of hot water for his bath and clean clothes to wear before supper. In 1945 I had a bathroom built which made this much easier. As long as the cold spells lasted, this was an everyday occurrence for not only me, but several other ladies in town. We did feel sorry for these frozen miners, but it was a way of life.

"My husband, Howard, had an uncle that everyone called 'Uncle Bud,' but his real name was Rufus Moore. In the bitter cold weather he would stop at our house on the way home just to sit on the floor by the kitchen stove, just to 'thaw-out' before going home.

"Uncle Bud, Snuffy [Oates], George, and Cherokee, all miners now deceased, would wait for spring to head up to Snuffy's claim and throw one big running drunk! Uncle Bud had a green Model A Ford truck that would go anywhere and it came back to town looking like it had been everywhere. After their drunk was over, they went back to work and they were very nice people to know."

Most mines are equipped with a "dry," where the miners can change from their street clothes into their work clothes, or "diggers," before their work shift begins. After work, the dry is used for a shower and to change back into street clothes. The dry is equipped with a shower room, lockers for the miners' street clothes, and baskets hung from the ceiling for dirty and/or wet "diggers." There is also a lamp room where lamps are furnished to the miners. There is no record of any mining company at Creede Camp providing a dry facility for their miners until Homestake's Bulldog Mountain Mine.

Mining towns had more bars and outlets for alcohol per capita than most towns and cities. Those who worked in the mines drank to excess to forget their working conditions and the hazards of mining. This certainly was and is a negative consequence of mining. The following story may help one understand why alcohol use was greater in mining towns:[29]

> "One of the first 'DO NOTS' impressed on aspiring miners of my age during their first shift underground was: 'Don't ride the skip buckets. Use the ladders. If I catch you riding a bucket to your level, you will be fired on the spot' — orders straight from the shifter's [shift boss'] mouth. Later, as you were tramming ore or hooking buckets, a slow traveling bucket would come into view and riding on the lip would be that same shifter.
>
> "Eugene 'Gene' Dooley started work in the Amethyst Mine in the late 1940s on 500 level with most of the ore being hoisted from winzes bottoming on the 900 level. Gene was a maverick and, though being warned about riding sump buckets, couldn't resist saving time and energy by hopping one up or down during the working day. He was on his way to 700 level to tram and upon arriving at the Albion winze a bucket was just being lowered, so Gene stepped on the lip of the bucket, grasped the cable, and was on his way without the hoistman's knowledge. The Albion winze changed dip [slope] about halfway down where the wooden skids guided the bucket in another direction. The bucket was moving downward with considerable speed when it made the flop over, for which Gene was totally unprepared. As luck would have it for an Irishman, the head of a spike protruded from an inner skid enough to snag the strap on one side of Gene's overalls and kept him from a bumpy, splintery ride the remainder of the distance. I don't remember whether he extricated himself or managed to hop the loaded bucket on its return, but he is still with us."

THE MINING CYCLE

The mining cycle for all types of underground mining consists of four basic functions: 1) drilling; 2) blasting; 3) mucking and tramming; and 4) supporting the newly mined opening as required. Drilling is making the holes in the rock in which explosives are placed; blasting is the process of placing and setting off the explosives to break the rock or ore; and mucking and tramming is the work of removing the broken rock or ore. Supporting the newly mined area first means the removal of loose rock and slabs that could be an immediate safety hazard and then using timber or rock-bolts or other support methods to make the opening safe. Then the mining cycle is repeated. Each of these phases has its own risks and is described as it developed through Creede Camp's century of mining.

DRILLING

Drilling at the beginning was done by hand that continued into the 1940s.[30] Four basic tools were used in the early-day drilling process at Creede Camp: 1) a "picky poke;" 2) a Johnson bar called a "bull prick"by the miners; 3) a singlejack hammer weighing approximately four pounds; and 4) a doublejack hammer weighing approximately eight to ten pounds. The miner's salutation, "tap 'er light," was coined during the era of hand drilling. The salutation means "don't hit the drill too hard," or "take it easy."

The picky poke and Johnson bar were unique to Creede Camp. As Emmons and Larsen stated, the rock along the veins was fractured and in many places the ore was crushed with plentiful mud seams. The picky poke, a long 1/2-inch diameter steel bar with one sharpened end that was bent at a thirty- to forty-degree angle about three inches from the end, was used by the miners to pick and poke holes into hard, but crushed, ore zones. The Johnson bar was a long steel tapered bar with a sharpened end. It was driven by a hammer into mud seams to make a hole and had lugs so that it could be hammered out of the hole if necessary.[31]

John Jackson remembers Noel "Snuffy" Oates, a Cousin Jack who was famed for working high grade from the great Commodore cave above the 300-foot level with a picky poke and a mountain of nerve:

> *"Snuffy liked to mine alone while in the cave working his picky poke to create holes for explosives, but he always had a helper near his working area with the explosives and to run for help if Snuffy's luck ran out. My brother, Joel, worked with Snuffy for a few weeks. On his first shift with Snuffy, they were climbing up a ladder with Snuffy in the lead. After they had climbed about 50 feet Snuffy stopped and told Joel, 'Hold up a minute, lad, I*

have to wind my watch, count me money, and take a leak.' So here's Joel, first day underground, thinking this old picky poke miner is going to wet all over him. He needn't have worried, Snuffy initiated all of his new helpers in the same manner."[32]

The singlejack hammer was swung by one man who held the hammer in one hand and a drill steel in the other. The doublejack hammer was swung by one man using both hands against a drill steel held by a second miner. Thus the reasoning behind the names — singlejack, one hand; doublejack, both hands. Drilling by single or doublejack hammers was a skill that took time to master. The singlejack hammer handle generally had a hole drilled through its free end in which was inserted a leather loop. This loop or thong allowed the miner to open his hand on the back swing to relax it while the thong held the hammer. Drill steel used in hand drilling was generally 5/8-inch in diameter and came in varied lengths, starting at about eight inches long. The bit end of the drill steel was chisel-shaped and the bit had to be turned while being hammered so that a round hole resulted.

Singlejack drilling was practical in softer rocks to a depth of about three feet. Doublejack drilling was used for deep holes or very hard rock. A horizontal hole was drilled at about half the speed of a vertical hole and up holes, or "uppers," were drilled at a speed considerably less than horizontal holes.[33]

Piston drills, or "sluggers," were introduced into the mining industry about the turn of the century. Steam "sluggers" were used to drive the first 1,000 feet of the Reynolds (Commodore No. 5) Tunnel in 1896. These drills used a piston actuated by steam to hammer a large non-rotating bit into the rock. The star-shaped bit was three inches in diameter and lasted for only two feet of drilling before it had to be sharpened. As one can imagine, a steady stream of steel and bits was required to keep the "sluggers" at work. Good blacksmiths were worth their weight in gold, as the sharpening of these bits required considerable metallurgical knowledge and skill. First, the bits were heated in a furnace to a malleable state, then swaged to the required dimensions and sharpness by hand, and finally tempered to withstand drilling without chipping from being too brittle or losing sharpness or gauge too fast from being too soft — a real challenge to the art of blacksmithing. The chief drawback to the piston drill was the high inertia of the piston assembly due to the heavy weight of the firmly attached drill steel and bit. This arrangement required heavy mountings and powerful machines. Piston drills were very heavy, clumsy, and hard to set up for drilling.[34]

Miners had a need for a lighter drill machine that was more easily handled than the "slugger," particularly in workings where access was limited. The hammer type of drill with hollow drill steel was invented by J.G. Leyner in 1897, but it did not become established until some years later. The hammer drill's success was based on a shuttling piston powered by compressed air that hammered a separate drill steel and bit. This feature made the Leyner drill lighter and much easier to handle than the piston drill. Beginning in 1905, it rapidly displaced the piston drill. The "stoper" drill was introduced in 1906 and the jackhammer or small hand-held type of drill in 1909, but they did not come into general use until 1912.[35]

The Leyner drill, or "drifter," was mounted on a shell and was moved forward and backward by a hand-cranked screw feed. The

drill with its shell was mounted on a horizontal arm that was clamped to a vertical column. The vertical column was placed in the center of the drift or tunnel and wedged tightly against the back of the opening. The arm could be moved up and down along the column by the clamps. Holes were drilled on one side of the face and then the arm was turned 180 degrees so that the holes on the other side could be drilled. Setting up a column and arm and drifter required, in the words of one miner, the efforts of "two men and a boy."

Stoper Drill at the Creede Mining Museum — circa 1990

Photo by Will Foreman

The "stoper" was so named because it was initially used for stoping in Colorado mines, where the drilling of up holes was required. It consists of a hammer drill solidly attached to an air leg that could be extended by the miner to hold the drill against the back or top of the stope. The initial stoper drill used a solid drill steel and, as a result, created clouds of small, sharp rock particles in the air around the miner using the drill. This rock dust, as it was breathed into the lungs, caused a terrible condition called silicosis or "miner's consumption." In fact, the stoper drill was given the name "widow maker" or worse by the miners. Even though it was successful mechanically, it was rejected until its design was modified for use with hollow drill steel, which allowed water to be introduced into the hole to eliminate the dust problem.

Drilling for drifting at Wagon Wheel Gap was done with a jackhammer mounted on a piece of 1 1/2-inch pipe to form a leg, called a "Mexican setup," probably because it was first used in Mexican mines. One person would sit on top of a set up and push with his feet while the other would lay his body against the pipe. A drift round at Wagon Wheel Gap consisted of sixteen four-foot holes. The Mexican setup was the predecessor of the jackleg drill. The fluorspar ore was drilled with stoper drills. The mine drifts at the Gap were all timbered and the holes were drilled between the lagging (three-inch boards overhead between timber sets on four-foot centers) so that the miners were always under timber for safety. It took an armload of drill steel and bits to drill six holes eight feet deep. The bits were sharpened by the blacksmith using a forge and an air hammer.[36]

The jackleg drill was developed in Europe in the early 1940s and was probably the greatest improvement in mining drills ever made. These drills maintained the flexibility of a hand-held drill and the jackleg allowed the drill to be heavier and more powerful. The jackleg itself is an air cylinder attached to the drill with a swivel connection and the piston rod is connected to a spiked foot plate that could be anchored behind a solid object on the floor of the opening. The jackleg provides support for the drill and forward thrust to keep the drill bit against the rock.[37]

The jackleg drills came to Creede Camp in the late 1940s and were nicknamed "Swede hammers" by the miners, since they were imported from Sweden. What a relief to the miners to be able to carry a much lighter seventy- to eighty-pound jackleg drill to the work face and immediately start drilling, as opposed to setting up a column and arm and drifter weighing well over 200 pounds and repositioning the drill for each hole during the drilling process. Another innovation, the tungsten carbide rock bit, which replaced steel bits that dulled rapidly, was introduced about the same time as the jackleg. These two innovations, the jackleg drill and the tungsten carbide bit, revolutionized mining at Creede Camp and elsewhere.

Jackleg drills used at Homestake's Bulldog Mountain Mine had a feature not normally found on a jackleg — backstroke rotation that allowed easier recovery of the drill steel after the hole is completed. This feature was made necessary by the unconsolidated nature of the ore.[38]

Homestake introduced modern mining machinery such as the "Alimak raise climber," the "raise borer," and the "drill jumbo" to Creede Camp. These improvements certainly made the miner's life easier! The Alimak raise climber, first developed in Finland, is a platform that rides on a track bolted to the side of the raise and is driven up or down by a cogged wheel system. This provides an easy, safe way for the miners to access the top of the raise and eliminates the need for timbering and ladders. The raise borer is patterned after tunnel boring machines and is capable of boring vertical or near vertical openings. The drill jumbo consists of a track- or rubber tire-mounted carriage equipped with one or more hydraulic booms that provide a stable base for drifter hammer drills equipped with automatic feed controls. With a drill jumbo, a single miner can operate more than one drill at the same time.[39]

Jackleg Drill at the Creede Mining Museum — circa 1990
Photo by Will Foreman

Drill Jumbo at
the Bulldog
Mountain Mine
— circa 1969
*Courtesy of
Sandy Kroll*

BLASTING

An old miner's saying states: "There are old powdermen and there
are bold powdermen, but there are no old, bold powdermen." A
"powderman" is a miner who handles explosives. The term "powder" as a name for explosives began when black blasting powder was
used. The use of explosives was a hazardous occupation at Creede
Camp. *The Engineering and Mining Journal's* March 18, 1899, issue
had this news item: "Commodore — An explosion of several hundred pounds of powder in this company's No. 2 Tunnel at Creede did
considerable damage to the mine and killed four men."

Black powder was first invented by the Chinese centuries ago
but was first used in mining about 1613 in Saxony. By 1689, black
powder was being used in the Cornish mines and remained the
explosive in general use in mining until the advent of dynamite.
Dynamite was developed by Alfred Nobel in Sweden about 1868. It
is a mixture of nitroglycerin and an neutral absorbent that creates a
relatively insensitive high explosive that can be detonated by a blasting cap. Nobel also invented the first reasonably safe and efficient
blasting cap, a metal capsule about 1/4-inch in diameter by two
inches long, filled with fulminate of mercury, that could be set off by
a spark from a safety fuse. In later years, the mercury compound
was replaced by lead azide to make a safer blasting cap. Safety fuse

was invented in 1851 by William Bickford and was first used in the Cornish mines to set off black powder. The Nobel Peace Prize was created by Alfred Nobel, the inventor of dynamite.[40]

In the early days of Creede Camp, dynamite had a serious problem — freezing. Nitroglycerin, the liquid component of dynamite used at the time, has a high freezing point, about fifty-two degrees Fahrenheit. Dynamite could be thawed with precautions, but if the precautions were disregarded, the consequences could be fatal. It was not until 1925 that the freezing problem was solved by the addition of a freezing point depressant to the nitroglycerine.[41]

The winters at Creede Camp were long and bitterly cold and this meant frozen dynamite. At least two special dynamite thawing facilities were built along the Amethyst Vein near the early mines at Creede Camp. One was west of the Commodore No. 4 Level and the other 2,000 to 3,000 feet further north. The northerly one was nearly gone in the 1980s. The facility at Commodore No. 4 was constructed of 1 x 12-inch lumber and was about 15 x 25 feet in size. At one end was a fireplace built of concrete and masonry. The fireplace had wells in the mantle that held boxes of dynamite for thawing. A metal bucket and mechanism was used to lower the boxes into the wells. Lore had it that one person only thawed the dynamite, which arrived frozen and very sensitive. After thawing, it was trammed underground for use.[42]

Dynamite, blasting caps, and safety fuse were used at Creede Camp for most of its history, probably until the Bulldog Mountain Mine was opened. Homestake Mining Company introduced more modern blasting techniques such as electric blasting and the use of a less sensitive explosive, ammonium nitrate-fuel oil mixture (ANFO), that could be injected into drill holes by compressed air. These methods greatly reduce the risks of blasting. Unfortunately, Homestake had to return to the use of dynamite to blast the ore because of its porous nature, but the use of ANFO continued in excavations away from the veins.[43] The use of dynamite, blasting caps, and safety fuse is described in the following paragraphs.

Dynamite cartridges, or "sticks," generally 1 1/8 inches in diameter by eight inches long in a treated paper wrapper, were inserted into the holes and tamped into place by the use of a wooden tamping stick to eliminate the chance of a spark that could cause a premature explosion. The second stick of dynamite placed into the hole had a blasting cap inserted into it and was called the primer. The primer was tamped into place with extra care and, perhaps, a little prayer. The miner then inserted as many additional sticks of dynamite as he felt was necessary to break the rock.

The blasting cap was attached to a length of safety fuse by "crimping" before it was inserted into the primer. The square-cut end of the safety fuse was carefully pushed into the metal capsule of the blasting cap to contact the detonating compound, and the end of the capsule was then crimped to the safety fuse to form a tight connection. The act of "crimping" was originally performed by miners with sometimes serious accidents. Later the function was performed in a central location with equipment designed to protect the crimper against premature explosions. The caps with attached fuses were then given to the miners.

A "round" is a series of drill holes designed to advance a tunnel, drift, shaft, winze, or raise or to break ore in a stope. The center holes in the round, called the "cut," when blasted provide a free face for the rest of the holes to break to. These center holes are drilled in a specific pattern to form a V-cut, a box-cut, a burn-cut, etc., as determined by the rock type. Creede miners used a "no cut" round to blast the ore wherever possible, using the natural fractures and fissures as the free face. Holes in a round were blasted in sequence. As an example: the "rib" holes (those along the sides of the drift) were blasted after the cut; then the "back" holes (those along the top of the drift); and last, the "lifters" (those holes along the bottom of the drift). The "lifter" holes were loaded with extra dynamite so that the broken rock would be "lifted" away from the face for easier removal or "mucking."

Blasting caps are ignited by the spark, or "spit," from burning safety fuse. Thus the miners' term for lighting the fuse — "spitting" the fuse, or in the case of a complete round, "spitting the round." Safety fuse has a constant rate of combustion, generally 120 seconds per yard of fuse with an accuracy of ten per cent. In order to blast the holes in proper sequence, "timed" fuses of different lengths were used. This was accomplished by first using the same length for all fuses in the round, then the exposed ends of the fuses in the first holes to detonate were cut back several inches. Next, the fuses from the remaining holes are sequenced by removing shorter pieces from the fuses to the final holes to detonate where the fuses remained full length.

The miner lit the fuses in the same timing sequence with a safety fuse lighter, generally lead spitter — a thin lead tubing filled with black powder. The miner cut off a section of the lead spitter sufficiently long to light all the holes in his round, lit the spitter with a

Spitting a Round at the Creede Mining Museum —
circa 1990

Photo by Will Foreman

match, and proceeded to spit his round. Prior to the development of lead spitter, miners lit their fuses with matches. First, the ends of the fuses were split for a short distance; then match heads were inserted into the splits; and the match heads were struck in the timing sequence. Lighting of more than a single fuse by a match is not considered a safe practice today. Lighting fuses with one's carbide lamp was not a good idea, but it was done. A particle of burning black powder from the fuse could block the acetylene gas orifice and put out the carbide lamp, leaving the individual in the dark next to a lit fuse attached to dynamite. Not a good situation! Reuben Wesander lit fuses in 1947 with a carbide lamp and the blast killed him before he could get safely away. His carbide lamp was driven through his skull.

After the miner spit his round, he informed any miners working in the area that there was "fire in the hole" so they could move to a safe place if necessary. Sound is transmitted through rock faster than through the air, and a click is heard when a hole goes off before the air blast occurs. At a safe distance from the blast, the miner would stop and listen to the rock as his round was blasted. By counting the clicks, the miner could determine if all his holes went off. This was very important. An unexploded primer in the muck pile or misfired hole was a serious hazard.

The use of dynamite caused other problems for miners. The explosion of dynamite created toxic fumes that affected miners who went back to their work place too soon, as was the case many times when the work was being done on a contract basis or who were in areas where mine ventilation was poor. Norman Birdsey was killed in 1966 when he fell 160 feet down a raise. Heavy powder smoke from the previous round caused him to black out and fall. Nitroglycerine can be absorbed through the skin when dynamite is handled without gloves, causing a bad headache, called a "powder headache" by miners.

MUCKING AND TRAMMING

"Muck" is a mining term for the broken rock or ore and "mucking" is the work of removing the broken rock or ore. Tramming is the transportation of the broken rock or ore.

A miner's shovel is called a "muck stick." Hand shoveling was the method of muck removal in the early mines and was continued at Creede Camp into the 1950s. In many cases a steel plate, called a "plat" or "slick sheet," was laid on the floor of a drift or tunnel at the face prior to blasting and the muck pile was lifted onto the steel plate by the bottom holes, or "lifters," in the round. It is much easier to shovel off the steel plate than off a rough rock surface.

The muck was loaded into one-ton mine cars that were then pushed by hand, or "hand trammed," away from the work place to an ore pass or a location where cars were coupled into a train for haulage out of the mine. An ore pass is a near vertical opening used to pass broken ore from an upper to a lower level where it is stored behind an ore chute. Chutes were used not only on ore passes between levels, but at shaft or winze loading stations, and on openings connecting the mine level to the stopes immediately above where the ore was excavated. Ore from the stope chutes was hand trammed to ore passes for haulage out of the mine. Frank Crampton describes mucking in the early-day mines:

> "Working conditions in the mines, wherever one went, were about the same. A mucker had to muck and tram sixteen one-ton cars in an eight-hour shift, or twenty if the shift were ten hours. Two cars an hour was the minimum wherever the stiff mucked and trammed. If there was a trammer to push the ore car, the job of the mucker increased, for it was continuous mucking to fill cars while the trammer took out a loaded car and brought back an empty." [44]

Ed Johnson describes mucking and tramming at the Wagon Wheel Gap Fluorspar Mine:

> *"One drilled twice a week, blasted, and then spent the rest of the week mucking the ore into 3/4-ton cars with a shovel. We would muck about 20 cars a shift, depending on how much of a hangover your partner had. The rock was very heavy and the blasting made it nearly like sand. The ore was trammed to and dumped into one of seven ore passes about 100 feet in height."*[45]

Hand Tramming

Pencil Sketch by Joel Tankersley

The ore from the seven ore passes was then trammed by a battery locomotive to the one ore pass to the mill level. Then it was moved by a mule-powered ore train, as described in Chapter Fourteen.

An ore chute is a structure, generally built from timber, with a sloping bottom and vertical sides with cleats to hold chute boards across the front. The chute boards regulate or stop the flow of muck. The miner who controlled the flow of ore through the chute was called a "chute puller" or "chute tapper." He first spotted the mine car or bucket beneath the chute, then opened the chute boards with a bar to allow the ore to start flowing, and adjusted the flow by further opening the chute boards or hammering them down. He had to be extremely careful to not let the ore overflow the car.

Mucking in a Creede Mine — 1942
Photo by Andreas Feininger, Courtesy of the Library of Congress

The most hazardous job the chute puller performed was eliminating a "hangup" in the opening above the chute. On occasion, when the muck was large, angular pieces could form an arch that blocked the flow, leaving a void between the hangup and the chute bottom. The procedure used to bring down the hangup was to tape a stick or two of dynamite on a wooden stick long enough to reach the hangup from the bottom of the chute. The dynamite was then primed with a blasting cap with a safety fuse. The chute puller would climb into the chute, light the fuse, and carefully lift the dynamite bomb up to the key rock holding the hangup in place; brace the stick on the chute bottom, gingerly slide out of the chute, replace the chute boards, and then run like hell to a safe place! John Jackson has an interesting story about a new miner hired in 1947 and a hangup:

> *"A young fellow from Oklahoma had been hired by our shifter, Glen Archer, and placed on 700 level of the Amethyst Mine and south of the Albion hoisting raise. He was assigned to pull ore from a filled stope with a single car and dump it in a pocket for hoisting to tunnel level. He had removed several tons of loose ore creating a pocket above the chute that was called a hangup. He*

wasn't familiar with explosives and was debating about getting someone to help him when it gave away with a rush of air and splintered a timbered wing closing off the only route he knew to safety. He worked his way south from the stope and happened on a ladder that reached 600 level where I was working. He saw my light and ran to me blurting out, 'Gawdamighty I'm glad to see you.' We weren't acquainted but he recognized me as one of the crew who rode in the same pickup from Creede. 'Listen feller,' he went on, 'if you'll show me how to get out of here, I'll never come back in a mine again.' I led him up the manway to 500 level then on to where he could see daylight. He thanked me and I never saw him again."[46]

Bill Swinehart lost his life in 1951 when a hangup collapsed prematurely and crushed him in the bottom of the chute. The use of electric blasting caps and detonating cord has eliminated much of the risk from this job since then.

Important changes in the way ore was handled occurred in the first part of the twentieth century. *The Engineering and Mining Journal* of July 3, 1926, had these comments on progress in underground loading equipment during the past quarter century:

A Chute
Puller at
Work in a
Creede Mine
— 1942
*Photo by
Andreas
Feininger,
Courtesy of
the Library of
Congress*

"Great attention has been given since the war period to underground loading by mechanical means, with the objective of eliminating hand shoveling, and a considerable degree of success has attended efforts to improve loading efficiency. ... The power drawn scraper has established itself in metal mining where conditions are suitable for its use. ... Electrical locomotives for underground transportation,

Mucking Machine at the Bulldog Mountain Mine — 1969

From Sharp Bits, Summer — 1969
*Courtesy of the
Barrick Gold Corporation*

both of the trolley and storage battery types, are now used in large-scale and even moderate-scale operations."

Unfortunately, Creede Camp did not benefit from this early mechanical loading equipment and electrical locomotives until much later. The first mechanical mucking machine in camp was used at the Clay Mine in 1933 or 1934. It was a rail-mounted Model 12-B unit manufactured by the Eimco Corporation and called a "rocker shovel." It had dual motors, one for lifting the bucket and the other for traction to move it along the rails.[47] The bucket was lowered in front and crowded into the muck pile. When the bucket was full, it was lifted over the top of the machine's carriage by the lift motor where it deposited the muck into a mine car coupled to the mucking machine. When the car was full it was switched and an empty car took its place and the process was repeated. John Jackson tells about the first mucking machine in Creede Camp at a later time, the renovation of the Commodore No. 5 Tunnel:

"When the tunnel had been renovated to an unstable area near the Last Chance boundary in 1944, Dave Brown and Billy Taylor contracted to drive a loop around the cave in the footwall of the fault. The work was contracted to them at $4 per foot advance and they were equipped with a Leyner drill and square point shovels. Later Fred Lane and Lyle Alspaugh would finish the contract and use the

*Eimco 12-B mucking machine that Al and Ashby Hibbs
rented to them for a fee of 50 cents per foot of advance. The
Hibbs brothers had acquired the mucking machine from
the Ben Birdsey estate. I had worn out several Number Six
square point shovels as a 'mucker' and to see this mechanical wonder in action was, in one word, awesome. A
1-1/2-ton tunnel car could be heaped full in less than two
minutes by an experienced operator. A train of six end
dump cars was pulled from the tunnel by a mule we affec-
tionately called 'Minnie Pearl.' Minnie Pearl would be
replaced by Mancha electric trammers while I was in the
Army and larger rocker dump cars would be employed in
a string of ten for a 20–ton payload."*[48]

The power drawn scraper, or "slusher," had a great impact on mining at Creede Camp and saved much hard labor and time in the mucking phase of the mining cycle. It could be used many places in the Creede
mines where mucking machines could not be accommodated. For some
reason it did not make its appearance in Creede until about 1948. John
Jackson stated: "To be equipped with a slusher and a jackleg drill in
1950 was like stepping from a Model T Ford into a Cadillac."[49]

The slusher used at Creede was a double-drum hoist powered by
a compressed air motor and a hoe-shaped scraper. Each drum of the
hoist could be turned by engaging a lever-operated clutch while the
other drum turned free. A pull rope from one of the drums was
attached to the bail of the scraper. A tail rope ran from the other
drum over a sheave located behind the muck pile and then to the
back of the scraper. The miner loaded the scraper at the muck pile
and pulled the ore onto a ramp and platform over an ore car. The
ore dropped into the ore car through a slot in the platform. Then,
by reversing the clutches, the tail rope moved the scraper back to the
muck pile as the pull rope was paid off the pull drum. When the car
was full, it was trammed and replaced by an empty car. As the drift
advanced, the ramp and platform and slusher were moved ahead.
Slushers were also used to slush ore directly into ore passes.

John Jackson relates stories about mules and horses used to tram
ore out of the Creede mines as late as 1949:[50]

*"Mules were used to pull trains to and from
Commodore 3 level in the 1930s. The handlers were cor-
rectly called mule skinners, but at Amethyst 5 level tunnel
we had two and sometimes three horses serving the same*

Slusher at the
Bulldog
Mountain Mine
— 1969
*Courtesy of
Sandy Kroll*

*purpose. Mule skinning was a dangerous job and the skin-
ners had to be ever alert for rock on the tracks or obstacles such as chutes and low timbers that could crush a
man against a loaded car. John 'Pip' Ward was a victim of
just such an accident in the Commodore Tunnel when
caught between a chute and the end car. Vic Miller took
over the mule skinner's post after Pip's tragic accident in
1937 and held the job until the mine closed.*

*"In 1947, at Amethyst 5 Tunnel, a skinner had
hooked a flat car on the end of his train on a return trip
to move a hoist from 580 raise. Two skinners were pulling
ore and waste rock at the time and the loaded train would
wait at 3 vein switch until the returning empty train
passed; the skinner would then flip the switch and head
out. Bill Mathews used Teddy, a faithful bay stud, and on
this day waved to the other skinner and clucked Teddy
into motion. He was unaware the flat car had come loose
in the tunnel and was resting there in darkness. There was
a fairly steep grade between 2 shaft and 3 shaft, putting
Teddy into a trot as he made the curve to the straightaway
and daylight 2000 feet east. The horses had large carbide
lamps hooked to the front of their harness that cast a wide*

and bright light, enabling Teddy to see danger ahead. There was no chance of Bill stopping the train, and he couldn't see the flat car, anyway, with Teddy's rear blocking his view. The first inkling Bill had of potential catastrophe was Teddy leaping upward to land with all four hooves on the flat car where he rode to a stop as Bill set the brakes from his step behind Teddy.

"I was driving a crosscut from 3 shaft west at the time, and the empty cars were consigned to me on his return, where I learned of Teddy's feat. Bill was still pasty white and shaking as he recounted the adventure. He quit not long after that and in 1949 Teddy retired to John A. Dabney's ranch near Saguache."

The "mule skinner" in the following photograph is Arthur Fairchild and the horse is "Brownie." Art had a knack for training horses to adapt to the underground environment. Both Art and Byron "Pappy" Fairchild were mule skinners in the first years of the Emperius Mining Company's Amethyst Mine operations. Art drove a truck part time for the Creede Transportation Company, his and Bill Kolish's company that hauled ore to the Emperius Mill.[51]

By 1950 all of the Emperius Mining Company's ore was transported out of the 1200 Level Transportation Tunnel (Commodore No. 5 Tunnel) to the ore bins that had been constructed in the mid-1940s. Battery locomotives pulling two-ton rocker cars replaced Teddy. The battery locomotives and cars provided haulage from the mines along the Amethyst Vein System until production ended.

Horse-Powered Ore Train at the Amethyst Mine — 1942
Courtesy of the Colorado Mining Association

Locomotive
and Ore Train
at the Bulldog
Mountain
Mine 9360
Level Portal
— 1969
*Courtesy of
Sandy Kroll*

The slusher-scraper combination was extensively used at the Bulldog Mountain Mine to move the ore excavated from the stopes into five-ton side-dump rail cars that were hauled to the mill by six- and seven-ton locomotives.[52] In 1981, Homestake introduced rubber-tired diesel loaders into the mine to improve productivity.[53]

GROUND SUPPORT

Many of the openings at Creede Camp mines, with the exception of those on the Bulldog Mountain Vein System, were "bald," meaning very little support was required since the walls of the veins were generally competent. There were short sections of drifts and other types of mine workings passing through broken zones of rock or "heavy ground" that required support by timber sets or stulls, but most openings did not. A timber set for a horizontal opening consists of two near vertical posts, one on each side of the opening, and a horizontal cap placed over the posts beneath the back that transmits any weight from the overlying rock through the posts to the rock beneath the opening. Timber sets for vertical or near vertical openings consisted of timbers in the form of a rectangle laid horizontally. Stulls are round timbers that are placed to transmit rock pressure across the mine opening. One end of the stull was set in a "hitch" that was cut into the rock by a miner using a singlejack hammer and "moil," a short, sharpened steel rod generally made from a section of drill steel. Moils that stayed sharp without chipping was another product of the blacksmith's art. The other end of the stull was tightly wedged to the rock with

Tunnel Timber
Sets at the
Creede
Mining
Museum —
circa 1990
Photo by
Will Foreman

miner's "wedges," wedge-shaped pieces of wood driven in oppos-
ing pairs to hold the stull tightly in place.

Oxidized ore was first excavated from the narrow, steep veins
that were rarely over ten feet wide by open, overhand stopes. In
overhand stoping, the ore was broken in horizontal slices progressing upward by miners working beneath and close to the top, or
"back," of the stope. The broken ore dropped to the bottom of the
stope where it was loaded through chutes into mine cars in the drift
beneath the stope. Only enough ore to cushion the chutes against
damage from ore dropped from above was left in the bottom of the
stope. This, of course, meant lots of open space between the miners
and the bottom of the stope, as mining progressed upward. Stulls
were installed mainly to provide access to the ore and to provide
support where needed. John Jackson noticed timber cribs filled with
waste rock in a few of the early-day stopes in the northern part of
the Amethyst vein where the hanging wall had been altered and was
loose.[54]

The Emperius Mining Company instituted the use of "shrinkage
stoping" in the sulfide ore zone. However, the first recorded shrinkage stoping at Creede Camp was in 1917 when Ray Morgan, caught
in a rock fall in a shrinkage stope timbered with stulls, later died
from his injuries.[55] As in open overhand stoping in a narrow, steep
vein, the ore is broken in horizontal slices progressing upward by
miners working beneath the back of the stope. Unlike open stoping,
the ore was left in place after it was broken. The broken ore was
"shrunk" by removing only that volume created by the swelling

effect of breaking the ore. The excess was removed from the stope through chutes at its bottom to leave a working place for the miners below the back. The balance of the ore was left in place for a working surface and temporary ground support until the stope was completed and the ore was drawn. Timbered manway raises at both ends of the stope provided access for miners, ventilation, and supplies. Shrinkage stoping did create several problems. Considerable amounts of ore were tied up in stopes for long periods

Installing a Stull

Pencil Sketch by Joel Tankersley

of time and this allowed the sulfide ore to oxidize, thus creating milling problems that could reduce metal recoveries. If broken ore was left in the stope too long, it could cement together and require re-mining.

Mining the Bulldog Vein System required drastic changes to ground support methods used at Creede Camp. Ore in the veins was essentially unconsolidated and required extensive ground support. Drifts were driven in the walls outside the vein where possible to take advantage of better rock conditions. Mine openings within the veins required special support. Drifts in areas of rubbly ore were driven using crown bars or booms ahead of the timbering operations. This provided protection for the miners, and the timbering was installed up to the face before the next round was drilled.[56]

Excavating the ore was complicated and made very expensive by the heavy ground encountered in the veins. The undercut and fill stoping method used at the Bulldog Mountain Mine was developed as an adaptation of a similar technique used to mine an ore body at the Magma Copper Company's mine at Superior, Arizona. The ore was mined in horizontal slices progressing downward. The first slice was mined to a depth of about twelve feet immediately beneath the track in the top level, and the slices were sequentially mined downward to the level below. When the ore was removed from a slice, the floor of the opening was lined with timber and wire mesh and then a cement-sand mixture was pumped into the excavation to a depth of about nine feet. Then the slice of ore below the consolidated fill was mined and the process was repeated. The sand fill was provided by the sand fraction of the mill tailings, thus solving two problems — ground support for the mining operation and the reduction of material stored in the tailings pond.[57] Heavy ground at the Bulldog created serious safety problems for the miners. Two miners, William C. "Scooter" Jackson and Dee Palmer, lost their lives in rock falls in 1969.

A unique method of excavating ore — sub-level caving — was used at the Wagon Wheel Gap Fluorspar Mine.[58] This method had been used in the underground iron mines in the Lake Superior Iron Range but rarely elsewhere. The ore is excavated in horizontal slices in descending order, so that the overburden, or "capping," will break up and subside as the ore beneath is removed. Timbered slice-drifts, or "sub-levels," were driven at twenty-foot vertical intervals along the vein, leaving a slice or lift of ore between the top of the timber sets and the bottom of the capping. The ore was excavated by mining and caving, starting at the far end of the sub-level and retreating toward the entrance. After the excavation of the ore in a slice was advanced, the sub-level beneath was driven and mined in the same retreating fashion. This mining method was developed for ore bodies of moderately firm ore overlain by rock that would cave readily, but coarsely, to form a capping that would arch and support itself temporarily over small openings.[59]

MINING CONTESTS

Miners, like cowboys, held contests to determine who was the best at their job-related skills. The cowboys held rodeos to test their skills at riding and roping. The miners also held contests to test their skills in drilling and mucking. Contests in the major mining centers brought contestants from all over the western United States and Canada who competed for large prizes. *Mining Reporter*'s October 31, 1901, issue reported on a drilling contest held at Leadville:

> *"The greatest drilling contest in the history of the West was concluded at Leadville last week. During last*

summer many drilling contests were held all over the West from British Columbia to Arizona; many records were made but owing to the varied kinds of rocks used no line could be made on the relative skill of the different miners. The Ouray drillers, Hupps and Linquist, hold a record of 41 1/2 inches in Gunnison granite, whilst the Butte men drilled considerably over fifty inches at Spokane. In order to settle the question as to the merits of the best drillers, Mr. James Knight of the Leadville Herald Democrat engineered a contest that brought all the best teams together. Seven teams in all entered, but the number would have been greater if the reputation of the contestants who actually drilled had not been so great. The wonderful talent of the men is shown by the fact that in 105 minutes they put down holes that aggregated 267 15/32 inches, or more than twenty-two feet, in the hardest rock known.

"The rules under which the contest proceeded were very simple. The time of drilling was fifteen minutes to each team. As many drills as the team thought sufficient could be used, size of the steel seven-eights of an inch. A timekeeper for the team and a coacher who could assist by advice. Eight pound hammers were used. The word 'go' was said and immediately the men went to work, one striking and the other turning alternately. The men drilled as long as they saw fit without changing, changed drills when they saw proper without restriction of rules.

"The most beautiful part about these drilling contests is the changing between the men and the changes of drills. It is always the same man who changes the drill. The changes of drills is one in this manner: The turner who is kneeling has the drills arranged by his knee, the bits pointing towards the hole. When he decides to change drills he turns with one hand and with the other grasps the next drill pointing at and close to the hole. Immediately the hammer was taken off the head of the drill the old drill was drawn out and immediately the new drill was inserted. So rapidly was this done that not a stroke would be lost. The rapid withdrawal of a thirty-six inch drill and the insertion of a forty-inch drill single handed and so rapidly that not a perceptible slacking up was seen as one the marvelous sights of a drilling contest. McKenzie of

Leadvillle and Freethy of Butte showed remarkable skill in this department. If the latter were a few inches taller he would be possibly the best change in the world. McKenzie deserves that honor now. The changes of men are done in this way: When the coacher gives the word to change, the turner rises just before the last blow of his partner, who immediately after striking the blow falls to his knees and commences to turn immediately after the other man has struck a blow. Thus but little time is lost. So expert are the champion drillers that some of them, for example McKenzie and Make, lost less than one-half second between all changes.

"We regret that we will be unable to give the entire analysis of the work of the performers, but in our next issue we will endeavor to work out the results so that the causes of victory and defeat will be more apparent. It seems obviously however, that McNichols and Ross of British Columbia lost the first prize through slowness in that all-important branch — changing.

"The results were as follows:

Malley and Chamberlain, Leadville, first prize $750, drilled 40 1/8 inches.

Ross and McNichols, British Columbia, second prize, $350, drilled 39 13/16 inches.

McKenzie and Make, Leadville, and Davey and Freethy, Butte, shared third and fourth prizes, $350, drilled 37 7/16 inches.

Hupps and Lindquist, Ouray, drilled 38 11/32 inches.

Tarr and Stewart, Leadville, drilled 36 11/16 inches.

Pittman and Coughlin, Boulder, Colorado, drilled 35 5/8 inches."

Creede was the site of mining contests throughout its history. Singlejack and doublejack drilling were the mainstays of the contests for many years; however, hand "mucking" competition was also important. Machine drilling and mucking was added to the competition in the 1930s and 1940s. Competition with the jackleg drill began in the 1950s.

George Wintz won the 1949 singlejack championship by drilling a hole 11 3/4 inches deep in an extremely hard rhyolite boulder in ten minutes. Les Turnipseed that year won the mucking contest by shoveling 2,900 pounds of rough silver-lead ore from one truck bed to another in three minutes, forty seconds.[60]

Ken Wyley remembers seeing the drilling contests at Creede in the late 1950s and early 1960s. He remembers Mike Smith and Tom Williams of Nederland, Colorado, coming to town, competing against the local champions, John Jackson and Gene Wardell, and actually beating them. The Creede Jaycees held the contests during those years. Lowell Hicks sponsored the contests during the 1970s. Doublejack drilling events had almost disappeared from mining contests by the early 1980s, but Dodie Vandermark from Buena Vista, Colorado, almost single-handedly brought them back. Creede miners Tom Payne, Lowell Hicks, and Les Hicks, under Vandermark's tutelage, placed in the top three in hand drilling events in nearly every mining contest held throughout the West. Payne was awarded "all around miner" at the Colorado State Mining Championships for four or five years before it was sponsored by Creede in 1988. Payne and Hicks placed first in the doublejack drilling contests for seven or eight years at the Nevada State Mining Championships, Tonopah, Nevada.[61]

In addition to mining contests, the whiskey race, whiskey drinking contest, and horse racing was part of the Fourth of July celebrations. The races were held on Main Street and one, a race to Monte Vista, covered fifty miles with four or five horse changes along the way. A professional prize fighter was brought to town so locals could challenge him. Several miners actually whipped the professional.[62]

CHAPTER 17

RHYMES OF THE MINES

CREEDE CAMP PRODUCED NOT ONLY METALS but poetry, too. The earliest published poet of the region was Harriet L. Wason, wife of Martin Van Buren Wason. Wason's poetry was written by her posing as a Harvard-educated young man who had come to the West for a vacation. The poems were supposedly written to his college friend in the East, describing scenes and incidents along the Rio Grande as well as from other sections of Colorado, flavored with local Indian legends. Her poems were published in *Letters from Colorado* in 1887 by Cupples and Heard of Boston.[1]

Cy Warman, the "Poet of the Cochetopas," was no doubt the most famous of the Creede poets. Warman was a native of Illinois who came West in the early 1880s as a locomotive engineer for the Denver and Rio Grande Railroad. His writing had taken him from the engineer's cab to the position of editor for a railroad publication in Denver. He established the *Creede Chronicle*, a weekly newspaper, in March 1892 and was the newspaper's editor. The *Chronicle* ceased publication in 1895. Warman wrote the well-known song poem, "Sweet Marie," for his wife-to-be while he was a locomotive engineer.[2] His poems written in Creede appeared in a privately printed book, *Mountain Melodies*, in 1892. One of the poems in the book put Creede Camp into the national limelight:

Creede
Here's a land where all are equal —
Of high or lowly birth —
A land where men make millions,
Dug from the dreary earth.
Here meek and mild-eyed burro
On mineral mountains feed —
It's day all day, in the day-time,
And there is no night in Creede.

The cliffs are solid silver,
With wond'rous wealth untold;
And the beds of running rivers
Are lined with glittering gold.
While the world is filled with sorrow,
And hearts must break and bleed —
It's day all day, in the day-time,
And there is no night in Creede.

More than forty poems were in Warman's *Mountain Melodies,* including the following four. The poem, "Stained Silver," speaks to politics and the price of silver:

The Columbine
Sweet Marie, here's a columbine,
The summer can surely spare it.
See! Here's a delicate twig to twine,
To braid in this beautiful hair of thine,
Sweet Marie, here's a columbine —
Take it, my queen, and wear it!

Waved by the wind in the summer time;
Wet by the summer showers;
Blown in the balm of this beautiful clime,
Over our heads where the hills are rime;
Waved by the winds in the summer time —
Fairest of forest flowers.

For I have brought you this boutonniere,
Plucked from the hills above you,
To weave in the waves of your beautiful hair,
Or wear in your breast where the love songs are,
I have brought you this boutonniere —
Take it, because I love you.

The Amethyst Vein
The sun o'er the summit is bringing
Chilled roses to life on the lea;
The rivers are laughing and singing,
And slipping away tow'rd the sea.

The winds in the cedars are sighing,
Their summer songs rhyme with the rills;
The miners are patiently trying
The traces that hide in the hills.

The tremulous tramways are creaking
'Neath the weight of each silvery train;
The men in the mountain are seeking
That source of the Amethyst vein.

The Miner's Lament
O'er the treacherous trail I've traveled
For nearly a dozen years,
I have sought the hidden treasure —
I have lived on hopes and fears,
And the dreams I dreamed at midnight
On the perfumed piñon bow;
Were I fancy, fairer — sweeter
Than the dreams I'm dreaming now.

I have been to see the city —
I have sat beside the sea,
And have heard its mystic music;
But it brings no bliss to me.
I am lone; I miss the melody
Made by the mountain winds;
As they creep across the craggy
Crest and dally with the pines.

'May be wrong to be ungrateful
For the good things God has given;
'May be wrong to under-estimate
The blessings sent from heaven;
But the joy that's in the seeking
Of the wealth beneath the ground
Is a joy the miner loses
When the hidden treasure's found.

So I leave these treasured millions
And again my feet I turn
Toward the silent, snowy mountains,

For my restive soul doth yearn
For the mournful, mystic melody
Made by the mountain winds,
And the scent of summer wild flow'rs
and the perfume of the pines.

Silver Stained
I am weary, said the miner,
And my limbs are growing cold;
I am weary of this seeking
After silver. I am told
That the dollar of our daddies
Is a dream of something fled,
And the silver in the Senate's
Just about as good as lead.

I had learned to love the mountains
As the sailor loves the sea,
As the song birds love the sunlight,
As the flowers love the lea.
But I'm weary, Oh, so weary,
I would lay me down and rest
Where the soft wind shakes the cedars,
Near the mountain's craggy crest.

I can see our silver dollar
Slowly driven to disgrace;
There's a mark upon her forehead
And a film before her face.
I am weary of this waiting;
I would lay me down to rest,
Where the soft wind shakes the cedars
Near the mountain's craggy crest.

The *Rocky Mountain News* issue of March 24, 1892, carried a poem written by "Joe":

Creede
Down from the hills one lucky day
There was news of value, so they say,
Carried to Denver, miles away,
With a terribly dangerous, thrilling roar —

The news that Creede had struck rich ore.
Only that and nothing more.

Only that, but that was enough
To drive men out to hunt the stuff,
To face the weather, calm or rough;
To drive men up in the hills so wild
That summer was never counted mild,
To dig in mountains on mountains piled.
Yes, men came in from far and near;
The sound was loud so all could hear,
And the news was greeted with lusty cheer,
For who was there, of men so great,
That thought not fortune would on him wait,
And moved not on with heart elate?

Four thousand strong took up the cry;
Four thousand strong to Creede drew nigh;
Four thousand strong with anxious eye
Took to the trails from regions scattered,
Marched in companies torn and tattered
To Creede, where wealth is freely plattered.

And there they are, so the papers say,
Scheming and scheming day after day,
Striving to make some lucky play
That will make them forever rich in gold,
That up their heads they may ever hold
Among the magnates mighty and bold.

Cy Warman wrote another poem about Creede in 1911 that is not as well known as the first one he wrote:[3]

The Rise And Fall of Creede
A thousand burdened burros filled
The narrow, winding, wriggling trail.
A hundred settlers came to build,
Each day, new houses in the vale.
A hundred gamblers came to feed
On these same settlers — this was Creede.
Slanting Annie, Gambler Joe

And bad Bob Ford, Sapolio, —
Or Soapy Smith, as he was known,—-
Ran games peculiarly their own,
And everything was open wide,
And men drank absinthe on the side.
And now the Faro bank is closed,
And Mr. Faro's gone away
To seek new field, it is supposed, —
More verdant fields. The gamblers say
The man who worked the shell and ball
Has gone back to the Capitol.
The winter winds blow bleak and chill,
The quaking, quivering aspen waves
About the summit of the hill —
Above the unrecorded graves
Where halt, abandoned burros feed
And coyotes call — and this is Creede.
Lone graves whose head-boards bear no name,
Whose silent owners lived like brutes
And died as doggedly, — but game,
And most of them died in their boots,
We mind among the unwrit names
The man who murdered Jesse James.
We saw him murdered, saw him fall,
And saw his mad assassin gloat
Above him. Heard his moans and all,
And saw the shot holes in his throat,
And men moved on and gave no heed
To life or death — and this was Creede.

When *The Creede Candle* closed its doors on December 27, 1930, the neighboring *Silver World* of Lake City, through editor William C. Blair, broke into verse. The poem errs in connecting Cy Warman and *The Creede Candle*:

In a land where all are equal —
Of high or lowly birth —
A land where poor made millions,
From good old Mother Earth:
Shown Warman's brilliant Candle,
Keeping Creede in constant light.

Now the Candle's doused, Jimtown's in gloom.
And Creede has always night —

Where once 'twas all day day-time
"And there was no night in Creede."
Now Stygian darkness blankets all
And hides whatever deed.
In a thousand towns throughout the land,
We laugh, sing, play and shout;
But Creede is sad all day and night —
The Candle's glare is out.

Now Creede's all dark the whole night through,
And from rise until setting sun;
But Creede's not in the garbage yet —
It's record has just begun.
'Twill return apace and have a place —
A gem of rays serene,
In a set of gold and wealth untold —
All day with no night between.

Creede continued to be a popular subject for poets over the years. Charles F. Thomas of Palmdale, California, wrote a poem, a parody of Warman's "Creede," that was published in the magazine *Explosives Engineer* of July/August 1958 and reprinted by permission of the copyright holder, Dyna Nobel, Inc.:

Ghost Town
Creede, wild city praised in story,
Famed in words of poets' song,
Silvered land with golden glory,
Peopled once with crowding throng.
But no shouts are heard in playtime;
Tales are lost of stirring deed.
Now the days are drear in the daytime,
And the nights are dark in Creede.

Where the toiling miner wrestled
Wealth from rugged Mother Earth.
Creede, whose nights seemed daytime, nestled
Mid the high hills' echoed mirth.
Old-time gamblers, girls of paytime,

Miners, mothers, every breed —
Now the days are lone in daytime,
And the nights are dark in Creede.

In Creede's graveyard, lone and cheerless,
On a rough, neglected hill
Rest the dead men, cowards or fearless,
And Creede's women, good with ill.
All faced hardship, bright or graytime;
Most earned joy in kindly deed.
Now the days are sad in daytime,
And the nights are dark in Creede.

From old shells of buildings dreary,
Once saloons or dancehalls bright.
Is that music? Ghostly, eerie,
Played for spirits of the night?
But sad hearts must dream the gaytime,
And there man is lone, indeed,
For the days are still in daytime,
And the nights are dark in Creede.

Mines deserted, rotted headframes
Stand like gallows on the hills.
Once-famed names are now just dead names;
Still, abandoned are the mills.
Here the winter's snow in Maytime
Casts cold chill on summer's seed.
Long, too long are the days in daytime,
Dark, so dark are nights in Creede.

Nellie Sloan, wife of William C. Sloan who was instrumental in the discovery of the hanging wall veins, wrote beautiful poetry and distributed it to friends. Unfortunately her poems were not published and have been lost.[4] Poems by other Creede Camp authors have been saved and samples of them along with biographical sketches of the authors follow.

Ed McCargish, an Irishman from the Trinidad, Colorado, coal mines, came to Creede about 1940 and worked for the Emperius and Outlet Mining Companies. John Jackson hired Ed at the Phoenix Mine and has this remembrance of him:[5]

"We drove to work in an old pickup, four of us, Art Davis, Pete Walker, Ed, and myself. Ed chewed tobacco and ate garlic cloves, a lethal combination. We would cope in summer with the windows of the pickup rolled down but in winter it became a problem. Ed would beg, 'Jeezuschrist boys, roll up the windows. I'm freezing.' It became worse and I finally had to tell him he would either have to forego the garlic or ride in back. He rode in back, bundled up like a Siberian Russian."

McCargish was a rhymster of some note and published his works in a privately printed booklet titled, *Odes and Poems By a Hard Rock Miner*, in 1948. The following poems are from his booklet:

The Wreck At Alby Shaft
*They had a wreck at Alby shaft, it wasn't any joke
Norm left 700 with a can of muck then the cable broke
Aby Taylor was filling cans in 700 sump
When the can and muck came tumbling Aby made a jump
He landed in behind the chute it was the only place to git
Aby was in a hurry he hadn't time to spit
But when the wreck was cleared away, Aby took
another chance
He kept right on working when he should have
changed his pants
He asked Norm to borrow his overalls, Norm said O nix
I know you are in a dirty mess for I am in the very
same fix!*

A Fourth In Creede
*We hope the folks that came to Creede to celebrate the 4th
Went away well satisfied that they got their money's worth
We had a few sham battles they didn't amount to much
A miner gave a girl a push of course he got in dutch
Red Johnson rode a bucking horse at least he done his best
But was tossed so high up in the sky blue birds made a nest
Now the dust has settled and the smoke has cleared away
I think I will close this little ode. I have no more to say.*

The Trials Of A Miner
*Strange things happen to the men in the mine
Some will have a coniption fit like a monkey on a vine
Some will shank a piece of steel, others burst a hose*

Others may lose their buzzy and down the stope she goes
But something happened recently that makes the men all pass
A miner named Dick Lehman just up and lost his ass
Everything was lovely 'til someone had to blast
Dick was very busy and forgot to watch his ass
You may think me lieing or just a plain damn fool
This pesky thing I call an ass is a damned old mule
But if you ever drive her be sure you tie her fast
Or you will be like Lehman — sure to lose your ass.

Watch Your Bones Rod

I worked with a man called Zero, of course his
name wasn't hot
The reason we call him Zero is because his name is Ott
One day I heard him cursing, it would chill the heart of God
When I asked the reason he had stuck his bones [bonus] rod
If he had a voice like some of us they could hear him in town
When I saw the formation he had drilled in something brown
So come all you hard rock miners, as over the Earth you trod
Watch which way you point your chuck and watch your
bones [bonus] rod.

The Prospector

When you go prospecting don't expect some lucky witch
To lead you to some lucky spot where you will strike it rich
You may live on flapjacks and wear patches on your pants
Only tinhorns want a cinch but the gambler takes a chance
The sourdough has courage, he toils the live-long day
And turns out in the morning when the jack begins to bray
So stick to pick and shovel tho it's tough going on the start
We hope Dame Fortune will have a smile for those two —
TY [Poxson] and ART. [Davis]

Hard Rock Casey

There was a hard rock miner up on the Rio Grande
Known as Hard Rock Casey a tough and dangerous man
When he climbed aboard his trusty steed and gave the
Indian yell
All the folks in the town of Creede knew he was
raising hell
But he finally met his Waterloo when he tried to
buck the law
He made a drive for his .45 but was too slow on the draw

So Hard Rock Casey passed away he met a bad man's fate
His last shot availed him not he was just 2 seconds late
Now we miss the crack of his .45 also his Indian yell
We nailed him up in a box of pine and sent him to Boot Hill.

Oppy was Creede Camp's mountain man. His given name was
Louis Chester Brechman and was born in Kansas in 1886. He was
given to a family named Oppy when he was seven. The Oppy family moved to Cripple Creek, Colorado, shortly after Louis joined
them. Oppy was "shell-shocked" while in the front lines in France
during World War I, and this left him prone to anger, suspicions, and
eccentricities. He received a pension after the war for his injuries.
His pension and grubstakes from individuals along the Rio Grande
allowed him to spend the summers prospecting and living in the hills
around Creede. He could live for weeks on the contents of his back
pack and he built cabins in the areas he frequented. The cabins were
made from materials on-site. He hand hewed boards for roof shin-
gles, doors, tables, and bedsteads with his axe. The window panes
were of waxed paper. During Creede's hard times, Oppy regularly
delivered fresh elk and deer meat to needy families and widows during and out of the legal hunting seasons.[6]

When he felt his better judgment being usurped by his mental
demons, he would have William T. Jackson, Jr. lock all of his guns
in the Jackson safe until he recovered. In the early 1960s, Oppy's
eccentricities and temper overcame him and he was sent to the Fort
Lyons Veterans Hospital, where he spent the rest of his life. John
Jackson has this remembrance of Oppy:[7]

> *"Lou was so well read that when he recited poetry to*
> *me I thought it was from the masters, not his own. The*
> *first and only time I saw a tear in the eyes of our revered*
> *'mountain man' was in the year 1953. We had learned the*
> *date of Lou Oppy's birthday, and my wife Inez baked him*
> *a two-tiered cake with white and pink icing in celebration*
> *of his birthday and his many favors to us in mining ven-*
> *tures. He exclaimed, 'That deserves a bear hug,' and*
> *nearly squeezed the life from Inez as he hid this brief show*
> *of tenderness from me by letting the tears drop in her*
> *hair."*

The following two poems were written by Oppy for his friend,
Ina Wetherill, after she had given him several gifts at Christmas time
in 1946.[8]

Fantasy in A Minor

For years and years I've roamed the hills
Listening to babbling brooks and rills;
The red fox plaintive, mournful cry,
And the night birds soothing lullabye.

Content to live in solitude,
Think wholesome tho'ts eat simple food,
Lie down at night on my pine bough bed,
And pull the tarp up over my head.

Last Christmas to me, a friend did send,
A gift which started another trend;
To dormant ideas in a callous mind;
And suggested a help mate I better find.

Two lovely wives, identical twins,
Exquisite hand, adorable fins,
Modest sunbonnets, ruffled skirts,
Good housewives, they're no flirts.

One on my left, one on my right,
In connubial bliss, we rest at night;
They shower kisses on my bald pate,
I'm a dad-gum "Oriental Potentate."

Today, this Christmas, Nineteen and forty-seven,
Comes added bliss, housewives seven;
To scrub and feed me to the grave,
And then to Church, my soul to save.

Such devotion I have never met,
Seven in one, "my Pantalet,"
Seven phases of that Gift Divine,
Brighter than gold, Sweeter than wine.

Forgive this meager, senseless verse,
The Creator of this Universe,
Ages ago spoke a mournful moan,
It is not good, man should live alone.

I echo that sentiment, good and true,
As I gaze into the starry blue,
And wonder where will I next Christmas be,
With my Pantalets, Ruffles, and Fantasy.

Prospector's Lament
My head rests on a pillow case,
In a woman's lap, who has no face,
Her ruffled skirt wrapped around my neck,
I bet I choke to death, by heck.

I snooze, I dream, in a vision I see,
A lady fair as fair can be
But when I check and double check
I'm hugging a pillow and the bed's a wreck.

A mere suggestion is all I need,
Imagination stirs and gets up speed,
I grab a passing angel's wing,
We mount on high and there we sing.

There's a beautiful home far over the sea,
A beautiful home for you and for me,
Its glittering towers forever will shine,
That beautiful home some day will be mine.

John Jackson is a poet of note. The following poems are a sampling written by John starting with his beautiful tribute to his wife's memory: Inez shared John's life not only as his wife but his helpmate and supporter in his mining ventures. She was willing to do most any job, but hated to crimp dynamite caps onto fuses. Understandably so!

In Memory of Inez
1933-2002
Ah, what a life, we played it well
in roles we didn't seek
and now it's time to say "farewell"
with memories at their peak

We dreamed there'd be another spring
and smell it's fragrant breath

that coaxed the Meadowlark to sing
before our date with death

But through the softly falling snow
the Owl of darkness came
to cover you with death's warm glow
and, gently, call your name

A special love, we always knew
the bond would never part
and I am still a part of you
because we shared one heart

I love you
John

Priorities

Oh what a tragic waste of time
to shift one's feet and start to climb
the path that leads to wealth and fame
then find you're old, deranged and lame

The air is crisp, the sun is bright
the goal so near I think I might
roll back the years and labor on
before the will to fight is gone

But what is fame without a love
and how could wealth lift one above
the warmth and comfort of old friends
the peace of mind a family lends

So.....I'll turn back, accept my lot
with memories my journey brought
for after all, I did succeed
in fending off the clutch of greed

A cheery smile when skies are gray
will do much more to make my day
than wealth or fame for ego's sake
and better frost contentment's cake.

Blasphemy

I think every word worth sounding
would be ever so less confounding
if restricted in vowels
punctuated by growls
then arranged for simple compounding

Oratory is gilded by intellect
embellished and most circumspect
magnified in pretension
for the ego's ascension
to heights that I deem quite suspect

A growl from a dog gets attention
plainly signaling "no intervention"
in his mood or direction
lest you have a connection
with a route to another dimension

I've Been There, Pard

I was born at home in the town of Creede
with a midwife to cut the cord
went to work the next day and found my pay
would be just room and board
I cut my wisdom teeth on a tamping stick and
combed my hair with a scaling bar
had to learn real fast how to muck and blast
and run the wheels off a tunnel car
I got peppered with rock from a runaway fuse
and broke my back in a fall in a shaft
got throttled and kicked and soundly licked
while my pards sat back and laughed
So I'll listen to your bellyachin' and I'll drink
with you now and then
just don't tell me where I'm goin' when you
don't know where I've been

I joined our Uncle Sam's army, thought I'd
earn me a medal or two
took a one way trip on a Liberty ship held
together with rivets and glue

I tramped over Heidelberg's castles and washed
my feet in the muddy Rhine
traded cigarettes for a Fraulein's gebets and
a bottle of Bordeaux wine
Then I went and married a Kansan with webs
between her toes
a solid brunette with her curls in a net and
a chicken bone run through her nose
So, if you haven't spent a day in my diggers or
bedded down in a wildcat's den
don't tell me where I'm goin' 'cause you
don't know where I've been

Cirrhosis has spotted my liver, I've got rocks
in the box to boot
lumbago in my spine has my chassis out of line
but I plain don't give a hoot
No more shafts or stopes or tunnels, no more
smelling stale powder smoke
no more drilling wet lifters, arguing with
shifters or laughing at a super's joke
Drilled 'er out in my dreams last night and I'm
ready for the last pink slip
there's fire in the hole and the devil's got my soul,
Mr. Hoistman let 'er rip
Now we both know where I'm going and a
little bit of where I've been
remember those hard rock miners and drink a
toast to 'em now and then

Graveyard Poker
The moon was full and the tidal pull
made the timbers creak and groan
in the Last Chance shaft where a natural draft
brought forth a quavering moan

Near the end of our shift in a square set drift
mucked out, timbered and clean
the rail spiked true for the day shift crew
Erick Nelson, Gus Prince and Al Dean

We learned at the station of a minor complication
when Red belled for a lift to the collar
the skip got hung when a guide rail sprung
the overtime would earn us a dollar

With nothing to do 'til the maintenance crew
got everything back on track
Bill says "what the heck" and pulls out a deck
"a little poker will take up the slack"

A make shift table on top of old cable
was level enough for a deal
he shuffled the cards for his mining pards
though he knew each one by feel

A hair raising feeling as Bill started dealing
made me turn to a ghostly arrival
an eerie apparition with roots in perdition
searching for means of survival

A rumbling cough dislodged a thick broth
of silica dust and green phlegm
that he spat toward the wall, rolled into a ball
and quivered in silent requiem

I fingered three Jacks and tried to relax
from a haunting premonition
things wouldn't go right on this fateful night
with this refugee from perdition

Relieved when I saw, two Kings on the draw
a full house the very first caper
I scribbled IOU, ten dollars would be due
the bearer of this slip of paper

Red says "I'm through" and Bill folded, too
as the ghost slowly pushed in his poke
a prospector's pride, gold gleaming inside
this wraith was going for broke

My senses went numb as the stub of a thumb
fanned his cards to see what he drew
he whispered "I'll call if it's winner take all
and your soul goes with the IOU"

It was then I remembered a miner dismembered
at this very shaft, I was told
crushed by a skip that fell from the lip
I shuddered and said "I'll fold"

Glasgow Bill

Put it on the cuff, that's enough of your guff
It's a boilermaker for me
and Scotch on the rocks for old Bill Cox
my pard from the Bessie G
he's a "Cousin Jack" and I've lost track
of where his home should be

The Couer D'Alene and Butte we've seen
Grass Valley along the way
a helluva hand but I can't understand
that lingo of Glasgow bay
where an ore shoot's a nipple and a bin is a tipple
and a hillside is a Bonny Brae

He's a pickypoke man, gather around if you can
and look at this scar on his chest
we were working the breast when he says "take a rest
while I tickle this devil's nest"
the back looked loose and when he gave it a goose
Bill Cox very nearly went West

The first slab to drop slid over the top
of the load on our last tunnel car
the next one hit Bill then shattered a sill
with a thund'rous, earth shaking jar
and there on the track lay a mashed Cousin Jack
groaning "Jackson, where is my bar"

His trusty pickypoke was bent, sprung and broke
laying under the slab on the sill
then he looked at his blood mixing slowly with mud
and says "well, let's set up and drill"
let's drink to this miner, there ain't any finer
from a tipple to a "Bonny Brae" hill

EPILOGUE

AN ESTIMATED FIVE MILLION TONS OF ORE were mined during Creede Camp's century of mining. The production records indicate that 3,994,020 tons of metallic ore were mined in the period from 1904 through 1985. *The Creede Candle* of January 6, 1893, lists the estimated total tonnage of ore shipped up to December 31, 1892, as 46,155 tons. An estimated 800,000 tons of metallic ore were mined between 1893 and 1904.[1] Production at the Wagon Wheel Gap Fluorspar Mine was 190,000 tons mined between 1911 and 1950.[2]

CREEDE CAMP MINERAL PRODUCTION
1891-1985

	Unit	Total Production	Average Price Year 2000*	Total Value
GoldTroy	Ounce	159,028	$ 280.32	$ 44,578,729
SilverTroy	Ounce	85,694,169	5.00	428,470,845
Copper	Short Ton	3,412	1,809.44	6,173,809
Lead	Short Ton	168,552	872.05	146,985,772
Zinc	Short Ton	54,117	1,116.15	60,402,690
Fluorspar	Short Ton	190,000	113.43	21,551,700
				$708,163,545

* U.S. Geological Survey's Mineral Yearbook prices for 2000.

Mineral production from 1891 through 1985 for gold, silver, copper, lead, zinc, and fluorspar at year 2000 prices has a value of more than $708 million. An additional $500,000 of gold, silver, and lead recovered in 1988 from ore mined by Homestake from the Equity Mine and $115,154 from cadmium mined by the Emperius Mining Company from 1965 to 1972 bring Creede Camp's total production for its century of mining to just under $709 million.

The production of ore from Creede Camp's mines required an estimated 182 miles of mine workings, including tunnels, adits, drifts, shafts, raises, and winzes to develop the ore bodies:

Area	Miles of Mine Openings
Amethyst Vein System	125[3]
Bulldog Mountain Mine	24[4]
East Willow Creek Mines	20[5]
Equity Mine	2.5[6]
Mammoth Mountain Mines	1[7]

Sunnyside and Monon Hill Mines	7.5[8]
Wagon Wheel Gap Fluorspar Mine	2[2]
	182

The Bulldog Mountain Mine was shut down at the end of January 1985 and was kept on a standby status until 1988, when Homestake Mining Company discontinued their exploration program at their Equity or North Amethyst property. Homestake Mining Company announced the decommissioning and final reclamation of the Bulldog Mountain Mine in a news release dated August 5, 1992:

> "Al Winters, Vice President and General Manager of Homestake Mining Company, announced the company will begin the decommissioning and final reclamation of the Bulldog Mountain Mine. Closure activities will include removal of the mill, sealing of portals, and recontouring and revegetation of disturbed areas.
>
> "During the late 1970s and early 1980s, the Bulldog Mountain Mine was the largest silver producer in Colorado and the fourth largest primary silver producer in the nation. From beginning of production in 1969 through placement on standby in 1985, the mine produced 25.3 million ounces of silver and 48.6 million pounds of lead.
>
> "During the past decade every primary silver producer in the nation has severely curtailed or ceased operations. A combination of factors including increased costs of production brought on by escalating regulatory demands, widespread environmental opposition, lack of access to mineralized areas on federal lands, and the continuing low price of silver, led Homestake to this decision to decommission the mine and complete final reclamation."

All of the mine and mill equipment was sold in 1993 as were the water treatment plant, warehouses, machine shop, and storage sheds. Dismantling of the buildings and reclamation of tailing ponds commenced in 1993. The Equity (North Amethyst) Mine site was reclaimed in 1993 and all tunnel portals were sealed. The Bulldog Mountain Mine site was reclaimed in 1994. The decommissioning and reclamation work was completed in July of that year.

In 2001, Homestake Mining Company held patented and unpatented claims at both the Bulldog Mountain and Equity Mines.

Reclamation of the Homestake Mine and
Mill Complex — 2003

Photo by the Author

The company did sell surface rights to most of their patented claims and retained mineral rights on all claims.[10] Since then, Homestake Mining Company has been absorbed into American Barrick, Inc., a subsidiary of Barrick Gold Corporation, a Canadian mining company.

Tyrus Poxson, son of Ben Poxson, the co-founder of the Emperius Mining Company, sold the mill complex to Minerals Engineering Company but retained title to the Emperius Mine properties. Title to the mill complex was transferred from Minerals Engineering to CoCa and finally to Hecla Mining Company. Reclamation of the Emperius Mill and tailing pond occurred in 2000. San Luis Valley Earthmovers of Monte Vista, Colorado, dismantled the mill, cleaned up the mill site, and capped the tailings pond for Hecla's subsidiary, Creede Resources, for an estimated $600,000. Hecla Mining Company now owns the mill site, the Cowboy Johnson Mine, and patented claims at Sunnyside.[11]

Many of the claims owned by Creede Mines have been sold. The famous Last Chance claim was sold by Ralph Granger's heirs to Jack Morris, who plans to turn it into a tourist attraction.

According to the *Federal Census*, Creede's population in 1960, at the beginning of the second boom, was 350; was 653 in 1970 at the beginning of production at the Bulldog Mountain Mine; and was 610 at the height of the second boom in 1980. The population dropped to 362 in 1990 after the mines closed and rebounded slightly in 2000 to 377.

Reclamation of
the Emperius
Mill Complex
— 2003. Mill
Site in the
Background
and the
Capped Tailing
Pond in the
Foreground
*Photo by the
Author*

THE TRANSITION FROM A MINING CAMP

Throughout its history, Creede had been a center for hunting, fishing, and other outdoor activities in the surrounding San Juan Mountains and this has continued unabated. When mining stopped, the town of Creede transformed itself into a mecca for tourists. In addition to outdoor activities, it has become a center for culture and an artist's paradise. Paul Davis, who spent the 1940s at Creede Camp as a miner and engineer, had these comments about Creede:

> *"What a transition, from a rough, tough mining camp born in the late 1800s, to a barely existent community 40 years later; in the years of the depression held together by pride and concern for one another. It was at the end of the depression that I showed up on the scene, just as there was a resurgence in the mining industry. The 1940s were exciting years. The Poxson — Nelson efforts kept the mines profitably working and the community in good shape. With the entry of Homestake in the 1960s, mining changed for the better.*
>
> *"As impressive to me as all the above is the innovative thinking, perseverance, courage, and resourcefulness with which the people of Creede have transformed the community to one basically existing on the fine arts and tourism from one totally dependent on mining for its existence. It resulted from a fierce resolve to keep Creede a viable community. The residents have much to be proud of and I join them in their pride."*[12]

The Creede Repertory Theater, started in 1966 during Creede's mining days by the Creede Junior Chamber of Commerce, is well known throughout the theatrical world. The Jaycees wanted to bring new business to Creede and felt that, since the movie house had been sponsoring amateur melodramas, a theater company would be appropriate. A letter describing the idea of a theater company was drafted and sent to ten universities and colleges but elicited no interest. One student, Steve Grossman at the University of Kansas, saw the letter and contacted Pastor Jim Livingston in Creede. As a result, twelve freshmen and sophomore students from the University of Kansas drove to Creede from Lawrence, Kansas, to begin "Operation Summer Theater."

The students were housed in the home of one of the local ranch owners and the restaurants in Creede took turns feeding them. The theater company was accepted by the citizens of Creede with open arms, and five plays were produced that first year in rotating repertory. The first play produced was *Mr. Roberts*. The KU students built sets, sewed costumes, rehearsed their lines, sold tickets, advertised their productions, and even installed a lighting system for the stage. The dressing room beneath the stage had originally been used to store coal. At the end of the first season, each student left Creede with a $50 paycheck for the summer and, most importantly, the satisfaction that he or she had been a part of a unique and satisfying experience. Kansas University supplied most of the actors during the early years of the Creede Repertory Theater, and several of the original twelve came back to Creede in 1977.

Over the years since its humble beginnings, the Creede Repertory Theater has evolved into an important economic asset to Creede and a training ground for young professional actors and actresses, many of whom have gone on to successful acting careers. The theater building was first renovated and then expanded to include an art gallery. The University of Colorado conducted an economic impact study of the arts in Colorado in 1982. The study concluded that the Creede Repertory Theater was responsible for generating nearly two million dollars in revenue that year. Aspiring young actors and actresses from all over the country vie for a place in the theater company. As an example, in 2001, applications from 2,500 aspiring individuals were received to fill forty-two openings.

The Creede Repertory Theater renovated the Rio Grande Hotel, built in 1892 and a survivor of floods and fires, to provide living quarters for the theater's cast. The renovation was supported by the

Colorado Historical Society, which awarded the Stephen Hart Award in 2001 in recognition of the Creede Repertory Theater's outstanding restoration of the hotel. The Rio Grande Hotel was added to the Colorado State Register of Historic Properties in 1995.

The theater was, no doubt, the most important factor in Creede's transition from dependence on the mines to a town supported by tourism and the arts. It sponsored other art forms, and art galleries now line Creede's Main Street. Creede is recognized as one of the top hundred art towns in the United States.[13]

The original Denver and Rio Grande Railroad depot was renovated and turned into the Creede Historical Museum. It is sponsored by the Creede Historical Society and supported by grants from the Colorado Historical Fund. Creede has maintained its mining town ambience and has honored its heritage by hosting mining contests at its annual "Days of '92" celebration; by building an underground fire station and an underground mining museum where all can see what the mines and the miners' work were like; and by creating the Bachelor Historic Tour, Creede's historic silver trail.

MINING CONTESTS

The "Days of '92" celebrations held on the Fourth of July are considerably different from those of days past — no whiskey drinking contests, no whiskey, or horse races. The modern celebrations include parades through Creede with floats sponsored by local businesses interspersed with various marching groups. Children along the parade are showered with candies from the floats. Raft races down the Rio Grande River were part of the celebration. Pie baking and eating contests, fly casting matches, barbecues, street dancing, and fireworks displays have been a part of the celebration. Mining contests are still an important part of the Days of '92. In fact, the annual Colorado State Mining Championship contests have been held in Creede since 1988. The singlejack contest at Creede lasts five minutes and the holes are drilled in Gunnison Blue Granite by using a five-pound hammer and wedge bits no less than 3/4-inches in diameter. The top ten winning depths for singlejack holes in the Creede contests range from 8.638 to 9.791 inches. The two-man doublejack contest lasts ten minutes and the holes are drilled in Gunnison Blue Granite using a ten-pound hammer and no less than a 7/8-inch wedge drill bit. The top winning depths at the Creede doublejack drilling contests range from 25.321 to 26.906 inches. The machine drilling contest is a timed event for drilling two

three-foot deep holes in rhyolite. Contestants come to
Creede to compete from all
over the West.[14]

UNDERGROUND
FIRE STATION

Work commenced in 1976 on
Creede's underground fire station, located under the cliff on
the west side of Willow Creek
Canyon above Windy Gulch in
what was called "Stringtown."
A tunnel eighteen feet wide
and fourteen feet high was
driven into the face of the cliff
a distance of 139 feet. Six lateral tunnels were driven off
the main tunnel to house the
fire equipment and provide
space for an office and
kitchen. The laterals are thirty

Singlejack Drilling Contest —
Tom Payne
Courtesy of Ken Wyley

feet long, twelve feet wide, and twelve to fourteen feet in height. The
fire station was constructed by Creede's volunteer firemen, miners,
and engineers who donated their labor. Explosives were donated by
the Atlas Powder Company and the DuPont Company. Other companies donated the use of mining equipment and blasting supplies.
The fire station, completed in August 1982, is a unique facility and
a tribute to Creede's mining heritage. Colorado Governor Richard
Lamm sent a letter to the community commending the volunteers
for their work.

UNDERGROUND MINING MUSEUM

The Underground Mining Museum, located immediately north of
the fire station, was also excavated beneath the cliff on the west side
of Willow Creek. Work began in November 1990 and was completed in time for Creede's centennial celebration on July 4, 1992.

The project commenced with the blasting of the cliff face to
make room for construction equipment and parking. Tunneling
began in the spring of 1993. Tom Payne, Chuck Fairchild, and
Robert Hosselkus drove a 450-foot long horseshoe-shaped tunnel, a

cross-shaped community center, a gift shop area, and a small theater into the cliff. They also excavated chambers along the tunnel to hold mining exhibits that illustrate the equipment, tools, and methods used during Creede Camp's century of mining. A wood cribbing facade was added to the outside of the museum's entrance.[15]

The tunnel and display areas were left rough with a coating of wire mesh and gunite, a concrete mixture sprayed on the rock surfaces to cover the wire mesh, for ground support. The wire mesh is attached by rock bolts anchored in holes drilled into the sides and back of the openings. The museum contains twenty-two mining displays. In 1992, the first year of its operation, the museum was visited by 14,000 people. The Community Center, after being coated with gunite, was finished with conventional walls and ceiling. It contains 3,500 square feet of floor space, has a seating capacity of 200, a full kitchen, bathroom facilities, audio and video equipment, and a dance floor.

BACHELOR HISTORIC TOUR

The Bachelor Historic Tour is seventeen miles long and starts from the south end of Creede. It proceeds north through the town of Creede past the Underground Mining Museum to the confluence of East and West Willow Creeks, the site of the Humphreys Mill. It then follows West Willow Creek past the Commodore, Amethyst, Last Chance, and Midwest Mines to its northernmost point, the Equity Mine. It then backtracks south to Allen's Crossing where the route crosses West Willow Creek and passes the Park Regent Mine, Bachelor Town Site, and the Bulldog Mountain Mine to its starting point. There are eighteen interpretive stops on the tour that are marked by signs and described in a brochure prepared for the tour.

Creede, Colorado — circa 1978

Courtesy of Pan Eimon

APPENDICES

	ORE	GOLD		SILVER		COPPER	
Year	Tons	Ounces	Value	Ounces	Value	Pounds	Value
1891			$10,055	378,889	$374,382		
1892			$87,219	2,391,514	$2,080,617		
1893			$53,252	4,897,684	$3,820,194		
1894			$40,336	1,866,927	$1,176,164		
1895			$114,482	1,423,038	$924,975		
1896			$52,238	1,560,865	$1,061,388		
1897			$61,328	3,070,576	$1,842,346	1,500	$180
1898			$46,383	4,177,184	$2,464,539	14,729	$1,826
1899			$91,671	3,796,899	$2,278,139	20,223	$3,458
1900			$209,387	2,280,038	$1,413,623	2,614	$434
1901			$102,813	1,816,023	$1,089,614	1,007	$168
1902			$112,838	1,923,973	$1,019,706		
1903			$178,961	1,608,788	$868,746	133	$18
1904	124,278		$222,864	1,664,633	$965,487	1,337	$171
1905	91,338		$216,994	1,193,442	$728,000	107	$17
1906	126,124		$176,150	1,254,058	$852,759		
1907	104,977		$142,803	1,246,961	$822,994	12,711	$52,542
1908	61,131		$127,549	830,951	$440,404	41	$5
1909	64,941		$108,825	891,185	$463,416	17,401	$2,262
1910	62,956		$121,181	773,722	$417,810	29,031	$3,687
1911	65,932		$179,196	545,319	$289,019	33,384	$4,173
1912	66,488		$86,002	714,909	$439,669	23,885	$3,941
1913	56,763		$50,282	805,343	$486,427	31,647	$4,905
1914	27,952		$19,304	615,734	$340,501	32,586	$84,334
1915	28,071		$33,039	291,807	$147,946	8,943	$1,565
1916	38,103		$31,124	373,956	$246,063	13,138	$3,232
1917	32,755		$10,101	361,517	$297,890	19,297	$5,268
1918	28,372	674	$13,943	640,959	$640,959	3,490	$862
1919	16,718	469	$9,083	369,575	$413,924	355	$66
1920	12,597		$5,710	272,322	$296,831	1,120	$208
1921	7,076		$3,816	192,468	$192,468	1,899	$245
1922	3,978		$1,654	106,903	$106,903	3,422	$462
1923	6,462		$2,394	228,867	$187,871	1,088	$160
1924	4,647	72	$1,494	239,149	$160,230		
1925	8,047	43	$885	738,735	$512,682		
1926	8,855	33	$672	551,468	$344,116		
1927	3,592	12	$246	214,850	$121,820		
1928	4,021	24	$490	210,159	$122,943		
1929	5,436	122	$2,517	612,497	$326,461		
1930	4,576	114	$2,364	396,044	$152,477		
1931	0						
1932	0						
1933		9	$186				
1934	5,907	55	$1,922	479,890	$310,232		
1935	9,312	22	$753	499,600	$359,145		
1936	10,738			422,071	$326,894		
1937	12,734	4	$154	321,546	$248,716		
1938	35,656	187	$6,545	457,595	$295,819		
1939	37,083	709	$24,815	596,858	$405,140	1,300	$135
1940	41,113	893	$31,255	866,402	$616,108	10,200	$1,153
1941	41,568	904	$31,640	906,712	$644,773	32,000	$3,776
1942	39,243	644	$22,540	805,202	$572,588	77,600	$9,390
1943	30,290	465	$16,275	630,952	$448,677	101,000	$13,130
1944	27,883	444	$15,540	518,161	$368,470	75,000	$10,125
1945	18,354	238	$8,330	433,177	$308,037	69,400	$9,369
1946	16,032	175	$6,125	355,110	$266,929	61,000	$9,882

Mineral Production for Mineral County, Colorado, Page 1

LEAD		ZINC		CADMIUM	TOTAL VALUE	
Pounds	Value	Pounds	Value	Value		Year
354,854	$15,259				$399,696	1891
3,000,000	$120,000				$2,287,836	1892
7,500,000	$277,500				$4,150,946	1893
6,500,000	$214,500				$1,431,000	1894
8,220,870	$263,068				$1,302,525	1895
6,021,109	$180,633				$1,294,259	1896
6,080,673	$218,904				$2,122,758	1897
5,453,104	$207,218	200,000	$9,200		$2,729,166	1898
5,677,162	$255,472	100,000	$5,800		$2,634,540	1899
14,951,956	$657,886	450,000	$19,800		$2,301,130	1900
10,519,895	$452,355	1,800,000	$73,800		$1,718,750	1901
9,291,358	$380,946	2,047,555	$96,283		$1,611,773	1902
8,600,646	$361,227	2,634,000	$142,236		$1,551,188	1903
13,348,436	$573,897	4,402,697	$224,538		$1,986,957	1904
11,880,797	$558,397	2,515,628	$148,422		$1,651,830	1905
14,886,356	$848,522	2,892,061	$176,416		$2,053,847	1906
12,980,288	$687,955	2,691,216	$158,782		$1,815,076	1907
8,238,025	$345,997	1,100,107	$51,705		$965,660	1908
9,036,816	$388,583	1,817,296	$98,134		$1,061,220	1909
8,246,000	$362,824	2,421,926	$130,784		$1,036,286	1910
7,674,556	$345,355	1,258,561	$71,738		$889,481	1911
5,730,222	$257,860	308,681	$21,299		$808,771	1912
3,398,364	$149,528	454,875	$25,473		$716,615	1913
1,401,795	$54,670				$418,809	1914
2,382,128	$111,960	85,984	$10,662		$305,172	1915
2,295,087	$158,361	240,575	$32,237		$471,017	1916
1,305,744	$112,294	54,971	$5,607		$431,160	1917
989,620	$70,263				$726,027	1918
934,113	$49,508	96,274	$7,028		$479,609	1919
531,537	$42,523				$345,270	1920
156,778	$7,055				$203,584	1921
153,455	$8,440				$117,459	1922
237,557	$16,629	41,000	$2,788		$209,642	1923
191,562	$15,325	41,000	$2,665		$179,714	1924
501,000	$43,587	8,000	$608		$557,762	1925
354,700	$28,376				$373,164	1926
75,286	$4,743				$126,809	1927
23,000	$1,334				$124,767	1928
271,000	$17,073				$346,051	1929
148,600	$7,430				$162,271	1930
					$0	1931
					$0	1932
					$186	1933
176,900	$6,545				$318,699	1934
351,800	$14,072				$373,970	1935
370,800	$17,057				$343,951	1936
278,000	$16,402				$265,272	1937
241,006	$11,806				$314,170	1938
718,000	$33,746				$463,836	1939
1,299,000	$64,950				$713,466	1940
1,140,000	$64,980				$745,169	1941
1,051,600	$70,457				$674,975	1942
1,155,000	$86,625	13,000	$1,404		$566,111	1943
957,000	$76,560	15,000	$1,710		$472,405	1944
605,000	$52,030	9,000	$1,035		$378,801	1945
492,000	$53,628	6,000	$732		$357,296	1946

Mineral Production for Mineral County, Colorado, Page 2

Year	ORE Tons	GOLD Ounces	Value	SILVER Ounces	Value	COPPER Pounds	Value
1947	24,760	245	$8,575	317,712	$287,529	46,600	$9,786
1948	28,614	247	$8,645	297,926	$269,638	36,000	$7,812
1949	38,262	779	$27,265	263,867	$238,813	74,000	$14,578
1950	47,072	803	$28,105	345,247	$312,466	68,000	$14,144
1951	45,422	804	$28,140	236,652	$214,182	50,000	$12,100
1952	41,685	1,122	$39,270	174,219	$157,677	48,000	$11,616
1953	37,372	1,257	$43,995	173,966	$157,488	24,000	$6,888
1954	45,399	1,964	$68,740	238,685	$216,022	50,000	$14,750
1955	28,596	1,025	$35,875	135,640	$122,761	36,000	$13,428
1956	29,432	802	$28,070	111,731	$101,122	47,200	$20,060
1957	50,010	2,822	$98,770	279,249	$252,734	136,200	$40,996
1958	26,981	785	$27,745	92,841	$84,026	79,400	$20,882
1959	29,314	800	$28,000	131,433	$118,954	125,900	$38,651
1960	38,541	833	$29,155	237,364	$214,826	315,000	$101,115
1961	41,657	624	$21,840	303,995	$281,040	549,000	$164,700
1962	44,382	570	$19,950	276,356	$299,846	434,900	$133,949
1963	26,039	440	$15,400	252,555	$323,043	281,800	$86,794
1964	41,993	495	$17,325	284,716	$368,138	530,400	$172,910
1965	43,182	547	$19,145	185,449	$239,785	477,500	$169,035
1966	44,895	618	$21,630	143,034	$184,943	464,000	$167,829
1967	44,135	446	$15,610	111,365	$172,616	482,000	$184,326
1968	41,004	516	$20,258	96,740	$207,469	182,000	$75,743
1969	101,489	822	$30,460	1,226,285	$1,835,339	352,000	$154,124
1970	138,474	595	$21,266	1,670,691	$3,268,031	226,000	$121,863
1971	119,951	185	$7,631	2,063,993	$3,190,933	290,000	$151,164
1972	104,750	91	$4,879	1,979,132	$2,595,701	100,000	$49,848
1973	86,683			2,091,483	$4,600,000		
1974	100,285	77	$25,103	1,248,875	$5,476,717	18,000	$21,823
1975	172,485	955	$853,722	1,717,586	$6,422,811	390,000	$359,897
1976	149,983	875	$109,655	1,827,343	$5,649,042	208,000	$131,040
1977	113,672			2,047,009	$8,064,327		
1978	110,385			2,102,050	$10,348,104		
1979	97,438			1,413,244	$15,672,876		
1980	100,579			1,453,439	$29,998,981		
1981	104,000			1,414,000	$14,875,280		
1982	89,000			1,358,000	$10,796,100		
1983	82,000			1,262,000	$14,437,280		
1984	90,000			1,275,000	$10,378,500		
1985	2,000			30,000	$184,200		
1988							
TOTAL	**3,994,020**	**159,028**	**$4,601,710**	**85,694,169**	**$188,743,171**	**6,824,488**	**$2,572,998**

Production figures, 1891 – 1923, from Henderson, Charles W., Mining in Colorado, Professional
    Paper No. 138, 1926, pg. 181.
Production figures, 1924 – 1968, compiled by the U. S. Bureau of Mines.
Production figures, 1969 – 1985, from Nelson, Martin A., Summary Report on the Creede
    Formation Project, 1989, pg. 18.
Value of gold, silver, and lead from ore processed by Homestake in 1988 by Robert A. Boppe.

LEAD		ZINC		CADMIUM	TOTAL VALUE	
Pounds	Value	Pounds	Value	Value		Year
658,400	$94,810	14,730	$1,694		$402,394	1947
902,000	$161,458	176,000	$23,408		$470,961	1948
2,324,000	$367,192	1,342,000	$166,408		$814,256	1949
2,844,000	$383,940	1,746,000	$247,932		$986,587	1950
2,334,000	$403,782	1,784,000	$324,688		$982,892	1951
3,026,000	$487,186	2,048,000	$339,968		$1,035,717	1952
3,392,000	$444,352	1,716,000	$197,340		$850,063	1953
4,356,000	$596,772	2,222,000	$239,976		$1,136,280	1954
2,384,000	$355,216	1,490,000	$183,270		$710,550	1955
2,531,100	$397,383	1,853,400	$253,918		$800,551	1956
4,462,200	$638,095	3,638,800	$422,101		$1,452,698	1957
2,466,400	$298,434	2,038,200	$209,935		$641,022	1958
3,229,000	$393,938	2,549,600	$293,204		$872,747	1959
4,353,300	$509,336	3,836,500	$496,827		$1,351,259	1960
3,767,800	$388,083	4,742,200	$545,353		$1,401,016	1961
3,934,400	$377,702	4,647,100	$534,417		$1,365,884	1962
2,409,800	$267,489	3,287,600	$381,362		$1,074,088	1963
3,083,000	$403,573	4,876,200	$663,163		$1,625,409	1964
3,098,200	$483,319	4,571,200	$667,395	$23,189	$1,601,868	1965
3,077,000	$465,089	3,975,100	$576,390	$31,000	$1,446,881	1966
2,902,000	$406,378	4,296,000	$594,820	$18,000	$1,391,750	1967
3,186,000	$420,948	3,058,000	$412,911	$170	$1,137,499	1968
5,254,000	$742,544	4,130,000	$605,045		$3,367,512	1989
6,306,000	$910,857	3,222,000	$493,610	$35,943	$4,851,570	1970
5,280,000	$728,736	4,764,000	$767,020		$4,845,484	1971
3,964,000	$395,469	890,000	$157,975	$6,852	$3,210,724	1972
3,708,000	$500,000				$5,100,000	1973
3,126,000	$776,893	262,000	$94,189		$6,394,725	1974
7,732,000	$1,739,175	4,550,000	$1,772,680		$11,148,285	1975
7,538,000	$959,958	2,802,000	$1,037,020		$7,886,715	1976
4,078,000	$970,503				$9,034,830	1977
4,106,000	$985,596				$11,333,700	1978
2,756,000	$937,040				$16,609,916	1979
2,088,000	$876,960				$30,875,941	1980
2,600,000	$962,000				$15,837,280	1981
1,800,000	$468,000				$11,264,100	1982
1,800,000	$396,000				$14,833,280	1983
1,800,000	$324,000				$10,702,500	1984
68,000	$12,240				$196,440	1985
					$500,000	1988
337,103,149	$30,872,341	108,234,037	$14,226,903	$115,154	$241,632,337	TOTAL

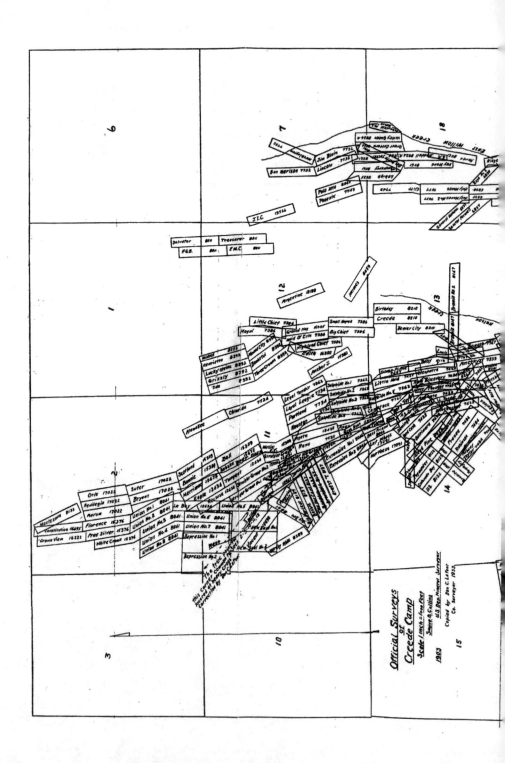

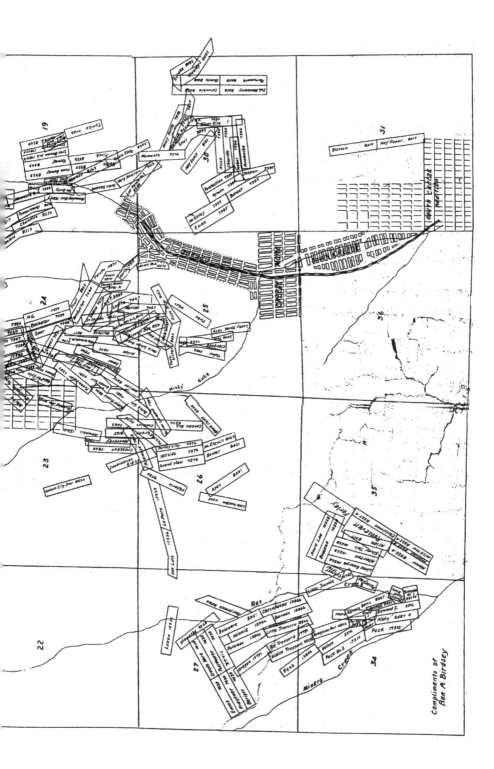

Compliments of
Ben A. Birdsey

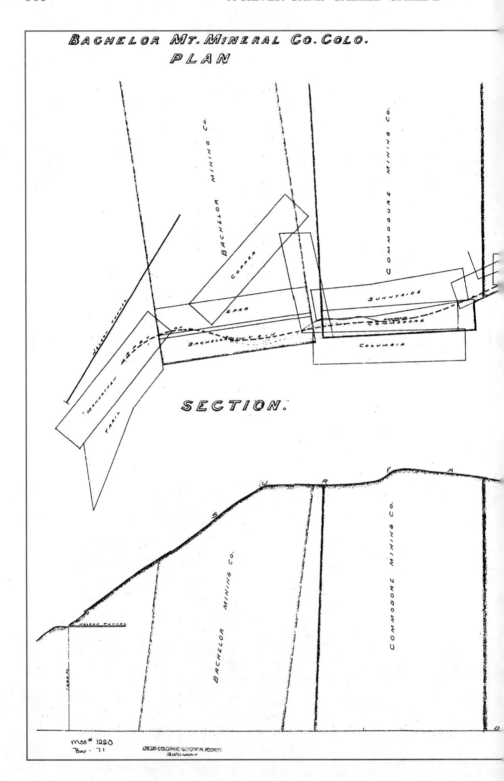

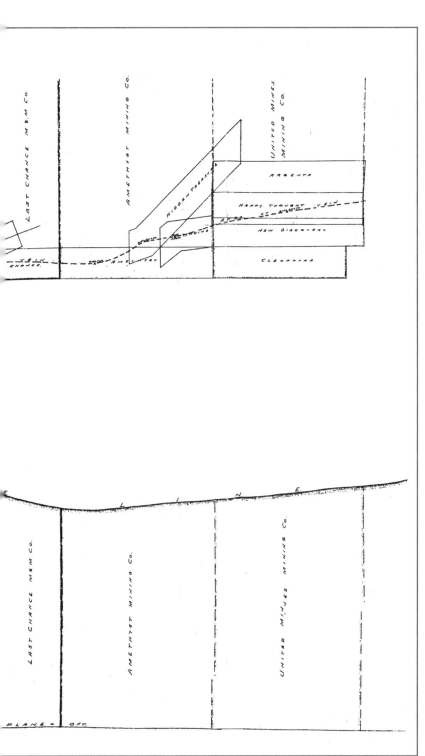

NOTES

PROLOGUE

1. Cross, Whitman; Howe, Earnest; Ransome, F.L., *Geologic Atlas of the United States: Silverton Folio*, U.S. Geological Survey, Washington, D.C., Government Printing Office, 1905.
2. Emmons, W.H. and Larsen, E.S., *Geology and Ore Deposits of the Creede District*, U.S. Geological Survey Bulletin 718, Washington, D.C., Government Printing Office, 1923.
3. Steven, Thomas A. and Ratté, James C., *USGS Professional Paper 487: Geology and Structural Control of Ore Deposition in the Creede District, San Juan Mountains, Colorado*, U.S. Geological Survey, Washington, D.C., Government Printing Office, 1965.
4. *Yearbook*. U.S. Geological Survey, Washington, D.C., Government Printing Office, 1980, pg. 48.
5. Smith, R.L. and Bailey, R.A., *Resurgent Cauldrons*, in Coats, R.R., Hag, R.L. and Anderson, C.A., eds., *Studies in Volcanology*; Geological Society of America Memoir 116, Boulder, CO, 1968.
6. Francis, Peter, "Giant Volcanic Calderas," *Scientific American*, June, 1983.
7. Lipman, Peter W., *Central San Juan Cluster: Regional Volcanic Framework in Ancient Lake Creede*, Geological Society of America Special Paper 346, Boulder, CO, 2000, pg. 74.
8. Emmons, W.H. and Larsen, E.S., *Geology and Ore Deposits of the Creede District*, U.S. Geological Survey Bulletin 718, Washington, D.C., Government Printing Office, 1923, pg. 61.
9. Steven, Thomas A. and Ratté, James C., *USGS Professional Paper 487: Geology and Structural Control of Ore Deposition in the Creede District, San Juan Mountains, Colorado*, U.S. Geological Survey, Washington, D.C., Government Printing Office, 1965, pg. 84.
10. Eckel, Edwin B., *Minerals of Colorado*, Golden, Colorado, Fulcrum Publishing, 1997, pg. 23.
11. Ibid.
12. Axelrod, Daniel I., *The Late Oligocene Creede Flora, Colorado*, University of California Publications in Geological Sciences, vol. 130, 1987.
13. Spero, Vince, Monte Vista, Colorado, Telephone Interview, 2002.
14. Martorano, et al., *Colorado Prehistory: A Context for the Rio Grande Basin*, Denver, Colorado, Colorado Council of Professional Archeologists, 1999.
15. Bean, Luther E., "Land of the Blue Sky People," Monte Vista, Colorado, *The Monte Vista Journal*, 1962, pg. 43.
16. Brown, *An Empire of Silver: A History of the San Juan Silver Rush*, Caldwell, Idaho, Caxton Printers, Ltd., 1965, pg. 55.
17. McCullough, Frances, "The Barlow and Sanderson Stage Line in the San Luis Valley," *The San Luis Valley Historian*, Volume XXX, No. 3, 1998, pg. 18.
18. Kindquist, Cathy E., *Stony Pass: The Tumbling and Impetuous Trail*, Silverton, Colorado, San Juan Book Company, 1987, pg. 23.
19. McCullough, Frances, "The Barlow and Sanderson Stage Line in the San Luis Valley," *The San Luis Valley Historian*, Volume XXX, No. 3, 1998, pp. 22-23.
20. Mumey, Nolie, *Creede: History of a Colorado Silver Mining Town*, Denver, Colorado, Artcraft Press, 1949, pg. 5.
21. LaFont, John, *The Homesteaders of the Upper Rio Grande*, Birmingham, Alabama, Oxmoor Press, 1971, pg. 14.
22. Ibid., pg. 40.
23. Mumey, Nolie, *Creede: History of a Colorado Silver Mining Town*, Denver, Colorado, Artcraft Press, 1949, pp. 26-27.
24. Getz, Carol Ann Wetherill, "The Wason Legend," *The San Luis Valley Historian*, Volume XI, Number 4, Alamosa, Colorado, 1979.

CHAPTER 1 – DISCOVERY

1. *The Engineering and Mining Journal*, August 5, 1893.
2. Emmons, W.H. and Larsen, E.S., *Geology and Ore Deposits of the Creede District*, U.S. Geological Survey Bulletin 718, Washington, D.C., Government Printing Office, 1923, pg. 3.
3. LaFont, John, *The Homesteaders of the Upper Rio Grande*, Birmingham, Alabama, Oxmoor Press, 1971, pg. 34.
4. Canfield, John G., *Mines and Mining Men of Colorado: The Principal Producing Mines of Gold and Silver, The Bonanza Kings and Successful Prospectors, The Picturesque Camps and Thriving Cities*, Denver, Colorado, John G. Canfield, Publisher, 1893, pg. 62; and Meeves, Henry C. and Darnell, Richard P., *Study of the Silver Potential, Creede District, Mineral County, Colorado*, U.S. Department of the Interior, Bureau of Mines Information Circular 8370, Washington, D.C., Government Printing Office, 1968, pg. 29.
5. Emmons, W.H. and Larsen, E.S., *Geology and Ore Deposits of the Creede District*, U.S. Geological Survey Bulletin 718, Washington, D.C., Government Printing Office, 1923, pg. 3.
6. Ibid.
7. *The Creede Candle*, January 7, 1892.
8. Canfield, John G., *Mines and Mining Men of Colorado: The Principal Producing Mines of Gold and Silver, The Bonanza Kings and Successful Prospectors, The Picturesque Camps and Thriving Cities*, Denver, Colorado, John G. Canfield, Publisher, 1893, pg. 59.
9. Ibid., pg. 61.
10. Emmons, W.H. and Larsen, E.S., *Geology and Ore Deposits of the Creede District*, U.S. Geological Survey Bulletin 718, Washington, D.C., Government Printing Office, 1923, pg. 148.
11. Canfield, John G., *Mines and Mining Men of Colorado: The Principal Producing Mines of Gold and Silver, The Bonanza Kings and Successful Prospectors, The Picturesque Camps and Thriving Cities,* Denver, Colorado, John G. Canfield, Publisher, 1893, pg. 68.
12. Emmons, W.H. and Larsen, E.S., *Geology and Ore Deposits of the Creede District*, U.S. Geological Survey Bulletin 718, Washington, D.C., Government Printing Office, 1923, pg. 3.
13. Ibid., pg. 159.
14. Canfield, John G., *Mines and Mining Men of Colorado: The Principal Producing Mines of Gold and Silver, The Bonanza Kings and Successful Prospectors, The Picturesque Camps and Thriving Cities*, Denver, Colorado, John G. Canfield, Publisher, 1893, pg. 61.
15. Emmons, W.H. and Larsen, E.S., *Geology and Ore Deposits of the Creede District*, U.S. Geological Survey Bulletin 718, Washington, D.C., Government Printing Office, 1923, pg. 4.
16. Canfield, John G., *Mines and Mining Men of Colorado: The Principal Producing Mines of Gold and Silver, The Bonanza Kings and Successful Prospectors, The Picturesque Camps and Thriving Cities*, Denver, Colorado, John G. Canfield, Publisher, 1893, pg. 62. John MacKenzie's biography is, for the most part, from Canfield.
17. LaFont, John, *The Homesteaders of the Upper Rio Grande*, Birmingham, Alabama, Oxmoor Press, 1971, pg. 34.
18. Mumey, Nolie, *Creede: History of a Colorado Silver Mining Town*, Denver, Colorado, Artcraft Press, 1949, pg. 19.
19. Canfield, John G., *Mines and Mining Men of Colorado: The Principal Producing Mines of Gold and Silver, The Bonanza Kings and Successful Prospectors, The Picturesque Camps and Thriving Cities,* Denver, Colorado, John G. Canfield, Publisher, 1893, pg. 62. Richard Irwin's biography is, for the most part, from Canfield.
20. Guyot, N.E., "Cripple Creek: An Inside Story — II," *Engineering and Mining Journal-Press*, December 20, 1924.
21. *The Denver Republican*, July 13, 1897. Nicholas C. Creede's biography is, for the most part, from *The Denver Republican* article.
22. Letter from John Jackson to the author, dated January 23, 2001.
23. Emmons, W.H. and Larsen, E.S., *Geology and Ore Deposits of the Creede District*, U.S. Geological Survey Bulletin 718, Washington, D.C., Government Printing Office, 1923, pg. 3.
24. Canfield, John G., *Mines and Mining Men of Colorado: The Principal Producing Mines of Gold and Silver, The Bonanza Kings and Successful Prospectors, The Picturesque Camps and Thriving Cities*, Denver, Colorado, John G. Canfield, Publisher, 1893, pg. 61.
25. *The Creede Candle*, February 2, 1920.
26. Born's obituary copied from a Silverton, Colorado, newspaper dated June, 1908, in the Creede Historical Society files.
27. Canfield, John G., *Mines and Mining Men of Colorado: The Principal Producing Mines of Gold and Silver, The Bonanza Kings and Successful Prospectors, The Picturesque Camps and Thriving Cities*, Denver, Colorado, John G. Canfield, Publisher, 1893, pp. 62-63.

28. *The Monte Vista Journal*, October 17, 1975. Julius Haase's biography is, for the most part, from the *Journal* article.
29. *The Denver Republican*, July 13, 1897. Eric Van Buddenbrock's biography is, for the most part, from *The Denver Republican* article.
30. Ibid.
31. Canfield, John G., *Mines and Mining Men of Colorado: The Principal Producing Mines of Gold and Silver, The Bonanza Kings and Successful Prospectors, The Picturesque Camps and Thriving Cities*, Denver, Colorado, John G. Canfield, Publisher, 1893, pp. 60-63.

CHAPTER 2 – HERE COMES THE RAILROAD
1. Athearn, Robert G., *Rebel of the Rockies: A History of the Denver and Rio Grande Western Railroad*, New Haven and London, Yale University Press, 1962, pg. 5.
2. Author's calculations.
3. Griswold, Don L. and Harvey, Jean, *The Carbonate Camp Called Leadville*, Denver, Colorado, The University of Denver Press, 1951, pg. 61-61.
4. Henderson, Charles W., *Mining in Colorado: A History of Discovery, Development and Production*, U.S. Geological Survey Professional Paper No. 138, Washington, D.C., Government Printing Office, 1926, pg. 41.
5. *The Engineering and Mining Journal*, October 2, 1897.
6. Athearn, Robert G., *Rebel of the Rockies: A History of the Denver and Rio Grande Western Railroad*, New Haven and London, Yale University Press, 1962, pp. 175-176.
7. *The Denver Republican*, December 12, 1891.
8. Mumey, Nolie, *Creede: History of a Colorado Silver Mining Town*, Denver, Colorado, Artcraft Press, 1949, pp. 49 and 54.
9. *The Engineering and Mining Journal*, February 13, 1892.
10. *The Rocky Mountain News*, January 17, 1892.
11. Davis, Richard Harding, *The West From a Car Window*, New York, Harper & Bros., 1892.
12. Mumey, Nolie, *Creede: History of a Colorado Silver Mining Town*, Denver, Colorado, Artcraft Press, 1949, pg. 50.

CHAPTER 3 – POLITICS AND THE PRICE OF SILVER
1. Henderson, Charles W., *Mining in Colorado: A History of Discovery, Development and Production*, U.S. Geological Survey Professional Paper No. 138, Washington, D.C., Government Printing Office, 1926, pg. 181.
2. Griswold, Don L. and Harvey, Jean, *The Carbonate Camp Called Leadville*, Denver, Colorado, The University of Denver Press, 1951, pg. 56. Jacob Sanders (Saunders) was a Leadville mine investor. He and two others divided $150,000 on the sale of the Small Hopes Mining Pool property about 1879.
3. Nye, Robert E., Nycon Resources, Inc., Lakewood, Colorado, Interview, July, 2001.

CHAPTER 4 – THE PROSPECTORS
1. Canfield, John G., *Mines and Mining Men of Colorado: The Principal Producing Mines of Gold and Silver, The Bonanza Kings and Successful Prospectors, The Picturesque Camps and Thriving Cities*, Denver, Colorado, John G. Canfield, Publisher, 1893, pp. 59-60.
2. *The Engineering and Mining Journal*, March 5, 1892.
3. Ibid.
4. Ibid., March 10, 1894.
5. *Mining and Scientific Press*, May 14, 1921.
6. *Colorado Business Directory*, 1895.
7. *Mining and Scientific Review*, XXVIII, January-June, 1892, Rio Grande County, pg. 9; and Emmons, W.H. and Larsen, E.S., *Geology and Ore Deposits of the Creede District*, U.S. Geological Survey Bulletin 718, Washington, D.C., Government Printing Office, 1923, pg. 4.
8. Barnes, Chuck, *The Creede Candle: A compilation of news reports appearing in The Creede Candle beginning with the January 7, 1892, edition and depicting the history of Creede*, Creede, Colorado, 1993.
9. Ibid.
10. Peele, Robert, *Mining Engineers' Handbook*, New York, John Wiley & Sons, Inc., 1950, pp. 24-06.
11. Ibid.

12. Ibid., pp. 24-07.
13. Costigan, George P., Jr., *Cases on the American Law of Mining*, Indianapolis, Indiana, Bobbs-Merrill Company, 1929, pg. 445.
14. Peele, Robert, *Mining Engineers' Handbook*, New York, John Wiley & Sons, Inc., 1950, pp. 24-03.

CHAPTER 5 – THE EARLY INVESTORS
1. Canfield, John G., *Mines and Mining Men of Colorado: The Principal Producing Mines of Gold and Silver, The Bonanza Kings and Successful Prospectors, The Picturesque Camps and Thriving Cities*, Denver, Colorado, John G. Canfield, Publisher, 1893, pg. 59.
2. *The Creede Candle*, January 7, 1892.
3. Hubbard, Judson Slater, *A Man of Business and the Enterprises: Memoirs of Judson Slater Hubbard*, 1979, pg. 18.
4. Albert E. Reynolds Collection No. 1220, Colorado Historical Society's Stephen H. Hart Library, Denver, Colorado.
5. Emmons, W.H. and Larsen, E.S., *Geology and Ore Deposits of the Creede District*, U.S. Geological Survey Bulletin 718, Washington, D.C., Government Printing Office, 1923, pp. 3-4.
6. Ibid., pg. 4.
7. *American National Biography*, Auspices of the American Council of Learned Societies, New York, Oxford University Press, 1999.
8. Bollinger, Edward T. and Bauer, Frederick, *The Moffat Road*, Denver, Colorado, Sage Books, 1962, pg. 15.
9. Athearn, Robert G., *Rebel of the Rockies: A History of the Denver and Rio Grande Western Railroad*, New Haven and London, Yale University Press, 1962, pp. 160-161.
10 Beebe, Lucius and Clegg, Charles, *Narrow Gauge in the Rockies*, Berkeley, California, Howell-North, 1958, pg. 123.
11. Ibid, pg. 167.
12. Bollinger, Edward T. and Bauer, Frederick, *The Moffat Road*, Denver, Colorado, Sage Books, 1962, pp. 20-21.
13. Kohl, Edith Eudora, *Denver's Historic Mansions*, Denver, Colorado, Sage Books, 1957, pg. 249.
14. Berteloop, Paul Gordon, *The History of Creede: A Mining Camp in its Early Days*, University of Denver, Thesis for a Master's Degree, August, 1953, pg. 22.
15. Edwin L. Bennett, Names of Residents and Business Firms of Creede, Colorado, to 1901.
16. LaFont, John, *The Homesteaders of the Upper Rio Grande*, Birmingham, Alabama, Oxmoor Press, 1971, pg. 37; and *The Creede Candle*, December 30, 1892.
17. Ambrose, Stephen E., *Nothing Like It in the World: The Men Who Built the Transcontinental Railroad, 1863-1869*, New York, Simon & Schuster, 2000, pg. 344.
18. *Pliny Fisk Sharp Scrapbooks*, Denver Public Library, Western History Collection, Denver, Colorado, Volume 8, pg. 53. Original source of the obituary not known.
19. *American National Biography*, Auspices of the American Council of Learned Societies, New York, Oxford University Press, 1999.
20. Carter, C. Joe, "The San Luis Valley Senator, Thomas Meade Bowen," *The San Luis Valley Historian*, Volume XXIII, Number 1, Alamosa, Colorado, 1991, pg. 5.
21. Henderson, Charles W., *Mining in Colorado: A History of Discovery, Development and Production*, U.S. Geological Survey Professional Paper No. 138, Washington, D.C., Government Printing Office, 1926, pg. 203.
22. *American National Biography*, Auspices of the American Council of Learned Societies, New York, Oxford University Press, 1999.
23. Riggenbach, Emma M., *A Bridge to Yesterday*, Monte Vista, Colorado, High Valley Press, 1982, pg. 299.
24. Hall, Frank, *History of the State of Colorado*, Chicago, Illinois, Blakely Printing Company, 1895.
25. Scamehorn, Lee, *Albert Eugene Reynolds: Colorado's Mining King*, Norman, Oklahoma, University of Oklahoma Press, 1995, pp. 5-6. Reynold's biography is, for the most part, taken from Scamehorn's book.
26. Hubbard, Judson Slater, *A Man of Business and the Enterprises: Memoirs of Judson Slater Hubbard*, 1979, pg. 16. Humphrey's biography is, for the most part, taken from Hubbard's unpublished work.

27. LaFont, John, *The Homesteaders of the Upper Rio Grande*, Birmingham, Alabama, Oxmoor Press, 1971, pg. 60.
28. Riggenbach, Emma M., *A Bridge to Yesterday*, Monte Vista, Colorado, High Valley Press, 1982, pg. 57.
29. Ferguson, Charles W., "Unforgettable DeWitt Wallace," *Readers' Digest*, February, 1987.

CHAPTER 6 – BOOM TIMES
1. *The Engineering and Mining Journal*, June 6, 1891.
2. Mumey, Nolie, *Creede: History of a Colorado Silver Mining Town*, Denver, Colorado, Artcraft Press, pg. 9, 1949.
3. Ibid.
4. *The Engineering and Mining Journal*, February 13, 1892.
5. *Colorado Business Directory*, 1893.
6. Emmons, W.H. and Larsen, E.S., *A Preliminary Report on the Geology and Ore Deposits of Creede, Colorado*, U.S. Geological Survey Bulletin 530, Washington, D.C., Government Printing Office, pg. 43, 1913 and *Mining and Scientific Review*, January-June, 1892, Rio Grande Co., pg. 9.
7. Warman, Cy, *Mountain Melodies*, Creede, Colorado, privately printed, 1892.
8. Barnes, Chuck, *The Creede Candle: A compilation of news reports appearing in The Creede Candle beginning with the January 7, 1892, edition and depicting the history of Creede*, Creede, Colorado, Introduction, 1993.
9. *The Creede Candle*, January 14, 1892.
10. Mumey, Nolie, *Creede: History of a Colorado Silver Mining Town*, Denver, Colorado, Artcraft Press, pp. 15-16, 1949.
11. Ibid., pg. 17.
12. LaFont, John, *The Homesteaders of the Upper Rio Grande*, Birmingham, Alabama, Oxmoor Press, 1971, pg. 37.
13. Smith, Duane A., *Mining America: The Industry and the Environment*, Lawrence, Kansas, University Press of Kansas, 1987, pg. 117.
14. Clark, V.V., *A Geological Study with Historical Notes of Creede Mines, Inc.*, made to A.E. Humphreys, Denver, Colorado, September 25, 1934, pg. 3.
15. Wolle, Muriel Sibell, *Stampede to Timberline: The Ghost Towns and Mining Camps of Colorado*, Boulder, Colorado, published by Muriel S. Wolle, 1949, pg. 332.
16. Mumey, Nolie, *Creede: History of a Colorado Silver Mining Town*, Denver, Colorado, Artcraft Press, 1949, pg. 157.
17. Wheeler, Harold, Family History, Date Unknown, Creede Historical Society Library.
18. Letter from John Jackson to the author dated December 7, 2000.
19. Ibid.
20. Letter from Paul Davis to the author dated June 17, 2002.
21. Mineral County Commissioner Proceedings, Volume 1.
22. Ogburn, Robert W., "Law and Mostly Order in Mineral County," *The San Luis Valley Historian*, Volume XXVII, No. 2, 1995, pg. 7.
23. *The Denver Times*, September 22, 1899.

CHAPTER 7 – CONFLICTS AND LITIGATION
1. Albert E. Reynolds Collection No. 1220, Colorado Historical Society's Stephen H. Hart Library, Denver, Colorado.
2. *The Engineering and Mining Journal*, April 6, 1895.
3. Costigan, George P., Jr., *Cases on the American Law of Mining*, Indianapolis, Indiana, Bobbs-Merrill Company, 1929, pp. 445-447.
4. Peele, Robert, *Mining Engineers' Handbook*, New York, John Wiley & Sons, Inc., 1950, pp. 24-21.
5. Colorado Bureau of Mines Manuscripts, Box 640, Volume 24, Colorado Historical Society's Stephen H. Hart Library, Denver, Colorado.
6. Albert E. Reynolds Collection No. 1220, Colorado Historical Society's Stephen H. Hart Library, Denver, Colorado.

CHAPTER 8 – THE EARLY MINES AND MINING COMPANIES: 1884-1899
1. Emmons, W.H. and Larsen, E.S., *Geology and Ore Deposits of the Creede District*, U.S. Geological Survey Bulletin 718, Washington, D.C., Government Printing Office, 1923, pg. 187.

2. Henderson, Charles W., *Mining in Colorado: A History of Discovery, Development and Production*, U.S. Geological Survey Professional Paper No. 138, Washington, D.C., Government Printing Office, 1926, pg. 181.

3. Emmons, W.H., *U.S. Geological Survey Mineral Resources*, 1892, U.S. Geological Survey, Washington, D.C., 1893, pg. 68.

4. *Colorado Rail Annual No. 14: Narrow Gauge Byways in the San Juans*, pg. 170.

5. Ibid, pg. 171.

6. *The Engineering and Mining Journal*, January 6, 1893.

7. Ibid., November 24, 1894.

8. *The Mining Reporter*, May 25, 1899; and *The Engineering and Mining Journal*, October 21, 1899.

9. Emmons, W.H. and Larsen, E.S., *A Preliminary Report on the Geology and Ore Deposits of Creede, Colorado*, U.S. Geological Survey Bulletin 530, Washington, D.C., Government Printing Office, 1913, p. 59.

10. Emmons, W.H. and Larsen, E.S., *Geology and Ore Deposits of the Creede District*, U.S. Geological Survey Bulletin 718, Washington, D.C., Government Printing Office, 1923, pg. 142.

11. Clark, V.V., *A Geological Study with Historical Notes of Creede Mines, Inc.*, made to A.E. Humphreys, Denver, Colorado, September 25, 1934, pg. 9.

12. Emmons, W.H. and Larsen, E.S., *Geology and Ore Deposits of the Creede District*, U.S. Geological Survey Bulletin 718, Washington, D.C., Government Printing Office, 1923, pg. 148.

13. Albert E. Reynolds Collection No. 1220, Colorado Historical Society's Stephen H. Hart Library, Denver, Colorado.

14. Emmons, W.H. and Larsen, E.S., *Geology and Ore Deposits of the Creede District*, U.S. Geological Survey Bulletin 718, Washington, D.C., Government Printing Office, 1923, pp. 148-149.

15. Albert E. Reynolds Collection No. 1220, Colorado Historical Society's Stephen H. Hart Library, Denver, Colorado.

16. Ibid.

17. Notes from Various Sources, Creede Historical Society.

18. Stack, Barbara, *Handbook of Mining and Tunnelling Machinery*, New York, John Wiley & Sons, Inc., 1982, pp. 166-168.

19. The author researched mining magazines of the time but did not find the tunneling machine article remembered by John Jackson. Given the facts that Karns developed a tunneling machine at Ouray at A.E. Reynolds' mine and that John's memory of the machine's description is so vivid led the author to include the tunneling machine in the history of Commodore Mine.

20. *The Engineering and Mining Journal*, June 16, 1900.

21. Albert E. Reynolds Collection No. 1220, Colorado Historical Society's Stephen H. Hart Library, Denver, Colorado.

22. Emmons, W.H. and Larsen, E.S., *Geology and Ore Deposits of the Creede District*, U.S. Geological Survey Bulletin 718, Washington, D.C., Government Printing Office, 1923, pg. 153.

23. Canfield, John G., *Mines and Mining Men of Colorado: The Principal Producing Mines of Gold and Silver, The Bonanza Kings and Successful Prospectors, The Picturesque Camps and Thriving Cities*, Denver, Colorado, John G. Canfield, Publisher, 1893, pg. 68.

24. *The Engineering and Mining Journal*, June 4, 1898; and Albert E. Reynolds Collection No. 1220, Colorado Historical Society's Stephen H. Hart Library, Denver, Colorado.

25. *The Creede Candle*, January 7, 1892, and February 4, 1892; and *The Engineering and Mining Journal*, February 13, 1892.

26. *The Engineering and Mining Journal*, March 12, 1892.

27. Canfield, John G., *Mines and Mining Men of Colorado: The Principal Producing Mines of Gold and Silver, The Bonanza Kings and Successful Prospectors, The Picturesque Camps and Thriving Cities*, Denver, Colorado, John G. Canfield, Publisher, 1893, pg. 65.

28. *The Engineering and Mining Journal*, August 4, 1894.

29. Emmons, W.H. and Larsen, E.S., *Geology and Ore Deposits of the Creede District*, U.S. Geological Survey Bulletin 718, Washington, D.C., Government Printing Office, 1923, pg. 155.

30. Meeves, Henry C. and Darnell, Richard P., *Study of the Silver Potential, Creede District, Mineral County, Colorado*, U.S. Department of the Interior, Bureau of Mines Information Circular 8370, Washington, D.C., Government Printing Office, 1968, pg. 18.

31. *The Engineering and Mining Journal*, June 10, September 23 and December 9, 1899.

32. Canfield, John G., *Mines and Mining Men of Colorado: The Principal Producing Mines of Gold and Silver, The Bonanza Kings and Successful Prospectors, The Picturesque Camps and Thriving Cities*, Denver, Colorado, John G. Canfield, Publisher, 1893, pg. 61.
33. *The Creede Candle.* August 26, 1892.
34. Ibid., January 6, 1893.
35. Clark, V.V., *A Geological Study with Historical Notes of Creede Mines, Inc.*, made to A.E. Humphreys, Denver, Colorado, September 25, 1934, pg. 4.
36. Canfield, John G., *Mines and Mining Men of Colorado: The Principal Producing Mines of Gold and Silver, The Bonanza Kings and Successful Prospectors, The Picturesque Camps and Thriving Cities*, Denver, Colorado, John G. Canfield, Publisher, 1893, pg. 65.
37. *The Engineering and Mining Journal*, October 14, 1893.
38. *Mining Reporter*, May 1, 1902.
39. Emmons, W.H. and Larsen, E.S., *Geology and Ore Deposits of the Creede District*, U.S. Geological Survey Bulletin 718, Washington, D.C., Government Printing Office, 1923, pg. 159.
40. *The Engineering and Mining Journal*, May 28, 1892.
41. Canfield, John G., *Mines and Mining Men of Colorado: The Principal Producing Mines of Gold and Silver, The Bonanza Kings and Successful Prospectors, The Picturesque Camps and Thriving Cities*, Denver, Colorado, John G. Canfield, Publisher, 1893, pp. 71-72.
43. *The Engineering and Mining Journal*, March 3 and June 30, 1894.
43. Ibid., August 18, 1894.
44. Ibid.
45. Ibid., June 17, 1899.
46. *Mining Science*, July 14, 1910.
47. *The Engineering and Mining Journal*, March 12, 1892.
48. Ibid., April 23, 1892.
49. *Prospectus* for 400 Acre Consolidated Diamond Drill Mining Company, 1892, pg. 2.
50. *The Creede Candle*, December 23, 1892.
51. Ibid., Volume I, 1892.
52. Hubbard, Judson Slater, *A Man of Business and the Enterprises: Memoirs of Judson Slater Hubbard*, 1979, pg. 18.
53. Ibid., pg. 56.
54. Canfield, John G., *Mines and Mining Men of Colorado: The Principal Producing Mines of Gold and Silver, The Bonanza Kings and Successful Prospectors, The Picturesque Camps and Thriving Cities*, Denver, Colorado, John G. Canfield, Publisher, 1893, pg. 63.
55. *The Engineering and Mining Journal*, April 21, 1894.
56. Ibid., June 30, 1894.
57. Ibid, February 2, 1895.
58. Ibid., September 21, 1895.
59. Hubbard, Judson Slater, *A Man of Business and the Enterprises: Memoirs of Judson Slater Hubbard*, 1979, pg. 19.
60. *The Engineering and Mining Journal*, March 12, 1892.
61. Canfield, John G., *Mines and Mining Men of Colorado: The Principal Producing Mines of Gold and Silver, The Bonanza Kings and Successful Prospectors, The Picturesque Camps and Thriving Cities*, Denver, Colorado, John G. Canfield, Publisher, 1893, pp. 66-67.
62. *The Engineering and Mining Journal*, April 21, 1894.
63. Ibid., February 2, April 6, and June 29, 1895.
64. Emmons, W.H. and Larsen, E.S., *Geology and Ore Deposits of the Creede District*, U.S. Geological Survey Bulletin 718, Washington, D.C., Government Printing Office, 1923, pg. 168.
65. Ibid., pg. 173.
66. *The Creede Candle*, January 7, 1892; and Canfield, John G., *Mines and Mining Men of Colorado: The Principal Producing Mines of Gold and Silver, The Bonanza Kings and Successful Prospectors, The Picturesque Camps and Thriving Cities*, Denver, Colorado, John G. Canfield, Publisher, 1893, pg. 62.
67. Canfield, John G., *Mines and Mining Men of Colorado: The Principal Producing Mines of Gold and Silver, The Bonanza Kings and Successful Prospectors, The Picturesque Camps and Thriving Cities*, Denver, Colorado, John G. Canfield, Publisher, 1893, pg. 61.
68. *The Creede Candle*, January 7, 1892.
69. *The Engineering and Mining Journal*, August 8, 1891.
70. *Del Norte Prospector:* Creede's 50th Anniversary Edition, June 2, 1942.
71. *The Denver Republican*, December 12, 1891, pg. 12.

72. Meeves, Henry C. and Darnell, Richard P., *Study of the Silver Potential, Creede District, Mineral County, Colorado*, U.S. Department of the Interior, Bureau of Mines Information Circular 8370, Washington, D.C., Government Printing Office, 1968, pg. 27.

73. *The Creede Candle*, January 7, 1892.

74. Ibid., December 30, 1892.

75. Ibid., October 15, 1898.

76. Canfield, John G., *Mines and Mining Men of Colorado: The Principal Producing Mines of Gold and Silver, The Bonanza Kings and Successful Prospectors, The Picturesque Camps and Thriving Cities*, Denver, Colorado, John G. Canfield, Publisher, 1893, pg. 62.

77. Emmons, W.H. and Larsen, E.S., *Geology and Ore Deposits of the Creede District*, U.S. Geological Survey Bulletin 718, Washington, D.C., Government Printing Office, 1923, pg. 181.

78. Canfield, John G., *Mines and Mining Men of Colorado: The Principal Producing Mines of Gold and Silver, The Bonanza Kings and Successful Prospectors, The Picturesque Camps and Thriving Cities*, Denver, Colorado, John G. Canfield, Publisher, 1893, pg. 62.

79. *The Engineering and Mining Journal*, March 12, 1892.

80. *The Creede Candle*, Volume I, 1892.

81. *The Engineering and Mining Journal*, October 28, 1893.

82. *Mineral Resources of the United States*, 1908, U.S. Geological Survey, Washington, D.C.

83. *The Engineering and Mining Journal*, April 6, 1895.

84. Ibid., July 27, 1895.

85. Ibid., April 9 and July 9, 1898.

86. Ibid., September 23, 1899.

87. Emmons, W.H. and Larsen, E.S., *Geology and Ore Deposits of the Creede District*, U.S. Geological Survey Bulletin 718, Washington, D.C., Government Printing Office, 1923, pg. 175.

88. *The Engineering and Mining Journal*, November 23, 1895.

89. Ibid., April 9, 1898.

90. Emmons, W.H. and Larsen, E.S., *Geology and Ore Deposits of the Creede District*, U.S. Geological Survey Bulletin 718, Washington, D.C., Government Printing Office, 1923, pg. 177.

91. *The Engineering and Mining Journal*, March 12, 1892.

92. Ibid., July 9, 1898.

93. Ibid., December 8, 1894.

94. *The Creede Candle*, January 6, 1893. Other histories state that these early mineral locations were abandoned and then relocated in later years, but do not give the name(s) of the 1870s discoverers.

95. *The Creede Candle*, July 1, 1892.

96. *The Engineering and Mining Journal*, July 15, 1893, and March 10, 1894.

97. Emmons, W.H. and Larsen, E.S., *Geology and Ore Deposits of the Creede District*, U.S. Geological Survey Bulletin 718, Washington, D.C., Government Printing Office, 1923, pg. 3.

98. *The Engineering and Mining Journal*, July 15, 1893.

99. Ibid., December 9, 1899.

100. Ibid., November 24, 1900.

101. Steven, Thomas A. and Ratté, James C., *USGS Professional Paper 487: Geology and Structural Control of Ore Deposition in the Creede District, San Juan Mountains, Colorado*, U.S. Geological Survey, Washington, D.C., 1965, pp. 8-9.

102 Emmons, W.H. and Larsen, E.S., *Geology and Ore Deposits of the Creede District*, U.S. Geological Survey Bulletin 718, Washington, D.C., Government Printing Office, 1923, pp. 187-188.

103. Canfield, John G., *Mines and Mining Men of Colorado: The Principal Producing Mines of Gold and Silver, The Bonanza Kings and Successful Prospectors, The Picturesque Camps and Thriving Cities*, Denver, Colorado, John G. Canfield, Publisher, 1893, pg. 71.

104. Rickard, T.A., "Across the San Juan Mountains" as published in *The Engineering and Mining Journal*, September 12, 1903.

105. *The Engineering and Mining Journal*, December 17, 1892.

106. Ibid., May 26, June 2, and August 25, 1894.

107. *Prospectus* for 400 Acre Consolidated Diamond Drill Mining Company, 1892, pg. 6.

108. Steven, Thomas A. and Ratté, James C., *USGS Professional Paper 487: Geology and Stuctureal Control of Ore Deposition in the Creede District, San Juan Mountains, Colorado*, U.S. Geological Survey, Washington, D.C., 1965, pg. 78.

109. *The Engineering and Mining Journal*, August 31, 1895.

CHAPTER 9 – THE NELSON-WOOSTER-HUMPHREYS TUNNEL TO THE RESCUE

1. *The Creede Candle*, February 21, 1920.
2. Ibid., April 1, 1892.
3. Ibid., February 21, 1920.
4. *The Engineering and Mining Journal*, April 9, 1892.
5. Emmons, W.H. and Larsen, E.S., *Geology and Ore Deposits of the Creede District*, U.S. Geological Survey Bulletin 718, Washington, D.C., Government Printing Office, 1923, pg. 5.
6. Nelson Tunnel and Mining Company Letterhead, circa 1893, in the files of the Creede Historical Society.
7. Canfield, John G., *Mines and Mining Men of Colorado: The Principal Producing Mines of Gold and Silver, The Bonanza Kings and Successful Prospectors, The Picturesque Camps and Thriving Cities*, Denver, Colorado, John G. Canfield, Publisher, 1893, pg. 64 and pp. 66-67.
8. Nelson Tunnel and Mining Company Letterhead, circa 1893, in the files of the Creede Historical Society.
9. *The Engineering and Mining Journal*, May 26, 1894.
10. Ibid., March 9, 1895.
11. Emmons, W.H. and Larsen, E.S., *Geology and Ore Deposits of the Creede District*, U.S. Geological Survey Bulletin 718, Washington, D.C., Government Printing Office, 1923, pg. 5.
12. *The Engineering and Mining Journal*, August 31, 1895.
13. Clark, V.V., *A Geological Study with Historical Notes of Creede Mines, Inc.*, made to A.E. Humphreys, Denver, Colorado, September 25, 1934, pg. 6.
14. Ibid.
15. Bank of Monte Vista letter from R.B. Wallace to Bertha C. Bowen, dated January 15, 1909.
16. *The Engineering and Mining Journal*, November 5, 1898.
17. Ibid., June 16, 1900.
18. Ibid., February 15 and March 22, 1902.
19. *Mining Reporter*, December 4, 1902.
20. Lakes, Arthur, "Creede Mining Camp," *Mines and Minerals*, Volume 23, 1903, pp. 433-435.
21. *Mining Reporter*, July 20, 1905.
22. *Mining Science*, December 16, 1909.
23. Meeves, Henry C. and Darnell, Richard P., *Study of the Silver Potential, Creede District, Mineral County, Colorado*, U.S. Department of the Interior, Bureau of Mines Information Circular 8370, Washington, D.C., Government Printing Office, 1968, pg. 12.
24. Clark, V.V., *A Geological Study with Historical Notes of Creede Mines, Inc.*, made to A.E. Humphreys, Denver, Colorado, September 25, 1934, pg. 45.
25. Hubbard, Judson Slater, *A Man of Business and the Enterprises: Memoirs of Judson Slater Hubbard*, 1979, pg. 57.
26. Colorado State Bureau of Mines Biennial Report for 1917 and 1918.
27. Clark, V.V., *A Geological Study with Historical Notes of Creede Mines, Inc.*, made to A.E. Humphreys, Denver, Colorado, September 25, 1934, pg. 44.

CHAPTER 10 – A TIME FOR CONCENTRATION

1. *Mineral Resources of the United States*, U.S. Geological Survey, Washington, D.C., 1906 - 1918.
2. "Mills and Milling Practice at Creede, Colorado," *Mining Reporter*, November 15, 1906.
3. *The Engineering and Mining Journal*, August 29, 1896.
4. H.C. Parmelee, "Zinc Ore Dressing in Colorado — III, The Creede District," *Metallurgical and Chemical Engineering*, December, 1910.
5. Taggart, Arthur F., *Elements of Ore Dressing*, New York, John Wiley & Sons, Inc., 1951, pp. 225, 185 and 210.
6. Smith, Duane A., *Mining America: The Industry and the Environment*, Lawrence, Kansas, University Press of Kansas, 1987, pg. 117.
7. Emmons, W.H. and Larsen, E.S., *Geology and Ore Deposits of the Creede District*, U.S. Geological Survey Bulletin 718, Washington, D.C., Government Printing Office, 1923, pg. 6.
8. *Mining Reporter*, November 15, 1906.

9. Steven, Thomas A. and Ratté, James C., *USGS Professional Paper 487: Geology and Structural Control of Ore Deposition in the Creede District, San Juan Mountains, Colorado*, U.S. Geological Survey, Washington, D.C., 1965, pg. 9.
10. *The Engineering and Mining Journal*, March 15, 1902.
11. Lakes, Arthur, "Creede Mining Camp," *Mines and Minerals*, Volume 23, 1903, pp. 433-435.
12. *The Engineering and Mining Journal*, May 5 and November 24, 1900.
13. Ibid., June 7, 1902.
14. *Mining Reporter*, 1903.
15. Lakes, Arthur, "Creede Mining Camp," *Mines and Minerals*, Volume 23, 1903, pp. 433-435.
16. *Mineral Resources of the United States*, U.S. Geological Survey, Washington, D.C., 1906-1916.
17. Emmons, W.H. and Larsen, E.S., *Geology and Ore Deposits of the Creede District*, U.S. Geological Survey Bulletin 718, Washington, D.C., Government Printing Office, 1923, pg. 142.
18. Albert E. Reynolds Collection No. 1220, Colorado Historical Society's Stephen H. Hart Library, Denver, Colorado.
19. *The Engineering and Mining Journal*, November 24, 1900.
20. Ibid., May 4, 1901.
21. Ibid., September 5, 1901 and November 27 and December 4, 1902.
22. Lakes, Arthur, "Creede Mining Camp," *Mines and Minerals*, Volume 23, 1903, pp. 433-435.
23. Albert E. Reynolds Collection No. 1220, Colorado Historical Society's Stephen H. Hart Library, Denver, Colorado.
24. Ibid.
25. *Mining Reporter*, March 21 and 28, 1907.
26. *Mineral Resources of the United States*, U.S. Geological Survey, Washington, D.C., 1906-08, 1910-12, 1915-18; and Albert E. Reynolds Collection No. 1220, Colorado Historical Society's Stephen H. Hart Library, Denver, Colorado.
27. Albert E. Reynolds Collection No. 1220, Colorado Historical Society's Stephen H. Hart Library, Denver, Colorado.
28. Ibid.
29. Ibid.
30. Ibid.
31. Colorado State Bureau of Mines Biennial Report for 1917 and 1918.
32. Emmons, W.H. and Larsen, E.S., *Geology and Ore Deposits of the Creede District*, U.S. Geological Survey Bulletin 718, Washington, D.C., Government Printing Office, 1923, pg. 152.
33. Albert E. Reynolds Collection No. 1220, Colorado Historical Society's Stephen H. Hart Library, Denver, Colorado.
34. Ibid.
35. Emmons, W.H. and Larsen, E.S., *Geology and Ore Deposits of the Creede District*, U.S. Geological Survey Bulletin 718, Washington, D.C., Government Printing Office, 1923, pg. 152.
36. *Mining Reporter*, December 4, 1902.
37. Ibid., July 23, 1903.
38. Ibid., July 20, 1905.
39. *Mining Science*, May 27, 1909, 1910, and April 27, 1911.
40. *Mineral Resources of the United States*, U.S. Geological Survey, Washington, D.C., 1911.
41. *The Engineering and Mining Journal*, October 12, 1912.
42. *Mineral Resources of the United States*, U.S. Geological Survey, Washington, D.C., 1915 1916, 1917 and 1918.
43. Emmons, W.H. and Larsen, E.S., *Geology and Ore Deposits of the Creede District*, U.S. Geological Survey Bulletin 718, Washington, D.C., Government Printing Office, 1923, pp. 152-153. Note: Even though the report was published in 1923, the author believes the description of the mines was that when the field work was done in 1911 and 1912.
44. Albert E. Reynolds Collection No. 1220, Colorado Historical Society's Stephen H. Hart Library, Denver, Colorado.
45. *The Engineering and Mining Journal*, June 17, 1899.
46. Ibid., June 23, 1900.
47. *Mining Reporter*, June 26, 1902.

48. *The Engineering and Mining Journal,* May 14, 1910.
49. *Mining Reporter,* September 28, 1905.
50. *Mineral Resources of the United States,* U.S. Geological Survey, Washington, D.C., 1908.
51. *Mining Science,* May 27, 1909.
52. Ibid., July 14, 1910.
53. H.C. Parmelee, "Zinc Ore Dressing in Colorado-III, The Creede District," *Metallurgical and Chemical Engineering,* December, 1910.
54. Emmons, W.H. and Larsen, E.S., *Geology and Ore Deposits of the Creede District,* U.S. Geological Survey Bulletin 718, Washington, D.C., Government Printing Office, 1923, pg. 159.
55. Garrey, George H., *Report on the Mines Along the Amethyst Lode, Creede, Mineral County, Colorado,* 1916.
56. Meeves, Henry C. and Darnell, Richard P., *Study of the Silver Potential, Creede District, Mineral County, Colorado,* U.S. Department of the Interior, Bureau of Mines Information Circular 8370, Washington, D.C., Government Printing Office, 1968, pg. 22.
57. *Mining Science,* December 21, 1911.
58. Ibid., February 12, 1912.
59. *The Engineering and Mining Journal,* July 20, 1912.
60. Ibid., September 28 and October 12, 1912.
61. Albert E. Reynolds Collection No. 1220, Colorado Historical Society's Stephen H. Hart Library, Denver, Colorado.
62. *The Engineering and Mining Journal,* June 23, 1900.
63. *Mining Reporter,* October 10, 1901.
64. *The Engineering and Mining Journal,* March 22, 1902.
65. *Mining Reporter,* July 19, 1902.
66. Ibid., December 4, 1902.
67. Ibid.
68. Ibid., July 23, 1903.
69. Lakes, Arthur, "Creede Mining Camp," *Mines and Minerals,* Volume 23, 1903, pp. 433-435.
70. *Mining Reporter,* May 12 and June 16, 1904.
71. Lescohier, Roger P., *Lester Pelton and the Pelton Water Wheel,* reproduced by Buttonworks-Printworks through the cooperation of the Empire Mine Park Association, California, 1992, pp. 14 and 19.
72. *Mining Reporter,* April 28, 1904.
73. Hubbard, Judson Slater, *A Man of Business and the Enterprises: Memoirs of Judson Slater Hubbard,* 1979, pg. 19.
74. Smith, Duane A., *Mining America: The Industry and the Environment,* Lawrence, Kansas, University Press of Kansas, 1987, pg. 117.
75. LaFont, John, *The Homesteaders of the Upper Rio Grande,* Birmingham, Alabama, Oxmoor Press, 1971, pg. 37.
76. Costilla Combined Courts Records, San Luis, Colorado, 1905.
77. The author knew "Grandma Pfeiffer," Albert Pfeiffer's daughter-in-law, as a child. When he was about 8 or 9, his parents took him on Sunday afternoon drives and visits with "Grandma" — a gracious lady about 80 years old. He still remembers her tales about the Indians, soldiers, and buffalo in Colorado's San Luis Valley. She let him play "Indians" in a beautiful beaded deerskin jacket with a bullet hole in the back that had been given to her by her father-in-law. The jacket had belonged to a Comanche chief killed by Pfeiffer.
78. Costilla Combined Courts Records, San Luis, Colorado, 1905.
79. Letter from John Jackson to the author dated May 27, 2001.
80. Clark, V.V., *A Geological Study with Historical Notes of Creede Mines, Inc.,* made to A.E. Humphreys, Denver, Colorado, September 25, 1934, pg. 7.
81. Hubbard, Judson Slater, *A Man of Business and the Enterprises: Memoirs of Judson Slater Hubbard,* 1979, pg. 19.
82. *Mining Reporter,* July 20, 1905.
83. Ibid., September 21, 1905.
84. *Mineral Resources of the United States,* U.S. Geological Survey, Washington, D.C., 1906 and 1907.
85. *Mining Reporter,* August 22, 1907.
86. *Mineral Resources of the United States,* U.S. Geological Survey, Washington, D.C., 1908.
87. Emmons, W.H. and Larsen, E.S., *Geology and Ore Deposits of the Creede District,* U.S. Geological Survey Bulletin 718, Washington, D.C., Government Printing Office, 1923, pg. 164.

88. *Mining Science,* December 16, 1909.
89. *Mineral Resources of the United States,* U.S. Geological Survey, Washington, D.C., 1910; and *Mining Science,* April 27, 1911.
90. *Mining Science,* November 16, 1911.
91. Hubbard, Judson Slater, *A Man of Business and the Enterprises: Memoirs of Judson Slater Hubbard,* 1979, pg. 19.
92. Emmons, W.H. and Larsen, E.S., *Geology and Ore Deposits of the Creede District,* U.S. Geological Survey Bulletin 718, Washington, D.C., Government Printing Office, 1923, pg. 168.
93. *The Engineering and Mining Journal,* September 28, 1912.
94. *Mineral Resources of the United States,* U.S. Geological Survey, Washington, D.C., 1915.
95. Ibid., 1916 and 1917.
96. *Mineral Resources of the United States,* U.S. Geological Survey, Washington, D.C., 1918; and Fifteenth Biennial Report, Bureau of Mines of the State of Colorado, 1917 and 1918.
97. Clark, V.V., *A Geological Study with Historical Notes of Creede Mines, Inc.,* made to A.E. Humphreys, Denver, Colorado, September 25, 1934, pg. 44.
98. Ibid., pg. 6.
99. Emmons, W.H. and Larsen, E.S., *Geology and Ore Deposits of the Creede District,* U.S. Geological Survey Bulletin 718, Washington, D.C., Government Printing Office, 1923, pp. 164 and 168.
100. Clark, V.V., *A Geological Study with Historical Notes of Creede Mines, Inc.,* made to A.E. Humphreys, Denver, Colorado, September 25, 1934, pg. 21.
101. Albert E. Reynolds Collection No. 1220, Colorado Historical Society's Stephen H. Hart Library, Denver, Colorado.
102. Ibid.
103. Letter from G. Hardy, Consulting Engineer, to H.A. Guess, President of the Creede Exploration Company, dated March 29, 1919.
104. Fifteenth Biennial Report, Bureau of Mines of the State of Colorado, 1917 and 1918.
105. *The Engineering and Mining Journal,* December 8, 1917.
106. Albert E. Reynolds Collection No. 1220, Colorado Historical Society's Stephen H. Hart Library, Denver, Colorado.
107. Ibid.
108. Ibid.
109. *The Engineering and Mining Journal,* March 7, 1903.
110. Emmons, W.H. and Larsen, E.S., *Geology and Ore Deposits of the Creede District,* U.S. Geological Survey Bulletin 718, Washington, D.C., Government Printing Office, 1923, pg. 169.
111. *Mineral Resources of the United States,* U.S. Geological Survey, Washington, D.C., 1915, 1917, and 1918.
112. *The Engineering and Mining Journal,* February 25, 1899.
113. *Mining Reporter,* May 1, 1902.
114. Fifteenth Biennial Report, Bureau of Mines of the State of Colorado, 1917 and 1918.
115. Steven, Thomas A. and Ratté James C., *USGS Professional Paper 487: Geology and Structural Control of Ore Deposition in the Creede District, San Juan Mountains, Colorado,* U.S. Geological Survey, Washington, D.C., 1965, pp. 8-9.
116. *Mining Science,* November 17, 1910.
117. *Mineral Resources of the United States,* U.S. Geological Survey, Washington, D.C., 1915-1918.
118. *The Engineering and Mining Journal,* April 6, 1895.
119. Ibid., May 26 and July 28, 1900.
120. *The Denver Times,* March 5, 1901 and February 21, 1902.
121. *The Mining Reporter,* November 23, 1905.
122. *Mineral Resources of the United States,* U.S. Geological Survey, Washington, D.C., 1906-1912.
123. H.C. Parmelee, "Zinc Ore Dressing in Colorado-III, The Creede District," *Metallurgical and Chemical Engineering,* December, 1910.
124. Clark, V.V., *A Geological Study with Historical Notes of Creede Mines, Inc.,* made to A.E. Humphreys, Denver, Colorado, September 25, 1934, pg. 35.
125. *The Engineering and Mining Journal,* June 23 and July 28, 1900.
126. *Mining Reporter,* December 4, 1902.

127. Ibid., October 10, 1903.
128. *Mineral Resources of the United States,* U.S. Geological Survey, Washington, D.C., 1907 and 1910.
129. Ibid., 1916-1918.
130. Clark, V.V., *A Geological Study with Historical Notes of Creede Mines, Inc.,* made to A.E. Humphreys, Denver, Colorado, September 25, 1934, pg. 36.
131. *The Denver Times,* December 4, 1901.
132. *Mineral Resources of the United States,* U.S. Geological Survey, Washington, D.C., 1906 and 1907.
133. Ibid., 1912-1918.
134. Emmons, W.H. and Larsen, E.S., *Geology and Ore Deposits of the Creede District,* U.S. Geological Survey Bulletin 718, Washington, D.C., Government Printing Office, 1923, pp. 182-183.
135. *The Engineering and Mining Journal,* July 4, 1901.
136. *Prospectus* of the Monte Carlo Gold and Silver Mining Company, September 15, 1904.
137. *Mineral Resources of the United States,* U.S. Geological Survey, Washington, D.C., 1906, 1907, and 1908.
138. Letter from John Jackson to the author dated February 14, 2001.
139. Steven, Thomas A. and Ratté, James C., *USGS Professional Paper 487: Geology and Structural Control of Ore Deposition in the Creede District, San Juan Mountains, Colorado,* U.S. Geological Survey, Washington, D.C., 1965, pg. 9.
140. *The Engineering and Mining Journal,* November 24, 1900.
141. *The Denver Times,* March 5, 1901.
142. *Mining Reporter,* December 4, 1902, and *The Engineering and Mining Journal,* August 29, 1903.
143. Emmons, W.H. and Larsen, E.S., *Geology and Ore Deposits of the Creede District,* U.S. Geological Survey Bulletin 718, Washington, D.C., Government Printing Office, 1923, pg. 189.
144. *Mining Reporter,* June 16, 1904, and July 27, 1905.
145. *Mineral Resources of the United States,* U.S. Geological Survey, Washington, D.C., 1906 -1918.
146. Emmons, W.H. and Larsen, E.S., *Geology and Ore Deposits of the Creede District,* U.S. Geological Survey Bulletin 718, Washington, D.C., Government Printing Office, 1923, pg. 191.
147. Ibid., pg. 141.
148. *The Engineering and Mining Journal,* November 24, 1900.
149. *The Denver Times,* December 4, 1901.
150. *Mineral Resources of the United States,* U.S. Geological Survey, Washington, D.C., 1910.
151. Emmons, W.H. and Larsen, E.S., *Geology and Ore Deposits of the Creede District,* U.S. Geological Survey Bulletin 718, Washington, D.C., Government Printing Office, 1923, pg. 193.
152. Larsen, Esper S., *Recent Mining Developments in the Creede District, Colorado,* U.S. Geological Survey Bulletin 811-B, Washington, D.C., Government Printing Office, 1929, pg. 103.
153. *Mineral Resources of the United States,* U.S. Geological Survey, Washington, D.C., 1916 -1918.
154. Fifteenth Biennial Report, Bureau of Mines of the State of Colorado, 1917 and 1918.
155. Emmons, W.H. and Larsen, E.S., *Geology and Ore Deposits of the Creede District,* U.S. Geological Survey Bulletin 718, Washington, D.C., Government Printing Office, 1923, pg. 186.
156. Letter to Geo. J. Bancroft from C.N. Blanchette, July 29, 1926 (attached to Bancroft Report on Bulldog Mine).
157. LaFont, John, *The Homesteaders of the Upper Rio Grande,* Birmingham, Alabama, Oxmoor Press, 1971, pp. 20-21.
158. Dr. Howell's biography and other information provided by his son, Dr. Thomas F. Howell of Abilene, Texas.
159. Interview with Marge Hosselkus by author, 2001.
160. *Minerals Yearbook,* U.S. Bureau of Mines, Washington, D.C., 1991.
161. LaFont, John, *The Homesteaders of the Upper Rio Grande,* Birmingham, Alabama, Oxmoor Press, 1971, pg. 44.

162. Aurand, Harry A., *Fluorspar Deposits of Colorado*, Colorado Geological Survey Bulletin 18, 1926, pp. 62-63.
163. Fifteenth Biennial Report, Bureau of Mines of the State of Colorado, 1917 and 1918.
164. Letter from John Jackson to the author dated April 13, 2001.
165. Eckel, Edwin B., *Minerals of Colorado*, Golden, Colorado, Fulcrum Publishing, 1997, pg. 172.

CHAPTER 11 – EARLY MINE TRANSPORTATION
1. LaFont, John, *The Homesteaders of the Upper Rio Grande*, Birmingham, Alabama, Oxmoor Press, 1971, pg. 34.
2. Smith, Frank W., "The Adventures of Frank W. Smith and Many Other Pioneer Miners in the State of Colorado," *The San Luis Valley Historian*, Volume IV, Spring, 1972, pg. 5.
3. Bennett, E.L., "A Creede Scrapbook," *The San Luis Valley Historian*, Volume IV, Spring, 1972, pg. 21.
4. Smith, Frank W., "The Adventures of Frank W. Smith and Many Other Pioneer Miners in the State of Colorado," *The San Luis Valley Historian*, Volume IV, Spring, 1972, pp. 3-4.
5. Ibid., pp. 5-6.
6. Bennett, E.L., "A Creede Scrapbook," *The San Luis Valley Historian*, Volume IV, Spring, 1972, pg. 21.
7. Clark, V.V., *A Geological Study with Historical Notes of Creede Mines, Inc.*, made to A.E. Humphreys, Denver, Colorado, September 25, 1934, pp. 1-2.
8. Letter from Paul Davis to the author dated March 13, 2003.
9. Letter from John Jackson to the author dated March 14, 2003.
10. Peele, Robert, *Mining Engineers' Handbook*, New York, John Wiley & Sons, Inc., 1950, pp. 24-08 and 24-39.
11. Trennert, Robert A., *Riding the High Wire: Aerial Mine Tramways in the West*, Boulder, Colorado, University Press of Colorado, 2001, pg. 38.
12. Letter from John Jackson to the author dated January 15, 1985.
13. *Mining and Scientific Review*, XXVIII, January-June, 1892, Rio Grande County, pg. 9.
14. *The Colorado Sun*, June 19, 1892, pg. 27, Col. 3.
15. Letter from John Jackson to the author dated July 30, 2001.
16. Canfield, John G., *Mines and Mining Men of Colorado: The Principal Producing Mines of Gold and Silver, The Bonanza Kings and Successful Prospectors, The Picturesque Camps and Thriving Cities*, Denver, Colorado, John G. Canfield, Publisher, 1893, pg. 72.
17. H.C. Parmelee, "Zinc Ore Dressing in Colorado-III, The Creede District," *Metallurgical and Chemical Engineering*, December, 1910.
18. *Mining Reporter*, October 4, 1906.
19. Albert E. Reynolds Collection No. 1220, Colorado Historical Society's Stephen H. Hart Library, Denver, Colorado.
20. Plan-Profile Drawing, Albert E. Reynolds Collection No. 1220, Colorado Historical Society's Stephen H. Hart Library, Denver, Colorado.
21. Albert E. Reynolds Collection No. 1220, Colorado Historical Society's Stephen H. Hart Library, Denver, Colorado.
22. Letter from John Jackson to the author dated January 15, 1985.
23. Letter from Paul Davis to the author dated March 13, 2003.
24. Albert E. Reynolds Collection No. 1220, Colorado Historical Society's Stephen H. Hart Library, Denver, Colorado.
25. Plan-Profile Drawing, Albert E. Reynolds Collection No. 1220, Colorado Historical Society's Stephen H. Hart Library, Denver, Colorado.
26. Letters from John Jackson to the author dated January 15, 1985 and July 30, 2001.
27. Ibid.
28. Letter from John Jackson to the author dated January 15, 1985.
29. *Mineral Resources of the United States*, U.S. Geological Survey, Washington, D.C., 1906.
30. Emmons, W.H. and Larsen, E.S., *Geology and Ore Deposits of the Creede District*, U.S. Geological Survey Bulletin 718, Washington, D.C., Government Printing Office, 1923, pg. 185.
31. The author climbed up to the Mollie S. Mine in 2001 along the alignment of the tramway.

32. Letter from John Jackson to the author dated April 13, 2001.
33. Aurand, Harry A., *Fluorspar Deposits of Colorado*, Colorado Geological Survey Bulletin 18, 1926, pg. 62.
34. *Mining Reporter*, October 4, 1906.
35. Interview with Ed Johnson and Gene Dooley, June 11, 2001.

CHAPTER 12 – HARD TIMES
 1. *The Mineral Industry*, McGraw-Hill Book Company, Inc., 1925.
 2. *The Engineering and Mining Journal*, February 2, 1929.
 3. Colorado Bureau of Mines *Annual Report* for 1932 and 1933.
 4. Larsen, Esper S., *Recent Mining Developments in the Creede District, Colorado*, U.S. Geological Survey Bulletin 811-B, Washington, D.C., Government Printing Office, 1929, pg. 90.
 5. Clark, V.V., *A Geological Study with Historical Notes of Creede Mines, Inc.*, made to A.E. Humphreys, Denver, Colorado, September 25, 1934, pg. 4.
 6. Garrey, George H., *Report on the Mines Along the Amethyst Lode, Creede, Mineral County, Colorado*, 1916, pp. 84-85.
 7. Steven, Thomas A. and Ratté, James C., *USGS Professional Paper 487: Geology and Structural Control of Ore Deposition in the Creede District, San Juan Mountains, Colorado*, U.S. Geological Survey, Washington, D.C., 1965, pg. 56.
 8. State of Colorado Bureau of Mines *Annual Report* for the year 1919, U.S. Geological Survey *Mineral Resources of the United States for 1920, 1924, 1925, 1926, and 1927*.
 9. *The Creede Candle*, January 1, 1927.
10. Larsen, Esper S., *Recent Mining Developments in the Creede District*, Colorado, U.S. Geological Survey Bulletin 811-B, Washington, D.C., Government Printing Office, 1929, pg. 94.
11. Clark, V.V., *A Geological Study with Historical Notes of Creede Mines, Inc.*, made to A.E. Humphreys, Denver, Colorado, September 25, 1934, pg. 17.
12. Colorado State Archives, Case No. 310, Archive No. 68931.
13. Albert E. Reynolds Collection No. 1220, Colorado Historical Society's Stephen H. Hart Library, Denver, Colorado.
14. Ibid.
15. U.S. Geological Survey *Mineral Resources in the United States* for 1927-1929.
16. Larsen, Esper S., *Recent Mining Developments in the Creede District, Colorado*, U.S. Geological Survey Bulletin 811-B, Washington, D.C., Government Printing Office, 1929, pg. 97.
17. Albert E. Reynolds Collection No. 1220, Colorado Historical Society's Stephen H. Hart Library, Denver, Colorado.
18. State of Colorado Bureau of Mines *Fifteenth Biennial Report, 1917 and 1918*; and the Colorado State Bureau of Mines *Annual Report for 1919*.
19. *Mineral Resources of the United States*, U.S. Geological Survey, Washington, D.C., 1920-1931.
20. *Mineral Resources of the United States*, U.S. Geological Survey, Washington, D.C., 1927.
21. Larsen, Esper S., *Recent Mining Developments in the Creede District, Colorado*, U.S. Geological Survey Bulletin 811-B, Washington, D.C., Government Printing Office, 1929, pg. 97.
22. Letters from John Jackson to the author, dated April 7, 2003, and April 21, 2003.
23. Letters from John Jackson to the author, dated November 11, 2001, and April 4, 2003.
24. *Mineral Resources of the United States*, U.S. Geological Survey, Washington, D.C., 1920-1930.
25. Larsen, Esper S., *Recent Mining Developments in the Creede District*, Colorado, U.S. Geological Survey Bulletin 811-B, Washington, D.C., Government Printing Office, 1929, pg. 97.
26. Albert E. Reynolds Collection No. 1220, Colorado Historical Society's Stephen H. Hart Library, Denver, Colorado.
27. *Mineral Resources of the United States*, U.S. Geological Survey, Washington, D.C., 1929 and 1930.
28. Larsen, Esper S., *Recent Mining Developments in the Creede District*, Colorado, U.S. Geological Survey Bulletin 811-B, Washington, D.C., Government Printing Office, 1929, pg. 98.

29. Scamehorn, Lee, *Albert Eugene Reynolds: Colorado's Mining King*, Norman, Oklahoma, University of Oklahoma Press, 1995, pg. 225.
30. Unknown Author, *Brief History of the Emperius Mining Company*, March 10, 1972.
31. Letter from John Jackson to the author, dated April 7, 2003.
32. *Annual Report for the Year 1919*, U.S. Bureau of Mines, Washington, D.C.
33. *Mineral Resources of the United States,* U.S. Geological Survey, Washington, D.C., 1926.
34. Robert A. Boppe Collection — *Prospectus* of the North Amethyst Mining Company.
35. *Mineral Resources of the United States*, U.S. Geological Survey, Washington, D.C., 1927 and 1928.
36. Larsen, Esper S., *Recent Mining Developments in the Creede District*, Colorado, U.S. Geological Survey Bulletin 811-B, Washington, D.C., Government Printing Office, 1929, pp. 100-102.
37. Ibid.
38. Colorado State Bureau of Mines Report for 1919.
39. Larsen, Esper S., *Recent Mining Developments in the Creede District*, Colorado, U.S. Geological Survey Bulletin 811-B, Washington, D.C., Government Printing Office, 1929, pg. 98.
40. *Mineral Resources of the United States,* U.S. Geological Survey, Washington, D.C., 1922 and 1923.
41. Clark, V.V., *A Geological Study with Historical Notes of Creede Mines, Inc.*, made to A.E. Humphreys, Denver, Colorado, September 25, 1934, pg. 37.
42. Larsen, Esper S., *Recent Mining Developments in the Creede District*, Colorado, U.S. Geological Survey Bulletin 811-B, Washington, D.C., Government Printing Office, 1929, pg. 109.
43. Ibid.
44. *Mineral Resources of the United States*, U.S. Geological Survey, Washington, D.C., 1921 -1923.
45. *Mineral Resources of the United States*, U.S. Geological Survey, Washington, D.C., 1927 and 1928.
46. Larsen, Esper S., *Recent Mining Developments in the Creede District*, Colorado, U.S. Geological Survey Bulletin 811-B, Washington, D.C., Government Printing Office, 1929, pg. 107.
47. Clark, V.V., *A Geological Study with Historical Notes of Creede Mines, Inc.*, made to A.E. Humphreys, Denver, Colorado, September 25, 1934, pg. 39.
48. Larsen, Esper S., *Recent Mining Developments in the Creede District*, Colorado, U.S. Geological Survey Bulletin 811-B, Washington, D.C., Government Printing Office, 1929, pg. 108.
49. Colorado State Bureau of Mines Reports for 1933 and 1934.
50. Bancroft, George J., *A Report on the Bulldog Mine*, Creede, Colorado, 1926.
51. Robert A. Boppe Collection — Letter from Herman Emperius to Fred Monkemeyer dated April 10, 1928.
52. Letter from Robert A. Boppe to the author dated October 2, 2001.
53. *Colorado Rail Annual No. 14: Narrow Gauge Byways in the San Juans*, pg. 198.

CHAPTER 13 – THE TOWNS OF CREEDE CAMP: FROM BOOM TO BUST

1. Johnson, Ed, Creede, Colorado, Telephone Interview, May 2002.
2. Clark, V.V., *A Geological Study with Historical Notes of Creede Mines, Inc.*, made to A.E. Humphreys, Denver, Colorado, September 25, 1934, pg. 37.
3. Wheeler, Harold, Family History, Date Unknown, Creede Historical Society Library.
4. Letter from John Jackson to the author, dated April 10, 2003.
5. *Colorado Business Directory for 1893*.
6. Letter from John Jackson to the author, dated April 4, 2003.
7. Clark, V.V., *A Geological Study with Historical Notes of Creede Mines, Inc.*, made to A.E. Humphreys, Denver, Colorado, September 25, 1934, pg. 3.
8. *Colorado Rail Annual No. 14: Narrow Gauge Byways in the San Juans,* pg. 195.
9. *The Creede Candle*, October 14, 1911.
10. *The Denver News*, October 18, 1895.
11. *Creede Firemen Ledger,* pg. 136.
12. Influenza Epidemic of 1918, A partial list of deaths from newspaper and death records, Creede Historical Society Library.
13. Feitz, Leland, *A Quick History of Creede: Colorado Boom Town*, Denver, Colorado, Golden Bell Press, 1969, pg. 35.

14. *The Creede Candle,* July 20, 1929, and March 29, 1930.
15. Oehlerts, Donald E., *Guide to Colorado Newspapers,* Denver, Colorado, Bibliographical Center for Research — Rocky Mountain Region, 1964, pp. 104-105.
16. *Creede Firemen Ledger,* pg. 175.
17. McCarty, Florence, *To Catch a Star,* Monte Vista, Colorado, High Valley Press, 1996, pg. 136.
18. Ibid., pg. 130.
19. *Historic Creede — A Walking Tour,* items 4, 7, and 8.

CHAPTER 14 – REBIRTH – THE HANGING WALL VEINS
1. *The Mineral Industry,* McGraw Hill Book Company, Inc., Vol. 50, 1941, pg. 206.
2. Albert E. Reynolds Collection No. 1220, Colorado Historical Society's Stephen H. Hart Library, Denver, Colorado.
3. State of Colorado Bureau of Mines *Annual Report for 1934.*
4. U.S. Bureau of Mines *Minerals Yearbook for 1935.*
5. *The Mineral Industry,* McGraw Hill Book Company, Inc., Vol. 43, 1934, pg. 201.
6. Ibid.,Vol. 47, 1938, pg. 191 and 1941, Vol. 50, pg. 206.
7. *The Engineering and Mining Journal,* February, 1949.
8. State of Colorado Bureau of Mines *Annual Report for 1961.*
9. Clark, V.V., *A Geological Study with Historical Notes of Creede Mines, Inc.,* made to A.E. Humphreys, Denver, Colorado, September 25, 1934, pg. 46; and a letter from John Jackson to the author dated July 30, 2001. Wallace Leary and associates had organized the Creede Reduction Company in about 1920 to sign up mine owners for the express purpose of milling ores of Creede Camp. A consultant, G.H. Dern, was hired to examine the properties and the feasibility of a custom mill.
10. U.S. Bureau of Mines *Minerals Yearbook for 1938.*
11. Letter from John Jackson to the author dated July 30, 2001.
12. Albert E. Reynolds Collection No. 1220, Colorado Historical Society's Stephen H. Hart Library, Denver, Colorado.
13. *Mining World,* Vol. 3, No. 12, 1941, pp. 15-18.
14. State of Colorado Bureau of Mines *Annual Report for 1946.*
15. Steven, Thomas A. and Ratté, James C., *USGS Professional Paper 487: Geology and Structural Control of Ore Deposition in the Creede District, San Juan Mountains, Colorado,* U.S. Geological Survey, Washington, D.C., 1965, pg. 10.
16. Albert E. Reynolds Collection No. 1220, Colorado Historical Society's Stephen H. Hart Library, Denver, Colorado.
17. Clark, V.V., *A Geological Study with Historical Notes of Creede Mines, Inc.,* made to A.E. Humphreys, Denver, Colorado, September 25, 1934, pp. 16-18.
18. Albert E. Reynolds Collection No. 1220, Colorado Historical Society's Stephen H. Hart Library, Denver, Colorado.
19. Scamehorn, Lee, *Albert Eugene Reynolds: Colorado's Mining King,* Norman, Oklahoma, University of Oklahoma Press, 1995, pp. 26, 28, 31, 220-221, 225, and 228.
20. Ibid., pp. 223-224.
21. Steven, Thomas A. and Ratté, James C., *USGS Professional Paper 487: Geology and Structural Control of Ore Deposition in the Creede District, San Juan Mountains, Colorado,* U.S. Geological Survey, Washington, D.C., 1965, pg. 10.
22. Clark, V.V., *A Geological Study with Historical Notes of Creede Mines, Inc.,* made to A.E. Humphreys, Denver, Colorado, September 25, 1934, pg. 32.
23. State of Colorado Bureau of Mines *Annual Reports for 1935 and 1937,* and U.S. Bureau of Mines *Minerals Yearbooks for 1936-1938.*
24. State of Colorado Bureau of Mines *Annual Report for 1939,* and U.S. Bureau of Mines *Minerals Yearbook for 1940.*
25. Albert E. Reynolds Collection No. 1220, Colorado Historical Society's Stephen H. Hart Library, Denver, Colorado.
26. Clark, V.V., *A Geological Study with Historical Notes of Creede Mines, Inc.,* made to A.E. Humphreys, Denver, Colorado, September 25, 1934, pg. 32.
27. State of Colorado Bureau of Mines *Annual Report for 1935.*
28. U.S. Bureau of Mines *Minerals Yearbook for 1940.*
29. State of Colorado Bureau of Mines *Annual Report for 1939.*
30. Albert E. Reynolds Collection No. 1220, Colorado Historical Society's Stephen H. Hart Library, Denver, Colorado; and Annual Report of the Emperius Mining Company 1940.
31. State of Colorado Bureau of Mines *Annual Report for 1935.*
32. State of Colorado Bureau of Mines *Annual Report for 1939*; and U.S. Bureau of Mines *Minerals Yearbook for 1940.*

33. Albert E. Reynolds Collection No. 1220, Colorado Historical Society's Stephen H. Hart Library, Denver, Colorado; and Annual Report of the Emperius Mining Company 1940.
34. Hubbard, Judson Slater, *A Man of Business and the Enterprises: Memoirs of Judson Slater Hubbard*, 1979, pg. 57.
35. Unknown Author, *Brief History of the Emperius Mining Company*, March 10, 1972.
36. *The Denver Post*, September 26, 1932.
37. *The Alamosa Journal*, August 24, 1922.
38. *The Rocky Mountain News*, August 1, 1990.
39. Scamehorn, Lee, *Albert Eugene Reynolds: Colorado's Mining King*, Norman, Oklahoma, University of Oklahoma Press, 1995, pp. 224-228.
40. Letter from John Jackson to the author, dated May 10, 2003.
41. Ibid., dated July 18, 2001.
42. Albert E. Reynolds Collection No. 1220, Colorado Historical Society's Stephen H. Hart Library, Denver, Colorado; and Annual Report of the Emperius Mining Company 1939.
43. Albert E. Reynolds Collection No. 1220, Colorado Historical Society's Stephen H. Hart Library, Denver, Colorado; and Comments by B.T. Poxson, no date.
44. U.S. Bureau of Mines *Mineral Yearbook Review of 1940*; Albert E. Reynolds Collection No. 1220, Colorado Historical Society's Stephen H. Hart Library, Denver, Colorado; and Annual Report of the Emperius Mining Company 1940.
45. Albert E. Reynolds Collection No. 1220, Colorado Historical Society's Stephen H. Hart Library, Denver, Colorado; and Comments by B.T. Poxson, no date.
46. Unknown Author, *Brief History of the Emperius Mining Company*, March 10, 1972.
47. Steven, Thomas A. and Ratté, James C., *USGS Professional Paper 487: Geology and Structural Control of Ore Deposition in the Creede District, San Juan Mountains, Colorado*, U.S. Geological Survey, Washington, D.C., 1965, pp. 10-11.
48. Cannaday, F.X., *The OH Vein and its Relation to the Amethyst Fault*, Colorado School of Mines Thesis for a Master of Science Degree, Golden, Colorado, March, 1950, pg. 1.
49. Letter from John Jackson to the author, dated April 21, 2003; and Meeves, Henry C. and Darnell, Richard P., *Study of the Silver Potential, Creede District, Mineral County, Colorado*, U.S. Department of the Interior, Bureau of Mines Information Circular 8370, Washington, D.C., Government Printing Office, 1968, pp. 33 and 35.
50. Poxson, B.T., "Mineral County's Annual Production Being Increased By Activity of Emperius Mining Company," Colorado Mining Association's *1942 Mining Year Book*.
51. Letters to the author from John Jackson dated September 28 and October 11, 2001, and from Paul Davis dated June 8, 2003.
52. Unknown Author, *Brief History of the Emperius Mining Company*, March 10, 1972.
53. Albert E. Reynolds Collection No. 1220, Colorado Historical Society's Stephen H. Hart Library, Denver, Colorado.
54. U.S. Bureau of Mines *Minerals Yearbook for 1943*; and Colorado Mining Association's *Mining Year Book for 1943*.
55. U.S. Bureau of Mines *Minerals Yearbook for 1945*.
56. Colorado Mining Association's *Mining Year Book for 1947*.
57. Voynick, Stephen M., *Climax: The History of Colorado's Climax Molybdenum Mine*, Missoula, Montana, Mountain Press Publishing Company, 1996, pg. 173.
58. Colorado Mining Association's *Mining Year Book for 1947*; and U.S. Bureau of Mines *Minerals Yearbook for 1947*.
59. Colorado Mining Association's *Mining Year Book for 1947*.
60. Steven, Thomas A. and Ratté, James C., *USGS Professional Paper 487: Geology and Structural Control of Ore Deposition in the Creede District, San Juan Mountains, Colorado*, U.S. Geological Survey, Washington, D.C., 1965, pg. 11.
61. U.S. Bureau of Mines *Minerals Yearbook for 1949*.
62. *The Engineering and Mining Journal*, March, 1951 and the U.S. Bureau of Mines *Minerals Yearbook for 1951*.
63. State of Colorado Bureau of Mines *Report for 1950-1951*.
64. U.S. Bureau of Mines *Minerals Yearbook for 1952*.
65. U.S. Bureau of Mines *Minerals Yearbook for 1953*.
66. State of Colorado Bureau of Mines *Report for 1954*, U.S. Bureau of Miners *Minerals Yearbook for 1955*, Creede Historical Society Library File; and Letter to the Author from John Jackson dated June 15, 2003.
67. U.S. Bureau of Mines *Minerals Yearbooks for 1955 and 1956*.
68. U.S. Bureau of Mines *Minerals Yearbook for 1957*.

69. *The Newsboy*, San Luis Valley Rural Electric Cooperative, October, 2001, pp.4-5.
70. U.S. Bureau of Mines *Minerals Yearbook for 1958* and *State of Colorado* Bureau of Mines *Report for 1958.*
71. U.S. Bureau of *Mines Minerals Yearbook for 1959 and 1960;* and State of Colorado Bureau of Mines *Annual Report for 1960.*
72. Full, Roy P. and Harty, Richard F., *Geologic Study of the Property of Creede Mines, Inc., Creede Mining District, Mineral County, Colorado,* Salt Lake City, Utah, January 29, 1969, pg. 54.
73. State of Colorado Bureau of Mines *Annual Report for 1961.*
74. The author was acquainted with Joe Salyer.
75. Unknown Author, *Brief History of the Emperius Mining Company,* March 10, 1972.
76. Scamehorn, Lee, *Albert Eugene Reynolds: Colorado's Mining King,* Norman, Oklahoma, University of Oklahoma Press, 1995, pg. 228.
77. State of Colorado Bureau of Mines *Annual Report for 1962.*
78. U.S. Bureau of Mines *Minerals Yearbook for 1963.*
79. Unknown Author, *Brief History of the Emperius Mining Company,* March 10, 1972.
80. U.S. Bureau of Mines *Minerals Yearbook for 1967.*
81. Ibid., 1968-1970.
82. Ibid., 1971.
83. Colorado Division of Mines *Mineral Industry Activities for 1972.*
84. Author's conversation with the "zinc specialist" at the U.S. Geological Survey.
85. U.S. Bureau of Mines *Minerals Yearbook for 1946.*
86. Letter from Paul Davis to the author dated May 27, 2001.
87. Letter from John Jackson to the author dated December 17, 2000, and a telephone interview with Les Turnipseed on November 5, 2001.
88. Unknown Author, *Brief Chronological Mining History Summary, Creede Mining District, Colorado,* January 1, 1983, pg. 5.
89. U.S. Bureau of Mines *Minerals Yearbook for 1935.*
90. U.S. Bureau of Mines *Minerals Yearbook for 1952.*
91. Letter from John Jackson to the author dated December 17, 2000.
92. U.S. Bureau of Mines *Minerals Yearbooks for 1956, 1957, 1958 and 1960;* a letter from John Jackson to the author dated June 15, 2003; and Unknown Author, *Brief Chronological Mining History Summary, Creede Mining District, Colorado,* January 1, 1983, pg. 4.
93. Letter from John Jackson to the author dated June 15, 2003.
94. Ibid., December 17, 2000.
95. Ibid.
96. U.S. Bureau of Mines *Minerals Yearbooks for 1952 through 1956, 1959;* and the State of Colorado Bureau of Mines *Annual Report for 1961.*
97. Steven, Thomas A. and Ratté, James C., *USGS Professional Paper 487: Geology and Structural Control of Ore Deposition in the Creede District, San Juan Mountains, Colorado,* U.S. Geological Survey, Washington, D.C., 1965, pg. 11.
98. Letter from John Jackson to the author dated December 7, 2000; and the State of Colorado Bureau of Mines *Annual Report for 1956.*
99. Clark, V.V., *A Geological Study with Historical Notes of Creede Mines, Inc.,* made to A.E. Humphreys, Denver, Colorado, September 25, 1934, pg. 36; and the State of Colorado Bureau of Mines *Annual Report for 1934.*
100. U.S. Bureau of Mines *Minerals Yearbooks for 1946 through 1949;* and Steven, Thomas A. and Ratté, James C., *USGS Professional Paper 487: Geology and Structural Control of Ore Deposition in the Creede District, San Juan Mountains, Colorado,* U.S. Geological Survey, Washington, D.C., 1965, pg. 11.
101. State of Colorado Bureau of Mines *Annual Report for 1962 through 1965.*
102. Letters from John Jackson to the author dated December 7 and 17, 2000; and Unknown Author, *Brief Chronological Mining History Summary, Creede Mining District, Colorado,* January 1, 1983, pg. 5.
103. U.S. Bureau of Mines *Minerals Yearbooks for 1946 through 1949;* Steven, Thomas A. and Ratté, James C., *USGS Professional Paper 487: Geology and Structural Control of Ore Deposition in the Creede District, San Juan Mountains, Colorado,* U.S. Geological Survey, Washington, D.C., 1965, pg. 11; the State of Colorado Bureau of Mines *Annual Report for 1946 and 1947;* and the U.S. Bureau of Mines *Minerals Yearbook for 1950.*

104. U.S. Bureau of Mines *Minerals Yearbooks for 1935 and 1951;* a Letter from John Jackson to the author dated December 7, 2000; and Steven, Thomas A. and Ratté, James C., *USGS Professional Paper 487: Geology and Structural Control of Ore Deposition in the Creede District, San Juan Mountains, Colorado*, U.S. Geological Survey, Washington, D.C., 1965, pg. 11.

105. Colorado Bureau of Mines *Mineral Industry Activities for 1966 through 1971;* and a letter from John Jackson to the author dated December 17, 2000.

106. U.S. Bureau of Mines *Minerals Yearbooks for 1935 through 1937;* and a letter from John Jackson to the author dated December 7, 2000.

107. Steven, Thomas A. and Ratté, James C., *USGS Professional Paper 487: Geology and Structural Control of Ore Deposition in the Creede District, San Juan Mountains, Colorado*, U.S. Geological Survey, Washington, D.C., 1965, pg. 11.

108. State of Colorado Bureau of Mines *Annual Reports for 1934, 1937 and 1939;* and the U.S. Bureau of Mines *Minerals Yearbooks for 1935 through 1940.*

109. Letters from John Jackson to the author dated December 17, 2000, and March 4, 2001.

110. Steven, Thomas A. and Ratté, James C., *USGS Professional Paper 487: Geology and Structural Control of Ore Deposition in the Creede District, San Juan Mountains, Colorado*, U.S. Geological Survey, Washington, D.C., 1965, pg. 11.

111. State of Colorado Bureau of Mines *Annual Reports for 1937 and 1941;* and U.S. Bureau of Mines *Minerals Yearbooks for 1936 through 1941.*

112. Letter from John Jackson to the author dated December 17, 2000; and State of Colorado Bureau of Mines *Annual Reports for 1953 through 1966.*

113. State of Colorado Bureau of Mines *Annual Reports for 1934, 1937, and 1939.*

114. Letter from John Jackson to the author dated December 17, 2000.

115. State of Colorado Bureau of Mines *Annual Report for 1934.*

116. Korzeb, Stanley L., "The Wagon Wheel Gap Fluorspar Mine, Mineral County, Colorado," *The Mineralogical Record*, Volume 24, January-February, 1993, pp. 23-24.

117. Letter from Charles E. "Ed" Johnson to the author dated October 15, 2003.

CHAPTER 15 – THE SECOND BOOM

1. Steven, Thomas A. and Ratté, James C., *USGS Professional Paper 487: Geology and Structural Control of Ore Deposition in the Creede District, San Juan Mountains, Colorado*, U.S. Geological Survey, Washington, D.C., 1965, pg. 84.

2. Ibid., pp 82-84.

3. Hilliard, Henry, *Silver — Metal Prices in the United States through 1998*, U.S. Geological Survey, 2003, pg. 140.

4. Moritz, Charles, Editor, *Current Biography Yearbook 1980*, H.W. Wilson Company, New York, 1980, pp. 162-194; and Hilliard, Henry, *Silver — Metal Prices in the United States through 1998*, U.S. Geological Survey, 2003, pg. 140.

5. Meeves, Henry C. and Darnell, Richard P., *Study of the Silver Potential, Creede District, Mineral County, Colorado*, U.S. Department of the Interior, Bureau of Mines Information Circular 8370, Washington, D.C., Government Printing Office, 1968, pp. 1 and 56.

6. Letter from Robert Boppe to the author dated October 2, 2001.

7. Claim Maps on File with the U.S. Bureau of Land Management, Wheatridge, Colorado.

8. *Del Norte Prospector and Candle*, April 7, 1961.

9. Unknown Author, *Brief Chronological Mining History Summary, Creede Mining District, Colorado*, January 1, 1983; and interview with John Jackson on September 16, 2001.

10. *Del Norte Prospector and Candle*, February 23, 1968.

11. Letters to the author from John Jackson dated March 4, 2001, and Mildred (Hosselkus) Hoffman, Fred Baker's ex-wife, dated January 22, 2002, and the author's remembrances. The author knew Fred Baker, Jr. The author and boyhood friends would stop and talk to Fred at the Baker home on their way home by bicycles from fishing at Home Lake east of Monte Vista. The Baker family was next door neighbors to the author's parents in Monte Vista before moving to Aspen.

12. Letters to the author from John Jackson dated March 4, 2001, and Mildred (Hosselkus) Hoffman, Fred Baker's ex-wife, dated January 22, 2002, and a Letter to the Editor, *The Engineering and Mining Journal*, September 1965.

13. Hull, Donald A., *Geology of the Puzzle Vein, Creede Mining District, Colorado*, Thesis for a Doctor of Science Degree, University of Nevada, Reno, Nevada, June, 1979, pp. 6-7; Boppe, Robert, Spearfish, South Dakota, Telephone Interview, July, 2003; and Jackson, John, Cedaredge, Colorado, Interview, September 2001.

14. Steven, Thomas A. and Ratté James C., *USGS Professional Paper 487: Geology and Structural Control of Ore Deposition in the Creede District, San Juan Mountains, Colorado*, U.S. Geological Survey, Washington, D.C., 1965, pg. 84.
15. U.S. Bureau of Mines *Minerals Yearbooks for 1969 and 1970.*
16. Howell, Frank M., *Homestake's Bulldog Mountain Mill, Creede, Colorado*, Colorado Mining Association's *1970 Mining Year Book*; and "Homestake's Bulldog Mountain Mine," *Skillings Mining Review,* March 21, 1970.
17. Letter from Robert Boppe to the author dated October 2, 2001.
18. U.S. Bureau of Mines *Minerals Yearbooks for 1971, 1972 and 1973.*
19. Letter from Robert Boppe to the author dated October 2, 2001; U.S. Bureau of Mines *Minerals Yearbook for 1976* ; and Unknown Author, *Brief Chronological Mining History Summary, Creede Mining District, Colorado,* January 1, 1983.
20. U.S. Bureau of Mines *Minerals Yearbook for 1974.*
21. Jackson, Daniel, Jr., "Homestake's Hard Work Pays Off at Bulldog Mountain Mine," *The Engineering and Mining Journal,* May 1974, pg 69. Used by permission of *The Engineering and Mining Journal.*
22. Ibid., pg. 68.
23. U.S. Bureau of Mines *Minerals Yearbooks for 1975 and 1976*; and Colorado Division of Mines *Mineral Industry Activities for 1976.*
24. U.S. Bureau of Mines *Minerals Yearbook for 1976.*
25. Ibid.
26. U.S. Bureau of Mines *Minerals Yearbook for 1977.*
27. Colorado Division of Mines *Mineral Industry Activities for 1978*; and U.S. Bureau of Mines *Minerals Yearbook for 1980.*
28. U.S. Bureau of Mines *Minerals Yearbook for 1981.*
29. U.S. Bureau of Mines *Minerals Yearbooks for 1982 and 1983.*
30. U.S. Bureau of Mines *Minerals Yearbook for 1984.*
31. Unknown Author, *Brief History of the Emperius Mining Company,* March 10, 1972.
32. U.S. Bureau of Mines *Minerals Yearbook for 1961.*
33. State of Colorado Bureau of Mines *Annual Report For the Year 1962.*
34. Creede Mines, Incorporated Company Records.
35. Interview with Charles Melbye on April 27, 2001.
36. Ibid.
37. Interview with Charles Melbye on April 27, 2001; and LaFont, John, *The Homesteaders of the Upper Rio Grande*, Birmingham, Alabama, Oxmoor Press, 1971, pp. 34, 36, and 43.
38. Colorado Division of Mines *Mineral Industry Activities for 1973*; and U.S. Bureau of Mines *Minerals Yearbook for 1974.*
39. Interview with Charles Melbye on April 27, 2001.
40. Colorado Division of Mines *Mineral Industry Activities for 1976*; and U.S. Bureau of Mines *Minerals Yearbook for 1975.*
41. Interview with Charles Melbye on April 27, 2001.
42. Colorado Division of Mines *Mineral Industry Activities for 1977*; and an interview with Charles Melbye on April 27, 2001.
43. *The Wall Street Journal,* August 28, 1980. Used by permission of *The Wall Street Journal.*
44. Interview with Charles Melbye on April 27, 2001.
45. *Mining Engineering,* Volume 31, No. 5, p. 478, 1979.
46. U.S. Bureau of Mines *Minerals Yearbook for 1980.*
47. Interview with Charles Melbye on April 27, 2001.
48. Ibid.
49. Minerals Engineering Company's 1983 *10-K Report* to the Securities and Exchange Commission, pg. 3.
50. U.S. Bureau of Mines *Minerals Yearbooks for 1983, 1984 and 1985.*
51. Telephone Interview with Martin Nelson on July 10, 2001. Martin Nelson served as a geologist at Creede from 1983 to 1990 for Pioneer, Minerals Engineering, and CoCa.
52. U.S. Bureau of Mines *Minerals Yearbook for 1986.*
53. Interview with Charles Melbye on April 27, 2001.
54. Colorado Bureau of Mines *Mineral Industry Activities for 1971.*
55. Telephone Interview with Les Turnipseed on November 5, 2001; and the U.S. Bureau of Mines *Minerals Yearbook for 1976.*
56. U.S. Bureau of Mines *Minerals Yearbook for 1985.*

57. U.S. Bureau of Mines *Mineral Yearbooks for 1986 and 1987*; and *The Northern Miner,* date unknown, circa 1985.
58. Letter from Robert Boppe to the author dated August 2003.
59. Colorado Division of Mines *Mineral Industry Activities for 1975.*
60. U.S. Bureau of Mines *Minerals Yearbook for 1985* and *The Mining Record*, November 6, 1985.
61. Unknown Author, *Brief Chronological Mining History Summary, Creede Mining District, Colorado*, January 1, 1983, pg. 5.
62. Colorado Division of Mines *Mineral Industry Activities for 1980.*
63. Minerals Engineering Company's 1983 *10-K Report* to the Securities and Exchange Commission, pg. 4.
64. U.S. Bureau of Mines *Minerals Yearbook for 1985.*
65. Nelson, Martin A., *Summary Report — Creede Formation Project*, CoCa Mines, Inc., January 25, 1989, pp. 23-24.
66. Ibid., pp. 25-27.
67. U.S. Bureau of Mines *Minerals Yearbook for 1981*; and Nelson, Martin A., *Summary Report — Creede Formation Project*, CoCa Mines, Inc., January 25, 1989, pp. 27 and 78.

CHAPTER 16 – THE MINERS

1. Young, Otis E., Jr., *Black Powder and Hand Steel,* Norman, Oklahoma, University of Oklahoma Press, 1975, pg. 4.
2. Ibid., pp. 4-5.
3. Letter from John Jackson to the author dated September 14, 2003.
4. Crampton, Frank A., *Deep Enough: A Working Stiff in the Western Mine Camps*, Denver, Colorado, Sage Books, 1956, Preface.
5. Letter from Paul Davis to the author dated September 18, 2003.
6. *The Engineering and Mining Journal*, October 28, 1893.
7. *The Engineering and Mining Journal*, August, 1897.
8. *The Engineering and Mining Journal*, June 24 and September 9, 1899.
9. Smith, Duane A., *Song of the Hammer and Drill*, Golden, Colorado, Colorado School of Mines Press, 1982, pp. 103 and 107.
10. Suggs, George G., Jr., *Colorado's War on Militant Unionism: James H. Peabody and the Western Federation of Miners*, Wayne State University Press, 1972, pp. 20-22.
11. Conversations between the author and Charles H. Chase about his father, Charles A. Chase. The senior Chase successfully managed the Liberty Bell at Telluride and the Shenandoah Dives at Silverton where he was given the nickname "Father Chase" by the town.
12. *The Engineering and Mining Journal*, June 13, 1903.
13. Letter from John Jackson to the author dated May 27, 2001.
14. Suggs, George G., Jr., *Colorado's War on Militant Unionism: James H. Peabody and the Western Federation of Miners*, Wayne State University Press, 1972, pg. 15.
15. Crampton, Frank A., *Deep Enough: A Working Stiff in the Western Mine Camps*, Denver, Colorado, Sage Books, 1956, Preface.
16. *New Law for Pay Day Makes Trouble at Creede*, July 4, 1901, Colorado Bureau of Mines Manuscripts, Box 640, Volume 24.
17. *The Engineering and Mining Journal*, February 18, 1922.
18. Letter from John Jackson to the author dated September 27, 2003.
19. Letter from Paul Davis to the author dated August 30, 2003.
20. Telephone Interview with Robert A. Boppe on October 28, 2001.
21. Clemmer, Gregg S., *American Miners' Carbide Lamps: A Collector's Guide to American Carbide Mine Lighting*, Tucson, Arizona, Westernlore Press, 1987, pg. 44.
22. Emmons, W.H. and Larsen, E.S., *Geology and Ore Deposits of the Creede District*, U.S. Geological Survey Bulletin 718, Washington, D.C., Government Printing Office, 1923, pg. 6.
23. Ibid., pp. 134-135.
24. Letter from Paul Davis to the author dated August 30, 2001.
25. Author's remembrances from working for the Emperius Mining Company in the early 1950s and as a mine surveyor for Paul Davis in the late 1950s.
26. Letter from John Jackson to the author dated December 7, 2000.
27. Letter from Paul Davis to the author dated September 18, 2003.
28. Letter from Mary Midkiff Johnson to the author dated September 23, 2003.

29. Letter from John Jackson to the author dated September 27, 2003.
30. Letter from John Jackson to the author dated August 10, 2003, in which he stated that he hand drilled holes in the hanging wall of the Amethyst fault in 1944. Paul Davis in a letter to the author dated August 25, 2001, states that hand mining was done on narrow, high-grade veins in 1940.
31. Lehman, Dick, *A Little History, A Creede Souvenir Book — Days of '92*, Mineral County Chamber of Commerce, 1985.
32. Letter from John Jackson to the author dated September 14, 2003.
33. Peele, Robert, *Mining Engineers' Handbook*, New York, John Wiley & Sons, Inc., 1950, pg. 5-07.
34. Letter from John Jackson to the author dated February 1, 2001; and Stack, Barbara, *Handbook of Mining and Tunnelling Machinery*, New York, John Wiley & Sons, Inc., 1982, pg. 29.
35. *The Engineering and Mining Journal*, July 3, 1926.
36. Letter from Charles E. "Ed" Johnson to the author dated October 15, 2003.
37. Stack, Barbara, *Handbook of Mining and Tunnelling Machinery*, New York, John Wiley & Sons, Inc., 1982, pg. 36.
38. Jackson, Daniel, Jr., "Homestake's Hard Work Pays Off at Bulldog Mountain Mine," *The Engineering and Mining Journal*, May, 1974, pg. 68. Used by permission of *The Engineering and Mining Journal*.
39. Ibid., pg. 69; and *Sharp Bits,* a Homestake Mining Company in-house publication, Summer, 1969.
40. _____, *Blasters' Handbook*, fifteenth edition, Wilmington, Delaware, E.I. DuPont de Nemours & Company, Inc., 1969, pp. 1-4.
41. Ibid., pg. 11.
42. Letter from Martin Nelson to the author dated October 1, 2003.
43. Jackson, Daniel, Jr., "Homestake's Hard Work Pays Off at Bulldog Mountain Mine," *The Engineering and Mining Journal*, May, 1974, pg. 68. Used by permission of *The Engineering and Mining Journal*.
44. Crampton, Frank A., *Deep Enough: A Working Stiff in the Western Mine Camps*, Denver, Colorado, Sage Books, 1956, Preface.
45. Letter from Charles E. "Ed" Johnson to the author dated October 15, 2003.
46. Letter from John Jackson to the author dated December 7, 2000.
47. Ibid.
48. Ibid.
49. Ibid.
50. Ibid.
51. Letter from John Jackson to the author dated November 22, 2003.
52. Jackson, Daniel, Jr., "Homestake's Hard Work Pays Off at Bulldog Mountain Mine," *The Engineering and Mining Journal*, May, 1974, pg. 67 and 70. Used by the permission of *The Engineering and Mining Journal*.
53. U.S. Bureau of Mines *Minerals Yearbook for 1981*.
54. Letter from John Jackson to the author dated August 23, 2003.
55. Bureau of Mines of the State of Colorado, *Fifteenth Biennial Report, 1917 and 1918*.
56. Jackson, Daniel, Jr., "Homestake's Hard Work Pays Off at Bulldog Mountain Mine," *The Engineering and Mining Journal,* May, 1974, pg. 67-68. Used by the permission of *The Engineering and Mining Journal*.
57. Ibid., pg. 68.
58. Korzeb, Stanley L., "The Wagon Wheel Gap Fluorspar Mine, Mineral County, Colorado," *The Mineralogical Record*, Volume 24, January-February, 1993, pg. 24.
59. Peele, Robert, *Mining Engineers' Handbook*, New York, John Wiley & Sons, Inc., 1950, pp. 10-324 and 325.
60. *A Creede Souvenir Book — Days of '92*, Mineral County Chamber of Commerce, 1987.
61. Letter from Ken Wyley to the author dated November 11, 2003.
62. Johnson, Ed and Dooley, Gene, Interview, June 11, 2001.

CHAPTER 17 – RHYMES OF THE MINES

1. Davidson, Levette J., *Poems of the Old West*, Denver, Colorado, Sage Books, 1951, pg. 236; and Collins, Hallie Chapman, *Creede Then And Now*, Date Unknown, Creede Historical Society Library.

2. Davidson, Levette J., *Poems of the Old West*, Denver, Colorado, Sage Books, 1951, pg. 236; Mumey, Nolie, *Creede: History of a Colorado Silver Mining Town*, Denver, Colorado, Artcraft Press, 1949, pg. 12; and Oehlerts, Donald E., *Guide to Colorado Newspapers*, Biographical Center For Research, Rocky Mountain Region, Inc., Denver, 1904, pp. 104-105.
3. Warman, Cy, *Songs of Cy Warman*, Boston, Massachusetts, Rand Avery Co., 1911, pp. 76-77.
4. Letter to the author from John Jackson dated December 23, 2000.
5. Ibid.
6. Getz, Carol Ann Wetherill, "Oppy," *The San Luis Valley Historian*, Volume VII, Number 1, Alamosa, Colorado, 1975, pg. 1; a letter to the author from John Jackson dated April 30, 2001; and the author's remembrances.
7. Letter to the author from John Jackson dated April 30, 2001.
8. Getz, Carol Ann Wetherill, "Oppy," *The San Luis Valley Historian*, Volume VII, Number 1, Alamosa, Colorado, 1975, pp. 2-3.

EPILOGUE

1. Author's estimate.
2. Ridge, J.D., *Ore Deposits of the United States, 1933-1967*, Graton-Sales Volume, American Institute of Mining and Metallurgical Engineers, New York, Vol. I, Part V, Colorado Rockies: Steven, T.A., Ore deposits of the central San Juan Mountains, Colorado, pp. 706-713.
3. Meeves, Henry C. and Darnell, Richard P., *Study of the Silver Potential, Creede District, Mineral County, Colorado*, U.S. Department of the Interior, Bureau of Mines Information Circular 8370, Washington, D.C., Government Printing Office, 1968, pg. 30.
4. Letter from Robert Boppe to the author dated October 2, 2001.
5. Letter from John Jackson to the author dated November 29, 2001.
6. Letter from Robert Boppe to the author dated October 2, 2001.
7. Letter from John Jackson to the author dated January 11, 2002.
8. Ibid.
9. Letter from Ed Johnson to the author dated October 15, 2003.
10. Letter from Robert Boppe to the author dated October 2, 2001.
11. Ward, Zeke, Creede, Colorado, Telephone Interview, June 7, 2001.
12. Letter from Paul Davis to the author dated November 22, 2003.
13. Villani, John, *The 100 Best Small Art Towns in America*, Santa Fe, New Mexico, John Muir Publications, 1998.
14. Letter from Ken Wyley to the author dated November 11, 2003.
15. *The Pueblo Chieftain*, Monday, August 12, 1991.

BIBLIOGRAPHY

ARCHIVES AND MANUSCRIPT COLLECTIONS

Colorado Historical Society's Stephen H. Hart Library, Denver, Colorado
    Albert E. Reynolds Collection No. 1220.
    Colorado Bureau of Mines Manuscripts, Box 640, Volume 24.
    Prospectus - 400 Acre Consolidated Diamond Drill Mining Company, 1892.
    Edwin L. Bennett, Names of Residents and Business Firms of Creede, Colorado to 1901.
    Prospectus of the Monte Carlo Gold and Silver Mining Company.

Creede Historical Society, Creede, Colorado
    A Creede Souvenir Book – Days of '92, Mineral County Chamber of Commerce, 1985 and 1987.
    Collins, Hallie Chapman, *Creede Then And Now,* Date Unknown.
    Wheeler, Harold, Family History, Date Unknown.
    Notes from Various Sources, Date Unknown.
    Nelson Tunnel and Mining Company Letter with "poem," circa 1893.
    Bank of Monte Vista Letter from R.B. Wallace to Bertha C. Bowen, dated January 15, 1909.
    Prospectus of the Bulldog Leasing, Mining & Milling Company.
    Influenza Epidemic of 1918, A partial list of deaths from newspaper and death records.
    Creede Firemen Ledger.
    Historic Creede — A Walking Tour, 1993.

Denver Public Library, Western History Collection, Denver, Colorado
    Pliny Fisk Sharp Scrapbooks, Volume 8.

State of Colorado, Colorado State Archives, Denver, Colorado
    Commodore Mining Company vs. Bachelor Mining and Milling Company, et. al., Case No. 310, Archive No. 68931.

Robert A. Boppe Collection
    Prospectus of the North Amethyst Mining Company.
    Letter from Herman Emperius to Fred Monkemeyer dated April 10, 1928.

GOVERNMENT DOCUMENTS
FEDERAL
Cross, Whitman; Howe, Earnest; Ransome, F.L., *Geologic Atlas of the United States: Silverton Folio,* U.S. Geological Survey, Washington, D.C., 1905.
Emmons, W.H., *U.S. Geological Survey Mineral Resources, 1892,* U.S. Geological Survey, Washington, D.C., 1893.
Emmons, W.H. and Larsen, E.S., *A Preliminary Report on the Geology and Ore Deposits of Creede, Colorado,* U.S. Geological Survey Bulletin 530, Washington, D.C., Government Printing Office, 1913.
Emmons, W.H. and Larsen, E.S., *Geology and Ore Deposits of the Creede District,* U.S. Geological Survey Bulletin 718, Washington, D.C., Government Printing Office, 1923.
Henderson, Charles W., *Mining in Colorado: A History of Discovery, Development and Production,* U.S. Geological Survey Professional Paper No. 138, Washington, D.C., Government Printing Office, 1926.
Hilliard, Henry, *Silver — Metal Prices in the United States through 1998,* U.S. Geological Survey, 2003.
Larsen, Esper S., *Recent Mining Developments in the Creede District, Colorado,* U.S. Geological Survey Bulletin 811-B, Washington, D.C., Government Printing Office, 1929.

Annual Report for the Year 1919, U.S. Bureau of Mines, Washington, D.C.

Meeves, Henry C. and Darnell, Richard P., *Study of the Silver Potential, Creede District, Mineral County, Colorado,* U.S. Department of the Interior, Bureau of Mines Information Circular 8370, Washington, D.C., Government Printing Office, 1968.

Steven, Thomas A. and Ratté, James C., *USGS Professional Paper 487: Geology and Structural Control of Ore Deposition in the Creede District, San Juan Mountains, Colorado,* U.S. Geological Survey, Washington, D.C., 1965.

Mineral Resources of the United States, U.S. Geological Survey, Washington, D.C.

Minerals Yearbook, U.S. Bureau of Mines, Washington, D.C.

Mineral Yearbook Review, U.S. Bureau of Mines, Washington, D.C.

Yearbook. U.S. Geological Survey, Washington, D.C.

STATE OF COLORADO

Aurand, Harry A., *Fluorspar Deposits of Colorado,* Colorado Geological Survey Bulletin 18, 1926.

Bureau of Mines of the State of Colorado, *Fifteenth Biennial Report, 1917 and 1918.*

Colorado Business Directory.

Colorado Division of Mines *Mineral Industry Activities.*

Colorado State Bureau of Mines *Report for 1919.*

Report of the Colorado State Bureau of Mines for 1897.

State of Colorado Bureau of Mines *Annual Reports.*

MINERAL COUNTY

Mineral County Commissioner Proceedings, Volume 1.

COSTILLA COUNTY

Costilla Combined Courts Records, 1905.

PROFESSIONAL JOURNALS

Axelrod, Daniel I., *The Late Oligocene Creede Flora, Colorado,* University of California Publications in Geological Sciences, vol. 130, 1987.

Bethke, Philip M. and Hay, Richard L, editors, *Ancient Lake Creede: Its Volcano-Tectonic Setting, History of Sedimentation, and Relation to Mineralization in the Creede Mining District,* Geological Society of America's Special Paper 346, 2000, that includes studies by Peter W. Lipman, Paul B. Barton, Phillip M. Bethke, Richard L. Hay, Thomas A. Steven, and others.

Smith, R.L. and Bailey, R.A., *Resurgent Cauldrons,* in Coats, R.R., Hag, R.L. and Anderson, C.A., eds., *Studies in Volcanology;* Geological Society of America Memoir 116, 1968.

Ridge, J.D., *Ore Deposits of the United States, 1933-1967,* Graton-Sales Volume, A.I.M.M.E., New York, Vol. I, Part V, Colorado Rockies: Steven, T.A., Ore deposits of the central San Juan Mountains, Colorado.

MINING JOURNALS

Colorado Mining Association's *Mining Year Books.*

The Engineering and Mining Journal.

The Engineering and Mining Journal-Press.

Explosives Engineer.

Metallurgical and Chemical Engineering.

The Mineral Industry.

Mines and Minerals.

Mining America.

Mining and Scientific Press.

Mining and Scientific Review.

Mining Engineering.

The Mining Record.

Mining Reporter.

Mining Science.

Mining World.

The Northern Miner.

Skillings Mining Review.

MAGAZINES

Carter, C. Joe, "The San Luis Valley Senator, Thomas Meade Bowen," *The San Luis Valley Historian*, Volume XXIII, Number 1, Alamosa, Colorado, 1991.

Colorado Rail Annual No. 14: "Narrow Gauge Byways in the San Juans."

Ferguson, Charles W., "Unforgettable DeWitt Wallace," *Readers' Digest*, February, 1987.

Francis, Peter, "Giant Volcanic Calderas," *Scientific American*, June, 1983.

Getz, Carol Ann Wetherill, "Oppy," *The San Luis Valley Historian* Volume VII, Number 1, Alamosa, Colorado, 1975.

Getz, Carol Ann Wetherill, "The Wason Legend," *The San Luis Valley Historian*, Volume XI, Number 4, Alamosa, Colorado, 1979.

Korzeb, Stanley L., "The Wagon Wheel Gap Fluorspar Mine, Mineral County, Colorado," *The Mineralogical Record*, Volume 24, January-February, 1993.

Majors, Mrs. A.H., "Life in Creede in the Early Days," *Colorado Magazine*, Volume XXII, No. 6, November, 1945.

Ogburn, Robert W., "Law and Mostly Order in Mineral County," *The San Luis Valley Historian*, Volume XXVII, No. 2, 1995.

Poxson, B.T., "Mineral County's Annual Production Being Increased By Activity of Emperius Mining Company," *Colorado Mining Association's 1942 Mining Year Book.*

_____, *Sharp Bits*, Summer, 1969, In-House Publication of the Homestake Mining Company, Lead, South Dakota. Used by permission of the Barrick Gold Corporation.

NEWSPAPERS

The Alamosa Journal.
The Arizona Daily Star.
The Carbonate Chronicle.
The Colorado Sun.
The Creede Candle.
Creede Chronicle.
Del Norte Prospector and Candle.
Del Norte Prospector.
The Denver News.
The Denver Post.
The Denver Republican.
The Denver Times.
Mineral County Miner.
The Monte Vista Journal.
The Newsboy, San Luis Valley Rural Electric Cooperative.
The Pueblo Chieftain and Star Journal.
The Rocky Mountain News.
San Diego Union.
San Luis Valley Graphic.
The Valley Courier.
The Wall Street Journal.

BOOKS

Ambrose, Stephen E., *Nothing Like It in the World: The Men Who Built the Transcontinental Railroad, 1863-1869*, New York, Simon & Schuster, 2000.

American National Biography, *Auspices of the American Council of Learned Societies*, New York, Oxford University Press, 1999.

Athearn, Robert G., *Rebel of the Rockies: A History of the Denver and Rio Grande Western Railroad*, New Haven and London, Yale University Press, 1962.

Bean, Luther E., *Land of the Blue Sky People*, Monte Vista, Colorado, The Monte Vista Journal, 1962.

Beebe, Lucius and Clegg, Charles, *Narrow Gauge in the Rockies*, Berkeley, California, Howell-North, 1958.

Bollinger, Edward T. and Bauer, Frederick, *The Moffat Road*, Denver, Colorado, Sage Books, 1962.

Brown, *An Empire of Silver: A History of the San Juan Silver Rush*, Caldwell, Idaho, Caxton Printers, Ltd., 1965.

Canfield, John G., *Mines and Mining Men of Colorado: The Principal Producing Mines of Gold and Silver, The Bonanza Kings and Successful Prospectors, The Picturesque Camps and Thriving Cities*, Denver, Colorado, John G. Canfield, Publisher, 1893.

Clemmer, Gregg S., *American Miners' Carbide Lamps: A Collector's Guide to American Carbide Mine Lighting*, Tucson, Arizona, Westernlore Press, 1987.

Colorado Press Association, *Who's Who in Colorado*, Boulder, Colorado, 1938.

Costigan, George P., Jr., *Cases on the American Law of Mining*, Indianapolis, Indiana, Bobbs-Merrill Company, 1929.

Crampton, Frank A., *Deep Enough: A Working Stiff in the Western Mine Camps*, Denver, Colorado, Sage Books, 1956.

Davidson, Levette J., *Poems of the Old West*, Denver, Colorado, Sage Books, 1951.

Davis, Richard Harding, *The West From a Car Window*, New York, Harper & Bros., 1892.

Eckel, Edwin B., *Minerals of Colorado*, Golden, Colorado, Fulcrum Publishing, 1997.

Feitz, Leland, *A Quick History of Creede: Colorado Boom Town*, Denver, Colorado, Golden Bell Press, 1969.

Griswold, Don L. and Jean Harvey, *The Carbonate Camp Called Leadville*, Denver, Colorado, The University of Denver Press, 1951.

Hall, Frank, *History of the State of Colorado*, Chicago, Illinois, Blakely Printing Company, 1895.

Kindquist, Cathy E., *Stony Pass: The Tumbling and Impetuous Trail*, Silverton, Colorado, San Juan Book Company, 1987.

Kohl, Edith Eudora, *Denver's Historic Mansions*, Denver, Colorado, Sage Books, 1957.

LaFont, John, *The Homesteaders of the Upper Rio Grande*, Birmingham, Alabama, Oxmoor Press, 1971.

Lescohier, Roger P., *Lester Pelton and the Pelton Water Wheel*, Reproduced by Buttonworks-Printworks through the cooperation of the Empire Mine Park Association, California, 1992.

Martorano, et al., *Colorado Prehistory: A Context for the Rio Grande Basin*, Denver, Colorado, Colorado Council of Professional Archeologists, 1999.

McCargish, Ed, *Odes and Poems By a Hard Rock Miner*, Creede, Colorado, privately printed, 1948.

McCarty, Florence, *To Catch a Star*, Monte Vista, Colorado, High Valley Press, 1996.

Moritz, Charles, Editor, *Current Biography Yearbook 1980*, H.W. Wilson Company, New York, 1980.

Mumey, Nolie, *Creede: History of a Colorado Silver Mining Town*, Denver, Colorado, Artcraft Press, 1949.

Oehlerts, Donald E., *Guide to Colorado Newspapers*, Denver, Colorado, Bibliographical Center for Research — Rocky Mountain Region, 1964.

Peele, Robert, *Mining Engineers' Handbook*, New York, John Wiley & Sons, Inc., 1950.

Riggenbach, Emma M., *A Bridge to Yesterday*, Monte Vista, Colorado, High Valley Press, 1982.

Scamehorn, Lee, *Albert Eugene Reynolds: Colorado's Mining King*, Norman, Oklahoma, University of Oklahoma Press, 1995.

Smith, Duane A., *Mining America: The Industry and the Environment*, Lawrence, Kansas, University Press of Kansas, 1987.

Smith, Duane A., *Song of the Hammer and Drill*, Golden, Colorado, Colorado School of Mines Press, 1982.

Stack, Barbara, *Handbook of Mining and Tunnelling Machinery*, New York, John Wiley & Sons, Inc.,1982.

Suggs, George G., Jr., *Colorado's War on Militant Unionism: James H. Peabody and the Western Federation of Miners*, Wayne State University Press, 1972.

Taggart, Arthur F., *Elements of Ore Dressing*, New York, John Wiley & Sons, Inc., 1951.

Trennert, Robert A., *Riding the High Wire: Aerial Mine Tramways in the West*, Boulder, Colorado, University Press of Colorado, 2001.

Villani, John, *The 100 Best Small Art Towns in America*, Santa Fe, New Mexico, John Muir Publications, 1998.

Voynick, Stephen M., *Climax: The History of Colorado's Climax Molybdenum Mine*, Missoula, Montana, Mountain Press Publishing Company, 1996.

Warman, Cy, *Mountain Melodies*, Creede, Colorado, privately printed, 1892.

Warman, Cy, *Songs of Cy Warman*, Boston, Massachusetts, Rand Avery Co., 1911.

Wolle, Muriel Sibell, *Stampede to Timberline: The Ghost Towns and Mining Camps of Colorado*, Boulder, Colorado, published by Muriel S. Wolle, 1949.

Young, Otis E., Jr., *Black Powder and Hand Steel*, Norman, Oklahoma, University of Oklahoma Press, 1975.

_____, *Blasters' Handbook,* fifteenth edition, Wilmington, Delaware, E.I. DuPont de Nemours & Company, Inc., 1969.

UNPUBLISHED MATERIAL

Bancroft, George J., *A Report on the Bulldog Mine, Creede, Colorado,* circa 1927, with attached letter to Geo. J. Bancroft from C.N. Blanchette, dated July 29, 1926.

Barnes, Chuck, *The Creede Candle: A compilation of news reports appearing in The Creede Candle beginning with the January 7, 1892, edition and depicting the history of Creede,* Creede, Colorado, 1993.

Berteloop, Paul Gordon, *The History of Creede: A Mining Camp in its Early Days,* University of Denver Thesis for a Master's Degree, Denver, Colorado, August, 1953.

Cannaday, F.X., *The OH Vein and its Relation to the Amethyst Fault,* Colorado School of Mines Thesis for a Master of Science Degree, Golden, Colorado, March, 1950.

Clark, V.V., *A Geological Study with Historical Notes of Creede Mines, Inc.,* made to A.E. Humphreys, Denver, Colorado, September 25, 1934.

Creede Mines, Incorporated Company Records.

Claim Maps on File with the U.S. Bureau of Land Management, Wheatridge, Colorado.

Full, Roy P. and Harty, Richard F., *Geologic Study of the Property of Creede Mines, Inc., Creede Mining District, Mineral County, Colorado,* Salt Lake City, Utah, January 29, 1969.

Garrey, George H., *Report on the Mines Along the Amethyst Lode, Creede, Mineral County, Colorado,* 1916.

Hardy, G., Consulting Engineer, Letter to H.A. Guess, President of the Creede Exploration Company, dated March 29, 1919.

Hubbard, Judson Slater, *A Man of Business and the Enterprises: Memoirs of Judson Slater Hubbard,* 1979.

Hull, Donald A., *Geology of the Puzzle Vein, Creede Mining District, Colorado,* Thesis for a Doctor of Science Degree, University of Nevada, Reno, Nevada, June, 1979.

Nelson, Martin A., *Summary Report — Creede Formation Project,* CoCa Mines, Inc., January 25, 1989.

Unknown Author, *Brief History of the Emperius Mining Company,* March 10, 1972.

Unknown Author, *Brief Chronological Mining History Summary, Creede Mining District, Colorado,* January 1, 1983.

CORRESPONDENCE AND INTERVIEWS

Boppe, Robert, Spearfish, South Dakota, Correspondence, 2001, 2003.
Davis, Paul, Del Norte, Colorado, Correspondence, 2001, 2002, 2003.
Hoffman, Mildred, Sequim, Washington, Correspondence, 2002.
Hosselkus, Marge, Creede, Colorado, Interview, 2001.
Howell, Dr. Thomas F., Abilene, Texas, Correspondence, 2001.
Jackson, John, Cedaredge, Colorado, Correspondence and Interview, 1985, 2000, 2001, 2002, 2003.
Johnson, Charles E. "Ed," Creede, Colorado, Correspondence and Interview, 2002 and 2003.
Johnson, Ed and Dooley, Gene, Interview, June 11, 2001.
Melbye, Charles, Sun City West, Arizona, Interview, April 27, 2001.
Nelson, Martin, Telephone Interview, July 10, 2001.
Nye, Robert E., Nycon Resources, Inc., Lakewood, Colorado, Interview, July, 2001.
Spero, Vince, Monte Vista, Colorado, Telephone Interview, 2002.
Wyley, Ken, Creede, Colorado, Correspondence and Interview, 2003.

INDEX